W9-ADZ-950

Elementary Numerical Analysis with Programming

GERALD B. HAGGERTY
University of Rhode Island

Elementary Numerical Analysis with Programming

Allyn and Bacon, Inc.

Printed in the United States of America.

Library of Congress Catalog Card Number: 79–126574

To My Wife

Contents

Preface

More often than not, texts in numerical analysis are oriented toward a mathematical treatment of the subject with very little mention, or none at all, of flow-charting, programming, and running of programs. In an attempt to bridge this gap without neglecting the mathematical aspects, this book throughout its entire content contains an abundance of flow-charts and programs with outputs ranging from the simple to rather sophisticated type of problem. Control cards, data cards, arrangement of a source deck, and subprograms are described and explained in detail with diagrams whenever needed. Problem sets were also organized with the above views in mind. Even in a course structured for the use of desk calculators and slide rules, the reader would most likely acquire an appreciation of the involved computer methods and a good insight into their mathematical processes. Thus the book's innovating features, if at all, lie in the closing of this gap.

Since this book is intended to be a text in a first course in numerical analysis, and because of the special emphasis on flow charts and programs with results calculated on an IBM 360 model computer in the language FORTRAN IV, no rigorous proofs of theorems are given. However, formulas used in algorithms are derived in detail. In view of the book's purpose, the only prerequisite for a course based upon this book as a text (excluding possibly Chapter 7 on Differential Equations) is the usual college calculus sequence.

Chapters 1 and 2 present a functional description of a digital computer and the language FORTRAN IV. They can be omitted if the reader already has a good understanding of programming.

Chapters 3 and 4 treat solutions of equations. In Chapter 3, the solution of a single polynomial or transcendental equation is considered. Both linear and nonlinear systems of equations are the main subjects in Chapter 4, with a section devoted to the calculation of eigenvalues and eigenvectors.

In Chapter 5 (Interpolation), finite difference techniques are emphasized because of their use in numerical differentiation and integration (Chapter 6), and also in the solution of differential equations (Chapter 7). The last part of Chapter 5 considers the method of Least Squares.

Besides techniques for numerical differentiation, Chapter 6 treats Newton–Cotes techniques for numerical integration and Gaussian quadrature.

Predictor-corrector technique and numerical stability are considered in Chapter 7. It was necessary to present a brief treatment of difference equations only to show how these techniques are used in determining the stability of a method.

As the Bibliography attests, the material upon which this book is based has been drawn from many sources, and I am indeed indebted to the scholarly works of these authors.

For the patient reading of parts of this book, it is a pleasure to thank professors John B. Fraleigh and James Lewis of the Mathematics Department of the University of Rhode Island. Also to Harry Aharonian, Robert Wilkinson, and Richard Gencarelli of the Computer Science Department at URI, I wish to express my appreciation for the running of programs on the University computer. I must express thanks to the typists of this manuscript namely Dorothy Cooney, Susan Cafferty, and Paula Najarian. I am also indebted to Robert Domosh, Kay Kelley, and Jennifer Adams, all of Allyn and Bacon, Inc., for their very patient and helpful efforts during the production of this book. No doubt, there may still be errors in this book for which I am solely responsible but had it not been for the diligent work of the typists and the constructive criticisms of the staff, there would have been more errors.

G. B. H.

1

The Computer and Fortran Language

A brief description of a computer,[1] from the viewpoint of the purpose of each of its major functional elements, is necessary so that in programming his problems the student can bring to mind what transpires within the computer. A computer consists of five functional parts or elements: input device, storage, arithmetic-logic element, control, and output device.

Input

Whatever information is required in a problem must be "fed in" to a computer. Unlike a desk calculator, complete instructions and all data must be encoded from the external form of statements and numbers into an internal form consisting of electronic symbols. For this purpose, instructions and data are keypunched on cards.[2]

The input device, when called into action by the operator, causes all instructions and data to be encoded into the internal form, a process that is called *loading*. It is important to accept the idea that *all* information is fed into the computer before any internal operations take place.

A note on some current input developments: One can "write" to a computer—an input device has been developed such that the operator

[1] From here on, the word *computer* will always mean a digital computer.

[2] Magnetic tape and access from remote control units can also be used.

can inform the computer by drawing a picture or by writing a message. And, it is even possible to speak to a computer.

Storage

Likened to the human brain, the storage of a computer is the *memory* of this "brain" wherein sets of instructions and problem data are located symbolically and remain there indefinitely until an instruction is given to erase them. But unlike the human brain, peripheral devices such as magnetic tapes and magnetic disks can be connected to the computer to store more information. Since these devices are mechanical or electromechanical, they operate at a much slower rate than the symbolic operations that take place inside the computer. It must be emphasized that *all* instructions, *all* data—a "package deal"—are stored in the computer.

Arithmetic-logic Element

This part of a computer performs the arithmetic operations of addition, subtraction, multiplication, and division. It can also perform simple logical operations. Is a number zero? Is the sign of a number positive or negative? The arithmetic-logic element can answer these questions.

But beyond this, if a complicated calculation is required, the numerical analyst must apply techniques of analysis by repeatedly asking simple questions: is a number zero; is it positive or negative?

Control

Within a computer there is a unit that controls the sequence of various operations. This unit governs the input, output, storage, and the arithmetic-logic operations, as well as the transmission of information from one element to another. It tells the machine what operation to perform, where to do it, and when to do it.

Output

Without an *output* unit, a computer would be of no value to the programmer. This is the unit that communicates with the user. Output can be recorded on punched cards, on magnetic tapes, or as printed information on large sheets of paper. Whatever means is used, it is important that the output be sufficiently identified and described so that other persons besides the programmer, who are knowledgeable in the given area, can understand it.

1.1 Fortran Statements

A Fortran IV program consists of statements classified as:

1. Arithmetic statements
2. Control statements
3. Input and output statements
4. Specification statements
5. Subprogram statements

The first three of these are called executable statements. Specification and subprogram are called nonexecutable statements and are descriptive in nature.

Arithmetic statements cause the arithmetic operations to be performed on the right side of the equality sign, and the result replaces the current value of the variable to the left of the equality sign. Control statements control the order in which statements are executed. Input and output statements cause information to be transmitted between memory on the one hand and an input device or output device on the other.

1.2 Coding

Fortran statements are punched on cards or printed on remote control units beginning in card column 7 and ending in or before column 72. If a statement contains more than 66 characters, it can be continued on cards immediately following by punching any of the integers, 1, 2, . . . , 9, in column 6.

A reference number may be punched in columns 1 through 5. Columns 73 through 80 may be used for any reasonable purpose of the programmer, such as an explanation of the statement. Explanatory or descriptive comments may be punched in columns 2 through 80 if the letter *C* is punched in column 1.

1.3 Constants

There are three types of constants, namely integer constants, real constants, and double-precision constants.

Integer

Any signed or unsigned whole number without a decimal point and without any other punctuation is an integer constant. Its maximum range is from -2^{31} to $2^{31} - 1$ (on IBM/360 systems).

Real

Type 1: Any signed or unsigned number of maximum width 7 decimal digits, with a decimal point but no other punctuation.
Type 2: Any signed or unsigned number, also of maximum width 7 decimals, written in E notation, such as $2.15E + 02$, which means $(2.15)(10^2) = 215$. In E notation, the range is from 10^{-75} to 10^{75}.

Double-precision

Type 1: Any signed or unsigned number with a decimal point, having 8 to 16 decimal digits and no other punctuation.
Type 2: Any signed or unsigned number of 1 to 7 decimal digits followed by D and an exponent with no other punctuation, e.g., $8.7D + 03 = (8.7)(10^3) = 8700$.

1.4 Variables

A variable is a quantity that may take on different values throughout a program. The variable name consists of letters and integers in any order, the only requirement being that the first character is a letter and the total number of characters does not exceed six. It may also include the dollar sign as one of its characters.[3]

Variables are also of three types: integer, real, and double-precision. If the first character of the variable name is *I, J, K, L, M,* or *N,* the variable is an integer. Otherwise, the variable is real or double-precision. The double-precision variable has eight storage locations reserved for it, whereas the integer or real variable has only four locations reserved. Hence, a double-precision quantity can be more accurate. These variables can be specified by a statement stating the type. For example,

```
INTEGER A,B
```

[3] The dollar sign ($) is an acceptable character on the RAX system (IBM/360 Remote Access Computing System).

would specify that the variables A and B are integers in the program. Without this statement, A and B would be real variables.

1.5 Arrays

In any kind of computation involving matrices, vectors, or a problem where subscripted variables are needed, it is necessary to use an *array* of variables. Arrays can be one-dimensional, two-dimensional, or three-dimensional. Hence, a Fortran array is a set of variables and is described by the following examples.

Example 1

$$A(1) \quad A(2) \quad \cdots \quad A(i) \quad A(i+1) \quad \cdots \quad A(m)$$

where A is the name of the array and the subscripts 1, 2, . . . indicate the position of the particular variable.

Example 2

$$\begin{array}{cccc}
B(1,1) & \mathrm{B}(1,2) & \cdots & B(1,n) \\
B(2,1) & \mathrm{B}(2,2) & \cdots & B(2,n) \\
\cdot & \cdot & \cdot & \cdot \\
\cdot & \cdot & \cdot & \cdot \\
\cdot & \cdot & \cdot & \cdot \\
B(i,1) & \cdots & B(i,j) & B(i,n) \\
\cdot & \cdot & \cdot & \cdot \\
\cdot & \cdot & \cdot & \cdot \\
\cdot & \cdot & \cdot & \cdot \\
B(m,1) & B(m,2) & \cdots & B(m,n)
\end{array}$$

where B is the name of the array and the subscripts indicate the position of a particular variable.

Example 3

$$\begin{array}{ccccc}
C(1,1,1) & \cdots & C(1,1,m) & \cdots & C(1,1,k) \\
C(1,2,1) & \cdots & C(1,2,m) & \cdots & C(i,j,k)
\end{array}$$

is an example of a three-dimensional array.

Arrays are stored in a computer in the following order: The first subscript is increased most rapidly; the second subscript is increased at the next fastest rate; and the third subscript increases at the slowest rate. For example, a three-dimensional array would be stored as:

$$
\begin{array}{cccc}
A(1,1,1) & \mathrm{A}(2,1,1) & \cdots & A(m,1,1) \\
A(1,2,1) & \mathrm{A}(2,2,1) & \cdots & A(m,2,1) \\
\vdots & \vdots & \vdots & \vdots \\
A(1,n,1) & \cdots & \cdots & A(m,n,1) \\
A(1,1,2) & \cdots & \cdots & A(m,1,2) \\
\vdots & \vdots & \vdots & \vdots \\
A(1,1,L) & \cdots & \cdots & A(m,1,L) \\
\vdots & \vdots & \vdots & \vdots \\
A(1,n,L) & \cdots & \cdots & A(m,n,L)
\end{array}
$$

A subscript may be an unsigned, nonsubscripted integer variable V, an unsigned integer constant C, or a combination of these in the following forms:[4]

```
V
C
V+C
V-C
C*V
C*V+C1
C*V-C1
```

The computer must be informed of the size of the array at the beginning of the program, so that a sufficient number of locations in storage will be reserved. This is accomplished by a dimension statement,[5] such as

```
DIMENSION A(15)
```

This statement will instruct the computer to reserve fifteen locations for the subscripted variable A. The same number of reservations could be reserved by any of the following statements with its appropriate meaning:

[4] For explanation of arithmetic operations, refer to Sec. 1.6.

[5] For explanation of the DIMENSION statement, refer to Sec. 1.17.

```
INTEGER A(15)
REAL IA(15)
DOUBLE-PRECISION A(15)
```

1.6 Arithmetic Operations

The arithmetic operators are

**	for exponentiation
*	for multiplication
/	for division
+	for addition
−	for subtraction

In Fortran there can be no ambiguity, no lack of programming grammar. There are three modes of expression—real, integer, and double-precision—in Fortran statements; a very general rule is that modes are not mixed. However, there are exceptions, and these will be described and explained as they occur throughout the text.

The order of computation in an arithmetic operation is: exponentiation first, multiplication and division next, and last, addition and subtraction. Whenever necessary, parentheses may be used as they are in algebra to specify the order of operations.

1.7 Arithmetic Statements

A statement of the form

```
A=B
```

is called an arithmetic statement. The most important feature is that the equality sign does not mean equivalence; it means replacement. For example,

```
A=B+C
```

is interpreted by the computer as: The values of B and C are added and the result replaces the current value of A. Another example,

```
X=X+D
```

will cause the current value of X to be added to the current value of D, and this result will replace the current value of X.

1.8 Control Statements

Unconditional transfer or conditional transfer from one statement to another can be made by means of control statements. For an unconditional transfer, an unconditional GO TO statement is used. The form of this statement is

```
          .
          .
       GO TO 50
          .
          .
          .
    50 A=B+C
          .
          .
          .
```

Whenever the statement GO TO 50 is executed, control is transferred to statement 50.

Another control statement is the computed GO TO statement of the form:

```
    10 A=B+C
       .
       .
       .
       GO TO(10,20,30),I
    30 E=F+D
       .
       .
       .
    20 G=E
```

Whenever $I = 1$, transfer is made to statement 10; if $I = 2$, transfer is made to statement 20; if $I = 3$, transfer is made to statement 30.

1.9 Arithmetic IF Statement

The statement

```
IF(A)M,N,L
```

is interpreted by the computer as: If the value of A is negative, transfer is made to statement M. If the value of A is zero, transfer is made to statement N. If the value of A is positive, transfer is made to statement L.

1.10 DO Statement

This Fortran statement in its most general form

```
DO K I=M,N,L
```

is a command to execute all statements immediately following this DO statement through the statement K for $I = M$ first, and repeatedly for $I = M + L$, $I = M + 2L$, . . . until the value of I equals N or is the maximum integer of the form $M + KL$ less than N. For example,

```
   SUM=0.0
   DO 50 I=1,5
50 SUM=SUM+A(I)
```

would cause SUM to have the initial value of zero and successively add to this $A(1)$, $A(2)$, $A(3)$, $A(4)$, $A(5)$. Hence, the final result is

```
SUM=A(1)+A(2)+A(3)+A(4)+A(5)
```

The same result can be computed by an IF statement as follows:

```
   SUM=0.0
   I=1
30 SUM=SUM+A(I)
   IF(I-5)10,20,20
10 I=I+1
   GO TO 30
```

In using DO loops, the following rules must be obeyed:

1. There can be no change within a DO loop of the indexing. The letters I, M, N, or L cannot be altered in value.
2. DO loops may be nested one within another.
3. But DO loops cannot overlap one another.
4. Transfer out of a DO loop is always permissible.
5. Transfer into a DO loop is not permitted except in transferring from an inner loop to an outer loop, and then transfer can also be made from the outer loop to the inner loop. An index of a DO loop is defined by the DO statement itself. Once the current value of the index of the inner loop is known, subsequent transfer can be made from an outer loop into the inner loop, and the current value of the inner DO loop index will be used. Figure 1.1 shows these different possibilities.
6. The range extends from the DO statement through the statement labeled K.
7. The last statement in the range of a DO statement must be an

executable statement, but not a transfer statement such as a GO TO, IF, STOP, or RETURN.

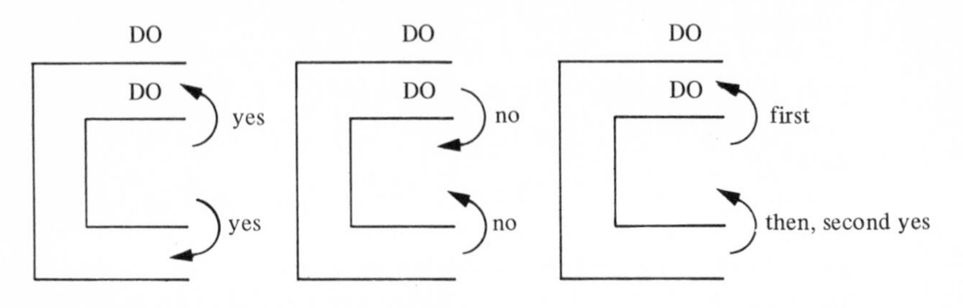

FIGURE 1.1 Nesting of DO Loops

8. In order to avoid the possibility of ending the range of a DO statement with a transfer statement, the CONTINUE statement may be used as an added statement of the DO loop and the range extended to this CONTINUE statement. It is a dummy statement that may be placed anywhere in a program without affecting the execution of the program. For example, it can be used as a branch statement as shown below:

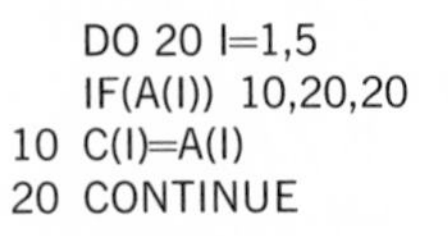

```
   DO 20 I=1,5
   IF(A(I)) 10,20,20
10 C(I)=A(I)
20 CONTINUE
```

1.11 PAUSE, STOP, END Statements

The statement PAUSE causes the computer to cease execution of the program. The operator must then give a command through the console to resume operation, and at that time the computer will begin with the next statement following PAUSE.

The statement STOP causes the computer to stop execution of the program, but the computer now expects that the next statement will be the END statement and not a continuing statement of the present program. The END statement is the last statement of the program and is interpreted by the computer as the end of all statements in the program. At this point the machine is in a waiting position and expects to receive data or a new program.

INPUT, OUTPUT

Any collection of data that is to be transferred between external devices, such as a card reader, a magnetic tape or disk unit, and storage is called a data set. Each data set may be subdivided into Fortran records, and this subdivision is accomplished by means of a FORMAT statement. The FORMAT statement can also describe the form of the data.

Thus, for transmittal of data between storage and the external form, an input or output statement is required; this I/O statement may refer to a FORMAT statement, which will specify the subdivision and describe the form of the data. There are five I/O statements: READ, WRITE, END FILE, REWIND, and BACK SPACE.[6]

1.12 READ, WRITE, FORMAT Statements

Although the FORMAT statement is not an I/O statement, it is necessary to consider it in conjunction with the READ statement and also with the WRITE statement. However, Secs. 1.13, 1.14, and 1.15 treat FORMAT statements more fully.

There are two general types of READ or WRITE statements. These are the READ or WRITE statements with FORMAT statements, and the READ or WRITE statements without FORMAT statements. If the data are already in internal form, a FORMAT statement is not required. But, if the data, as is the case in all programs in this book, are to be read in from the external form or to be printed in the external form, then an associated FORMAT statement is required with every I/O statement. Only I/O statements with formated data will be considered here.

The following example illustrates a READ statement with its FORMAT statement:

```
10 FORMAT(I6,F12.4)
   .
   .
   .
   READ(5,10)JOB,A
   .
   .
   .
```

[6] Only READ and WRITE statements will be defined in this text. For END FILE, REWIND, and BACK SPACE, the reader is referred to the *Manual IBM/360 Basic Programming Support*.

The statement

```
10 FORMAT(I6,F12.4)
```

describes, as it were, the data to be read in. *I*6 tells the computer that the first number (called *JOB*) to be read in by READ(5,10) is an integer and has a maximum of 6 places, and that the second number (called *A*) is a real number with a maximum of 12 places, four of which are to the right of the decimal point.

Thus, the data set is read in by calling upon the READ card device, whose reference number in the example is 5, and the data set of one integer and one real number is placed in locations *JOB* and *A*, respectively. With these two statements, READ and FORMAT, there would be at the end of the program one card for the data set, as shown in Fig. 1.2.

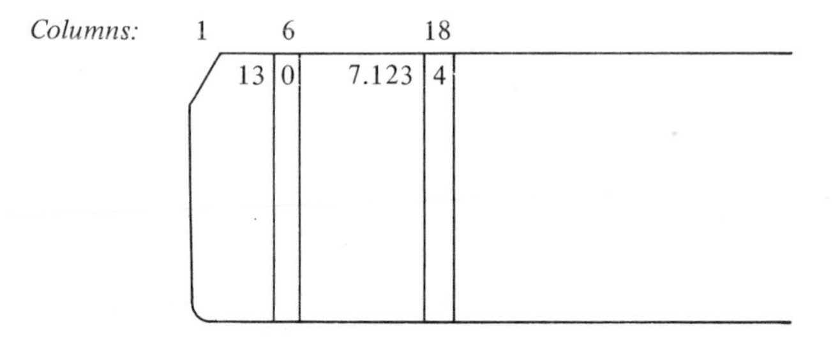

FIGURE 1.2 Data Card

The data set consisting of two numbers, 130 and 7.1234, is keypunched on this card in columns 4, 5, 6 and 13, 14, 15, 16, 17, 18, respectively. That is, keypunching data is right justified. It should be noted that only numbers appear on this card as a data set, with no other symbols or characters. If these two numbers had been computed by a program and had been stored in locations *JOB* and *A*, then an output statement with a FORMAT statement would appear in the program as

```
        .
        .
10 FORMAT(I6,F12.4)
        .
        .
        .
   WRITE(6,10)JOB,A
```

As output, the numbers 130 and 7.1234 would be printed on the output sheet of paper. The number 130 would be printed in the first six places,

1.16 Explicit Specification Statements

The explicit specification statement declares a particular variable or array to be real, integer, or double-precision, by a statement such as

```
REAL N,M,L
```

Such a statement would appear at the beginning of a program, and although by definition N, M, L are integer-type variables, this statement supersedes the definition; therefore, N, M, L will be considered as real variables. Several examples of explicit specification statements are given throughout the text.

1.17 DIMENSION Statement

For every subscripted variable in a program, there must be a statement providing information for allocation of storage for the variable, such as a DIMENSION statement or a DOUBLE-PRECISION statement. This statement must precede any statement using the subscripted variable. For example,

```
DIMENSION A(10,15)
```

is a command to reserve 150 storage locations for the array

$$A_{1,1} \quad \cdots \quad A_{10,15}.$$

1.18 COMMON Statement

Of widespread use in writing a main program containing subprograms within the main program is the COMMON statement. By this statement, variables or arrays in the main program will be allocated the same locations in storage as variables or arrays in a subprogram.

For example, consider a main program and a subprogram as shown below:

```
Main Program              Subprogram
     .                         .
     .                         .
     .                         .
COMMON A,B,C,D(50)     COMMON W,X,Y,Z(50)
```

These two COMMON statements cause the variable A to share the same location as the variable W, the variable B to share the same location as the variable X, and the same for the variables C and Y. For the subscripted variables D and Z, $D(1)$ and $Z(1)$ will share the same location. Likewise, $D(2)$ and $Z(2)$ will share the same location, and the same relation holds for all $D(I)$ and $Z(I)$.

Another feature of the COMMON statement is that it can be used as a specification statement, thereby eliminating the need for a DIMENSION statement. Hence, the two statements

Main Program	Subprogram
COMMON A(100)	COMMON X(100)

serve two purposes:

1. Replaces DIMENSION A(100) and DIMENSION X(100).
2. Causes the subscripted variables A and X to share the same locations.

If a programmer requires the use of variables of different modes, these variables should be arranged in order in the COMMON statement, as

```
COMMON
DOUBLE-PRECISION
REAL
INTEGER
```

1.19 EQUIVALENCE Statement

Within a single main program or within a subprogram, it may be feasible to permit several variables that may be subscripted to share the same location. The EQUIVALENCE statement provides for this possibility:

```
DIMENSION X(10),Z(5,10)
EQUIVALENCE (A,X(3),Z(5,1))
```

This EQUIVALENCE statement permits the same location in storage to be shared by the variables A, $X(3)$, and $Z(5,1)$.

Another method of using an EQUIVALENCE statement is by stating the order of the subscripted variable as it appears in storage. It should again be noted that a two-dimensional array such as $Z(5,10)$ is located in storage by columns. For example, $Z(5,10)$ is located in storage as

$Z(1,1)$	$Z(2,1)$	$\cdots$	$\cdots$	$Z(5,1)$	1st column
$Z(1,2)$	$Z(2,2)$	$\cdots$	$\cdots$	$Z(5,2)$	2nd column

$Z(1,3)$	$Z(2,3)$	$Z(3,3)$	$Z(4,3)$	$Z(5,3)$	
.	.	.	.	.	
.	.	.	.	.	
.	.	.	.	.	
$Z(1,10)$	$Z(2,10)$	...	...	$Z(5,10)$	10th column.

Hence, $Z(5,1)$ is in the fifth location of the whole array.

As another example, $Z(4,3)$ is in the fourteenth location; i.e., five locations in the first column, five locations in the second column, and four locations in the third column. The above EQUIVALENCE statement may be stated as

```
DIMENSION X(10), Z(5,10)
EQUIVALENCE (A,X(3),Z(5))
```

SUBPROGRAMS

Not too infrequently, a program may have a routine or a calculation that must be performed many times throughout the program, but each time with different data. For example, if the absolute value of a quantity is required many times with a different value of the quantity each time, it would seem that a subprogram could be called upon each time to perform this operation, rather than writing a set of statements for this purpose within the main program. For such a subprogram, there are Fortran-supplied subprograms; these are listed in Table 1.1, page 23.

However, for subprograms not supplied in the Fortran library, the programmer can use his own subprogram. These are called statement functions, function subprograms, and subroutine programs.

1.20 Statement Functions

The statement

```
FOF(X,Y)=X**2+Y**2
```

defines the expression $X^2 + Y^2$. *FOF* is the name of the function, and X and Y are its arguments.

Rules for using a *statement function* are:

1. A statement function must precede the first executable statement of the program.

2. The name consists of six or less characters, the first of which is a letter.
3. The arguments are nonsubscripted real variables.

The above function may be used in the program after it has been properly defined, with dummy variables such as

```
A=FOF(C,D)
```

This statement would cause $C^2 + D^2$ to be computed and the result to be placed in location A.

1.21 Function Subprograms

A statement function is an effective means of defining a function so that it can be called repeatedly throughout the program, by stating on the right side of a Fortran statement the name of the function with the dummy variables as arguments. But if the subprogram contains more than one statement, the function statement would not suffice. For this reason, a *function subprogram* may be used.

For example, to compute the absolute value of a number Z, whether Z is negative, zero, or positive, a function subprogram may be used as demonstrated below:

```
Main Program          FUNCTION ABSVAL(Z)
     .                IF(Z)5,6,7
     .              5 ABSVAL=-Z
     .                GO TO 8
     .              6 Z=0
     .                ABSVAL=Z
     .                GO TO 8
     .              7 ABSVAL=Z
     .              8 RETURN
A=ABSVAL(X)           END
     .
     .
```

The function subprogram takes the absolute value of the current value of X, and by the statement

```
A=ABSVAL(X)
```

places this value in location A.

Rules for using a function subprogram are:

1. The name of the subprogram (such as ABSVAL) consists of one to

six characters, the first of which is a letter. It also implies the type of result as being real, integer, or double-precision.

2. The arguments (at least one argument) such as Z can be non-subscripted variables, array names, or dummy variables. For example, in the above subprogram, ABSVAL(W), where W is a dummy variable, could have been used instead of ABSVAL(Z).
3. The statement RETURN causes a transfer of control to the CALL statement (A=ABSVAL(X)) in the main program.
4. The END statement (only one in a subprogram) specifies to the compiler the end of the subprogram.
5. The location of the set of cards for a function subprogram in relation to those for the main program is that the subprogram set follows the main program set (see Ch. 2).
6. The name of the subprogram, such as ABSVAL, must appear on the left side of an equality sign in the subprogram; also, the name and the current arguments in the main program, such as ABSVAL(X), must appear on the right side of an equality sign in the main program.
7. There can be several RETURN statements within a subprogram, as shown below:

```
Main Program              FUNCTION ABSVAL(W)
     .                    IF(Z)5,6,7
     .                  5 ABSVAL=-Z
     .                    RETURN
A=ABSVAL(X)             6 Z=0.0
     .                    ABSVAL=Z
     .                    RETURN
     .                  7 ABSVAL=Z
                          RETURN
                          END
```

As an overall concluding statement on function subprograms, it should be noted that the main program, i.e., the calling program, uses the set of instructions in the subprogram but uses its own values of variables within the main or calling program.

1.22 Subroutine Subprograms

The function subprogram always computes and returns a result to the calling program. The *subroutine subprogram* differs from the function subprogram in this respect, because the subroutine does not have to return any result to the calling program. Otherwise both are similar in the following respects:

1. Rules for naming each are the same, except the fact that the name implies that the result is real, integer, or double-precision is not relevant to a subroutine.
2. Both require RETURN statements and one END statement.
3. Both have dummy arguments.

The following is an example of a subroutine subprogram:

```
  SUBROUTINE ABSVAL(Z)
  IF(Z)5,6,7
5 Z=-Z
  RETURN
6 Z=Z
  RETURN
7 Z=Z
  RETURN
  END
```

In the calling program, the statement calling this subprogram would appear in the form:

```
      .
      .
      .
CALL ABSVAL(X)
      .
      .
      .
```

In this example, at the time that the statement CALL ABSVAL(X) is executed in the calling program, transfer is made to the subroutine ABSVAL(Z), and the absolute value of the number X is computed and return is made to the calling program at the statement immediately following CALL ABSVAL(X). Several subroutines are given throughout the text beginning with Ch. 2.

Rules for subroutine subprograms are:

1. The name consists of one to six alphameric characters, the first of which must be a letter.
2. Subroutine variables and statement numbers do not relate to other programs.
3. The arguments may be dummy variable names. These are replaced by the arguments in the calling program at the time of execution. Dummy arguments and true arguments must agree in number, order, and type. Dummy arguments may not appear in COMMON or EQUIVALENCE statements within the subroutine.
4. Dummy arguments are not, in all cases, needed.

5. The CALL statement in the calling program transfers control to the subroutine. At this time the dummy arguments are replaced by the arguments in the CALL statement.
6. The RETURN statement is the "stop" statement of a subroutine and transfers control to the calling program.

1.23 Fortran Words and Function Subprograms

The following list of words cannot be used except as specified by the Fortran compiler:

ABS	END	PAUSE
BACKSPACE	EQUIVALENCE	READ
CALL	FORMAT	REAL
COMMON	FUNCTION	RETURN
CONTINUE	GO	STOP
DIMENSION	GO TO	SUBROUTINE
DO	IF	WRITE
DOUBLE	INTEGER	

For example, it would be incorrect to write a statement such as

```
GO TO=A+B
```

As was mentioned previously, Fortran supplies the programmer with mathematical function subprograms. For example, the statement A=ABS(X) computes $|X|$ and stores it in location A.

TABLE 1.1 Mathematical Function Subprograms

Name of Function	*Fortran Name*	*Argument*	*Mode*
Exponential: e^x	EXP: EXP(X)	Real	Real
Natural logarithm: $\ln x$	ALOG: ALOG(X)	Real	Real
Common logarithm: $\log x$	ALOG10: ALOG10(X)	Real	Real
Arctangent: $\arctan x$	ATAN: ATAN(X)	Real	Real
Sine: $\sin x$	SIN: SIN(X)	Real	Real
Cosine: $\cos x$	COS: COS(X)	Real	Real
Square root: $\sqrt{x}$	SQRT: SQRT(X)	Real	Real
Hyperbolic tangent: $\tanh x$	TANH: TANH(X)	Real	Real
Absolute value: $\|x\|$	ABS: ABS(X)	Real	Real

In all of the names in Table 1.1, if the Fortran name is preceded by the letter D and the argument is double-precision, the mode of the function becomes double-precision.

1.24 Conclusion

The Fortran language and its basic features are defined and described quite fully in this chapter; however the major portion of the work of programming will be considered in the subsequent chapters.

Rules are inflexible; syntax and grammar *must* be correct. The slightest mistake—for example, a missing comma—can cause the whole program to be rejected. On the other hand, every statement in a program may be correct from all points of view, and yet, incorrect answers or no answers may be the result. For example, if a WRITE statement is omitted, some of the results may not be printed.

Whatever qualities are necessary to become a good programmer, whether these be insight and understanding or a love of digits and arithmetic, the following chapters should help in this development.

2

A Fortran Program

Imagine yourself as the teacher of someone capable of performing any kind of arithmetic operation at almost the speed of light, but who has no knowledge of numerical methods. This exceptional person can follow only the simplest of instructions. There can be no ambiguity in any instruction and no assumption made that this person has any intuition.

Now consider the task of instructing this person to sum the series:

$$\sin x = x - \frac{x^3}{3!} + \frac{x^5}{5!} - \cdots + (-1)^{n-1}\frac{x^{2n-1}}{(2n-1)!} \pm \cdots \tag{2.1}$$

for $x = x_0$ by forming partial sums until

$$\left|\frac{x^{2n-1}}{(2n-1)!}\right| < \epsilon.$$

Looking ahead to the results, it is seen that the partial sums become

$$\begin{aligned}
S_1 = x_0, \qquad S_2 &= x_0 - \frac{x_0^3}{3!} \quad \text{or} \quad S_2 = S_1 - \frac{x_0^3}{3!}, \\
S_3 &= x_0 - \frac{x_0^3}{3!} + \frac{x_0^5}{5!} \quad \text{or} \quad S_3 = S_2 + \frac{x_0^5}{5!}, \\
S_{n-1} &= x_0 - \frac{x_0^3}{3!} + \cdots \pm \frac{x_0^{2n-3}}{(2n-3)!} \quad \text{or} \quad S_{n-1} = S_{n-2} \pm \frac{x_0^{2n-3}}{(2n-3)!}, \\
S_n &= x_0 - \frac{x_0^3}{3!} + \cdots \pm \frac{x_0^{2n-1}}{(2n-1)!} \quad \text{or} \quad S_n = S_{n-1} \pm \frac{x_0^{2n-1}}{(2n-1)!}.
\end{aligned} \tag{2.2}$$

It certainly would not be desirable to tell him what to do at every step. It would be much better to state a few formulas that could be used repeatedly until the result is attained. These recursive instructions and formulas must be stated in such a way that there will be no ambiguity from beginning to end. The following is one way of instructing this person.

Set of Instructions

1. Set $x_0 = 1$.
2. Set $\epsilon = .001$.
3. Set SUM $= x_0$.
4. Set TERM $= x_0$.
5. Set XSQ $= -x_0^2$.
6. Set DENOM = 3.
7. Replace value of TERM by (TERM)XSQ/(DENOM−1)(DENOM).
8. Replace value of SUM by SUM+TERM.
9. If absolute value of TERM is less than ϵ, go to instruction 12; otherwise go to instruction 10.
10. Replace DENOM by DENOM+2.
11. Go to instruction 7.
12. Print the values of SUM, TERM, x_0, ϵ.
13. Stop.

Table 2.1, called a *level chart* of the operations, shows the input, intermediate results, and the final results.

TABLE 2.1 Level Chart

Level	x_0	ϵ	SUM	TERM	XSQ	DENOM	TERM<ϵ	PRINT
1	1	.001	1	1	−1	3		
2			.8333	−.1667		5	Is $\lvert -.1667 \rvert < .001$? NO	
3			.8416	.0083		7	Is $\lvert .0083 \rvert < .001$? NO	
4			.8412	−.0002			Is $\lvert -.0002 \rvert < .001$? YES	PRINT .8412, −.0002, +1, .001
								STOP

Perhaps not for the above computation, but for a more complicated problem, one can forsee that such a set of instructions might cause unnecessary confusion. To avoid this possibility, the Fortran language has been developed. But even in the simplified notation of Fortran, it is often quite difficult for an experienced programmer to keep in mind all of the various transfers from one statement to another as he writes a long program. Therefore, before writing a program, it is always a good first step to draw up a flow chart.

2.1 Flow Charts

A flow chart is a set of circles, diamonds, and rectangles arranged with directed line segments between these geometric figures. The whole picture graphically shows the flow of work to be done and the relation between the different statements. A *circle* indicates the beginning or end of a program. A *rectangle* with a statement inside indicates that this statement is to be executed, and shows the direction of the flow of work by the directed line segment. A *diamond* with a statement inside is used to ask a question.

As an example, a flow chart for the computation of sin x as set forth in the set of instructions is shown in Flow Chart 2.1.

In Flow Chart 2.1, at the time of execution of the program, each statement will be executed and the direction of the next executable statement is indicated by an arrow.

In particular, at the diamond wherein $|\text{TERM}| < \epsilon$ is inserted, a test is made at this juncture. As can be seen, if the answer is NO, i.e., $|\text{TERM}|$ is not less than ϵ, then DENOM is replaced by DENOM + 2 and transfer is made to the box containing

$$\text{TERM} = \frac{\text{(TERM)(XSQ)}}{\text{(DENOM)(DENOM}-1)}$$

This loop (steps 8, 9, 10) will be repeated until the answer is YES. At this time transfer is made to the PRINT statement (step 11); SUM, TERM, X_0, and ϵ are printed and a final transfer is made to END.

PROBLEMS

Write a flow chart for each of the following computations for $x = x_0$ and a given ϵ. Let $x_0 = .5$.

2-1. $\cos x = 1 - \frac{x^2}{2!} + \frac{x^4}{4!} - \frac{x^6}{6!} + \cdots.$

2-2. $e^x = 1 + x + \frac{x^2}{2!} + \frac{x^3}{3!} + \frac{x^4}{4!} + \cdots.$

FLOW CHART 2.1 Sin x

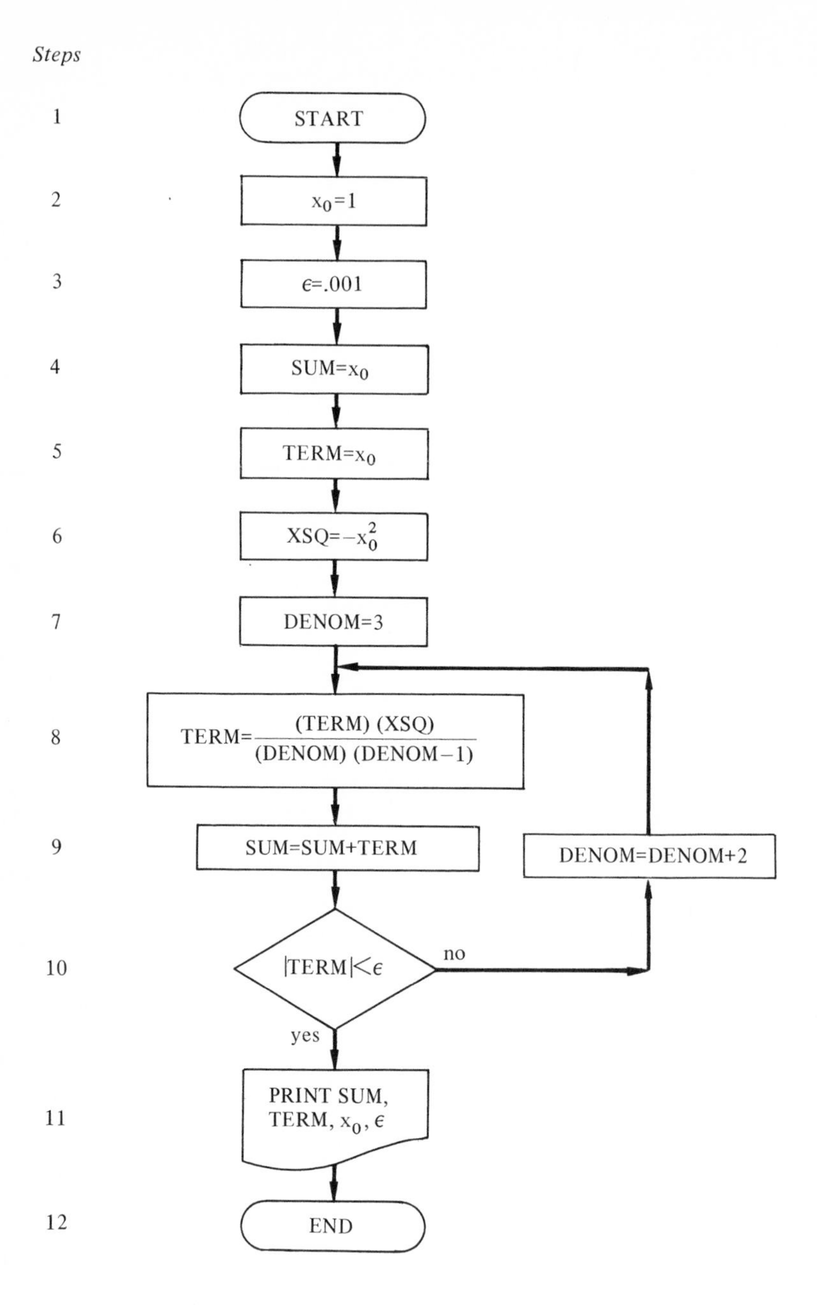

2-3. $\tan^{-1} x = x - \frac{x^3}{3} + \frac{x^5}{5} - \frac{x^7}{7} + \cdots.$

2-4. $(1 + x^2)^{-1/2} = 1 - \frac{x^2}{1!2^1} + \frac{1\cdot3x^4}{2!2^2} - \frac{1\cdot3\cdot5x^6}{3!2^3} + \frac{1\cdot3\cdot5\cdot7x^8}{4!2^4} - \cdots.$

2-5. $\ln(1 + x) = x - \frac{x^2}{2} + \frac{x^3}{3} - \frac{x^4}{4} + \cdots.$

2-6. $\sin^{-1} x = x + \frac{x^3}{1!2\cdot3} + \frac{1\cdot3x^5}{2!2^2\cdot5} + \frac{1\cdot3\cdot5x^7}{3!2^3\cdot7} + \frac{1\cdot3\cdot5\cdot7x^9}{4!2^4\cdot9} + \cdots.$

2.2 Fortran Program

As invaluable as a flow chart is to even an experienced programmer, the challenge lies in writing a program that will run on a computer. It is important at this point to realize that the output—groups of numbers row after row on a sheet of paper—would be quite incomprehensible to anyone, even to one well qualified in that field, unless some words of explanation accompany the numbers.

The following program, simple as it is, causes the output to be defined so that anyone acquainted with the sine function will understand the results. Before actually writing the program, a preview of the whole system will be presented to aid understanding of the processes involved.

A computer has a built-in control system, called a *monitor* system, that directs and controls the flow of work. If the program is written in Fortran, a problem-oriented language, the monitor system transfers control to the compiler. The *compiler* is a program in itself and causes the submitted Fortran program to be converted into machine language, i.e., a language that is acceptable to the computer. If the program had been written in machine language, the compiler would have been bypassed. Figure 2.1, a diagram employing the ideas of a flow chart, clarifies this design.

Varying from one machine to another but with the same purpose, control cards preceding the submitted Fortran program will direct the computer to take the path of monitor, compiler, assembler. To accomplish this, in one kind of system, for example, three control cards may be required, as shown in Fig. 2.2. Each control card has a slanted line in column 1. The first card, called an ID card, will be examined by the computer for an acceptable problem number that has been previously assigned to the programmer by the computer center. Additional information can be punched in this card out to column 72.

Card 2 notifies the computer that the set of cards to follow is a

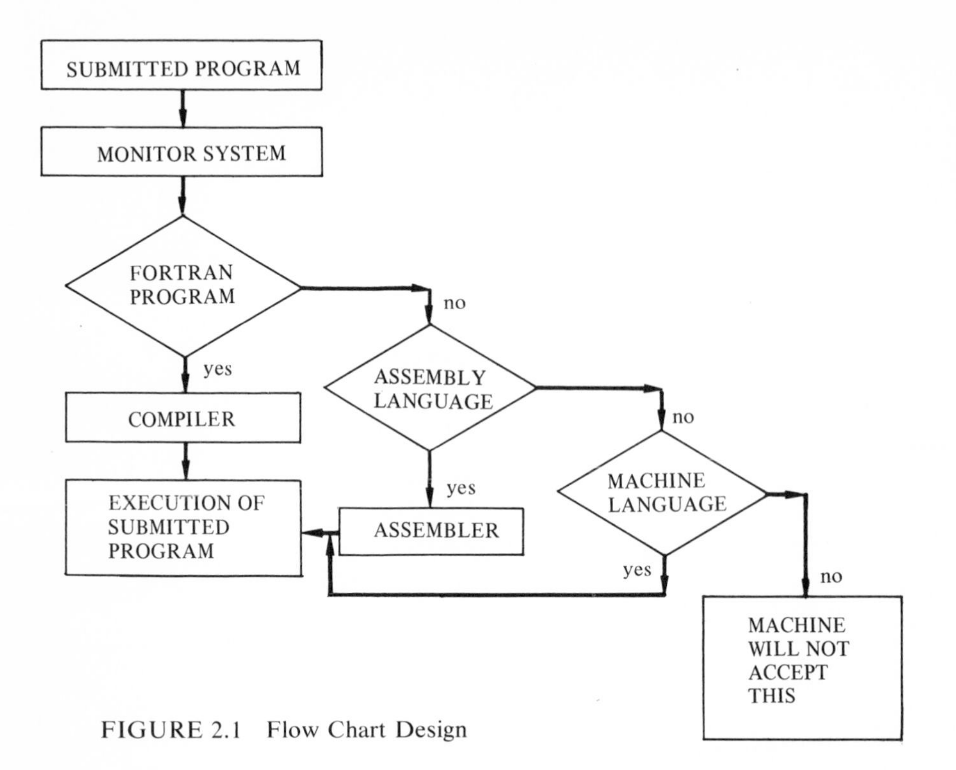

FIGURE 2.1 Flow Chart Design

complete job. The word MAP requests that a map of the internal storage of the program be printed as output. There are other variations of this card but /JOB must be punched.

Card 3 calls for a path through the Fortran compiler and requests that a list (the submitted program) be printed. REF requests that a list of references between the external form and the internal form be printed. There are other variations of this card also, but /FTC is required.

Immediately following these three cards is the Fortran deck of cards. The last card of this deck is the END card. If data (numbers) are to be read into the computer, the END card is followed by a DATA card, as shown in Fig. 2.3. This card informs the computer that data cards are expected. In the program for sin x, if the value of x is .5 and the value of ϵ is .001, then one card of data would follow the /DATA card, and would appear as in Fig. 2.4.

Finally, to indicate to the computer that this program with all its control cards and data is terminated, a last card, Fig. 2.5, is required.

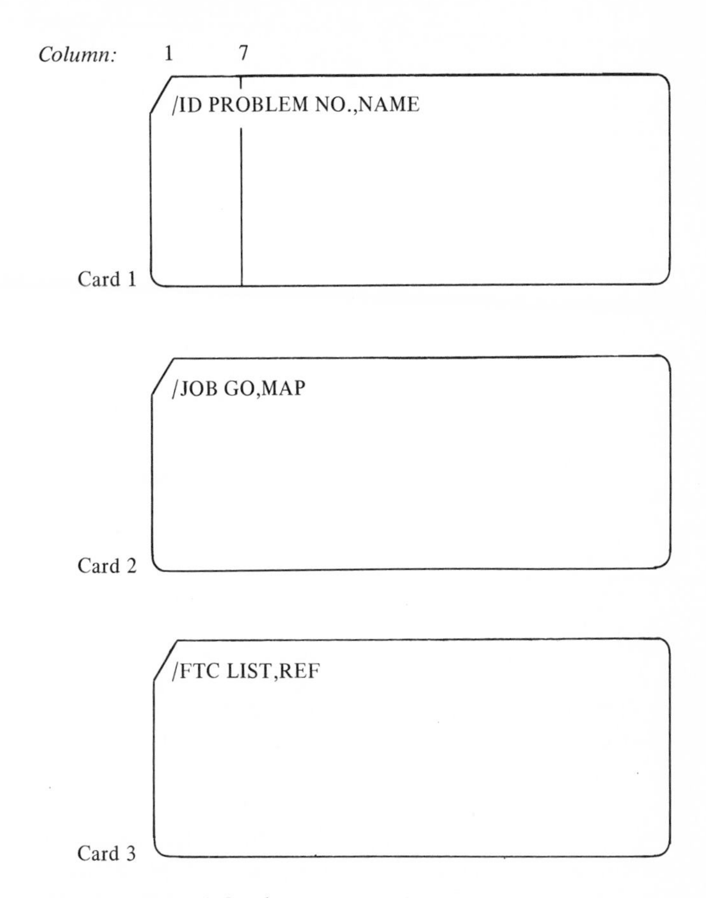

FIGURE 2.2 Control Cards

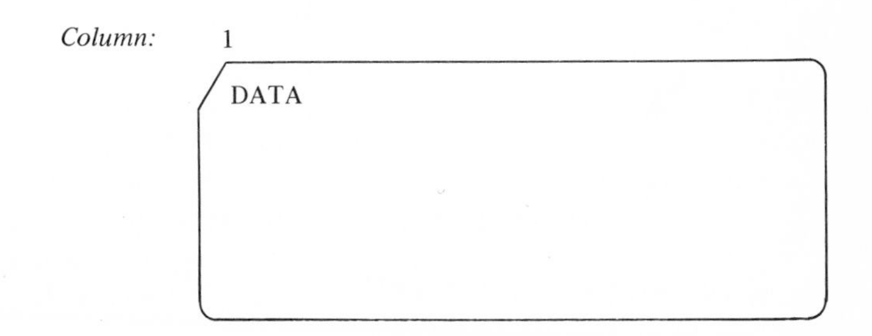

FIGURE 2.3 /DATA Control Card

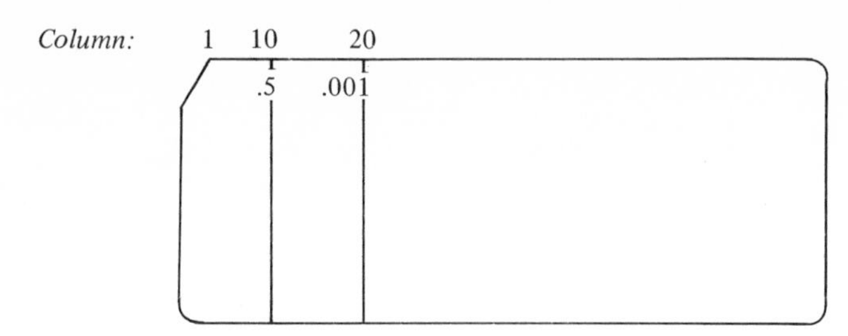

FIGURE 2.4 Data Card

FIGURE 2.5 /END Card

/END informs the computer that the next card to follow must be the first control card of another program. Thus, the whole "package deal" would appear as shown in Fig. 2.6.

Now to the punching of the program. Every Fortran statement of the program begins in column 7 and terminates on or before column 72. If a statement exceeds 66 columns, it can be continued on the card or cards immediately following the initial card for that statement, by punching in column 6 of the follow-up cards the unsigned integers 1, 2, 3, 4, 5, 6, 7, 8, 9.[1]

The complete program including control cards, program, /DATA, data cards, and /END is:

```
/ID 12500375,NAME
/JOB GO,MAP
/FTC LIST,REF
C         SIN(X)
01      1 FORMAT(1H1,30X,'NAME',//)
02      2 FORMAT(2F10.4)
03      3 FORMAT(30x,'X=',F10.4,10x,'EPS=',F10.4,//)
04      4 FORMAT(30x,'THE RESULT IS',//)
05      7 FORMAT(30x,'SIN(X)=',F10.4)
06        READ(5,2)X,EPS
07        WRITE(6,1)
```

[1] Any character is acceptable, except a zero or a blank.

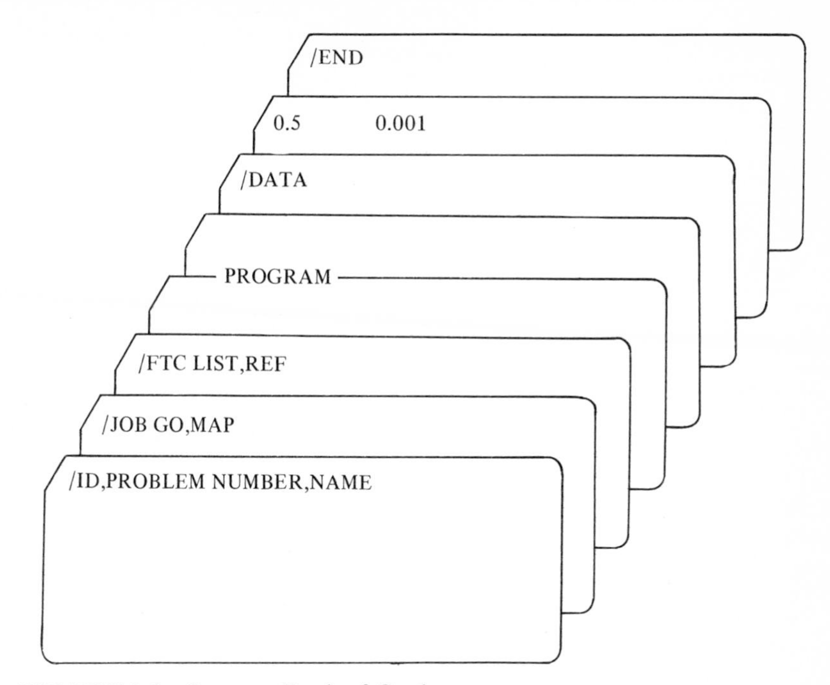

FIGURE 2.6 Program Deck of Cards

```
08        WRITE(6,3)X,EPS
09        WRITE(6,4)
10        SUM=X
11        TERM=X
12        XSQ=-(X*X)
13        DENOM=3.0
14     21 TERM=TERM*XSQ/(DENOM*(DENOM-1.0))
15        SUM=SUM+TERM
16        IF(ABS(TERM)-EPS)15,25,25
17     25 DENOM=DENOM+2.0
18        GO TO 21
19     15 WRITE(6,7)SUM
20        STOP
21        END
/DATA
0.5        0.001
/END
```

```
            X=0.500             EPS=0.0010

            THE RESULT IS

            SIN(X)=0.4794

STOP
```

2.2.1 Analysis

At the outset, what is the meaning of each of these statements? Are they truly algebraic? Has an equality sign the same meaning as it has in mathematics? And what about the FORMAT statements? the READ statements? the WRITE statements? In algebra, would it make sense to write DENOM=DENOM+2 or SUM=SUM+TERM? Hardly!

The equality sign is interpreted by the computer as a command to compute arithmetically the right-hand side of the equality sign, and assign the computed value to the term on the left side. For example, the computer interprets SUM=SUM+TERM as: Add the current value of SUM to the current value of TERM and assign this value to the left side SUM.

The program can be divided into three parts for the purpose of explanation:

1. Input statements with FORMAT statements.
2. Set of instructions to form partial sums of the SIN(X).
3. Output statements with FORMAT statements.

Input: Statements 2 and 6 will cause the values $X(0.5)$ and $EPS(0.001)$, which have been punched on the data card, to be stored in locations X and EPS.

Partial sums: The set of statements from 10 through 18 will repeatedly form partial sums, depending on |TERM| being greater than or equal to EPS.

Output: The result, namely the value of the sin x, is given by statements 5 and 19. The FORMAT statement

```
FORMAT(30X,'SIN(X)=',F10.4)
```

causes the printer to move to the 30th printing position by the 30X. The quotes of 'SIN(X)=' causes SIN(X)= to be printed beginning in the 30th printing position. The real number code, F10.4, in conjunction with WRITE(6,7)SUM, causes the value of sin x to be printed.

Additional output is contained in the other WRITE statements in conjunction with their associated FORMAT statements. Statements 1 and 7 cause the printer to move to a new sheet. This is indicated by 1H1. By 30X the printer moves to the 30th print position and proceeds to print the quote. The two slashes at the end of the FORMAT statement request the printer to double space before printing any other output. Statements 3 and 8 cause the next line of output, $X = 0.5000$ and $EPS = 0.0010$, to be printed; the printer then double spaces for the output of THE RESULT IS and again double spaces for the output of SIN(X)=0.4794.

EXERCISE

Write a program for each of Probs. 2-1 through 2-6.

2.3 Fortran Program With Subroutines

A program may consist of one main program and several subprograms. For each CALL statement of the main program there is a corresponding subprogram. Such a program with subprograms would appear as:

```
/ID
/JOB
/FTC
C       ANY PERTINENT COMMENT
        CALL SUB1(ARG11,ARG12,...ARG1P)
        CALL SUB2(ARG21,ARG22,...ARG2Q)
          .
          .
          .
        CALL SUBK(ARGK1,ARGK2,...ARGKR)
        STOP
        END
/FTC
        SUBROUTINE SUB1(ARG11,ARG12,...ARG1P)
          .
          .
          .
        RETURN
        END
/FTC
        SUBROUTINE SUB2(ARG21,ARG22,...ARG2Q)
          .
          .
          .
        RETURN
        END
          .
          .
          .
/FTC
        SUBROUTINE SUBK(ARGK1,ARGK2,...ARGKR)
          .
          .
          .
        RETURN
        END
```

```
/DATA
 DATA CARD NO.1
 DATA CARD NO.2
          .
          .
          .
 DATA CARD NO.L
/END
```

The CALL statements must be in logical order for correct execution of the total program, but the subroutines may be placed in any order. For example, subroutine *SUB*2 could have been placed before subroutine *SUB*1. The data cards must be located in the order in which they are required by the logic of the program.

A program can have not only subroutines but may also have subroutines within a subroutine of a subroutine. Only the capacity of the machine limits the number of subroutines. The example below illustrates a subroutine of a subroutine of the main program:

```
/ID
/JOB
/FTC
C       ANY PERTINENT COMMENT
        CALL SUB1(ARG11,ARG12,...ARG1P)
        CALL SUB2(ARG21,ARG22,...ARG2Q)
          .
          .
          .
        CALL SUBK(ARGK1,ARGK2,...ARGKR)
        STOP
        END
/FTC
        SUBROUTINE SUB1(ARG11,ARG12,...ARG1P)
        CALL SUB11(ARG1A,ARG1B,...ARG1L)
        RETURN
        END
/FTC
        SUBROUTINE SUB2(ARG21,ARG22,...ARG2Q)
          .
          .
          .
        RETURN
        END
/FTC
        SUBROUTINE SUB11(ARG1A,ARG1B,...ARG1L)
          .
          .
          .
        RETURN
        END
```

```
           .
           .
           .
/FTC
        SUBROUTINE SUBK(ARGK1,ARGK2,...ARGKR)
           .
           .
           .
        RETURN
        END
/DATA
 DATA CARD NO.1
 DATA CARD NO.2
           .
           .
           .
 DATA CARD NO.L
/END
```

2.4 Program for SIN(X) With Subprograms

The following program for computation of sin x is divided into a main program and two subprograms. The main program consists of a comment card and two CALL statements. The first CALL statement transfers control to the subroutine COMPUT, which computes the value of the sin x, and by the RETURN statement, control is transferred back to the main program. The main program then immediately transfers control to the subroutine RESULT, which prints the results; again by the RETURN statement, control is transferred to the main program at the statement STOP. Hence, control is now transferred to the monitor system.

What variables should be chosen as the arguments in a subroutine? Taking the subroutine COMPUT as an example, the arguments should include inputs and those variables that will become final results. For example, TERM and DENOM are intermediate results and need not be considered as arguments.

```
ID 12500375,NAME
/JOB GO,MAP
/FTC LIST,REF
C          SIN(X)
01         CALL COMPUT(SUM,X,EPS)
02         CALL RESULT(SUM,X,EPS)
03         STOP
04         END
```

```
/FTC
01          SUBROUTINE COMPUT(SUM,X,EPS)
02        2 FORMAT(2F10.4)
03          READ(5,2)X,EPS
04          SUM=X
05          TERM=X
06          XSQ=-(X*X)
07          DENOM=3.0
08       21 TERM=TERM*XSQ/(DENOM(DENOM-1.0))
09          SUM=SUM+TERM
10          IF(ABS(TERM)-EPS)15,25,25
11       25 DENOM=DENOM+2.0
12          GO TO 21
13       15 CONTINUE
14          RETURN
15          END
/FTC
01          SUBROUTINE RESULT(SUM,X,EPS)
02        1 FORMAT(1H1,//)
03        3 FORMAT(30X,'X=',F10.4,10X,'EPS=',F10.4,//)
04        4 FORMAT(30X,'THE RESULT IS',//)
05        7 FORMAT(30X,'SIN(X)=',F10.4)
06          WRITE(6,1)
07          WRITE(6,3)X,EPS
08          WRITE(6,4)
09          WRITE(6,7)SUM
10          RETURN
11          END
/DATA
/END
                X=0.5000          EPS=0.0010

                THE RESULT IS

                SIN(X)=0.4794
STOP
```

Is the SIN(X) program with or without subroutines a good program? Is there a sufficiently rapid convergence to the true value of sin x? Would another series approximation or polynomial approximation yield more accurate results in a fewer number of iterations than the Taylor Series? In a negative sense, the covering answer to the above questions can be stated that the Taylor Series approximation is not the best choice. It is, however, a good choice as a beginning in writing programs.

EXERCISE

Write a program with two subprograms for each of Probs. 2-1 through 2-6. The main program should consist principally of two CALL statements. One subprogram should be for the computation and the other for output.

2.5 Error

Another important question that will be considered again and again is that of error. There are four classes of error, namely:

1. *Truncation Errors:* These are caused by using a closed form that is not exact. For example, in the sin x computation, only a finite number of terms of the series was used. Other sources of truncation error are:
   (a) Solution of $f(x) = 0$ by an iterative process, which usually converges only as a limit as the number of iterations goes to infinity.
   (b) Approximation of the integral of a function by a finite summation of functional values.
2. *Round-off Errors:* Finite decimal numbers are used instead of the true numbers.
3. *Arithmetic Errors:* Human blunders—mistakes in addition, subtraction, multiplication, and division, and mistakes in transcribing numbers—may occur in any computation.
4. *Physical Law Error:* The physical law upon which a solution rests is usually only an approximation.

The physical law error will not be considered here. Round-off errors can be reduced to a great extent by using double-precision arithmetic. However, this has a disadvantage, since double-precision arithmetic requires twice as many storage locations as real arithmetic would require.

Truncation error is not known exactly, but in general can be estimated or bounded. As an example, since sin x is an alternating series whose terms decrease in magnitude, the true value of the sin x lies between s_n and s_{n+1}, where s_n is the nth partial sum, and

$$s_{n+1} = s_n \pm \frac{x^{2n+1}}{(2n+1)!}.$$

Hence, the truncation error is bounded by

$$E = \left| \frac{\pm x^{2n+1}}{(2n+1)!} \right|.$$

In any rapidly convergent series, the nth term in absolute value can be taken as a measure of the truncation error. In the program it would require one more term to be computed, i.e.,

$$\text{TERM} = \frac{\text{(TERM)(XSQ)}}{\text{(DENOM)(DENOM}-1.0)}$$

where DENOM has been increased by 2.0 after the final value of SUM has been computed.

EXERCISE

Write programs for Probs. 2-1 through 2-6, with the added requirement of computing an extra value of TERM as a measure of the truncation error.

3

Roots of an Equation

In this chapter, methods for finding roots of $f(x) = 0$, where $f(x)$ is a piecewise continuous function of x with real coefficients, will be presented. In Ch. 4, sets of linear and nonlinear equations will be considered.

The usual procedure for solving $f(x) = 0$ consists of two parts: approximate the root, and refine this approximation to the desired accuracy.

3.1 First Approximation

In finding the first approximation to a root r of $f(x) = 0$, probably the best method is a good guess based upon sound knowledge of the conditions that led to the equation. Another method consists of graphing $y = f(x)$ and determining x_0, where $y \cong 0$.

A third method is based upon the *intermediate value theorem:* If a real function $f(x)$ is continuous between $x = a$ and $x = b$, a and b being real numbers, and if $f(a)f(b) < 0$, then there is at least one real root between a and b.

In addition, the Bernoulli method will be considered in Sec. 3.13.

3.2 Method of False Position

Based on the theorem stated in Sec. 3.1, the method of false position can be effectively used to find a better approximation. From Fig. 3.1,

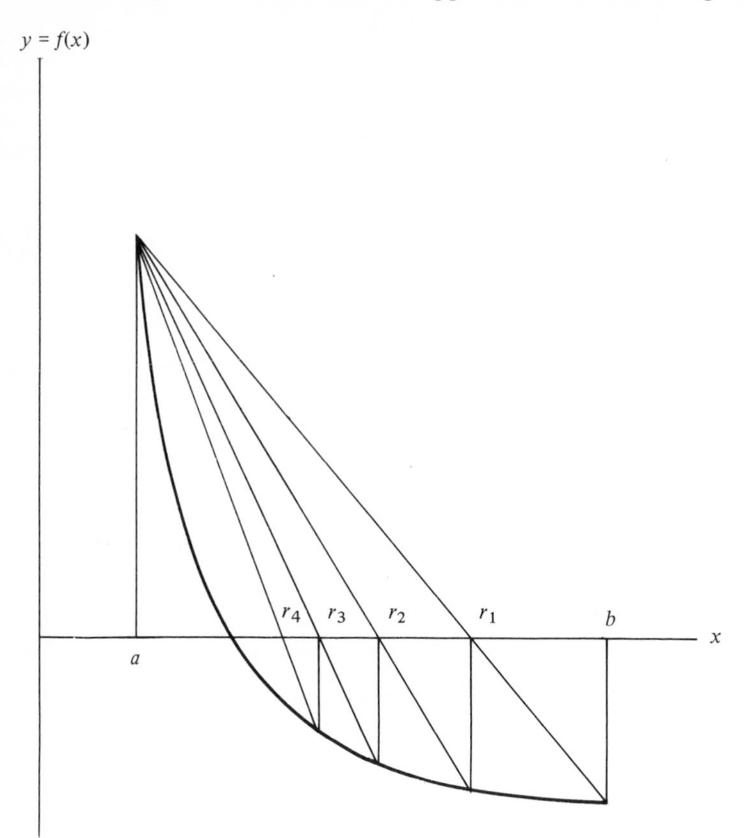

FIGURE 3.1 Method of False Position for a Convex Function

by use of similar triangles,

$$r_1 = a + \frac{f(a)(b - a)}{f(a) - f(b)}, \tag{3.1}$$

and again by similar triangles,

$$r_2 = a + \frac{f(a)(r_1 - a)}{f(a) - f(r_1)}. \tag{3.2}$$

Or, in general, by a process of iteration,

$$r_{i+1} = a + \frac{f(a)(r_i - a)}{f(a) - f(r_i)}. \tag{3.3}$$

Before each iteration to find r_{i+1}, a test should be made to determine whether or not $f(a)f(r_i)$ is negative. If it is negative, then the above formula (3.3) should be used. However, if the test shows that $f(a)f(r_i)$ is greater than zero, then according to the false position method, the value of r_i should replace a and the iteration should be

$$r_{i+1} = b + \frac{f(b)(r_i - b)}{f(r_i) - f(b)}. \tag{3.4}$$

From Fig. 3.1, it is clear that $f(a)f(r_i)$ is always negative; therefore, Eq. 3.3 will guarantee convergence without use of the test when a function is convex,[1] as is the case here. This will be true for any convex function. Thus, for the following problem this test is omitted.

3.2.1 Flow Chart

Let $f(x) = x^2 - 2$, for which $r = \sqrt{2}, -\sqrt{2}$. Hence, a root $r = \sqrt{2}$ lies between $a = 1.5$ and $b = 1.4$, for which $f(a)f(b) < 0$.

The algorithm can be stated as

$$r_{i+1} = a + \frac{f(a)(r_i - a)}{f(a) - f(r_i)}, \qquad (r_1 = b). \tag{3.5}$$

Steps

1. Read values of a, b, EPS.
2. Define $f(x)$. (See Sec. 1.20.)
3. Set $b = r_1$.
4. Compute

$$r_2 = a + \frac{f(a)(r_1 - a)}{f(a) - f(r_1)}.$$

5. If $|f(r_2)|$ is less than EPS, go to statement 8; otherwise go to statement 6.

[1] For a function $f(x)$ differentiable over $a < x < b$, if $f''(x) > 0$, $f(x)$ is said to be convex upward; if $f''(x) < 0$, $f(x)$ is said to be convex downward.

6. Replace r_1 by r_2.
7. Go to statement 4.
8. Print r_2, a, b, EPS.
9. Stop.

FLOW CHART 3.2.1 Method of False Position

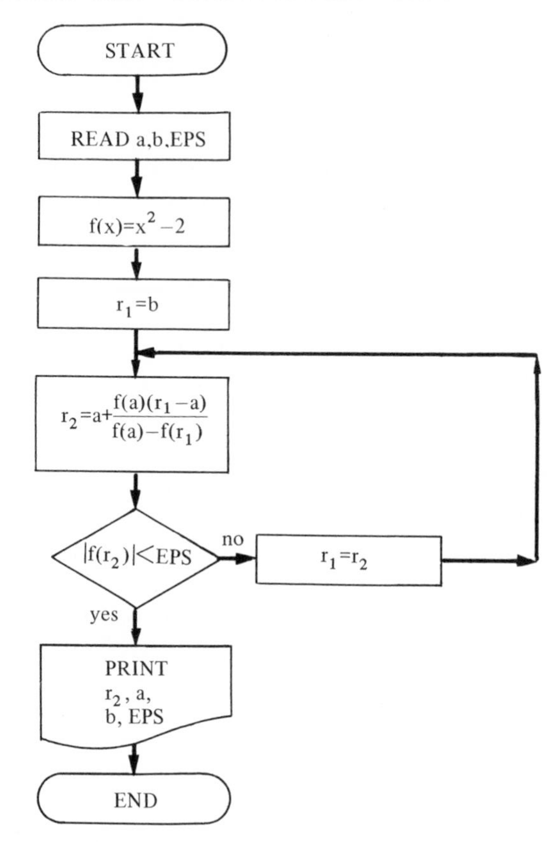

3.2.2 Discussion and Improvement of Program

Input/output and specification statements were discussed in Ch. 1 and examples given in Ch. 2. The function statement, $f(x) = X{*}{*}2\text{–}2$, described in Ch. 1, is an effective means of requesting the computer to compute $f(a)$ and $f(r_1)$. There is no need to use a subroutine.

However, there is no test other than the test for convergence, i.e., $|f(r_2)| < EPS$. In a more general case, safeguards against possible slow convergence must be included.

Safeguards

1. From the intermediate value theorem, $f(a)$ and $f(b)$ must be opposite in sign. In general, for each new approximation r_i, either $f(a)f(r_i)$ will be negative and r_i would replace b, or $f(b)f(r_i)$ will be negative and r_i would replace a.
2. When it is known by the computer that the interation will lead to convergence, there is no need to use any test to assure convergence. Thus, the above test may be avoided when convergence is certain.

   Hence, Eq. 3.3 or Eq. 3.4 may be changed so that the last two computed iterates are used to compute a new iterate, i.e.,

$$r_{i+1} = r_i + \frac{f(r_i)(r_i - r_{i-1})}{f(r_{i-1}) - f(r_i)}, \qquad (i = 2, 3, \ldots). \qquad (3.6)$$

3. A sequence of iterates $\{r_i\}$ determined by Eq. 3.6 will converge to the root r in most cases. However in some cases, e.g., where $f(x)$ is not convex, there may be divergence. Figure 3.2 (p. 48) illustrates an extreme case—the iterates $r_4, r_5, \ldots$ are diverging from the true root r.

   A safeguard against such possibility using Eq. 3.6 would be based upon a test to determine if each r_i falls within the interval (a, b). If any iterate such as r_4 or r_5 does not fall within this interval, the initial iterate r_1 may be adjusted so that successive iterates will fall within the interval.
4. One more precaution should be taken. To avoid an unnecessary number of iterations with no sufficiently better approximations, a running count of the number of iterations should be kept; if the number of iterations exceeds a given number (determined by the programmer), computation of the program should be terminated.

The revised Flow Chart 3.2.2 directs the flow of work to use Eq. 3.6 as long as the computed iterate r_3 falls in the interval (a,b).

For the first iteration, the false position test $f(r_3)f(r_2) < 0$ is used, and r_3 replaces r_1 or r_2 accordingly. For all successive iterations, as long as r_3 lies in the interval (a,b), the $f(r_3)f(r_2) < 0$ test is not applied. If r_3 is greater than b or less than a, then the $f(r_3)f(r_2) < 0$ test is applied once.

The test $|f(r_3)| < EPS$ does not assure true convergence. As an example of this condition, in Fig. 3.2 the absolute value of $f(r_5)$ is quite small and could be mistaken for true convergence in such a test.

FLOW CHART 3.2.2 Revised False Position Method *

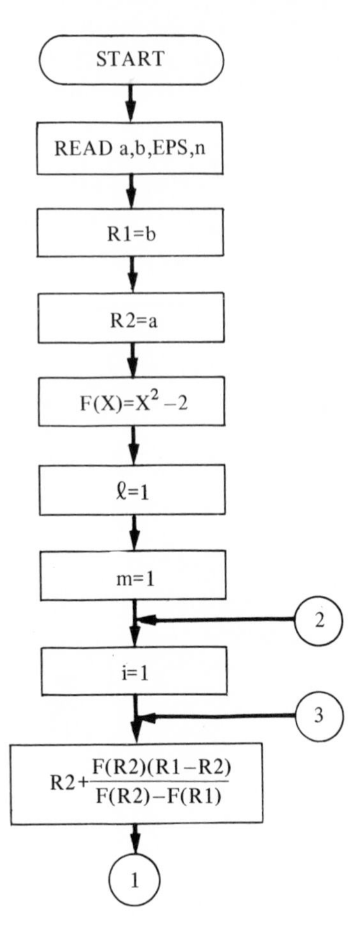

* To avoid confusion with the numeral "1," in the Flow Charts the letter "l" is replaced by the symbol "ℓ."

FLOW CHART 3.2.2 *(Continued)*

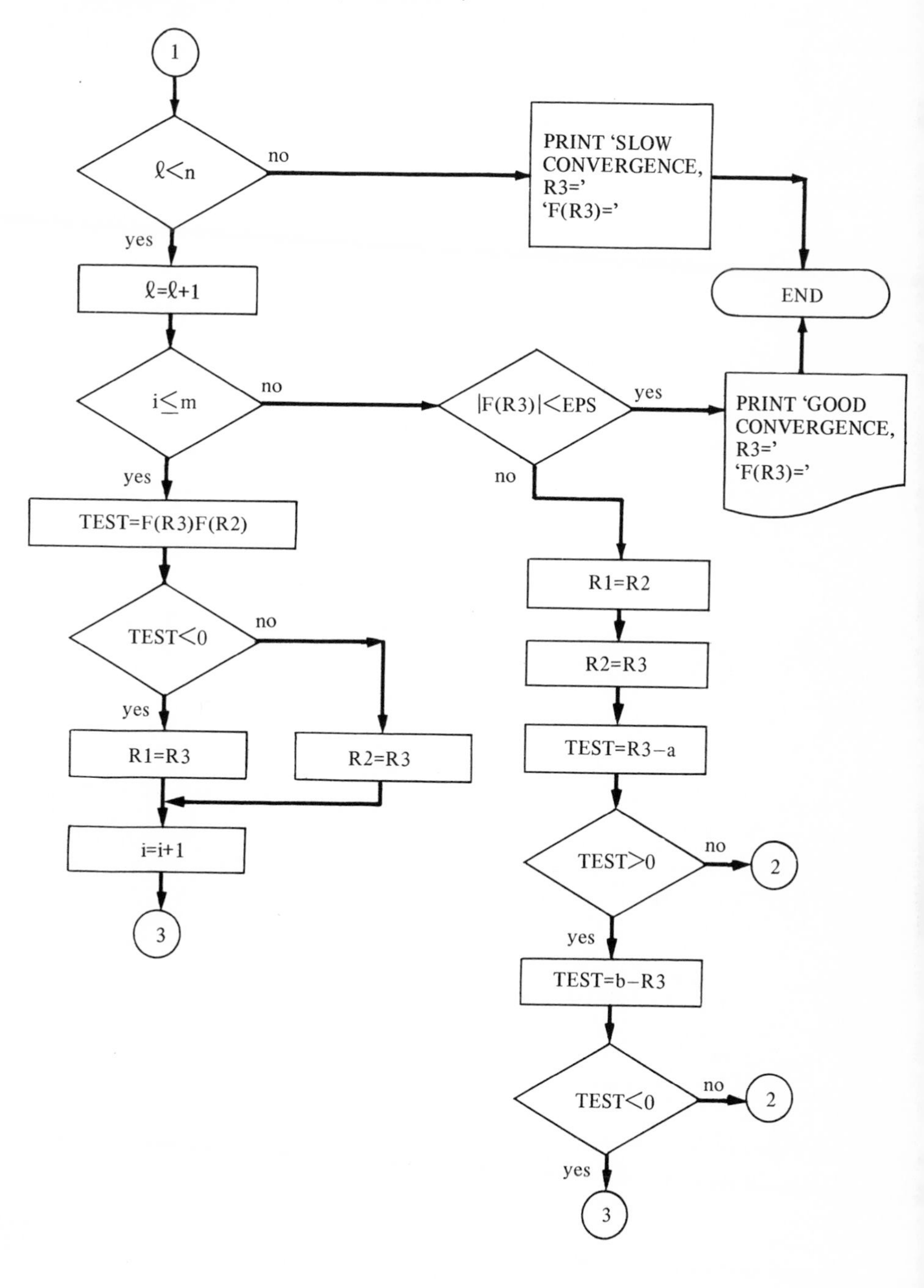

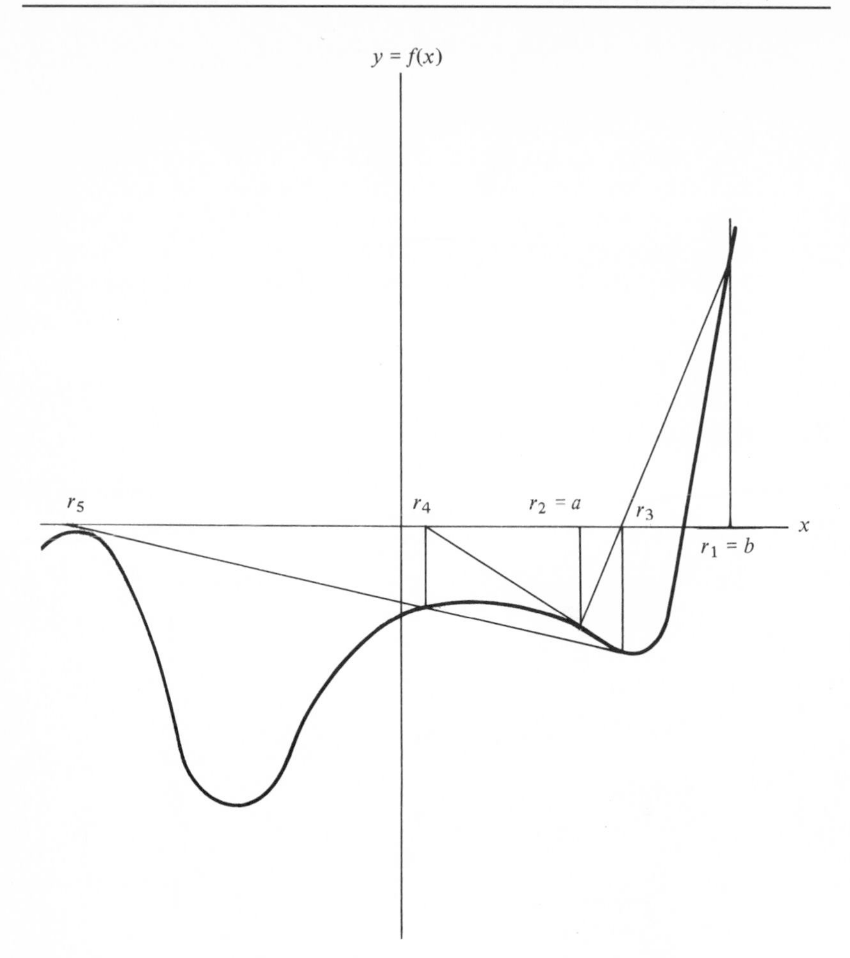

FIGURE 3.2 Method Using Eq. 3.6—Function Not Convex

3.2.3 Explanation of Revised Flow Chart

Consider the revised Flow Chart 3.2.2 in parts. The first part, from START through YES on the test of $I \leq M$, on through the test of $F(R3)F(R2) < 0$, and back to the computation of another $R3$ with I being replaced by $I + 1$, calculates two values of $R3$. The second part, which directs the flow through the NO direction of the test $I \leq M$ through the test $|F(R3)| < EPS$, uses the iterative formula

$$r_{i+1} = r_i + \frac{f(r_i)(r_i - r_{i-1})}{f(r_{i-1}) - f(r_i)}.$$

The two tests guaranteeing that $R3$ lies in the interval (a,b), provided that the tests are answered in the affirmative, computes successive values of $R3$ without using the test $F(R3)F(R2) < 0$. If either test shows that $R3$ does not lie within (a,b), the flow is redirected so that the test $F(R3)F(R2) < 0$ is again used; that is, the first part of Flow Chart 3.2.2 is used.

3.3 Newton-Raphson Method

Let x_0 be a first approximation to a root r of $f(x) = 0$. Then, by a truncated Taylor's series,

$$f(x_0 + \Delta x) \cong f(x_0) + f'(x_0)\Delta x = 0, \tag{3.7}$$

and

$$\Delta x \cong -f(x_0)/f'(x_0). \tag{3.8}$$

A second approximation is

$$x_1 = x_0 + \Delta x = x_0 - f(x_0)/f'(x_0). \tag{3.9}$$

By repeating this process, the iteration formula becomes

$$x_{i+1} = x_i - f(x_i)/f'(x_i). \tag{3.10}$$

What can be said about the rate of convergence of the iterates? By expanding $f(x)$ about the ith iterate in a Taylor's series with a remainder:

$$f(x) = f(x_i) + (x - x_i)f'(x_i) + \frac{(x - x_i)^2}{2} f''(\xi), \tag{3.11}$$

where ξ lies between x_i and x. Replacing x by $r, f(r) = 0$, Eq. 3.11 becomes

$$r = x_i - \frac{f(x_i)}{f'(x_i)} - \frac{(r - x_i)^2}{2} \frac{f''(\xi)}{f'(x_i)}, \tag{3.12}$$

assuming that $f'(x_i) \neq 0$. Then, by Eq. 3.10,

$$x_{i+1} - r = \frac{(x_i - r)^2 f''(\xi)}{2f'(x_i)}. \tag{3.13}$$

Since $x_i - r$ is the error in the ith iterate, Eq. 3.13 is a measure of the error of the next iterate. Equation 3.13 can be stated as

$$E_{i+1} = \frac{(E_i)^2 f''(\xi)}{2f'(x_i)}, \qquad (E_i = x_i - r). \tag{3.14}$$

Assuming that $|E_0| < 1$, it can be seen from Eq. 3.14 that if, for X in the region of interest,

$$\left|\frac{f''(\xi)}{2f'(X)}\right| < M \tag{3.15}$$

where M is an arbitrary positive number, the iterates x_i converge to r.

3.3.1 Flow Chart

The letter A is an arbitrary number chosen so that if $|f'(x)|$ should be too small at any time, transfer is made to an output statement of slow convergence. The rest of the flow chart is straightforward.

3.4 Square Root of a Number

In order to find the square root of a number A, let $f(x) = x^2 - A$ define the square root function. Applying the Newton–Raphson formula, Eq. 3.10, the square root iterative formula becomes

$$x_{i+1} = 1/2(x_i + A/x_i). \tag{3.16}$$

The error in the ith iterate is $x_i - r$, and the relative error is $(x_i - r)/r$, where $r = \sqrt{A}$.

Thus, if the relative error for the ith iterate is

$$RE_i = (x_i - r)/r,$$

then

$$RE_{i+1} = (x_{i+1} - r)/r. \tag{3.17}$$

It can also be shown that relative error in the $(i + 1)$th iterate is approximately equal to one-half the square of the relative error in the ith iterate.[2] Thus, if $|RE_0| < 1$, convergence is guaranteed. However, this test is not used in the flow chart or the program.

[2] See Kaiser L. Kunz, *Numerical Analysis* (New York: McGraw-Hill Book Company, Inc., 1957), p. 13.

FLOW CHART 3.3.1 Newton–Raphson Method

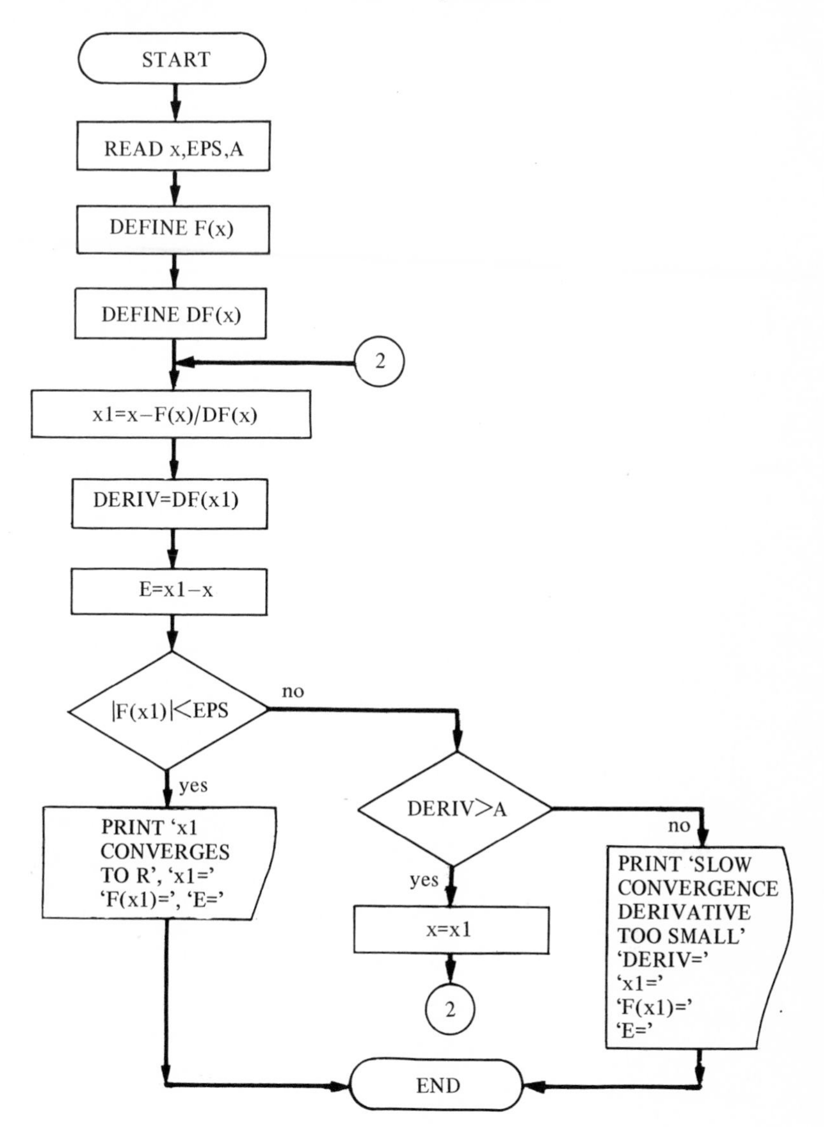

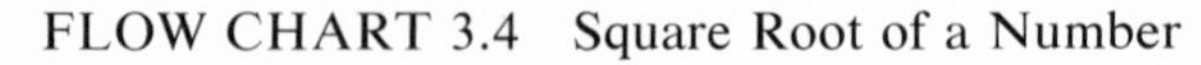

FLOW CHART 3.4 Square Root of a Number

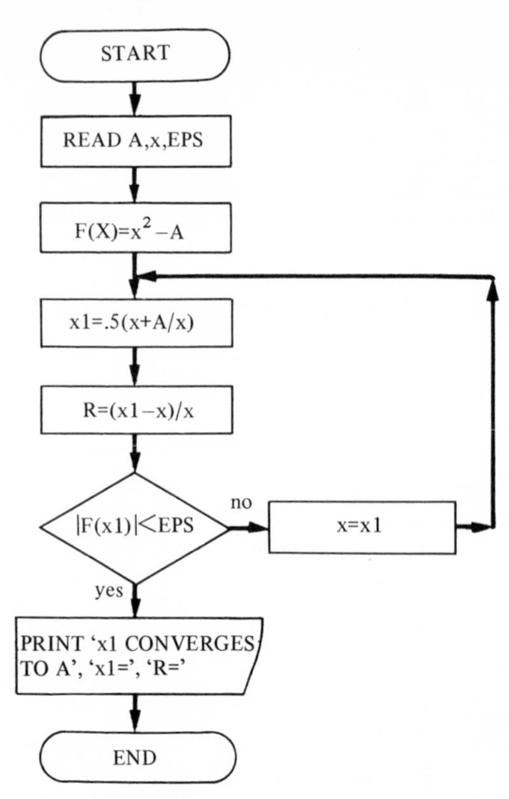

3.4.1 Program

Given: $f(x) = x^2 - A, \quad A = 2, \quad EPS = 10^{-4}$.
Starting value: $x = 1.5$.

```
      F(X)=X**2-A
      READ(5,100)A,X,EPS
100   FORMAT(3F10.4)
  1   X1=.5*(X+A/X)
      R=(X1-X)/X
      IF(ABS(F(X1))-EPS)2,3,3
  2   WRITE(6,101)X1,R
101   FORMAT(//,'X1 CONVERGES TO A',/,'X1=',F7.5,/,'R=',F8.5)
      STOP
  3   X=X1
      GO TO 1
      END
```

```
X1 CONVERGES TO A
X1=1.41422
R=-0.00173
```

PROBLEMS

3-1. (a) Derive a Newton–Raphson formula for the reciprocal of a real positive number A, $f(x) = 1/x - A = 0$. The iterates will approach $1/A$ if $0 < x_0 < 2/A$.

(b) Write a flow chart and program to approximate the reciprocal of the real positive number A. This should include tests for convergence and relative error. It should also include a test to insure that x_0 is within the range 0 to $2/A$.

3-2. (a) Derive a Newton–Raphson formula for the reciprocal of the square root of a real positive number A, $f(x) = 1/x^2 - A = 0$.

(b) Write a flow chart for a program to approximate $A^{-1/2}$. Test for convergence and relative error. $A^{1/2}$ can also be approximated by multiplying the result $A^{-1/2}$ by A. Include this routine.

3.5 The Secant Method

An improvement over the false position method is found in the secant method described below. The restriction that two consecutive approximations x_i and x_{i-1} be on opposite sides of the root is dropped. Hence, there is the possibility of no convergence. However, if convergence exists, it is much faster.

Let $(a, f(a))$ and $(b, f(b))$ be two sets of tabulated values of x and $f(x)$. Then

$$x = \left(\frac{f(x) - f(b)}{f(a) - f(b)}\right) a + \left(\frac{f(x) - f(a)}{f(b) - f(a)}\right) b. \tag{3.18}$$

Equation 3.18 is known as the Lagrange inverse interpolation formula for two tabulated points.

Let $f(x) = 0$, then

$$x = \left(\frac{f(b)}{f(b) - f(a)}\right) a + \left(\frac{f(a)}{f(a) - f(b)}\right) b. \tag{3.19}$$

Thus, x is the first approximation to the root r of $f(x) = 0$. Replacing b by x_1 and a by x_2, the formula can be stated as

$$x_3 = \left\{\frac{f(x_1)}{f(x_1) - f(x_2)}\right\} x_2 + \left\{\frac{f(x_2)}{f(x_2) - f(x_1)}\right\} x_1 . \tag{3.20}$$

And by replacing x_2 with x_3 and x_1 with x_2,

$$x_4 = \left\{\frac{f(x_2)}{f(x_2) - f(x_3)}\right\} x_3 + \left\{\frac{f(x_3)}{f(x_3) - f(x_2)}\right\} x_2 . \quad (3.21)$$

Thus, for the iterates x_{i-1}, x_i, x_{i+1}, the formula is

$$x_{i+1} = \left\{\frac{f(x_{i-1})}{f(x_{i-1}) - f(x_i)}\right\} x_i + \left\{\frac{f(x_i)}{f(x_i) - f(x_{i-1})}\right\} x_{i-1} . \quad (3.22)$$

Equation 3.22 is equivalent to Eq. 3.6. In this formula, two successive iterates are used to compute the next iterate.

3.5.1 Flow Chart

Let $f(x) = \sin x - x/2 = 0$. A root exists in the interval $x = \pi/2$ to $x = \pi$. Let a and b have starting values of $\pi/2$ and π, respectively; then the formula is

$$x = \left(\frac{f(a)}{f(a) - f(b)}\right) b + \left(\frac{f(b)}{f(b) - f(a)}\right) a. \quad (3.23)$$

3.5.2 Comparison of Methods

In both the false position method and the secant method, the only printed iterate was the last value, and all previously computed iterates are erased. To show how much more rapidly the secant method converges, subscripted variables can be used.

In Flow Chart 3.5.2, the false position method of Sec. 3.2 with the false position test $f(x_i)f(a) < 0$, and the secant method of Sec. 3.5 will be developed for the function

$$f(x) = \sin x - x/2, \qquad (x_1 = \pi/2, x_2 = \pi).$$

All iterates x_i for the false position method will be printed, and all iterates z_i for the secant method will be printed.[3]

[3] Note: $\pi = 3.14159265$,
$\pi/2 = 1.57079633$.

FLOW CHART 3.5.1 Secant Method

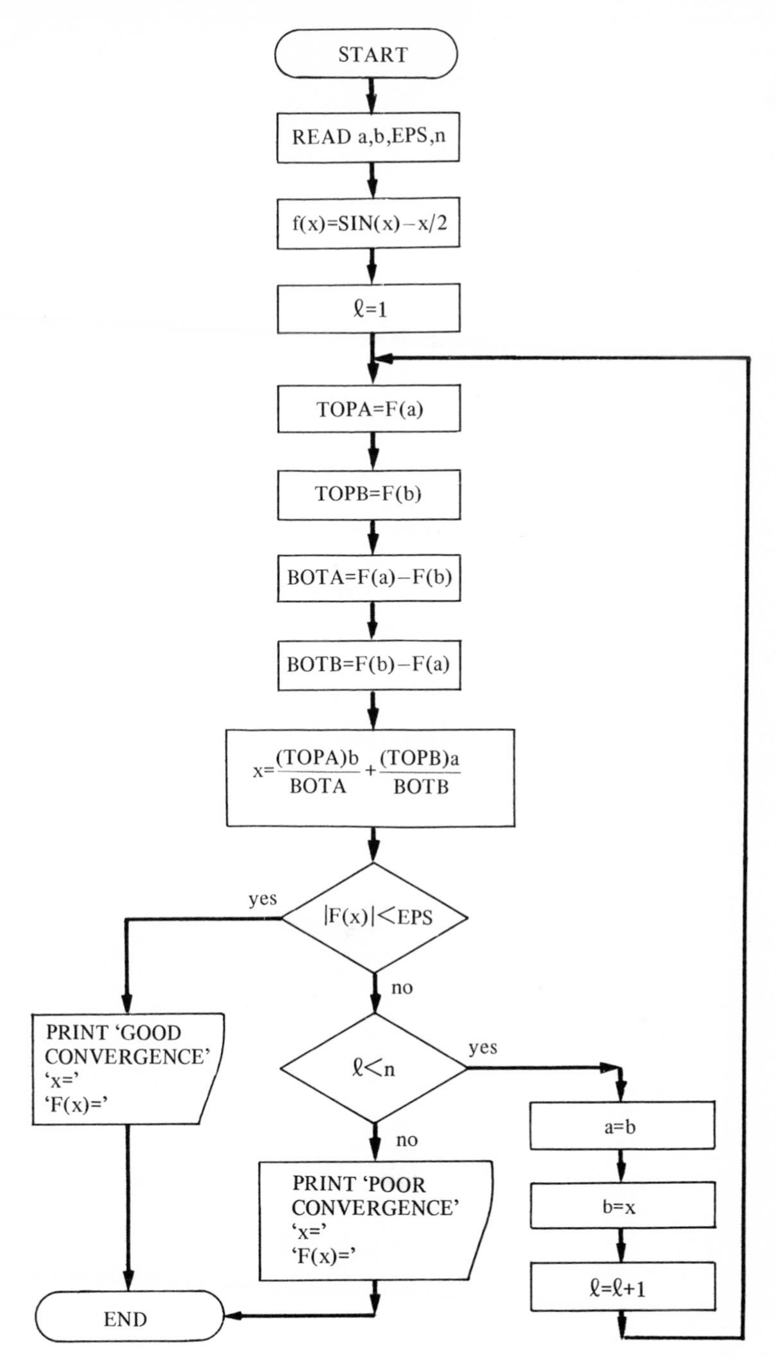

FLOW CHART 3.5.2 False Position and Secant Methods

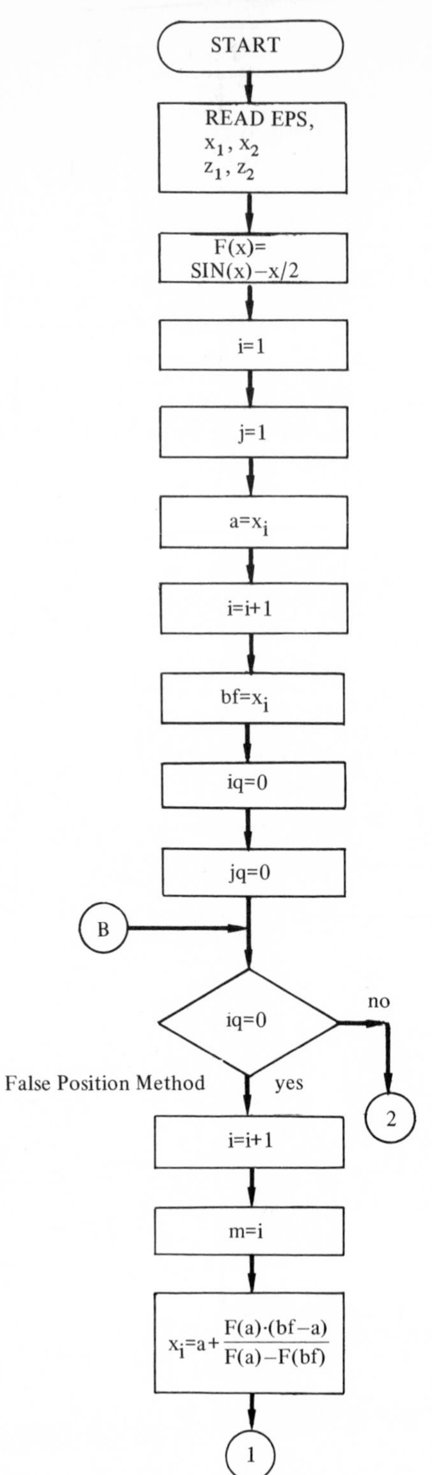

Flow Chart 3.5.2 *(Continued)*

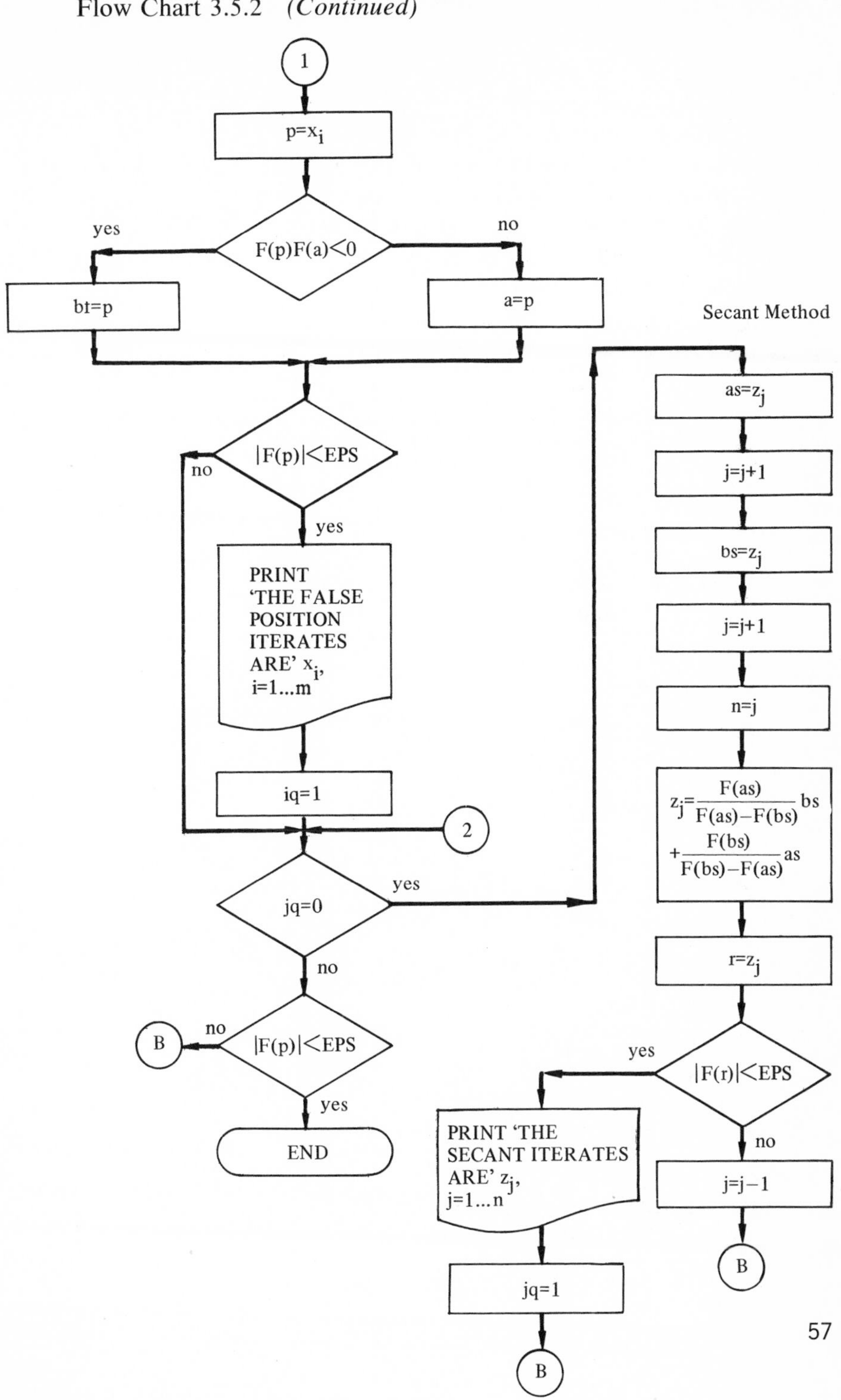

3.5.3 Program

It should be noted that the value of π in the output is $\pi = 3.14159203$, whereas the exact value of π to the eighth decimal place is 3.14159265, showing that this particular computer is accurate only to the sixth decimal place. A similar case can be made for the value of $\pi/2$. If double-precision arithmetic had been used, the output would have been exact to the eighth decimal place.

Starting values: $\pi = 3.14159265,$
$\pi/2 = 1.57079633.$

```
C     A COMPARISON OF THE RELATIVE SPEEDS
C     OF THE FALSE POSITION METHOD VERSUS
C     THE SECANT METHOD
C     F(X)=SIN(X)-X/2
C
      DIMENSION X(500),Z(500)
      F(X)=SIN(X)-X/2
    1 FORMAT(F15.8)
    2 FORMAT(1H1)
    3 FORMAT(//10X,'THE FALSE POSITION ITERATES ARE',//)
    4 FORMAT(//10X,'THE SECANT ITERATES ARE',//)
    5 FORMAT(15X,I2,5X,F15.8)
      WRITE(6,2)
      READ(5,1)X(1)
      READ(5,1)X(2)
      READ(5,1)EPS
      Z(1)=X(1)
      Z(2)=X(2)
      I=1
      J=1
C     TO COMPUTE A FALSE POSITION ITERATE
      A=X(I)
      I=I+1
      BF=X(I)
      IQ=0
      JQ=0
   10 IF(IQ)16,11,16
   11 I=I+1
      M=I
      X(I)=A+(F(A)*(BF-A)/(F(A)-F(BF)))
      P=X(I)
      IF(F(P)*F(A))12,13,13
   12 BF=P
      GO TO 14
   13 A=P
   14 IF(ABS(F(P))-EPS)50,16,16
```

```
   50 WRITE(6,3)
      DO 51 K=1,M
   51 WRITE(6,5)K,X(K)
      IQ=1
   16 IF(JQ)17,18,17
   17 IF(ABS(F(P))-EPS)99,10,10
C     TO COMPUTE SECANT ITERATE
   18 AS=Z(J)
      J=J+1
      BS=Z(J)
      J=J+1
      N=J
      Z(J)=(F(AS)/(F(AS)-F(BS)))*BS+(F(BS)/(F(BS)-F(AS)))*AS
      R=Z(J)
      IF(ABS(F(R))-EPS)60,19,19
   19 J=J-1
      GO TO 10
   60 WRITE(6,4)
      DO 61 K=1,N
   61 WRITE(6,5)K,Z(K)
      JQ=1
      GO TO 10
   99 STOP
      END
END OF COMPILATION MAIN
```

```
      THE SECANT ITERATES ARE
        1      1.57079601
        2      3.14159203
        3      1.75960255
        4      1.84420204
        5      1.90010929
        6      1.89535141
        7      1.89549351

      THE FALSE POSITION ITERATES ARE
        1      1.57079601
        2      3.14159203
        3      1.75960255
        4      1.84420204
        5      1.87701225
        6      1.88895416
        7      1.89319515
        8      1.89468765
        9      1.89521122
       10      1.89539433
       11      1.89545918
       12      1.89548111
       13      1.89548969
       14      1.89549255
       15      1.89549351
```

3.5.4 Explanation

Aside from the obvious fact that the output shows the secant method for a convex function converges in almost one-third the operating time of the false position method (five iterations against thirteen), there are some general programming features that should be noted. First, by using the control IQ, the flow of work is so directed to avoid computation of the false position iterates, or the printing of these, if $IQ = 1$. Only when $IQ = 0$ will either computation or the printing of these iterates occur. In this case, only one output of false position iterates will be printed.

The control JQ has the same effect on the secant method as IQ has on the false position method. In computing a secant iterate, the index J is reset equal to $J - 1$. This is necessary in computing the next iterate, Z_{J+1}. If this statement were omitted, the computer would be asked to compute Z_{J+2} in terms of Z_{J+1}, which has not at the time been computed.

EXERCISE

Let $f(x) = 0$ have a root r in the interval (a,b). For $f(a)$ and $f(b)$ opposite in sign, a process known as the bisectional method will always converge to the root r. The method consists of finding a sequence of points such that each point is the average of the two previous points, which are on opposite sides of the root r. Thus,

$$x_{i+1} = \frac{x_i + x_{i-1}}{2},$$

where $f(x_i)f(x_{i-1}) < 0$. The only formula required is $x_1 = (a + b)/2$, and x_1 replaces either a or b according to the answer of the test $f(x_1)f(a) < 0$.

Write a flow chart and program for the bisection method as applied to

$$f(x) = x^3 - 3x^2 + 4x - 5 = 0, \qquad (a = 2,\ b = 3).$$

Answer: $r = 2.21341$.

POLYNOMIALS

Before considering special methods of solving polynomial equations, it is appropriate first to develop methods of multiplying and dividing polynomials.

3.6 Multiplication of Polynomials

Let

$$P_n(x) = a_1x^n + a_2x^{n-1} + \cdots + a_nx + a_{n+1},$$

and (3.24)

$$P_m(x) = b_1x^m + b_2x^{m-1} + \cdots + b_mx + b_{m+1}.$$

The product of $P_n(x) \cdot P_m(x)$ is

$$P_{m+n}(x) = c_1x^{m+n} + c_2x^{m+n-1} + \cdots + c_{m+n}x + c_{m+n+1}. \quad (3.25)$$

The coefficients c_i can be determined by the usual method for multiplication of two polynomials, as shown below for $n = 5$, $m = 3$:

$$\begin{array}{l}
a_1x^5 + a_2x^4 + a_3x^3 + a_4x^2 + a_5x + a_6 \\
b_1x^3 + b_2x^2 + b_3x + b_4 \\
\hline
a_1b_1x^8 + a_1b_2x^7 + a_1b_3x^6 + a_1b_4x^5 \\
\quad + a_2b_1x^7 + a_2b_2x^6 + a_2b_3x^5 + a_2b_4x^4 \\
\quad\quad + a_3b_1x^6 + a_3b_2x^5 + a_3b_3x^4 + a_3b_4x^3 \\
\quad\quad\quad + a_4b_1x^5 + a_4b_2x^4 + a_4b_3x^3 + a_4b_4x^2 + a_5b_4x \\
\quad\quad\quad\quad + a_5b_1x^4 + a_5b_2x^3 + a_5b_3x^2 + a_6b_3x \\
\quad\quad\quad\quad\quad + a_6b_1x^3 + a_6b_2x^2 \\
\quad\quad\quad\quad\quad\quad + a_6b_4 \\
\hline
c_1x^8 + c_2x^7 + c_3x^6 + c_4x^5 + c_5x^4 + c_6x^3 + c_7x^2 + c_8x + c_9
\end{array}$$

The following set of equations shows the relationship between the coefficients c_i and a_i, b_i:

$$\begin{aligned}
c_1 &= a_1b_1 \\
c_2 &= a_1b_2 + a_2b_1 \\
c_3 &= a_1b_3 + a_2b_2 + a_3b_1 \\
c_4 &= a_1b_4 + a_2b_3 + a_3b_2 + a_4b_1 \\
c_5 &= a_2b_4 + a_3b_3 + a_4b_2 + a_5b_1 \\
c_6 &= a_3b_4 + a_4b_3 + a_5b_2 + a_6b_1 \\
c_7 &= a_4b_4 + a_5b_3 + a_6b_2 \\
c_8 &= a_5b_4 + a_6b_3 \\
c_9 &= a_6b_4
\end{aligned}$$

Thus, $P_{m+n}(x)$ may be expressed as

$$\sum_{k=1}^{mn} c_k x^{mn-k}, \qquad (mn = m + n + 1),$$

and

$$c_k = \sum_{j=k-m+l}^{\min(k,n1)} a_j b_{k-j+1}, \qquad (n1 = n + 1).$$

Initially, l takes on the value of m, and successively becomes $m - 1$, $m - 2, \ldots$ until it equals zero; $\min(k, n1)$ means that the smaller of the two values of k and $n1$ is always chosen as the upper limit of the summation.

3.6.1 Flow Chart

Let

$$P_n(x) = a_1 x^n + a_2 x^{n-1} + \cdots + a_n x + a_{n+1},$$
$$P_m(x) = b_1 x^m + b_2 x^{m-1} + \cdots + b_m x + b_{m+1}.$$

Then

$$P_{m+n}(x) = \sum_{k=1}^{mn} c_k x^{mn-k},$$

where

$$c_k = \sum_{j=k-m+l}^{\min(k,n1)} a_j b_{k-j+1}.$$

l takes on values of $m, m - 1, m - 2, \ldots, 0$, and $n > m$, $n1 = n + 1$, $mn = m + n + 1$.

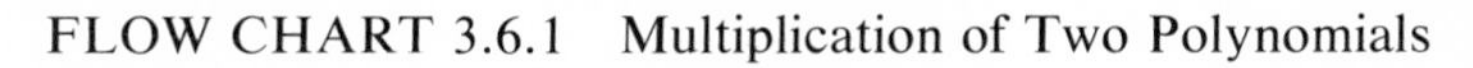

FLOW CHART 3.6.1 Multiplication of Two Polynomials

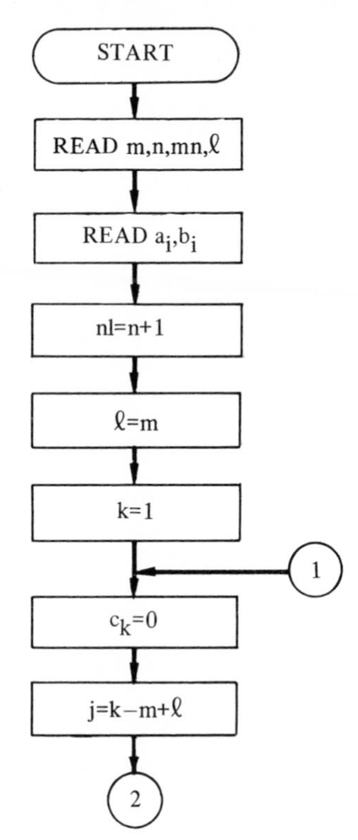

Flow Chart 3.6.1 *(Continued)*

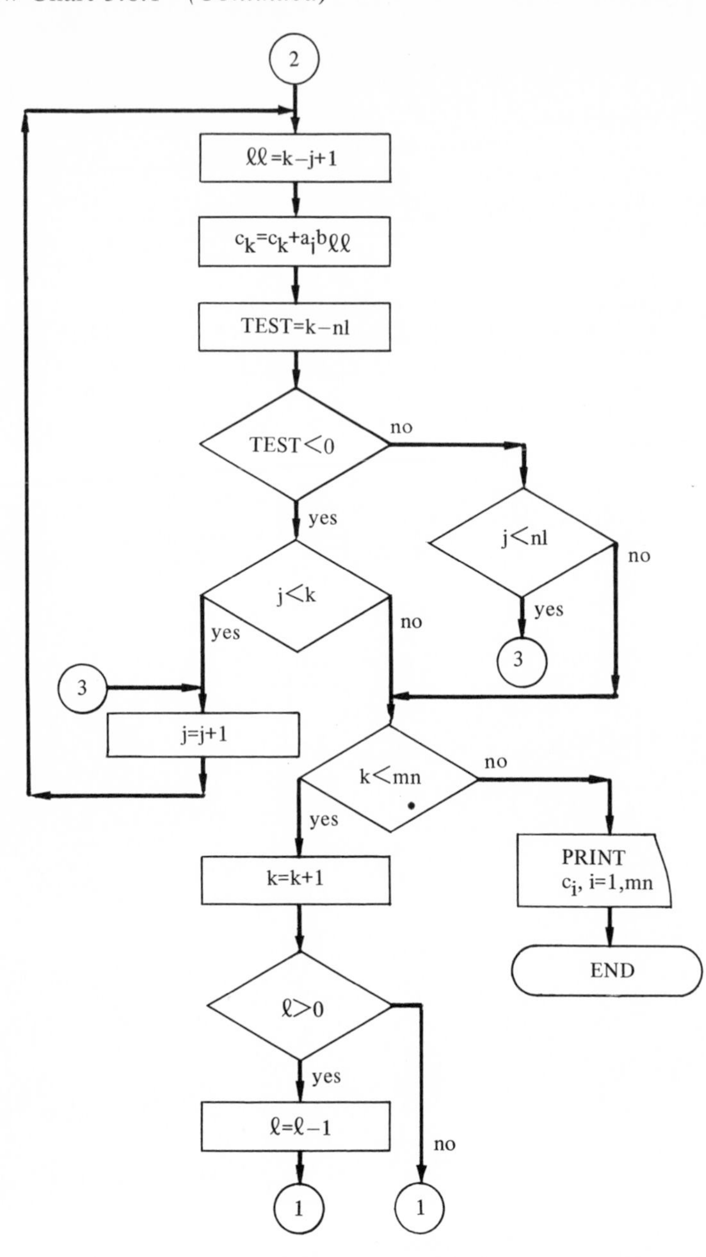

3.6.2 Program

For the product $p_m(x) \cdot P_n(X)$, where

$$P_n(x) = P_3(x) = x^3 + 3x^2 + 1 \quad \text{and} \quad P_m(x) = P_2(x) = x^2 + 2x + 1.$$

```
   MULTIPLICATION OF TWO POLYNOMIALS
   DIMENSION A(10),B(10),C(10)
 1 FORMAT(2I2)
 2 FORMAT (7F10.4)
 4 FORMAT (//5X,'THE POLYNOMIAL P(N) IS',//)
 5 FORMAT (//5X,'THE POLYNOMIAL P(M) IS',//)
 6 FORMAT (//5X,'THE PRODUCT OF P(N) P(M) IS',//)
   READ(5,1)N,M
   N1=N+1
   M1=M+1
   L=M
   MN=M+N+1
   READ(5,2) (A(I),I=1,N1)
   READ(5,2) (B(I),I=1,M1)
   DO 10 K=1,MN
   C(K)=0.0
   J=K-M+1
60 LL=K-J+1
   C(K)=C(K)+A(J)*B(LL)
   TEST=K-N1
   IF(TEST)20,30,30
20 IF(J-K)40,10,10
40 J=J+1
   GO TO 60
30 IF(J-N1)40,70,70
70 IF(L)10,10,80
80 L=L-1
10 CONTINUE
   WRITE(6,4)
   WRITE(6,2) (A(I),I=1,N1)
   WRITE(6,5)
   WRITE(6,2) (B(I),I=1,M1)
   WRITE(6,6)
   WRITE(6,2) (C(I),I=1,MN)
   STOP
   END
```

```
THE POLYNOMIAL P(N) IS
1.0000  3.0000  3.0000  1.0000

THE POLYNOMIAL P(M) IS
1.0000  2.0000  1.0000

THE PRODUCT OF P(N) P(M) IS
1.0000  5.0000  10.0000  10.0000  5.0000  1.0000
```

3.7 Division of Polynomials

Let n be greater than m. Then the division of $P_n(x)$ by $P_m(x)$ is expressed as shown below for $m=3$ and $n=4$:

$$
\begin{array}{r}
q_1x + q_2 \\
a_1x^3 + a_2x^2 + a_3x + a_4 \;\overline{)\,b_1x^4 + b_2x^3 + b_3x^2 + b_4x + b_5} \\
\underline{b_1x^4 + q_1a_2x^3 + q_1a_3x^2 + q_1a_4x} \\
b_2'x^3 + b_3'x^2 + b_4'x + b_5 \\
\underline{b_2'x^3 + q_2a_2x^2 + q_2a_3x + q_2a_4} \\
b_3''x^2 + b_4''x + b_5''
\end{array}
\tag{3.27}
$$

where, for $q_1 = b_1/a_1$,

$$b_2' = b_2 - (q_1)a_2, \qquad b_3' = b_3 - (q_1)a_3, \qquad b_4' = b_4 - (q_1)a_4;$$

for $q_2 = b_2'/a_1$,

$$b_3'' = b_3' - (q_2)a_2, \qquad b_4'' = b_4' - (q_2)a_3, \qquad b_5'' = b_5' - (q_2)a_4.$$

In a general problem, where m and n are positive integers, $n > m$, the quotient coefficients are

$$q_i = b_i^{i-1}/a_1, \qquad (i = 1, 2, \ldots, n - m + 1,\ b_1^0 = b_1),$$

and the superscript indicates the previous line of division. Then for each i, the coefficients of each next line of division, including the remainder, are expressed as

$$b_l^i = b_l^{i-1} - q_i a_{l+1-i},$$

where $l = i + 1, i + 2, \ldots, i + m$ (m terms), $l + m \leq n + 1$.

3.7.1 Flow Chart

Definitions

n, m are degrees, $n > m$.
$n1 = n + 1$ is the number of coefficients in the dividend.
$m1 = m + 1$ is the number of coefficients in the divisor.
$mn = n - m + 1$ is the number of coefficients in the quotient.
q_i, $i = 1, 2, \ldots, n - m + 1$ are the quotient coefficients.
b_l, $l = 2, 3, \ldots, m + 1$ are the coefficients of all intermediate steps of division.
b_l, $l = n - m + 2, n - m + 3, \ldots, n + 1$ are the coefficients of the remainder.

Notes on the Flow Chart

For each q_i formed, a line of division is formed. Thus, for $i = 1$ and $q_i = b_1/a_1$, then $b_2, b_3, \ldots, b_{m1}$ are formed. For each $i < mn$, i and $m1$ are incremented and another line of division is formed. When $i \geq mn$, the output statement is executed; that is, $q_1, q_2, \ldots, q_{mn}$ are printed as coefficients of the quotient, and $b_{mn+1}, b_{mn+2}, \ldots, b_{n1}$ are printed as coefficients of the remainder.

FLOW CHART 3.7.1 Division of Polynomials $P_n(x)/P_m(x)$

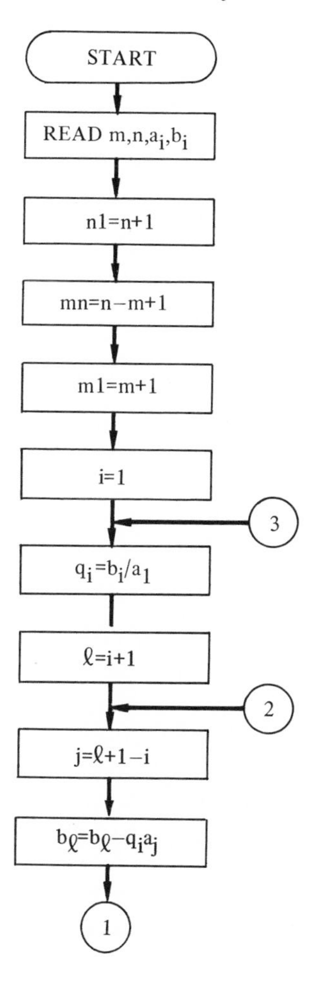

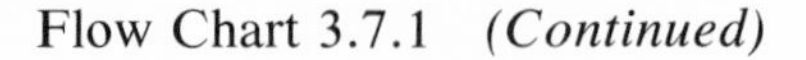
Flow Chart 3.7.1 *(Continued)*

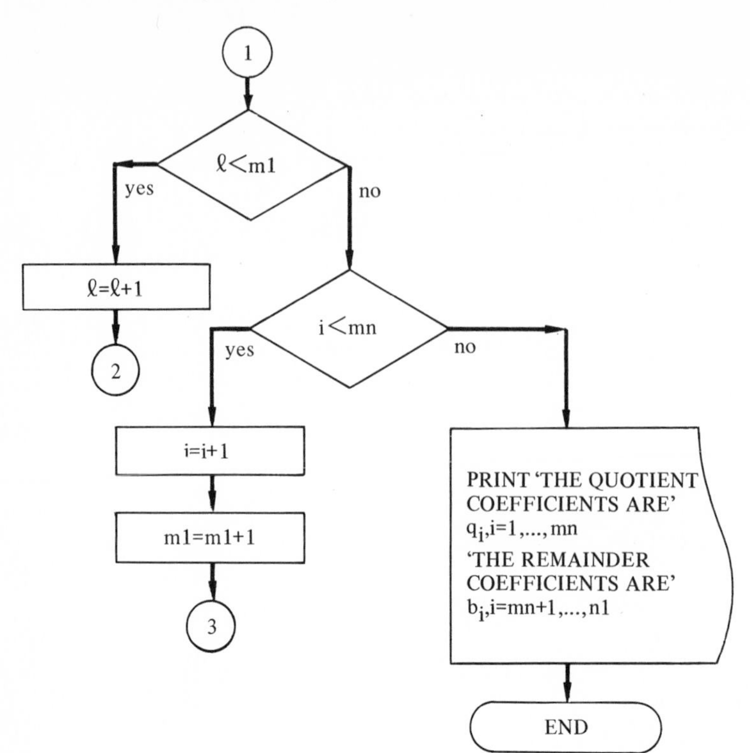

3.7.2 Program

To divide $x^5 - x^4 + 2x^3 - 16x^2 + 16x - 15$ by $x^2 - x + 1$, $(n = 5, m = 2)$.

```
C
C     PROGRAM TO DIVIDE Pn(x) by Pm(x)
C     DEGREE AND COEFFICIENTS OF POLYNOMIALS TO BE DATA
C     PROGRAM WRITTEN IN FORTRAN IV
C
      DIMENSION A(20),B(20),Q(20)
      READ(5,100)M,N
      N1=N+1
      M1=M+1
      READ(5,103)(A(I),I=1,M1)
      READ(5,103)(B(I),I=1,N1)
      WRITE(6,103)(A(I),I=1,M1)
```

```
      WRITE(6,103)(B(I),I=1,N1)
      MN=N-M+1
      I=1
    3 Q(I)=B(I)/A(1)
      L=I+1
    2 J=L+1-I
      B(L)=B(L)-Q(I)*A(J)
      IF(L-M1)4,5,5
    4 L=L+1
      GO TO 2
    5 IF(I-MN)6,7,7
    6 I=I+1
      M1=M1+1
      GO TO 3
    7 WRITE(6,101)(Q(I),I=1,MN)
  101 FORMAT('THE QUOTIENT COEFFICIENTS ARE',6F8.3/)
      LL=MN+1
      WRITE(6,102)(B(I),I=LL,N1)
  102 FORMAT('THE REMAINDER COEFFICIENTS ARE',6F8.3/)
  100 FORMAT(2I2)
  103 FORMAT(6F5.0)
      STOP
      END

      THE QUOTIENT COEFFICIENTS ARE
      1.000  0.000  1.000  -15.000

      THE REMAINDER COEFFICIENTS ARE
      0.0  0.0
```

3.8 Synthetic Division

It is often necessary to evaluate $P_m(x)$ for a given value of x and, in many cases, the values of $P'_m(x)$, $P''_m(x)$, . . . , $P^m_m(x)$ are also needed. If finding the quotient and the remainder were desired, the method of Sec. 3.7 could be used. But in most cases, all that is required is to find the remainder term, which is the value of the polynomial for the given value x.

Let

$$P_m(x) = a_0x^m + a_1x^{m-1} + \cdots + a_{m-1}x + a_m \quad \text{and} \quad x = x_0. \tag{3.28}$$

Then,

$$P_0(x_0) = a_0$$
$$P_1(x_0) = a_0x_0 + a_1 = x_0P_0(x_0) + a_1$$

$$
\begin{aligned}
P_2(x_0) &= a_0x_0^2 + a_1x_0 + a_2 = x_0P_1(x_0) + a_2 \\
&\;\;\vdots \\
P_i(x_0) &= x_0P_{i-1}(x_0) + a_i \\
&\;\;\vdots \\
P_{m-1}(x_0) &= x_0P_{m-2}(x_0) + a_{m-1} \\
P_m(x_0) &= x_0P_{m-1}(x_0) + a_m.
\end{aligned} \tag{3.29}
$$

Equations 3.29 may be expressed synthetically as

$$
\begin{array}{llllllll|l}
a_0 & a_1 & a_2 & a_3 & \cdots\ a_{m-3} & a_{m-2} & a_{m-1} & a_m & x_0 \\
 & x_0P_0(x_0) & x_0P_1(x_0) & x_0P_2(x_0) & \cdots\ x_0P_{m-4}(x_0) & x_0P_{m-3}(x_0) & x_0P_{m-2}(x_0) & x_0P_{m-1}(x_0) & \\
\hline
P_0(x_0) & P_1(x_0) & P_2(x_0) & P_3(x_0) & \cdots\ P_{m-3}(x_0) & P_{m-2}(x_0) & P_{m-1}(x_0) & P_m(x_0) &
\end{array}
$$

On the first line, the coefficients of x^m, x^{m-1}, . . . , 1 are given. Then $P_0(x_0) = a_0$ and all resulting $P_j(x_0)$ are formed by using the formula

$$P_j(x_0) = x_0P_{j-1}(x_0) + a_j,$$

the last element of which is

$$P_m(x_0) = x_0P_{m-1}(x_0) + a_m. \tag{3.30}$$

Some improvements are easily seen. $P_m(x)$ can be restated as

$$P_m(x) = a_1x^m + a_2x^{m-1} + \cdots + a_mx + a_{m+1}, \tag{3.31}$$

thereby eliminating the subscript zero.

In many problems it is not necessary to retain the coefficients a_i. Therefore, the coefficients can be called P_i. With these changes, the synthetic division appears as

$$
\begin{array}{lllllllll|l}
P_1 & P_2 & P_3 & \cdots & P_{m-3} & P_{m-2} & P_{m-1} & P_m & P_{m+1} & x_0 \\
 & x_0P_1 & x_0P_2 & \cdots & x_0P_{m-4} & x_0P_{m-3} & x_0P_{m-2} & x_0P_{m-1} & x_0P_m & \\
\hline
P_1 & P_2 & P_3 & \cdots & P_{m-3} & P_{m-2} & P_{m-1} & P_m & P_{m+1}, &
\end{array}
$$

or stated as a formula:

$$P_i = x_0P_{i-1} + P_i,$$

and $P_{m+1}(x_0)$ is the value of $P_m(x)$ at $x = x_0$.[4]

Differentiating the following equations:

$$
\begin{aligned}
P_1(x) &= a_1 \\
P_2(x) &= xP_1(x) + a_2 \\
P_3(x) &= xP_2(x) + a_3 \\
&\;\;\vdots \\
P_i(x) &= xP_{i-1}(x) + a_i \\
&\;\;\vdots \\
P_{m-1}(x) &= xP_{m-2}(x) + a_{m-1} \\
P_m(x) &= xP_{m-1}(x) + a_m \\
P_{m+1}(x) &= xP_m(x) + a_{m+1},
\end{aligned}
$$

the results are

$$
\begin{aligned}
P_1'(x) &= 0 \\
P_2'(x) &= xP_1'(x) + P_1(x) = P_1(x) \\
P_3'(x) &= xP_2'(x) + P_2(x) \\
&\;\;\vdots \\
P_i'(x) &= xP_{i-1}'(x) + P_{i-1}(x) \qquad (3.32) \\
&\;\;\vdots \\
P_{m-1}'(x) &= xP_{m-2}'(x) + P_{m-2}(x) \\
P_m'(x) &= xP_{m-1}'(x) + P_{m-1}(x) \\
P_{m+1}'(x) &= xP_m'(x) + P_m(x).
\end{aligned}
$$

A synthetic form of this division appears below:

$$
\begin{array}{cccccccc|l}
 & & & & & & & & \underline{x} \\
P_1(x) & P_2(x) & P_3(x) & \cdots & P_{m-2}(x) & P_{m-1}(x) & P_m(x) & P_{m+1}(x) & \\
 & xP_2'(x) & xP_3'(x) & \cdots & xP_{m-2}'(x) & xP_{m-1}'(x) & xP_m'(x) & & \\
\hline
P_2'(x) & P_3'(x) & P_4'(x) & \cdots & P_{m-1}'(x) & P_m'(x) & P_{m+1}'(x) & &
\end{array}
$$

[4] The expression $P_i = x_0P_{i-1} + P_i$ is not an equation in the usual sense. It merely means that $x_0P_{i-1} + P_i$ is computed and then replaces the value of P_i.

Combining the two synthetic divisions for $x = x_0$ in one synthetic division, and eliminating primes, the following form can be used, provided that the coefficients of $P_{m+1}(x)$ are not needed again:[5]

$$\begin{array}{cccccccc|l}
 & & & & & & & & x_0 \\
P_1 & P_2 & P_3 & \cdots & P_{m-2} & P_{m-1} & P_m & P_{m+1} & \\
 & x_0P_1 & x_0P_2 & \cdots & x_0P_{m-3} & x_0P_{m-2} & x_0P_{m-1} & x_0P_m & \\
\hline
P_1 & P_2 & P_3 & \cdots & P_{m-2} & P_{m-1} & P_m & P_{m+1} & \\
 & x_0P_1 & x_0P_2 & \cdots & x_0P_{m-3} & x_0P_{m-2} & x_0P_{m-1} & & \\
\hline
P_1 & P_2 & P_3 & \cdots & P_{m-2} & P_{m-1} & P_m & &
\end{array}$$

In the third line of division above, P_{m+1} is the value of the polynomial at $x = x_0$. In the fifth line of division, P_m is the value of the first derivative of $P_m(x)$ at $x = x_0$. For both divisions, only one formula is required, namely

$$P_i = x_0P_{i-1} + P_i, \qquad \begin{array}{l} i = 1, 2, \ldots, m1, \\ m1 = m + 1 \text{ in the first division,} \\ m1 = m \text{ in the second division.} \end{array} \tag{3.33}$$

Continuing with the d^2P_i/dx_i^2, $x = x_0$, the following set of equations is developed:

$$\begin{aligned}
P_1''(x_0) &= 0 \\
P_2''(x_0) &= P_1'(x_0) = 0 \\
P_3''(x_0) &= x_0P_2''(x_0) + 2P_2'(x_0) = 2P_2'(x_0) \\
P_4''(x_0) &= x_0P_3''(x_0) + 2P_3'(x_0) \\
&\ \vdots \\
P_i''(x_0) &= x_0P_{i-1}''(x_0) + 2P_{i-1}'(x_0) \\
&\ \vdots \\
P_{m-1}''(x_0) &= x_0P_{m-2}''(x_0) + 2P_{m-2}'(x_0) \\
P_m''(x_0) &= x_0P_{m-1}''(x_0) + 2P_{m-1}'(x_0) \\
P_{m+1}''(x_0) &= x_0P_m''(x_0) + 2P_m'(x_0).
\end{aligned} \tag{3.34}$$

If this set of equations is going to be appended to the two previous sets of equations (3.29) and (3.32) in the form of a table, it is necessary to

[5] $P_i = P_i(x)$ and x is a given value, x_0.

rewrite them as

$$
\begin{aligned}
\frac{P_3''(x_0)}{2} &= P_2'(x_0) \\
\frac{P_4''(x_0)}{2} &= x_0\left(\frac{P_3''(x_0)}{2}\right) + P_3'(x_0) \\
\frac{P_5''(x_0)}{2} &= x_0\left(\frac{P_4''(x_0)}{2}\right) + P_4'(x_0) \\
&\;\;\vdots \\
\frac{P_i''(x_0)}{2} &= x_0\left(\frac{P_{i-1}''(x_0)}{2}\right) + P_{i-1}'(x_0) \qquad (3.35)\\
&\;\;\vdots \\
\frac{P_{m-1}''(x_0)}{2} &= x_0\left(\frac{P_{m-2}''(x_0)}{2}\right) + P_{m-2}'(x_0) \\
\frac{P_m''(x_0)}{2} &= x_0\left(\frac{P_{m-1}''(x_0)}{2}\right) + P_{m-1}'(x_0) \\
\frac{P_{m+1}''(x_0)}{2} &= x_0\left(\frac{P_m''(x_0)}{2}\right) + P_m'(x_0).
\end{aligned}
$$

The synthetic division is rewritten below to include values of the polynomial, the first derivative and half of the second derivative:

$$
\begin{array}{cccccccc}
 & & & & & & & \underline{|x_0} \\
P_1(x_0) & P_2(x_0) & P_3(x_0) & \cdots & P_{m-2}(x_0) & P_{m-1}(x_0) & P_m(x_0) & P_{m+1}(x_0) \\
 & x_0P_1(x_0) & x_0P_2(x_0) & \cdots & x_0P_{m-3}(x_0) & x_0P_{m-2}(x_0) & x_0P_{m-1}(x_0) & x_0P_m(x_0) \\
\hline
P_1(x_0) & P_2(x_0) & P_3(x_0) & \cdots & P_{m-2}(x_0) & P_{m-1}(x_0) & P_m(x_0) & P_{m+1}(x_0) \\
 & x_0P_2'(x_0) & x_0P_3'(x_0) & \cdots & x_0P_{m-2}'(x_0) & x_0P_{m-1}'(x_0) & x_0P_m'(x_0) & \\
\hline
P_2'(x_0) & P_3'(x_0) & P_4'(x_0) & \cdots & P_{m-1}'(x_0) & P_m'(x_0) & P_{m+1}'(x_0) & \\
 & \frac{x_0P_3''(x_0)}{2} & \frac{x_0P_4''(x_0)}{2} & \cdots & \frac{x_0P_{m-1}''(x_0)}{2} & \frac{x_0P_m''(x_0)}{2} & & \\
\hline
\frac{P_3''(x_0)}{2} & \frac{P_4''(x_0)}{2} & \frac{P_5''(x_0)}{2} & \cdots & \frac{P_m''(x_0)}{2} & \frac{P_{m+1}''(x_0)}{2} & &
\end{array}
$$

By omitting the prime notation, the above form can then be written:

$$
\begin{array}{cccccccc}
 & & & & & & & \underline{|x_0} \\
P_1 & P_2 & P_3 & \cdots & P_{m-2} & P_{m-1} & P_m & P_{m+1} \\
 & x_0P_1 & x_0P_2 & \cdots & x_0P_{m-3} & x_0P_{m-2} & x_0P_{m-1} & x_0P_m \\
\hline
P_1 & P_2 & P_3 & \cdots & P_{m-2} & P_{m-1} & P_m & P_{m+1} \\
 & x_0P_1 & x_0P_2 & \cdots & x_0P_{m-3} & x_0P_{m-2} & x_0P_{m-1} & \\
\hline
P_1 & P_2 & P_3 & \cdots & P_{m-2} & P_{m-1} & P_m & \\
 & x_0P_1 & x_0P_2 & \cdots & x_0P_{m-3} & x_0P_{m-2} & & \\
\hline
P_1 & P_2 & P_3 & \cdots & P_{m-2} & P_{m-1} & &
\end{array}
$$

where the last computed values of P_{m+1}, P_m, P_{m-1} in each line of division are respectively the values of the polynomial, its first derivative, and half of its second derivative for a given value of x.

It can be shown that if this process is continued, the values of the polynomial and all

$$\frac{d^s x}{dx^s}\Big/ s!, \qquad (s = 1, 2, \ldots, m)$$

can be obtained for a given value of x. The algorithm for this process is

$$P_i = x_0 P_{i-1} + P_i, \qquad (i = 1, 2, \ldots, m1) \tag{3.36}$$

where $m1 = m + 1, m, m - 1, \ldots, 2$.

3.8.1 Flow Chart

For the evaluation of a polynomial of degree m, its first derivative and second derivative, for a given value of x, let

$$
\begin{aligned}
P_m(x) &= p_1 x^m + p_2 x^{m-1} + p_3 x^{m-2} + \cdots + p_{m-1} x^2 \\
&\quad + p_m x + p_{m+1}, \qquad (m \geq 3).
\end{aligned}
$$

For $m = 2$, what changes would be necessary in Flow Chart 3.8.1?

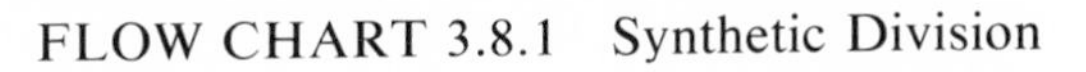

FLOW CHART 3.8.1 Synthetic Division

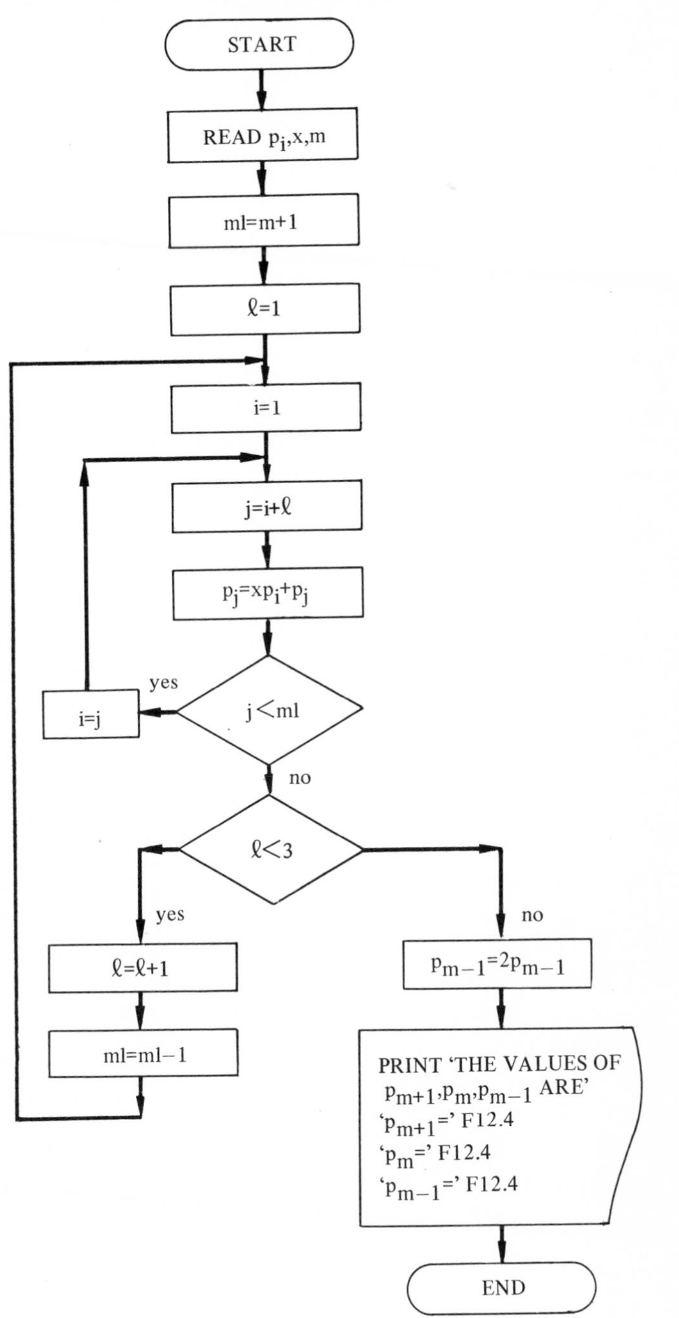

EXERCISE

Given the polynomial $P(x) = x^5 - 3x^2 + 4x - 5$, write a flow chart and program to compute values of $P(2)$, $P'(2)$, $P''(2)$, $P'''(2)$, $P''''(2)$, $P'''''(2)$.

Suggestions: When the principal algorithm has been completed for the last time, the values of $p_5(x)$, $p_4(x)$, $p_3(x)$, $p_2(x)$, and $p_1(x)$ will have been stored in the computer. It is now necessary to form a set of statements that will yield factorials. Each factorial $s!$ will become the coefficient of p_{m+1-s}, since p_{m+1-s} is

$$\frac{d^sP_m(x)}{dx^s} \bigg/ s!$$

To generate 1!, 2!, 3!, . . . , the set of statements shown in Flow Chart 3.8.1(a) can be appropriately inserted at the end of the program.

FLOW CHART 3.8.1(a) Forming Factorials

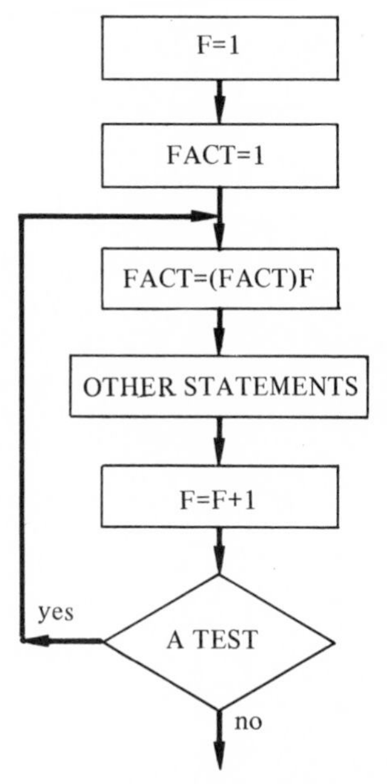

3.9 Improved Newton–Raphson Method for Polynomial Equations

Let $P_m(x) = 0$. Assume that a root r lies between $x = a$ and $x = b$. Then with $x_1 = a$, the combined formula from the Newton–Raphson formula (3.10) and synthetic division (3.36) is

$$x_{i+1} = x_i - \frac{P_m(x_i)}{P'_m(x_i)}, \tag{3.37}$$

or with the notation of Sec. 3.8, Eq. 3.37 becomes

$$x_{i+1} = x_i - \frac{p_{m+1}(x_i)}{p_m(x_i)}. \tag{3.38}$$

This method can be worthless unless a test is used to safeguard against the possibility of getting a false root. For example, consider the polynomial equation

$$P(x) = x^5 - 6x^4 + 24x + 3 = 0. \tag{3.39}$$

Since $P(1) = 22$ and $P(2) = -13$, a root r lies between $x = 1$ and $x = 2$. Using $x_0 = 1$ and Eq. 3.38, $x_1 = 1 - 22/5 = -3.4$. This approximation to a root between $x = 1$ and $x = 2$ is false. However, it is known that the slope of $P(x)$ at $x = 1$ is $+52$, whereas at $x = 2$, the slope is -88. Hence, it is true that somewhere between $x = 1$ and $x = 2$, the curve reaches a maximum and crosses the x axis before $x = 2$.

Hence, a program for this method should contain a test to make certain that each new approximation lies between $x = 1$ and $x = 2$. In the event that a new approximation x_i does not lie in the given interval, then x_{i-1} can be incremented so that it will have another value somewhere in the interval (1,2). With this new value of x_{i-1}, the value of x_i can be computed by the Newton–Raphson method.

In Flow Chart 3.9.1, the current value of x is incremented each time the test is not satisfied.

3.9.1 Flow Chart

Let

$$\begin{gathered} P(x) = x^5 - 6x^4 + 24x + 3 = 0, \\ P(1) = 22, \qquad P(2) = -13. \end{gathered} \tag{3.40}$$

Therefore, a root r lies between $x = 1$ and $x = 2$. Let m represent the degree and $m1$ the number of coefficients; x initially has the value 1, and $a = 1$, $b = 2$.

The coefficients are read in as q_i, $i = 1, 2, \ldots 6$. Following this, p_i are set equal to q_i for the purpose of using $P_{i+1} = xP_i + P_{i+1}$ with the original values of coefficients each time the process is repeated.

The control letter JOB keeps a count of the number of iterations. If

JOB should exceed the number K (in this case, 15) without good convergence, the program is terminated.

There are two principal parts in Flow Chart 3.9.1. If the computed value x_0 always falls in the interval (a,b), the Newton–Raphson method is applied repeatedly without incrementing x. If a computed value x_0 falls outside the interval (a,b), as is true of the first iteration in this problem, the initial value of x is adjusted to the value b. If $x = b$ is not a good choice, then x is given the value $(a + b)/2$. Subsequently, x may take on the values:

$$a + \frac{b-a}{4}, \qquad a + \frac{b-a}{8}, \qquad a + \frac{b-a}{16}.$$

Symbolically, x may take on the values:

$$a + \frac{b-a}{2^{ia-1}}, \qquad (ia = 1, \ldots, i \max, \text{ where } i \max = 5).$$

In Flow Chart 3.9.1, suppose that p_m vanishes; what provision should be made?

FLOW CHART 3.9.1 Improved Newton–Raphson Method

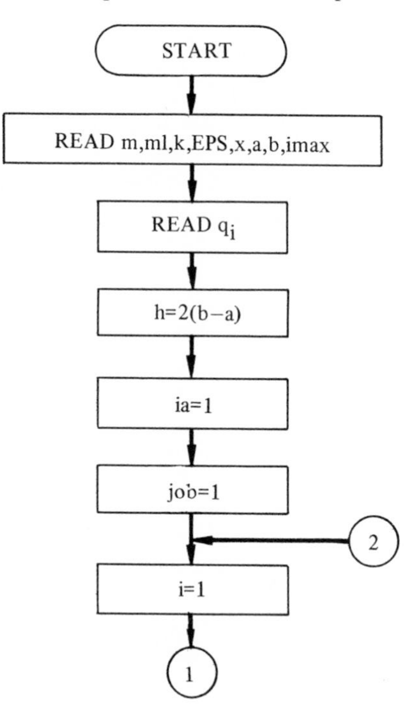

Flow Chart 3.9.1 *(Continued)*

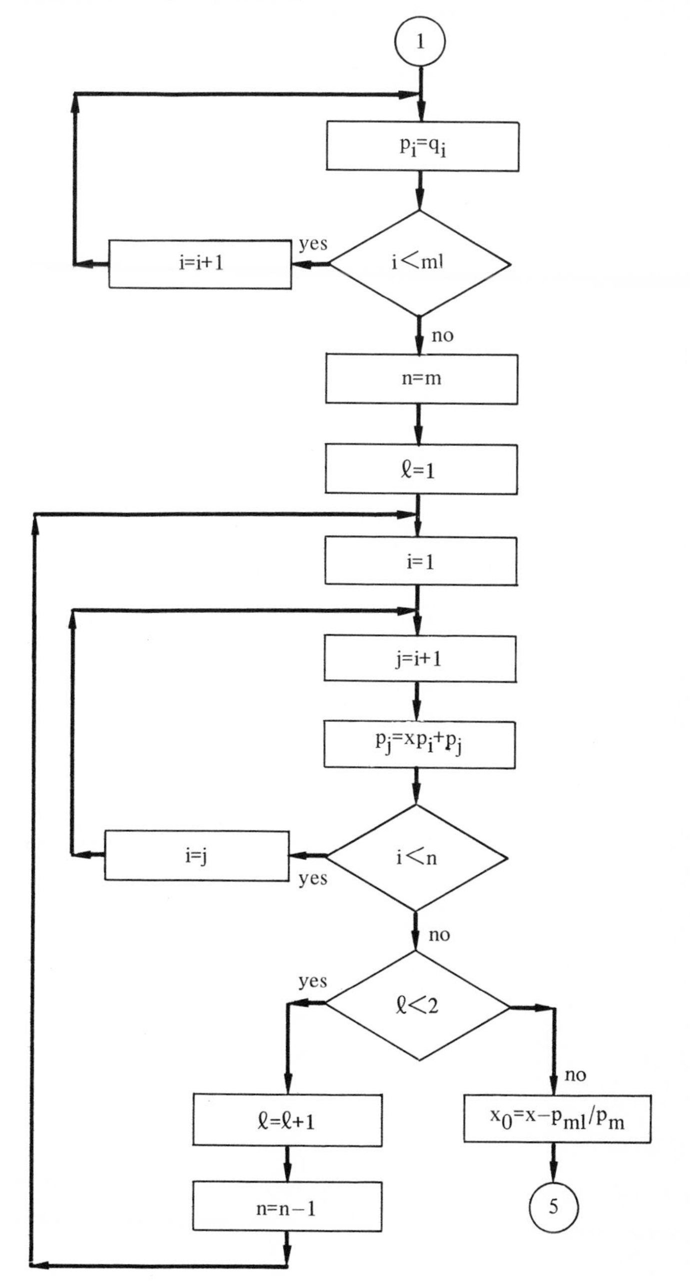

Flow Chart 3.91 *(Continued)*

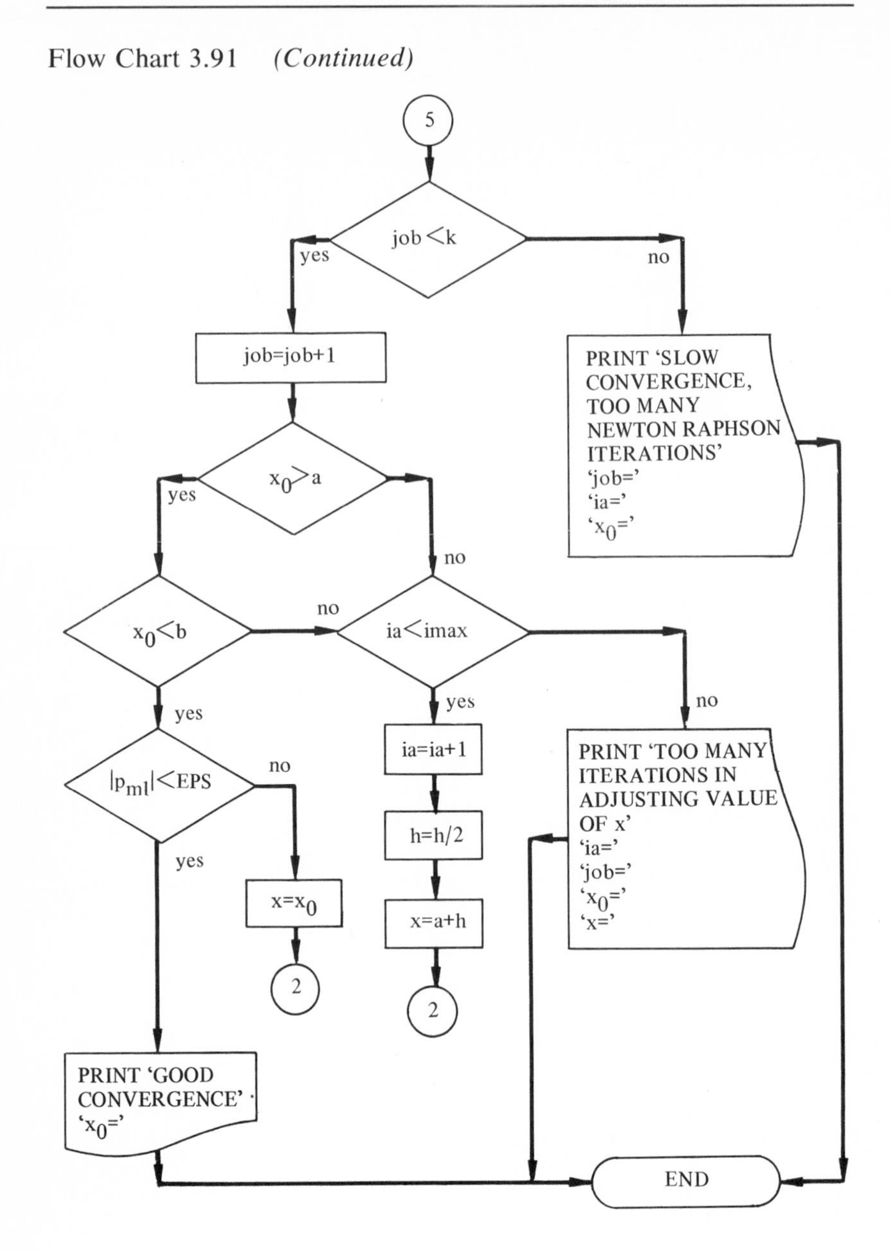

3.9.2 Program

Consider Eq. 3.40. The following program computes the value of the root r, $1 < r < 2$.

```
C
C       PROGRAM TO ILLUSTRATE IMPROVED NEWTON-RAPHSON TECHNIQUE
C       FOR A POLYNOMIAL EQUATION
C       PROGRAM WRITTEN IN FORTRAN IV
C
      DIMENSION P(20),Q(20)
      READ(5,300)M,ML,K,EPS,X,A,B,IMAX
300   FORMAT(3I2,F5.4,3F2.0,I2)
      WRITE(6,310)M,ML,K,EPS,X,A,B,IMAX
310   FORMAT(1X,3I2,2X,F5.4,2X,3F3.0,2X,I3)
      READ(5,301)(P(I),I=1,ML)
301   FORMAT(F5.0)
      WRITE(6,301)(P(I),I=1,ML)
      H=2*(B-A)
      IA=1
      JOB=1
  2   N=M
      DO 10 I=1,ML
 10   Q(I)=P(I)
      L=1
  4   I=1
  3   J=I+1
      Q(J)=X*Q(I)+Q(J)
      IF(I-N)12,14,14
 12   I=J
      GO TO 3
 14   IF(L-2)15,16,16
 15   L=L+1
      N=N-1
      GO TO 4
 16   XO=X-Q(ML)/Q(M)
      IF(XO-A)5,5,18
 18   IF(XO-B)19,5,5
 19   IF(ABS(Q(ML))-EPS)6,7,7
  6   WRITE(6,302)XO
302   FORMAT('GOOD CONVERGENCE XO= ',F8.3)
      GO TO 99
  7   IF(JOB-K)21,22,22
 21   JOB=JOB+1
      X=XO
      GO TO 2
 22   WRITE(6,303)L,IA,XO
303   FORMAT('SLOW CONVERGENCE',/,'TOO MANY ITERATES THROUGH NEW-
    1 TON-RAPHSON METHOD ',/,'L=',I2,/,'IA=',I2,/,'XO=',F8.3)
```

```
      GO TO 99
    5 IF(IA-IMAX)25,26,26
   25 IA=IA+1
      H=H/2
      X=A+H
      GO TO 2
   26 WRITE(6,304)IA,L,XO
  304 FORMAT('SLOW CONVERGENCE',/,'TOO MANY ITERATIONS IN ADJUSTING
    1 INITIAL VALUE OF X ',/,'IA=',I2,/,'L=',I2,/,'XO=',F8.3)
   99 STOP
      END

      THE RESULT IS

      GOOD CONVERGENCE XO=  1.832
```

PROBLEMS

3-3. Based on Flow Chart 3.9.1, write a flow chart and program such that all approximations lie between $x = 1$ and $x = 2$, including $x = 1$, and the count of all these approximations are printed.

3-4. Using $b = 2$ for the initial starting value of x, and including conditions given in Prob. 3-3, write a flow chart and program for Eq. 3.39. An initial value of h should be given, and h modified similar to the manner of Sec. 3.9.1 so that possible starting values of x may also be

$$b + \frac{(a-b)}{2},\ b + \frac{(a-b)}{2^2},\ \ldots,\ b + \frac{(a-b)}{2^4}.$$

How do the results compare?

3-5. Consider again Eq. 3.39. A root r lies in the interval (a,b). A combination of Flow Chart 3.9.1 and the flow chart of Prob. 3-4 can be made so that x initially set equal to a may take on the values:

(1) $$a + \frac{b-a}{2}, \qquad a + \frac{b-a}{2^2}, \qquad a + \frac{b-a}{2^3}$$

and

(2) $$b, \qquad b + \frac{a-b}{2^2}, \qquad b + \frac{a-b}{2^3}.$$

Allowing three iterations each for (1) and for (2), write a flow chart and program for this process.

3-6. The equation

$$48x^5 - 345x^4 + 970x^3 - 1335x^2 + 900x - 237$$

has a real root r in the interval $(1,2)$. Use the method of Sec. 3.9.1 and the method of Prob. 3-5 to approximate r. What additional test must be made in this problem and should always be a part of any such program?

Answer: $r = 1.793835$.

3.10 Root Squaring Method

If the roots of

$$P_m(x) = a_1x^m + a_2x^{m-1} + \cdots + a_mx + a_{m+1}$$

are known to be real and of different magnitudes, a technique known as the root squaring method can be applied to find all roots of the equation. The assumption is that

$$P_m(x) = a_1x^m + a_2x^{m-1} + \cdots + a_mx + a_{m+1}$$

has roots $r_1, r_2, \ldots, r_m$ such that

$$|r_1| > |r_2| > |r_3| > \cdots > |r_m|.$$

If the roots r_i differ greatly in magnitude, then an approximation to the roots follows from a theorem which states:

$$\begin{aligned}
\frac{a_2}{a_1} &= -\Sigma r_i \\
\frac{a_3}{a_1} &= \sum_{i<j} r_i r_j \\
\frac{a_4}{a_1} &= -\sum_{i<j<k} r_i r_j r_k \\
&\vdots \\
\frac{a_{m+1}}{a_1} &= (-1)^m (r_1 r_2 \cdots r_m).
\end{aligned} \tag{3.41}$$

Since r_1 is much larger than any other root, the first equation of (3.41) can be expressed as

$$\frac{a_2}{a_1} = -r_1\left(1 + \frac{r_2}{r_1} + \cdots + \frac{r_m}{r_1}\right) \qquad \text{or} \qquad a_2 \cong -r_1a_1.$$

From the second equation of (3.41),

$$\frac{a_3}{a_1} = r_1r_2\left[\left(1 + \frac{r_3}{r_2} + \cdots + \frac{r_m}{r_2}\right) + \cdots + \left(\frac{r_3}{r_1} \cdots \frac{r_m}{r_1}\right) + \cdots + \frac{r_{m-1}r_m}{r_1r_2}\right],$$

or

$$a_3 \cong r_1r_2a_1.$$

This process can be continued so that the following set of equations is developed:

$$\begin{aligned} a_2 &\cong -r_1 a_1 \\ a_3 &\cong r_1 r_2 a_1 \\ a_4 &\cong -r_1 r_2 r_3 a_1 \\ &\vdots \\ a_{m+1} &\cong (-1)^m r_1 r_2 \cdots r_m a_1 . \end{aligned} \tag{3.42}$$

From the above equations, by substituting from one equation into the following one, the set of equations below is derived:

$$\begin{aligned} a_2 + r_1 a_1 &\cong 0 \\ a_3 + r_2 a_2 &\cong 0 \\ a_4 + r_3 a_3 &\cong 0 \\ &\vdots \\ a_{m+1} + r_m a_m &\cong 0. \end{aligned} \tag{3.43}$$

Thus,

$$\begin{aligned} r_1 &\cong -\frac{a_2}{a_1} \\ r_2 &\cong -\frac{a_3}{a_2} \\ &\vdots \\ r_m &\cong -\frac{a_{m+1}}{a_m}. \end{aligned} \tag{3.44}$$

Example

$x^2 - 1001x + 1000 = 0$ has the roots $r_1 = 1000$ and $r_2 = 1$. From the relationship between roots and coefficients,

$$r_1 \cong -\left(\frac{-1001}{1}\right) \cong 1001,$$

$$r_2 \cong -\left(\frac{1000}{-1001}\right) \cong 1.$$

If, however, the roots of $P_m(x)$ differ in magnitude, but not greatly, it is necessary to apply a method whereby the resulting roots will differ greatly in magnitude. Then by an inverse process, the roots of $P_m(x)$ can be accurately approximated. Let

$$P_6(x) = a_1x^6 + a_2x^5 + a_3x^4 + a_4x^3 + a_5x^2 + a_6x + a_7,$$

and (3.45)

$$P_6(-x) = a_1x^6 - a_2x^5 + a_3x^4 - a_4x^3 + a_5x^2 - a_6x + a_7.$$

Then

$$\begin{aligned} P_6(x)P_6(-x) = a_1^2x^{12} &- (a_2^2 - 2a_1a_3)x^{10} + (a_3^2 - 2a_2a_4 + 2a_1a_5)x^8 \\ &- (a_4^2 - 2a_3a_5 + 2a_2a_6 - 2a_1a_7)x^6 \\ &+ (a_5^2 - 2a_4a_6 + 2a_3a_7)x^4 \\ &- (a_6^2 - 2a_5a_7)x^2 + a_7^2. \end{aligned} \tag{3.46}$$

Let $y = -x^2$ and Eq. 3.46 becomes

$$\begin{aligned} a_1^2y^6 &+ (a_2^2 - 2a_1a_3)y^5 + (a_3^2 - 2a_2a_4 + 2a_1a_5)y^4 \\ &+ (a_4^2 - 2a_3a_5 + 2a_2a_6 - 2a_1a_7)y^3 + (a_5^2 - 2a_4a_6 + 2a_3a_7)y^2 \\ &+ (a_6^2 - 2a_5a_7)y + a_7^2 = F(y). \end{aligned}$$

Hence, $F(y) = F(-x^2) = P_6(x)P_6(-x) = 0$.

If the roots of $P_6(x)$ are $r_1, r_2, \ldots, r_6$, then the roots of $P_6(-x)$ are $-r_1, -r_2, \ldots, -r_6$, and the roots of $F(y) = 0$ are $q_1 = -r_1^2$, $q_2 = -r_2^2, \ldots, q_6 = -r_6^2$. Thus,

$$|r_1| = |q_1|^{1/2},\ |r_2| = |q_2|^{1/2},\ \ldots,\ |r_6| = |q_6|^{1/2}.$$

This procedure can be repeated as many times as necessary to sufficiently separate the roots.

Then the set of Eqs. 3.44 is used to find the roots of the last equation resulting from squaring. If the root squaring method has been applied p times, then the relation between the roots r_k of the given equation and the roots q_k of the last equation is

$$|q_k| = |a_{k+1}|/|a_k| = |r_k|^{2^p}.$$

Let $2^p = L$, then $|r_k| = |q_k|^{1/L}$. Once the magnitude of all r_k have been determined, the sign can be determined by substituting r_k in $P(x)$. If $|P(r_k)|$ is sufficiently small, then r_k is a root; otherwise $-r_k$ is a root.

Consider one squaring of $P_6(x)$ as shown in the table below:

a_1	a_2	a_3	a_4	a_5	a_6	a_7
a_1^2	a_2^2	a_3^2	a_4^2	a_5^2	a_6^2	a_7^2
	$-2a_1a_3$	$-2a_2a_4$	$-2a_3a_5$	$-2a_4a_6$	$-2a_5a_7$	
		$2a_1a_5$	$2a_2a_6$	$2a_3a_7$		
			$-2a_1a_7$			
c_1	c_2	c_3	c_4	c_5	c_6	c_7

where

$$\begin{aligned} c_1 &= a_1^2 \\ c_2 &= a_2^2 - 2a_1a_3 \\ c_3 &= a_3^2 - 2a_2a_4 + 2a_1a_5 \\ &\;\;\vdots \\ c_7 &= a_7^2 . \end{aligned} \tag{3.47}$$

Each of these relationships can be expressed as

$$c_j = (a_j)^2 + 2 \sum_{k=1}^{\min(n-j,j-1)} (-1)^k (a_{j-k})(a_{j+k}). \tag{3.48}$$

The upper limit of the Σ means summation continues to $k = j - 1$, if $j - 1 < n - j$ $(n = m + 1)$, and otherwise to $n - j$. It should be noted (see Ch. 4) that

$$\sum_{i=n}^{n-1} a_i = 0 \qquad \text{and} \qquad \sum_{i=n}^{n} a_i = a_n .$$

3.10.1 Flow Chart

To find the roots of:

$$P(x) = x^3 - 5x^2 - 17x + 21 = 0, \tag{3.49}$$

where $n = 4$, $m = 3$, $nf = 3$ (the number of iterations in the root squaring process).

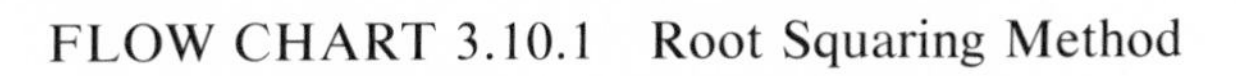

FLOW CHART 3.10.1 Root Squaring Method

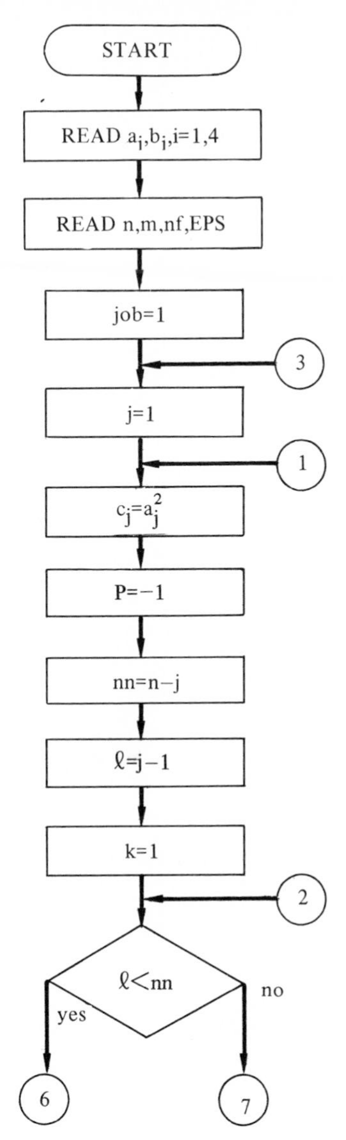

Flow Chart 3.10.1 *(Continued)*

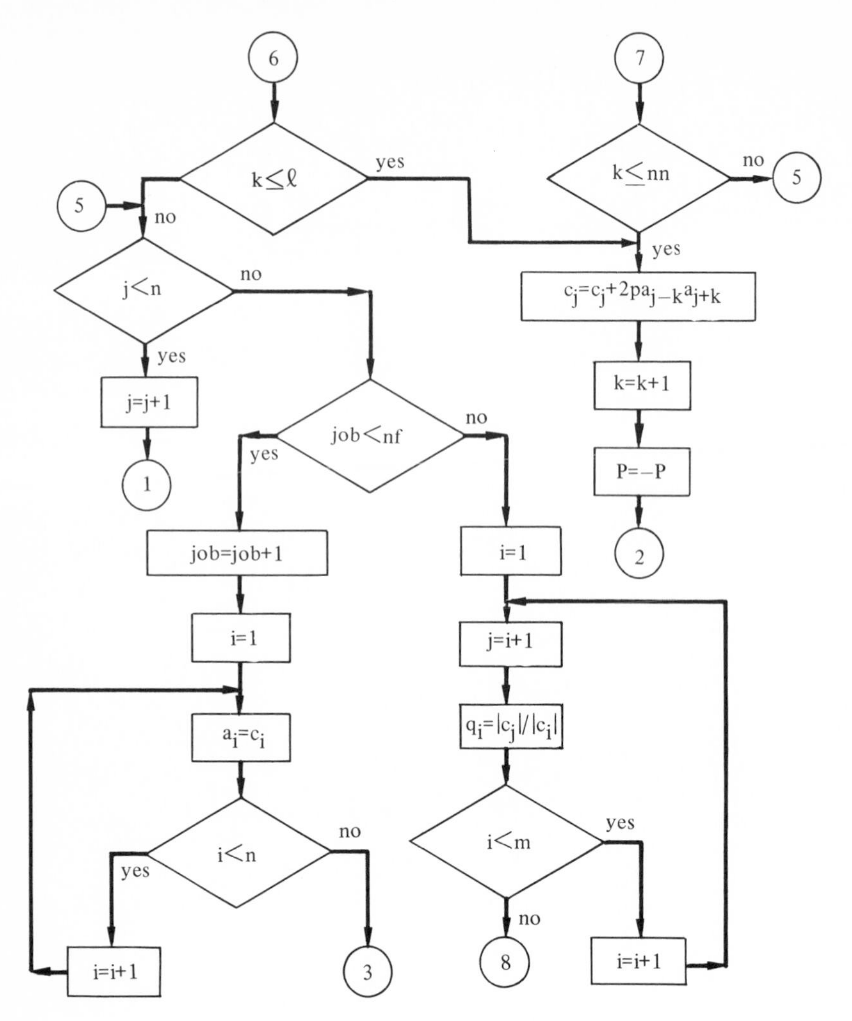

Flow Chart 3.10.1 *(Continued)*

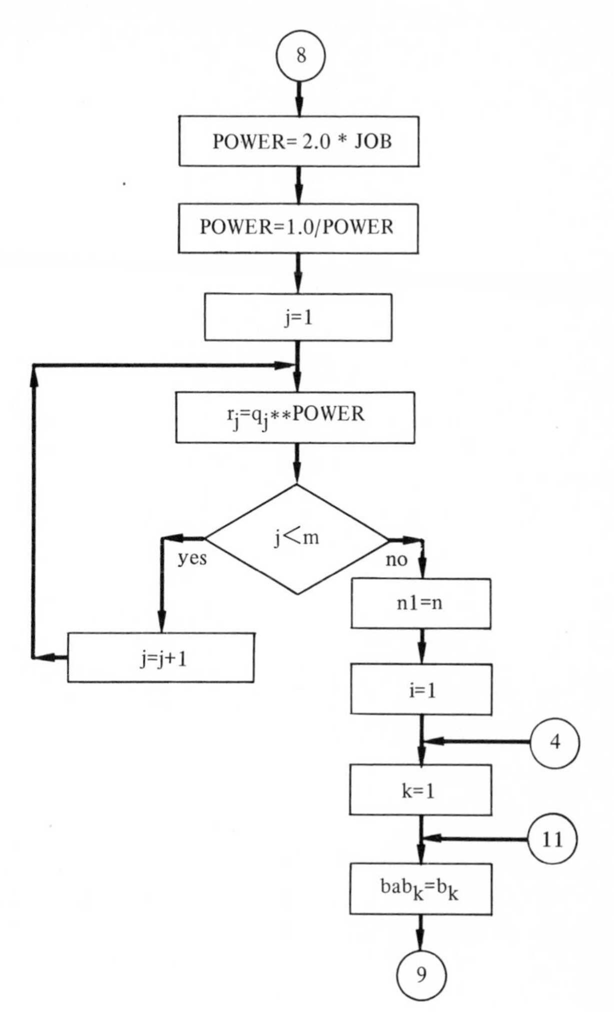

Flow Chart 3.10.1 *(Continued)*

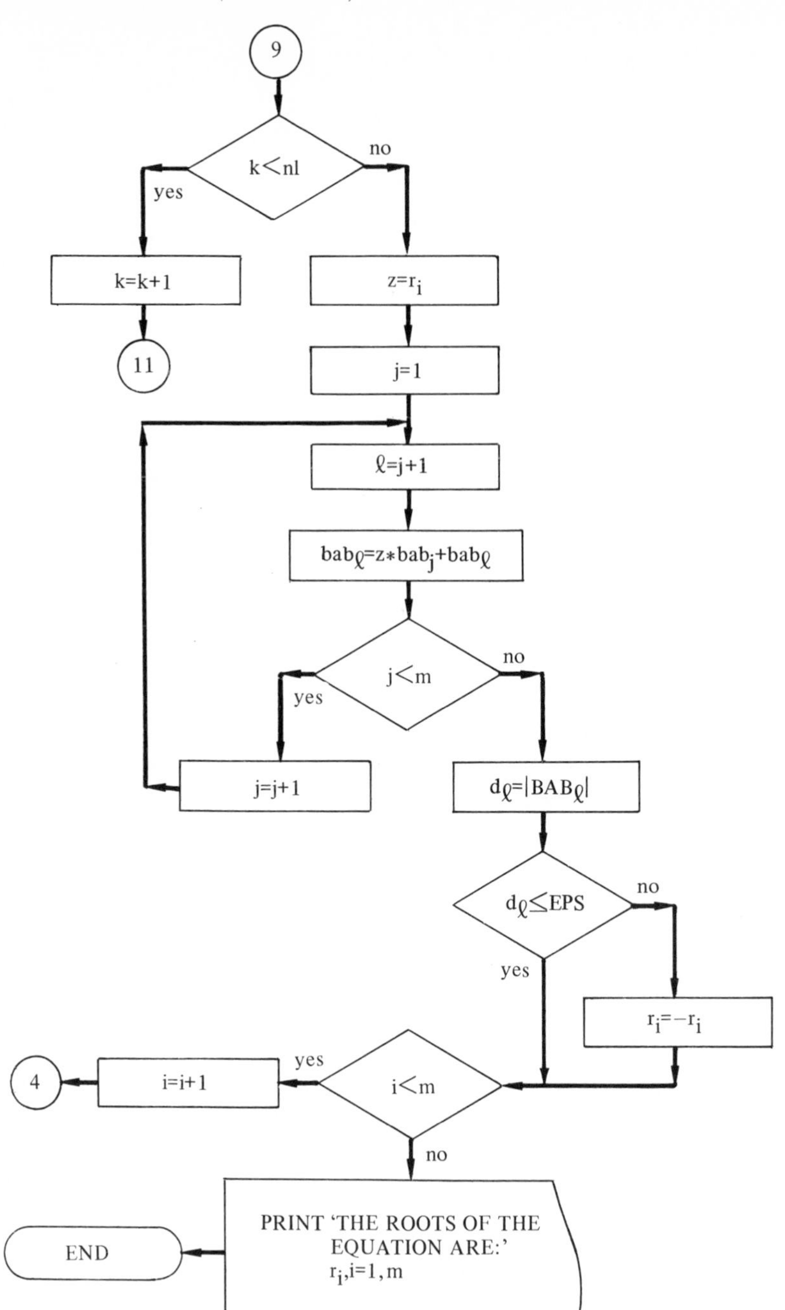

3.10.2 Program

The following program computes all roots of Eq. 3.49.

```
      DIMENSION A(10),B(10),C(10),D(10),Q(10),R(10),BAB(10),
      READ(5,700)N,M,NF,EPS
      READ(5,701)(A(I),I=1,N)
      DO 20 I=1,N
   20 B(I)=A(I)
      JOB=1
    3 J=1
    1 C(J)=A(J)**2
      P=-1
      NN=N-J
      L=J-1
      K=1
    2 IF(L-NN)6,7,7
    6 IF(K-L)21,21,5
    5 IF(J-N)22,23,23
   22 J=J+1
      GO TO 1
    7 IF(K-NN)21,21,5
   21 JK1=J-K
      JK2=J+K
      C(J)=C(J)+2*P*A(JK1)*A(JK2)
      K=K+1
      P=-P
      GO TO 2
   23 IF(JOB-NF)24,25,25
   24 JOB=JOB+1
      I=1
   35 A(I)=C(I)
      IF(I-N)26,3,3
   26 I=I+1
      GO TO 35
   25 I=1
   14 J=I+1
      Q(I)=ABS(C(J))/ABS(C(I))
      IF(I-M)27,8,8
   27 I=I+1
      GO TO 14
    8 POWER=2.0**JOB
      POWER=1.0/POWER
      J=1
   15 R(J)=Q(J)**POWER
      IF(J-M)13,16,16
   13 J=J+1
      GO TO 15
   16 N1=N
```

```
      I=1
    4 K=1
   11 BAB(K)=B(K)
      IF(K-NL)17,18,18
   17 K=K+1
      GO TO 11
   18 Z=R(I)
      J=1
   19 L=J+1
      BAB(L)=Z*BAB(J)+BAB(L)
      IF(J-M)28,29,29
   28 J=J+1
      GO TO 19
   29 TEST=ABS(BAB(L))-EPS
      IF(TEST)10,40,40
   40 R(I)=-Z
   10 IF(I-M)31,32,32
   31 I=I+1
      GO TO 4
   32 WRITE(6,702)
      DO 33 L1=1,M
   33 WRITE(6,703)L1,R(L1)
  703 FORMAT(/10X,'R(',I2,')=',F6.2)
  702 FORMAT('1',5X,'THE ROOTS OF THE EQUATION ARE')
  701 FORMAT(8F10.3)
  700 FORMAT(3I2,F10.9)
      STOP
      END

      THE ROOTS OF THE EQUATION ARE
      R(1)= +7.00
      R(2)= -3.00
      R(3)= +1.00
```

3.10.3 Explanation

The program consists of three principal parts: first, the root squaring process, whereby

$$c_j = a_j^2 + 2 \sum_{k=1}^{\min(n-j,j-1)} (-1)^k a_{j-k} a_{j+k}$$

are determined. This set of statements, beginning with the statement JOB=1 through the subset of statements in which a_i are replaced by c_j, is executed three times. When JOB becomes equal to *nf*, which was set equal to 3 at the beginning, the roots of the given equation will have been raised to the eighth power. Hence the roots are fairly well separated.

Calculation of the roots r_j, extending from POWER=2**JOB down to the last IF statement, IF($i < m$), is the second part. In this set of statements, each r_i must be tested to determine whether r_i or $-r_i$ is a root. This is accomplished by the synthetic division of r_i. If the remainder d_l is small, then r_i is a root; if the remainder is large, then $-r_i$ is a root.

The third part consists of the output statement.

EXERCISE

When the root squaring method nears convergence, the cross-product terms will become negligible; accordingly, Eq. 3.48,

$$c_j = (a_j)^2 + 2 \sum_{k=1}^{\min(n-j,j-1)} (-1)^k(a_{j-k})(a_{j+k})$$

approximately becomes $c_j = a_j^2$. Therefore, instead of arbitrarily allowing n iterations of each Eq. 3.48, a test can be made after each iteration to determine if $c_j \cong a_j^2$. If this test is satisfied within the desired degree of accuracy for all j, the iteration can be terminated and the next part of the program begun.

It should be noted that c_j is very rapidly becoming large, and that the cross-products are relatively smaller, though still quite large. Hence, in using a test to determine if $c_j \cong a_j^2$, it is necessary to use a factor 10^{-n}, where n is 2^{JOB} and JOB indicates the current iteration. The test requires that after every c_j is computed, $(c_j)10^{-n}$ will be stored in T_j, and also each $a_j^2(10^{-n})$ will be stored in s_j. Then, if $|T_j - s_j| < EPS$ for all j, the iteration is terminated and the program continues with the next part.

Write a flow chart and program based on this type of test to find the roots of Eq. 3.49.

3.10.4 Comments

If the roots of $P(x) = 0$ are not real and distinct, it is still possible to use this method at least in two cases. First, suppose that two roots are complex and that all other roots are real and distinct. That is, suppose that a pair of complex roots $r \pm is$ exists such that

$$|r \pm is| > |r_3| > |r_4| > \cdots > |r_m|.$$

Then the root squaring method will not separate $r + is$ from $r - is$, but after p squarings, a set of equations can be derived:

$$c_1y^2 + c_2y + c_3 = 0$$
$$c_3y + c_4 = 0$$
$$\cdot$$
$$\cdot$$
$$\cdot$$
$$c_m y + c_{m+1} = 0.$$

Such a condition would be indicated by the fact that c_2 would not be approximately equal to a_2^2; that is, the cross-product terms would not vanish. Thus, if after several squarings $c_2(10^{-n}) \neq a_2^2(10^{-n})$ approximately, the flow of work would be directed to solve the quadratic equation $c_1y^2 + c_2y + c_3 = 0$, and the usual routine would be followed for the other roots.

Second, suppose that two real roots are equal in magnitude—that is, suppose

$$|r_1| = |r_2| > |r_3| > \cdots > |r_m|.$$

Since $|r_1| = |r_2|$, the root squaring method will not separate these two roots and will give rise to a quadratic equation $c_1y^2 + c_2y + c_3 = 0$.

This possibility of two real roots equal in magnitude would be indicated by the fact that the cross-product terms would approach one-half the squared term. However, for a pair of complex roots or for two roots equal in magnitude, the following procedure can be used. Referring to the exercise of Sec. 3.10.3, if $|T_j - s_j| \nless EPS$ after p squarings, then $c_{j-1}y^2 + c_jy + c_{j+1} = 0$ must be solved. A flow chart and program covering such possibilities are left as an exercise for the student (see Prob. 3-7).

3.11 Lin–Bairstow Method

In Sec. 3.8, synthetic division of polynomials was developed. This section continues with a method for determination of a quadratic factor of $P_n(x)$.[6] Let

$$P_n(x) = a_1x^n + a_2x^{n-1} + a_3x^{n-2} + \cdots + a_nx + a_{n+1},$$

and let $x^2 + px + q$ be a possible quadratic factor. Therefore,

$$a_1x^n + a_2x^{n-1} + \cdots + a_nx + a_{n+1}$$
$$= (x^2 + px + q)(b_1x^{n-2} + b_2x^{n-3} + \cdots + b_{n-3}x^2 + b_{n-2}x + b_{n-1}) + (Px + Q),$$

[6] In Sec. 3.8 a general synthetic division process was developed, but here it is also required that a formula relating a_i, b_i, p, and q be derived.

where $Px + Q$ is the remainder. Equating coefficients, the following coefficient relations are developed:

$$
\begin{aligned}
a_1 &= b_1 \\
a_2 &= b_2 + pb_1 \\
a_3 &= b_3 + pb_2 + qb_1 \\
&\ \ \vdots \\
a_i &= b_i + pb_{i-1} + qb_{i-2} \\
&\ \ \vdots \\
a_n &= pb_{n-1} + qb_{n-2} + P \\
a_{n+1} &= qb_{n-1} + Q.
\end{aligned}
\tag{3.50}
$$

Let P be called b_n, and further, let $b_0 = b_{-1} = 0$. Then

$$a_i = b_i + pb_{i-1} + qb_{i-2}, \qquad (i = 1, 2, \ldots, n + 1)$$

is true for all i, if $b_{n+1} = Q - pP$. This is true, since by the formula

$$a_k = b_k + pb_{k-1} + qb_{k-2},$$

$$a_{n+1} = b_{n+1} + pb_n + qb_{n-1},$$

or

$$a_{n+1} = Q - pb_n + pb_n + qb_{n-1} = Q + qb_{n-1}.$$

Then Eqs. 3.50 can be rewritten as

$$b_k = a_k - pb_{k-1} - qb_{k-2}, \qquad (k = 1, 2, \ldots, n + 1).$$

In order to find a new p and q such that $P(p,q) = 0$ and $Q(p,q) = 0$, it is necessary to expand $P(p,q)$ and $Q(p,q)$ in Taylor series. Hence,

$$P(p + \Delta p, q + \Delta q) = P(p,q) + \frac{\partial P}{\partial p}\Delta p + \frac{\partial P}{\partial q}\Delta q = 0$$

and

$$Q(p + \Delta p, q + \Delta q) = Q(p,q) + \frac{\partial Q}{\partial p}\Delta p + \frac{\partial Q}{\partial q}\Delta q = 0 \tag{3.51}$$

must be solved for Δp and Δq.

By taking partial derivatives of b_k, $k = 1, 2, \ldots, n + 1$, it can be shown that

$$\frac{\partial b_k}{\partial p} = -b_{k-1} - p\frac{\partial b_{k-1}}{\partial p} - q\frac{\partial b_{k-2}}{\partial p} \tag{3.52a}$$

and

$$\frac{\partial b_k}{\partial q} = -b_{k-2} - p\,\frac{\partial b_{k-1}}{\partial q} - q\,\frac{\partial b_{k-2}}{\partial q} \tag{3.52b}$$

for $k = 1, 2, \ldots, n + 1$. It can also be shown that[7]

$$\frac{\partial b_k}{\partial p} = \frac{\partial b_{k+1}}{\partial q}. \tag{3.53}$$

If $\partial b_k/\partial p = \partial b_{k+1}/\partial q$ is set equal to $-c_{k-1}$, then by substituting in either of Eqs. 3.52,

$$c_k = b_k - pc_{k-1} - qc_{k-2}, \qquad k = 1, 2, \ldots, n + 1. \tag{3.54}$$

Thus, to find $\partial P/\partial p$, $\partial P/\partial q$, $\partial Q/\partial p$, $\partial Q/\partial q$ the equations $P = b_n$ and $Q = b_{n+1} + pP$ are differentiated:

$$\frac{\partial P}{\partial p} = \frac{\partial b_n}{\partial p} = -c_{n-1}$$

$$\frac{\partial P}{\partial q} = \frac{\partial b_n}{\partial q} = -c_{n-2}$$

$$\frac{\partial Q}{\partial p} = \frac{\partial b_{n+1}}{\partial p} + P + p\,\frac{\partial P}{\partial p} = -c_n + b_n - pc_{n-1}$$

$$\frac{\partial Q}{\partial q} = \frac{\partial b_{n+1}}{\partial q} - p\,\frac{\partial P}{\partial q} = -c_{n-1} - pc_{n-2}.$$

Thus, Eqs. 3.51 become

$$\begin{gathered} b_n - c_{n-1}(\Delta p) - c_{n-2}(\Delta q) = 0, \\ b_{n+1} + pb_n + (-c_n + b_n - pc_{n-1})\Delta p + (-c_{n-1} - pc_{n-2})\Delta q = 0. \end{gathered} \tag{3.55}$$

Rearranging terms and using the relation $b_n = c_{n-1}(\Delta p) + c_{n-2}(\Delta q)$ in the second equation of (3.55), Eqs. 3.55 become

$$\begin{gathered} c_{n-1}(\Delta p) + c_{n-2}(\Delta q) = b_n, \\ (c_n - b_n)\Delta p + (c_{n-1})\Delta q = b_{n+1}, \end{gathered} \tag{3.56}$$

and Eqs. 3.56 can be solved by use of determinants. Hence, replacing p by $p + \Delta p$ and q by $q + \Delta q$, $x^2 + px + q$ is more nearly a factor of $P_n(x)$, and $P \cong 0$, $Q \cong 0$.

3.11.1 Flow Chart

Let

$$P(x) = x^3 - x - 1 = 0. \tag{3.57}$$

Choose $x^2 + x + 1$ as a trial quadratic factor. The two equations are

[7] This can be shown by mathematical induction, i.e., show that it is true for $K = 1$; then by mathematical induction Eq. 3.53 can be shown to be true in general.

$$b_k = a_k - pb_{k-1} - qb_{k-2}$$

and (3.58)

$$c_k = b_k - pc_{k-1} - qc_{k-2},$$

from which the coefficients of Δp and Δq in Eqs. 3.56 can be determined. Then Eqs. 3.56 can be solved for Δp and Δq. Thus, p becomes $p + \Delta p$ and q becomes $q + \Delta q$.

A hand computation can be more easily done by a table, with the aid of Eqs. 3.58:

k	a_k	b_k	c_k	p	q
1	1	1	1	1	1
2	0	−1	−2		
3	−1	−1	0		
4	−1	1	3		

Equations 3.56 become

$$-2\Delta p + \Delta q = -1,$$
$$\Delta p - 2\Delta q = 1, \qquad (\Delta q = -1/3,\ \Delta p = 1/3).$$

Hence, now $\bar{p} = p + \Delta p = 4/3$ and $\bar{q} = q + \Delta q = 2/3$. Repeating the process again:

k	a_k	b_k	c_k	$\bar{p}$	$\bar{q}$
1	1	1	1	4/3	2/3
2	0	−4/3	−8/3		
3	−1	1/9	3		
4	−1	−7/27			

and Eqs. 3.56 become

$$-8\Delta p + 3\Delta q = 1/3,$$
$$26\Delta p - 24\Delta q = -7/3, \qquad (\Delta p = -1/114, \quad \Delta q = 10/114).$$

Thus, $\bar{\bar{p}} = 1.324$ and $\bar{\bar{q}} = .753$. The true values are $p = 1.3247$, $q = .7549$.

n = degree.
$EPS = .00001$.
$n1 = n + 1$, the number of a_i.
$n2 = n - 1$, the number of b_i.[8]
m = maximum number of iterations.
$RMDP = P$.
$RMDQ = Q$.

[8] A DIMENSION statement for all b_i must be $(n + 1)$ since b_n and b_{n+1} are to be computed.

FLOW CHART 3.11.1 Lin–Bairstow Method

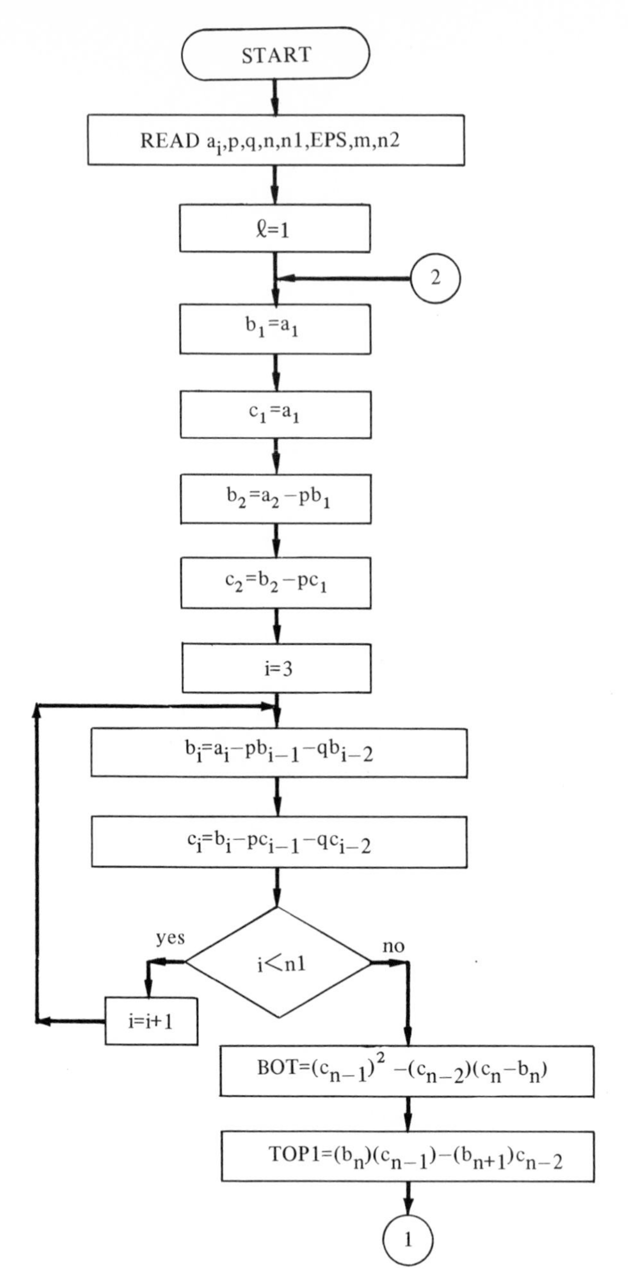

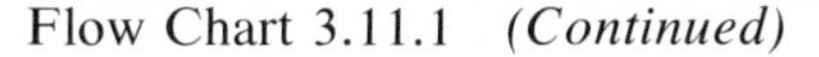

Flow Chart 3.11.1 *(Continued)*

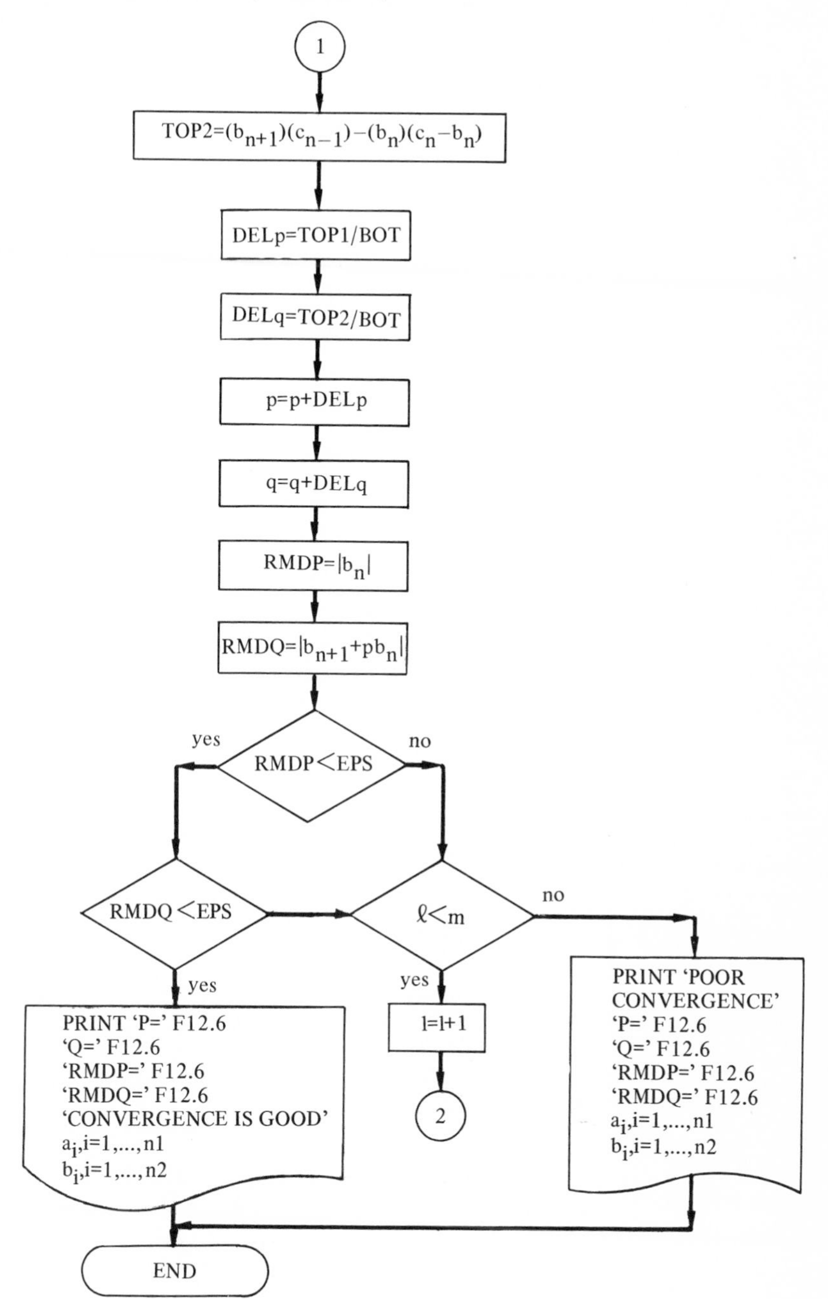

3.11.2 Program

The following program computes the values of p and q, as well as the values of P and Q, for Eq. 3.57.

```
      DIMENSION A(10),B(10),C(10)
  100 FORMAT(3F10.0,3I2)
  101 FORMAT(F10.0)
  102 FORMAT('1','P=',F12.6,/,'Q=',F12.6,/,'RMDP=',F12.6,/,'RMDQ=
    1 ',F12.6,/,'CONVERGENCE IS GOOD',/)
      READ(5,100)P,Q,EPS,N,N1,M
      READ(5,101)(A(I),I=1,N1)
      N2=N-1
      L=1
    2 B(1)=A(1)
      C(1)=A(1)
      B(2)=A(2)-P*B(1)
      C(2)=B(2)-P*C(1)
      I=3
    7 B(I)=A(I)-P*B(I-1)-Q*B(I-2)
      C(I)=B(I)-P*C(I-1)-Q*C(I-2)
      IF(I-N1)5,6,6
    5 I=I+1
      GO TO 7
    6 BOT=C(N-1)**2-C(N-2)*(C(N)-B(N))
      TOP1=B(N)*C(N-1)-B(N+1)*C(N-2)
      TOP2=B(N+1)*C(N-1)-B(N)*(C(N)-B(N))
      DELP=TOP1/BOT
      DELQ=TOP2/BOT
      P=P+DELP
      Q=Q+DELQ
      RMDP=ABS(B(N))
      RMDQ=ABS(B(N+1)+P*B(N))
      IF(RMDP-EPS)4,8,8
    4 IF(RMDQ-EPS)3,8,8
    3 WRITE(6,102)P,Q,RMDP,RMDQ
      WRITE(6,104)(A(I),I=1,N1)
      WRITE(6,104)(B(I),I=1,N2)
      STOP
    8 IF(L-M)9,1,1
    9 L=L+1
      GO TO 2
    1 WRITE(6,103)P,Q,RMDP,RMDQ
      WRITE(6,104)(A(I),I=1,N1)
      WRITE(6,104)(B(I),I=1,N2)
  103 FORMAT('1','POOR CONVERGENCE',/,'P=',F12.6,/,'Q=',F12.6,/,'RMDP=',
    1 F12.6,/,'RMDQ=',F12.6,/)
  104 FORMAT(10F7.2)
      STOP
      END
```

```
THE RESULTS ARE

p=1.324718
q=0.754878
RMDP=P=0.000001
RMDQ=Q=0.000000
```

3.12 Multiple Roots

If r is a root of multiplicity greater than 1, then the previous methods of this chapter would not be of any value, since the inverse function of a multiple root does not exist. There is also the possibility that a programmer would not know a priori the multiplicity of a root. Therefore, a method that is not dependent on the multiplicity of the root is needed. If

$$f(x) = (x - r)^{\alpha} g(x) = 0, \qquad (g(r) \neq 0),$$

then

$$f'(x) = (x - r)^{\alpha} g'(x) + \alpha(x - r)^{\alpha-1} g(x).$$

Thus, $f(x)/f'(x)$ has a single root, $x = r$.

Let $F(x) = f(x)/f'(x)$. Then

$$F'(x) = 1 - \frac{f(x)f''(x)}{[f'(x)]^2},$$

and since $F(x)$ has only one root at $x = r$, the Newton–Raphson formula may be modified to

$$x_{i+1} = x_i - F(x_i)/F'(x).$$

Regardless of the multiplicity of the root r in $f(x)$, $F(X)$ has only a single root r and the modified Newton–Raphson formula may be used; this is true even if $f(x)$ is not a polynomial.

3.12.1 Flow Chart

Let

$$\begin{aligned} f(x) &= (\sin x - x/2)^2 = 0, \\ f'(x) &= 2(\sin x - x/2)(\cos x - 1/2), \\ f''(x) &= 2[(\cos x - 1/2)^2 - \sin x(\sin x - x/2)]. \end{aligned} \tag{3.59}$$

Hence,

$$F(x) = \frac{\sin x - x/2}{2(\cos x - 1/2)}$$

and

$$F'(x) = 1 - \frac{f(x)f''(x)}{[f'(x)]^2}.$$

The first approximation to the root r is $x = \pi/2$.

3.12.2 Program

The following program computes the double root r, $\pi/2 < r < \pi$. Starting value: $x = \pi/2 \cong 1.57079633$.

```
    DIMENSION Z(20)
110 FORMAT(2F10.0,I5)
111 FORMAT('1','METHOD CONVERGES',/,10F12.6)
112 FORMAT('1','SLOW CONVERGENCE',/,10F12.6)
    F(X)=(SIN(X)-X/2)**2.
    PRIME(X)=2*.((SIN(X)-X/2.)*(COS(X)-1./2.))
    QRIME(X)=2*.((COS(X)-1./2.)**2-SIN(X)*(SIN(X)-X/2.))
    CAPF(X)=F(X)/PRIME(X)
    CAP2(X)=1-F(X)*QRIME(X)/PRIME(X)**2
    READ(5,110) X,EPS,M
    L=1
  1 XL=X-CAPF(X)/CAP2(X)
    IF(ABS(F(X))-EPS)2,3,3
  2 Z(L)=XL
    WRITE(6,111)(Z(I),I=1,L)
    STOP
  3 X=XL
    Z(L)=XL
    IF(L-M)4,5,5
  4 L=L+1
    GO TO 1
  5 WRITE(6,112)(Z(I),I=1,L)
    STOP
    END
```

THE RESULTS ARE

METHOD CONVERGES

z_1=1.801748
z_2=1.889629
z_3=1.895473
z_4=1.895494

FLOW CHART 3.12.1 Multiple Roots

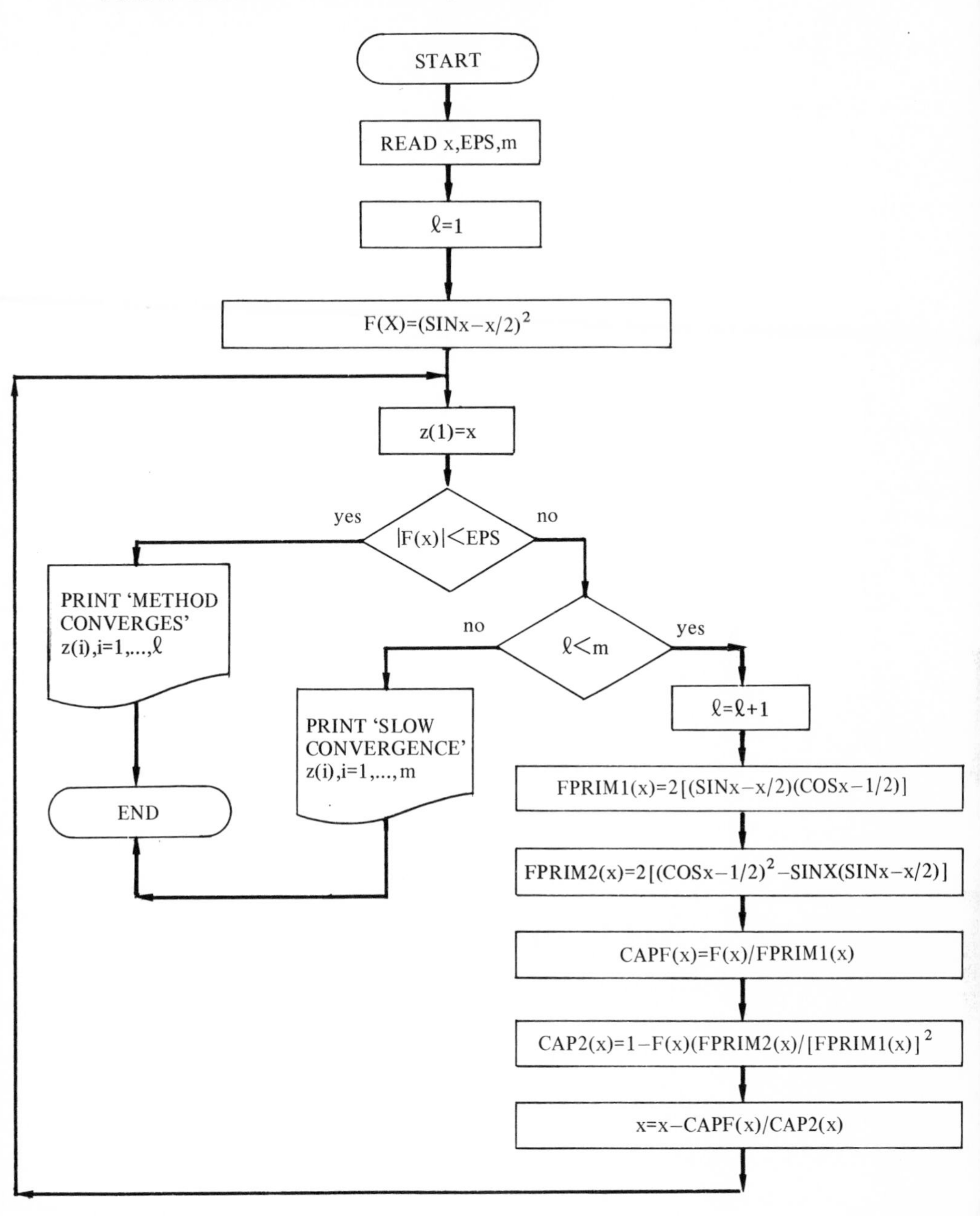

3.13 Bernoulli's Method

If it is known that in a polynomial equation, one real root r is dominant, i.e., $|r| > |r_k|$ where r_k represents any other root, then the method described below may be used to find the first approximation. This method may also be continued in some cases to find an approximation to the desired degree of accuracy, although convergence may be slow. Let

$$P(x) = a_1x^n + a_2x^{n-1} + \cdots + a_{n+1} = 0, \qquad (a \neq 0). \tag{3.60}$$

Assume that roots are $r, r_1, \ldots, r_{n-1}$ where $|r| > |r_k|$, $k = 1, 2, \ldots, n-1$. Rewrite $P(x)$ as

$$P(x) = a_nx^n + a_{n-1}x^{n-1} + \cdots + a_1x + a_0x^0 = 0. \tag{3.61}$$

Replace Eq. 3.61 by a difference equation:[9]

$$a_nx_n + a_{n-1}x_{n-1} + \cdots + a_1x_1 + a_0x_0 = 0. \tag{3.62}$$

Thus x^i is replaced by the subscripted variable x_i, and

$$x_n = -\frac{(a_{n-1}x_{n-1} + a_{n-2}x_{n-2} + \cdots + a_0x_0)}{a_n}. \tag{3.63}$$

Letting $x_0 = x_1 = \cdots = x_{n-2} = 0$, and $x_{n-1} = 1$, a first value of x_n is

$$x_n = -\frac{a_{n-1}x_{n-1}}{a_n} = -\frac{a_{n-1}}{a_n}.$$

Then the ratio $q_1 = x_n/x_{n-1}$ is a first approximation to the root r.

Replacing x_0 by x_1, x_1 by x_2, $\ldots$, x_{n-2} by x_{n-1}, and x_{n-1} by x_n, repeat the process so that

$$x_n = -\frac{(a_{n-1}x_{n-1} + a_{n-2}x_{n-2})}{a_n} \qquad \text{and} \qquad q_2 = \frac{x_n}{x_{n-1}}$$

is the next approximation to r.

This process of replacing x_i by x_{i+1} $(i = 0, \ldots, n-1)$, computing an x_n, and forming the sequence of quotients $q_i = x_n/x_{n-1}$ can be repeated so that[10]

$$\lim_{i\to\infty} q_i = r.$$

[9] See Ch. 7, Sec. 7.10 for a treatment of difference equations.

[10] See Peter K. Henrici, *Elements of Numerical Analysis* (New York: John Wiley & Sons, Inc., 1964).

Example 1

Let

$$P(x) = x^2 - x - 1 = 0. \qquad r_1 = (1 + \sqrt{5})/2, r_2 = (1 - \sqrt{5})/2.$$

The difference equation is $x_2 = x_1 + x_0$. Letting $x_0 = 0$, $x_1 = 1$, then $x_2 = 1$ and $q_1 = x_2/x_1 = 1$. Now replacing x_0 by x_1 and x_1 by x_2, $x_0 = 1$, $x_1 = 1$, and $x_2 = 1 + 1 = 2$; also, $q_1 = x_2/x_1 = 2$.

Repeating, the values of x_2 and q_i become:

$$\begin{aligned} x_2 &= 2 + 1 = 3 & q_3 &= 3/2 \\ x_2 &= 3 + 2 = 5 & q_4 &= 5/3 \\ x_2 &= 5 + 3 = 8, & q_5 &= 8/5. \end{aligned}$$

The values of x_2, namely 1, 2, 3, 5, 8, 13, . . . are called Fibonacci numbers, and it also can be shown that

$$\lim_{i\to\infty} q_i = \frac{1 + \sqrt{5}}{2}.$$

Example 2

Let

$$P(x) = x^3 - 13x^2 + 32x - 20, \qquad r_1 = 10, r_2 = 2, r_3 = 1.$$

Then, the difference equation is $x_3 = 13x_2 - 32x_1 + 20x_0$.

Letting $x_0 = x_1 = 0$ and $x_2 = 1$, then $x_3 = 13$ and $q_1 = x_3/x_2 = 13$. Letting $x_0 = x_1 = 0$, $x_1 = x_2 = 1$, $x_2 = x_3 = 13$, then $x_3 = (13)^2 - 32 = 137$ and $q_2 = x_3/x_2 = 137/13$. Again, let

$$\begin{aligned} x_0 &= x_1 = 1 \\ x_1 &= x_2 = 13 \\ x_2 &= x_3 = 137 \\ x_3 &= 13(137) - 32(13) + 20 = 1385, \end{aligned}$$

and

$$q_3 = 1385/137.$$

This procedure can be repeated, so that $\lim_{i\to\infty} q_i = 10$.

3.13.1 Flow Chart

Equation 3.63 may be restated as

$$x_{n+1} = -\frac{(a_n x_n + a_{n-1}x_{n-1} + \cdots + a_1 x_1)}{a_{n+1}}. \tag{3.64}$$

Comments

1. The letter k is a control for the maximum number of iterations.
2. The test of $x_n = 0$ is used in order to avoid division by zero in $q_i = x_{n+1}/x_n$.
3. $QONE$ initially set equal to zero is used for the purpose of testing $|q_{i+1} - q_i| < EPS$. $QTWO$, the currently computed value of x_{n+1}/x_n, replaces $QONE$ for each iteration when the test is not satisfied.
4. The data x_i ($i = 1, 2, \ldots, n-1$) are all zero, and $x_n = 1$. The values a_i ($i = 1, 2, \ldots, n+1$) are the coefficients in $P(x)$.

FLOW CHART 3.13.1 Bernoulli's Method

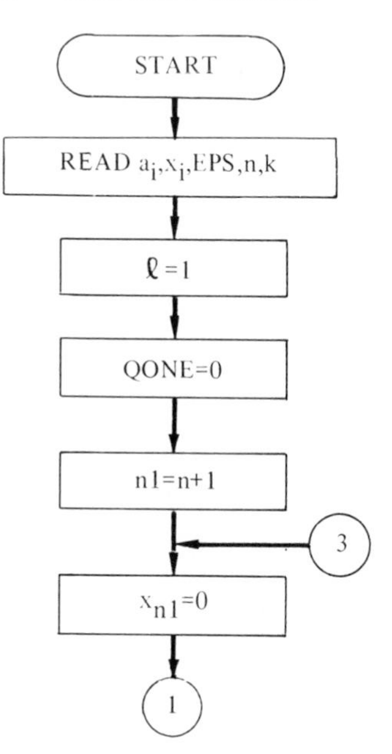

Flow Chart 3.13.1 *(Continued)*

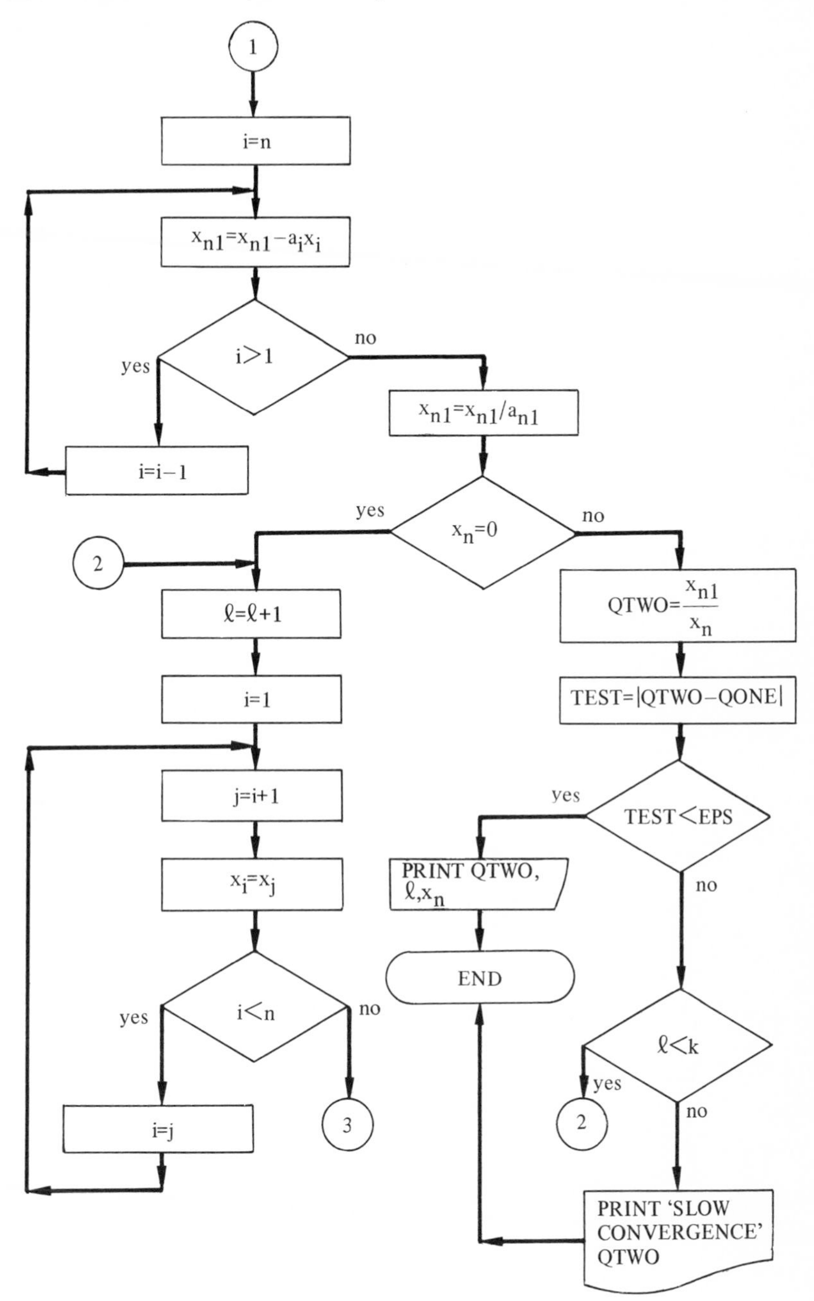

3.13.2 Program

To find the dominant root of $x^3 - 13x^2 + 32x - 20 = 0$.

```
      DIMENSION A(20),X(20)
      READ(5,100)N,K,EPS
      N1=N+1
      READ(5,101)(A(I),I=1,N1)
      READ(5,101)(X(I),I=1,N)
101   FORMAT(16F5.0)
102   FORMAT(//,'QTWO=',F10.4,/,'L=',I4,/,'X(N)=',F10.4)
103   FORMAT(//,'SLOW CONVERGENCE',/,'QTWO=',F10.4)
100   FORMAT(2I2,F5.0)
      L=1
      QONE=0
  3   X(N1)=0
      I=N
  6   X(N1)=X(N1)-A(I)*X(I)
      IF(I-1)7,7,8
  8   I=I-1
      GO TO 6
  7   X(N1)=X(N1)/A(N1)
      IF(X(N))9,2,9
  9   QTWO=X(N1)/X(N)
      TEST=ABS(QTWO-QONE)
      IF(TEST-EPS)10,11,11
 10   WRITE(6,102)QTWO,L,X(N)
 15   STOP
 11   IF(L-K)2,13,13
 13   WRITE(6,103)QTWO
      GO TO 15
  2   L=L+1
      I=1
 12   J=I+1
      X(I)=X(J)
      IF(I-N)14,3,3
 14   I=J
      GO TO 12
      END
```

```
      RESULT

      THE DOMINANT ROOT IS
      QTWO=10.0000
```

3.13.3 Bernoulli's Method Continued

If the roots of Eq. 3.60 are ordered in magnitude, i.e., $|r_1| > |r_2| > \cdots > |r_n|$, then, after the dominant root has been found and the equation reduced in degree by synthetic division, Bernoulli's method can be applied again to find the next root of greatest magnitude. Thus, all roots (if so ordered) can be found by this method.

The root smallest in magnitude can be found by considering $x^n P(1/x) = 0$; the smallest root of $P(x)$ then becomes the reciprocal of the largest root of $x^n P(1/x) = 0$.

Example 1

Consider

$$P(x) = x^3 - 13x^2 + 32x - 20 = 0.$$

In Sec. 3.13, $r_1 = 10$ was found to be the largest root. The reduced equation becomes $x^2 - 3x + 2 = 0$ and the difference equation is $x_2 = 3x_1 - 2x_0$.

Letting $x_0 = 0$ and $x_1 = 1$, then $x_2 = 3$ and $q_1 = 3$. Successive values of x_2 and q_i become:

i	x_2	q_i
2	7	7/3
3	15	15/7
4	31	31/15
5	63	63/31
6	127	127/63 .

Thus

$$\lim_{i \to \infty} q_i = 2.$$

Example 2

To find the smallest root in absolute value, consider

$$x^3 P(1/x) = -20x^3 + 32x^2 - 13x + 1 = 0.$$

The difference equation is

$$x_3 = \frac{32x_2 - 13x_1 + x_0}{20}.$$

Letting $x_0 = x_1 = 0$ and $x_2 = 1$, then $x_3 = 32/20$ and $q_1 = 32/20$; successive values of x_3 and q_i are:

i	x_3	q_i
2	191/100	191/160
3	1033/500	1033/955

Thus, $\lim_{i\to\infty} q_i = 1$, and $r_3 = 1$.

3.13.4 Final Comments on Bernoulli's Method

1. Convergence is usually slow. This can be avoided by applying another method (such as Newton–Raphson) after a fairly good approximation is found by the Bernoulli method.
2. Bernoulli's method can be used to find a dominant multiple real root. For example, $P(x) = x^3 - 5x^2 + 8x - 4 = 0$ has the roots 2, 2, 1 ($x_3 = 5x_2 - 8x_1 + 4x_0$). The values of x_3 and q_i are:

i	x_3	q_i
1	5	5
2	17	17/5
3	49	49/17
4	129	129/49
5	321	321/129

3. The method can be modified so that it will apply to the case where dominant roots may be complex.
4. The computed numbers may become very large in the intermediate steps.

3.14 The Lehmer–Schur Method

The statement that all methods so far considered, to solve $f(x) = 0$ for one root or more than one root,[11] are dependent upon some a priori knowledge of the root, is in general true. There is one method, however, that requires no knowledge of the nature of the roots and will converge for all roots of $f(x) = 0$.

This technique, known as the Lehmer–Schur method, is based upon the idea of determining whether there exists a root (or roots) within

[11] $f(x)$ is a polynomial.

the unit circle about the origin. If there is a single root, then a method such as Newton–Raphson can be used to approximate the root. If there are two complex roots, the Lin–Bairstow method may be applied. If there is no root within the unit circle, or if after the root(s) within the unit circle has been determined and the degree of $f(x)$ is reduced, a technique to determine a root within a circle of radius 2 can be applied.

Thus, by this method, one can determine whether or not there are roots within the unit circle. If any such roots exist, a suitable method may be used to approximate the root or roots more accurately. The method can be applied again to determine whether or not roots exist within a circle of radius 2. Hence, any such root would lie in the annulus of $1 < |r| < 2$. These roots can be approximated by appropriate methods. The Lehmer–Schur method can be applied as many times as are required, and in each case for the ith repeated time the roots would lie in the annulus of $2^{i-1} < |r| < 2^i$. For a root in the annulus $2^{i-1} < |r| < 2^i$, use will be made of the fact that if $f(x)$ has a root inside the circle $|x| = \rho$, then $g(x) = f(\rho x)$ has a root inside the unit circle.

3.14.1 Procedure

1. Define $f(x) = a_1 x^n + a_2 x^{n-1} + \cdots + a_{n+1}$ where a_i are real, $a_1 \neq 0$; $f(0)$ is assumed $\neq 0$.
2. Define $\bar{f}(x) = x^n f(x^{-1}) = a_{n+1} x^n + \bar{a}_n x^{n-1} + \cdots + a_1$.
3. Define $\phi[f(x)] = a_{n+1}\{f(x)\} - a_1\{\bar{f}(x)\}$. (Note: $\phi[f(x)]$ will be of degree $n-1$ if not identically zero. Let $\phi[f(x)] = f_1(x)$. Then by defining $\bar{f}_1(x) = x^{n-1} f_1(x^{-1})$ and applying ϕ again, $\phi[f_1(x)] = f_2(x)$ is in general of degree $n-2$. Thus, a sequence of polynomials $f_1(x)$, $f_2(x), \ldots, f_n(x)$, which will be of degrees $n-1, n-2, \ldots, 0$, is formed.
4. If for the smallest integer j, $f_j(0) = 0$, then for $i = 1, 2, \ldots, j-1$, if $f_1(0) < 0$, $f(x)$ has at least one root inside the unit circle. If, however, $f_i(0) > 0$ for $1 \leq i < j$, and if $f_{j-1}(x)$ is a constant, then $f(x)$ has no root inside the unit circle.[12]
5. Thus, if $f_i(0) > 0$ and $f_{j-1}(x)$ is a constant, let $x = 2z$ and repeat steps 1 through 4 for $f(2z) = g(z)$. If $g(z)$ has at least one root in the unit circle, then $f(x)$ has at least one root within the annulus $1 < |x| < 2$.
6. Step 5 can be repeated for $x = 2^2 z, 2^3 z, \ldots$, and in each case, if $f(\rho z) = 0$ ($\rho = 2, 2^2, 2^3, \ldots$) has a root within $|z| < 1$, then $f(x) = 0$

[12] For $j = 0$, $f_j(x) = f(x)$ and $f_j(0) = f(0)$.

has a root inside $|x| < \rho$. For each root found, $f(x)$ can be reduced in degree by synthetic division by one or by two according to whether $f(x)$ has a single root or a quadratic factor with two roots.

7. If for some j, $f_j(0) = 0$ but $f_{j-1}(x)$ is not a constant, let $x = \delta z$ where $1/2 < \delta < 1$. If $f(\delta z)$ has at least one root in the unit circle, then $f(x) = 0$ has a root or roots in $|x| < \delta$. With this substitution, repeat steps 1–7. This unusual case will occur if $a_1 = a_{n+1}$.
8. By repeating steps 1–7, the polynomial $f(x)$ will be reduced in degree to a constant—thus, all roots will be determined. If $f(0)f(1) < 0$, then at least one real root exists between 0 and 1. The Newton–Raphson method may be applied to approximate this root. If, however, there is a multiple root in (0,1) it would be necessary to use the Newton–Raphson improved process for a multiple root. Similar remarks apply for the interval (−1,0).

   If $f(0)f(1) > 0$ and $f(-1)f(0) > 0$,[13] and if the Lehmer–Schur process showed there are roots in the unit circle, then these conditions would indicate that there exist pairs of complex roots, or an even number of distinct real roots or real roots of even multiplicity. In such cases it would indicate that there would be at least a quadratic factor $x^2 + px + q$. Hence, the Lin–Bairstow method could be used. The roots of $x^2 + px + q$, after p and q have been sufficiently well approximated, can be found by the routine for solving a quadratic factor. The following examples illustrate the various possibilities described above.

Example 1

$$f(x) = 16x^3 - 64x^2 + 30x - 7 = 0,$$

$$\bar{f}(x) = x^3 f(x^{-1}) = -7x^3 + 30x^2 - 64x + 16 = 0,$$

$$\phi[f(x)] = f_1(x) = -7[16x^3 - 64x^2 + 30x - 7] - 16[-7x^3 + 30x^2 - 64x + 16],$$

or

$$f_1(x) = -32x^2 + 814x - 207 \qquad \text{and} \qquad f_1(0) = -207.$$

Hence, $f(x)$ has some roots in the unit circle $|x| < 1$. Also since $f(-1) < 0$, $f(0) < 0$, and $f(1) < 0$, either $f(x)$ has an even number of real roots, a root of even multiplicity, or a pair of complex roots inside the unit circle.

[13] If, for example, $f(0)f(1) < 0$ and $f(-1)f(0) > 0$, then a real root is indicated in the interval (0,1). This root would have to be determined and the process repeated to test for other possible roots.

Apply the Lin–Bairstow method with $x^2 + px + q = x^2 + x + 1$. By this process $x^2 + px + q$ finally becomes $x^2 - x/2 + 1/8$. The zeros of $x^2 - x/2 + 1/8$ are $(1 \pm i)/4$. Using synthetic division to divide one polynomial by another, the reduced equation is $g(x) = 16x - 56 = 0$. Then

$$\bar{g}(x) = xg(x^{-1}) = -56x + 16 = 0,$$
$$\phi[g(x)] = -56[16x - 56] - 16[-56x + 16],$$

or

$$g_1(x) = 56^2 - 16^2 > 0.$$

Thus there is no root of $g(x)$ inside the unit circle.

Let $x = 2z$, then $g(x) = g(2z) = H(z) = 32z - 56$; also let $\overline{H}(z) = -56z + 32$, then $\phi[H(z)] = -56(32z - 56) - 32(-56z + 32)$ or $\phi[H(z)] = 56^2 - 32^2 > 0$. Hence, $H(z)$ has no root in $|z| < 1$; therefore $f(x)$ has no root in $|x| < 2$.

Let $z = 2y$, $H(2y) = K(y) = 64y - 56$. Also let $\overline{K}(y) = -56y + 64$; then $\phi[K(y)] = -56(64y - 56) - 64(-56y + 64)$ or $K_1(y) = 56^2 - 64^2 < 0$. Hence $K(y) = 0$ has a root $|y| < 1$ and $f(x)$ has a corresponding root $2 < |x| < 4$.

By synthetic division, it is found that $y = 7/8$; hence $x = 4(7/8) = 7/2$. Thus, the roots of $f(x) = 0$ are $7/2$, $(1 \pm i)/4$. Only for the purpose of illustration is the last part of this method given. When by the Lehmer–Schur process $f(x)$ has been reduced to a quadratic or a linear factor, this factor can be solved by an appropriate routine.

Example 2

This next example illustrates the procedure used if $f_j(0) = 0$ and $f_{j-1}(x)$ is not a constant. Let

$$f(x) = 2x^2 - 5x + 2$$
$$\bar{f}(x) = 2x^2 - 5x + 2$$
$$\phi[f(x)] = f_1(x) = 2[2x^2 - 5x + 2] - 2[2x^2 - 5x + 2] = 0.$$

Thus, $f_1(x) = 0$, hence $f_1(0) = 0$, but $f(x)$ is not a constant. The procedure must be altered in such a case as follows.

Let $x = 3z/4$; then

$$f(3z/4) = g(z) = 9z^2 - 30z + 16 = 0,$$
$$\bar{g}(z) = z^2 g(z^{-1}) = 16z^2 - 30z + 9 = 0,$$
$$\phi[g(z)] = 16[9z^2 - 30z + 16] - 9[16z^2 - 30z + 9],$$

or

$$g_1(z) = -210z + 175 \qquad \text{and} \qquad g_1(0) = 175.$$

Since $g_1(0) > 0$ and $g(z)$ is not a constant, the process is repeated. Thus,

$$\bar{g}_1(z) = zg_1(z) = 175z - 210,$$

and

$$\phi[g_1(z)] = g_2(z) = 175(-210z + 175) + 210(175z - 210),$$

or

$$g_2(z) = 175^2 - 210^2 < 0.$$

Hence, $g(z) = 0$ has a root in $|z| < 1$; therefore $f(x)$ has a root in $|x| < 3/4$. Since $g(0) = 16$ and $g(1) = -5$, $g(z)$ has a real root in (0,1). By synthetic division, $z = 2/3$ is found to be a root of $g(z)$, hence $x = (3/4)^z = 1/2$ is a root of $f(x) = 0$. The other root of $f(x)$ is 2.

These two examples bring out the fact that the coefficients in $f_i(x)$ can become quite large. Therefore, each $f(x)$ should be normalized before the method is applied. This can be accomplished by dividing all coefficients by the coefficient of greatest magnitude.

PROBLEMS

3-7. Write a flow chart and program for the root squaring method to solve the equation

$$P(x) = 4x^4 - 44x^3 + 149x^2 - 126x - 81 = 0.$$

The true roots are 9/2, 9/2, $1 + \sqrt{2}$, $1 - \sqrt{2}$. If the test $|T_j - S_j| < EPS$ where $T_j = 10^{-n}c_j$ and $S_j = 10^{-n}a_j^2$ is not satisfied after several iterations for a current j, the indication is that there is a quadratic factor $c_{j-1}x^2 + c_jx + c_{j+1}$; these two roots are not being separated and hence they are the same real root or they are a pair of complex roots.

At this juncture, it is necessary to solve $a_{j-1}x^2 + a_jx + a_{j+1} = 0$. But such a solution would be worthless without a better approximation to the quadratic. Therefore, the Lin–Bairstow method must be applied. That is, express $a_{j-1}x^2 + a_jx + a_{j+1}$ as $x^2 + px + q$ where $p = a_j/a_{j-1}$ and $q = a_{j+1}/a_{j-1}$, and then use the Lin–Bairstow method.

The other two roots can be found by the root squaring process directly. However, as each root is approximated, a better approximation can be found by applying the Newton–Raphson method.

3-8. In

$$P(x) = 4x^4 - 44x^3 + 149x^2 - 126x - 81 = 0$$

it is known that there is a root between $x = 4$ and $x = 5$, namely $x = 9/2$; but $P(4)P(5) > 0$, and the Newton–Raphson method is not applicable. Therefore, the modified Newton–Raphson method for a multiple root should be used.

Write a flow chart and program to solve for all the roots of $P(x) = 0$. The steps are:

1. Use the modified Newton–Raphson method to find the dominant root. For this let the initial value of the root be $x = 4$.
2. Use synthetic division to reduce the degree of the equation.
3. Use synthetic division again to reduce the degree.
4. The reduced equation is now a quadratic. Solve the quadratic equation.

3-9. Apply the Bernoulli method to

$$P(x) = 4x^4 - 44x^3 + 149x^2 - 126x - 81 = 0$$

in the following manner:

1. Find the dominant root by application of the Bernoulli method for six iterations.
2. Use the modified Newton–Raphson method to find a better approximation.
3. Find the smallest root by application of the Bernoulli method for six iterations.
4. Use the Newton–Raphson method to find a better approximation for the smallest root.
5. Reduce the degree of the equation by synthetic division by the largest root and again by the smallest root.
6. Solve the quadratic equation.

3-10. Similar to the modified Newton–Raphson method for a multiple root, develop a modified secant method for a multiple root. That is, consider $F(x) = f(x)/f'(x)$ and derive a formula for x_{i+1} similar to Eq. 3.22. Then write a formula for this method similar to Eq. 3.19.

Write a flow chart and program for the modified secant method to approximate the double root r of $(\sin x - x/2)^2 = 0$, $\pi/2 < r < \pi$.

3-11. In Sec. 3.9 an improved Newton–Raphson method was developed for polynomial equations. In a like manner, develop an improved secant method for polynomial equations. Note that Eq. 3.22 may be stated as

$$x_{i+1} = x_i + \frac{f(x_i)(x_i - x_{i-1})}{f(x_{i-1}) - f(x_i)}.$$

Write a flow chart and a program for the improved secant method to approximate the root r of $P(x) = x^5 - 6x^4 + 24x + 3 = 0$ where $1 < r < 2$.

3-12. Use the Lehmer–Schur technique to solve:

(a) $f(x) = 4x^3 - 24x^2 + 39x - 14 = 0$, roots $1/2, 2, 7/2$,

(b) $f(x) = 4x^3 - 10x^2 + 8x - 3 = 0$, roots $(1 \pm i)/2, 3/2$,

(c) $f(x) = 2x^3 - 9x^2 + 14x - 10 = 0$, roots $1 \pm i, 5/2$.

4

Simultaneous Equations

Since the Σ and π notations are used quite extensively throughout this text, the basic features of these notations are presented here.

4.1 Σ Notation

The Σ notation indicates a sum. Thus, $u_1 + u_2 + u_3$ can be written as

$$\sum_{i=1}^{3} u_i \quad \text{or} \quad \sum_{j=1}^{3} u_j,$$

and in general,

$$u_1 + u_2 + \cdots + u_n = \sum_{i=1}^{n} u_i, \tag{4.1}$$

and

$$\sum_{i=m}^{n} u_i = u_m + u_{m+1} + \cdots + u_n, \qquad (m \le n). \tag{4.2}$$

Also,

$$u_m + u_{m+1} + \cdots + u_{k-1} + u_k + \cdots + u_n = \sum_{i=m}^{n} u_i,$$

$$\begin{aligned}\sum_{i=m}^{n} u_i &= (u_m + u_{m+1} + \cdots + u_{k-1}) + (u_k + \cdots + u_n)\\ &= \sum_{i=m}^{k-1} u_i + \sum_{i=k}^{n} u_i, \qquad (m \le k \le n).\end{aligned} \tag{4.3}$$

Further, from Eq. 4.3, if $k = m$, then

$$\sum_{i=m}^{m-1} u_i = 0. \tag{4.4}$$

The letter i (or j) called the index of summation, is entirely arbitrary, and hence is referred to as a dummy index.

4.1.1 Double Sums

A set of mn quantities,

$$\begin{matrix} u_{11} & u_{12} & \cdots & u_{1n} \\ u_{21} & u_{22} & \cdots & u_{2n} \\ \cdot & \cdot & \cdots & \cdot \\ u_{m1} & u_{m2} & \cdots & u_{mn}, \end{matrix}$$

may be summed by first summing rows and then summing the row totals:

$$\sum_{j=1}^{n} u_{1j} + \sum_{j=1}^{n} u_{2j} + \cdots + \sum_{j=1}^{n} u_{mj}.$$

This sum of sums may be expressed as

$$\sum_{i=1}^{m} \left(\sum_{j=1}^{n} u_{ij} \right) = \sum_{i=1}^{m} \sum_{j=1}^{n} u_{ij}. \tag{4.5}$$

If the quantities were summed first by columns and then by rows, the final sum would be

$$\sum_{j=1}^{n} \sum_{i=1}^{m} u_{ij}.$$

Thus,

$$\sum_{i=1}^{m} \sum_{j=1}^{n} u_{ij} = \sum_{j=1}^{n} \sum_{i=1}^{m} u_{ij}. \tag{4.6}$$

For a triangular set of quantities,

$$\begin{matrix} u_{11} & & & & \\ u_{21} & u_{22} & & & \\ u_{31} & u_{32} & u_{33} & & \\ \cdot & \cdot & \cdot & & \\ u_{m1} & u_{m2} & u_{m3} & \cdots & u_{mm}, \end{matrix}$$

the sum by rows is

$$\sum_{j=1}^{1} u_{1j} + \sum_{j=1}^{2} u_{2j} + \sum_{j=1}^{3} u_{3j} + \cdots + \sum_{j=1}^{m} u_{mj},$$

and this may be written as

$$\sum_{i=1}^{m} \sum_{j=1}^{i} u_{ij}.$$

EXERCISE

Show that the above sum may be stated as

$$\sum_{j=1}^{m} \sum_{i=j}^{m} u_{ij}.$$

Another double sum may be derived, letting

$$u_{ij} = a_{ij}x_i y_j, \qquad (i = 1, 2, \ldots, m \quad \text{and} \quad j = 1, 2, 3, \ldots, n).$$

Then the sum of all u_{ij} is

$$\sum_{i=1}^{m} \sum_{j=1}^{n} a_{ij}x_i y_j. \tag{4.7}$$

As an example, let $m = n = 2$; then,

$$\sum_{i=1}^{2} \sum_{j=1}^{2} a_{ij}x_i y_j = a_{11}x_1 y_1 + a_{12}x_1 y_2 + a_{21}x_2 y_1 + a_{22}x_2 y_2.$$

Such sums are known as bilinear forms, since they are linear in both x_i and y_i.

When $m = n$, only one summation sign may be used, as in

$$\sum_{i=1}^{m} \sum_{j=1}^{m} a_{ij}x_i y_j \equiv \sum_{i,j=1}^{m} a_{ij}x_i y_j. \tag{4.8}$$

In this simpler notation, both i and j start with one and continue to the upper limit m. A variation of this notation is seen in the summing of $x_i x_j$ where $i \neq j$ and both i and j begin with one and end with m.

Suppose, for example, that from the set $\{x_1, x_2, x_3\}$, the sum of all products $x_i x_j$, $i \neq j$ is required, i.e.,

$$x_1 x_2 + x_1 x_3 + x_2 x_1 + x_2 x_3 + x_3 x_1 + x_3 x_2.$$

This sum may be expressed as

$$\sum_{i,j=1}^{3} x_i x_j, \qquad (i \neq j).$$

But since $x_i x_j = x_j x_i$, this sum may also be written as $2(x_1x_2 + x_1x_3 + x_2x_3)$, and in Σ notation, this becomes

$$2 \sum_{i,j=1}^{3} x_i x_j, \qquad (i < j).$$

Hence,

$$\sum_{i,j=1}^{m} x_i x_j = \sum_{i,j=1}^{m} x_i x_j, \tag{4.9}$$

where on the left side of the equality $i \neq j$, and on the right-hand side $i < j$ (terms not satisfying restrictions are to be omitted).

4.2 π Notation

The π notation indicates a product. Thus,

$$u_1 u_2 u_3 \cdots u_n = \prod_{i=1}^{n} u_i.$$

The product

$$(u_1 u_2 u_3 \cdots u_n) \cdot (v_1 v_2 \cdots v_n) = (u_1 v_1)(u_2 v_2) \cdots (u_n v_n)$$

may be written as

$$\left(\prod_{i=1}^{n} u_i\right)\left(\prod_{i=1}^{n} v_i\right) \quad \text{or} \quad \prod_{i=1}^{n} u_i v_i. \tag{4.10}$$

The product of all quantities in

$$\begin{matrix} u_{11} & u_{12} & \cdots & u_{1n} \\ u_{21} & u_{22} & \cdots & u_{2n} \\ \cdot & \cdot & \cdots & \cdot \\ u_{m1} & u_{m2} & \cdots & u_{mn} \end{matrix}$$

may be expressed as

$$\prod_{i=1}^{m}\left(\prod_{j=1}^{n} u_{ij}\right) \quad \text{or} \quad \prod_{j=1}^{n}\left(\prod_{i=1}^{m} u_{ij}\right). \tag{4.11}$$

EXERCISE

Derive two double products in π notation, each of which indicates the product of

$$
\begin{matrix}
u_{11} & & & & \\
u_{21} & u_{22} & & & \\
u_{31} & u_{32} & u_{33} & & \\
\cdot & \cdot & \cdot & & \\
u_{m1} & u_{m2} & u_{m3} & \cdots & u_{mm}.
\end{matrix}
$$

Another example of π notation is contained in the product

$$(x_1 - x_2)(x_1 - x_3)(x_2 - x_3).$$

Symbolically this may be expressed as

$$\prod_{1 \le i < j \le 3} (x_i - x_j)$$

or

$$\prod_{\substack{i=1,2 \\ j=i+1,\cdots 3}} (x_i - x_j).$$

The general forms are

$$\prod_{1 \le i < j \le n} (x_i - x_j)$$

or

$$\prod_{\substack{i=1,2,\cdots,n-1 \\ j=i+1,\cdots,n}} (x_i - x_j).$$

4.3 Matrices

A rectangular array of numbers or functions is called a *matrix* and may be represented as [1]

$$A = \begin{bmatrix} a_{11} & a_{12} & \cdots & a_{1n} \\ a_{21} & a_{22} & \cdots & a_{2n} \\ \cdot & \cdot & \cdots & \cdot \\ a_{m1} & a_{m2} & \cdots & a_{mn} \end{bmatrix}. \tag{4.12}$$

A is said to be an m by n matrix since it has m rows and n columns; thus A can be expressed as $[a_{ij}]_{(m,n)}$.

When $m = n$, A is a *square* matrix and is said to be of order n. If all the elements of a square matrix above and below the main diagonal [2]

[1] In this text, a matrix is indicated by brackets, a determinant by vertical bars (see Sec. 4.5).

[2] The main diagonal consists of the elements $a_{11}, a_{22}, \ldots, a_{mn}$.

are zero, the matrix is called a *diagonal* matrix and is written as

$$[a_1, a_2, \ldots, a_n] = \begin{bmatrix} a_1 & 0 & \cdots & 0 \\ 0 & a_2 & \cdots & 0 \\ \cdot & \cdot & \cdots & \cdot \\ 0 & 0 & \cdots & a_n \end{bmatrix}. \tag{4.13}$$

If all $a_i = a$, the matrix is called a *scalar* matrix and is written as

$$[a] = \begin{bmatrix} a & 0 & \cdots & 0 \\ 0 & a & \cdots & 0 \\ \cdot & \cdot & \cdots & \cdot \\ 0 & 0 & \cdots & a \end{bmatrix}. \tag{4.14}$$

If $a = 1$, the matrix is called the *identity* matrix and is written as

$$I_n = \begin{bmatrix} 1 & 0 & \cdots & 0 \\ 0 & 1 & \cdots & 0 \\ \cdot & \cdot & \cdots & \cdot \\ 0 & 0 & \cdots & 1 \end{bmatrix}. \tag{4.15}$$

If all elements of a matrix are zero, the matrix is called a *null* matrix. If the rows and columns of a matrix are interchanged, the resulting matrix is called the *transpose* of the matrix. The transpose of A (4.12) is

$$A^T = \begin{bmatrix} a_{11} & a_{21} & \cdots & a_{m1} \\ a_{12} & a_{22} & \cdots & a_{m2} \\ \cdot & \cdot & \cdots & \cdot \\ a_{1n} & a_{2n} & \cdots & a_{mn} \end{bmatrix}. \tag{4.16}$$

In a square matrix A, if $a_{ij} = a_{ji}$ for all pairs of values (i, j), A is said to be *symmetric*. If $a_{ij} = -a_{ji}$, A is said to be *skew-symmetric*. What is the value of a_{ii} in a skew-symmetric matrix?

4.3.1 Addition and Subtraction of Matrices—Scalar Multiplication

If two matrices A and B are of the same order, their sum is defined as $[a_{ij} + b_{ij}]_{(m,n)}$. That is, their corresponding elements are added. Similarly, $A - B$ is defined as $[a_{ij} - b_{ij}]_{(m,n)}$. The operation of multiplying all elements of a matrix by a scalar not equal to zero is called scalar multiplication.

Thus,

$$\alpha A = \alpha \begin{bmatrix} a_{11} & a_{12} & \cdots & a_{1n} \\ a_{21} & a_{22} & \cdots & a_{2n} \\ \cdot & \cdot & \cdots & \cdot \\ a_{m1} & a_{m2} & \cdots & a_{mn} \end{bmatrix} = \begin{bmatrix} \alpha a_{11} & \alpha a_{12} & \cdots & \alpha a_{1n} \\ \alpha a_{21} & \alpha a_{22} & \cdots & \alpha a_{2n} \\ \cdot & \cdot & \cdots & \cdot \\ \alpha a_{m1} & \alpha a_{m2} & \cdots & \alpha a_{mn} \end{bmatrix}. \tag{4.17}$$

4.3.2 Multiplication of Matrices

If A is of order m by n and b is of order n by l, then $A \cdot B = C$, and C is a matrix of order m by l. This is expressed symbolically as

$$[a_{ik}]_{(m,n)} \cdot [b_{kj}]_{(n,l)} = [c_{ij}]_{(m,l)}. \tag{4.18}$$

The rule for multiplication is demonstrated by the following equation:

$$c_{ij} = a_{i1}b_{1j} + a_{i2}b_{2j} + \cdots + a_{in}b_{nj}, \tag{4.19}$$

or

$$c_{ij} = \sum_{k=1}^{n} (a_{ik})(b_{kj}). \tag{4.20}$$

Loosely expressed, the kth element of row i of A multiplies the kth element of column j of B, and these products are added to form c_{ij}:

$$[a_{ik}]_{(m,n)} \cdot [b_{kj}]_{(n,l)} = \left[\sum_{k=1}^{n} a_{ik}b_{kj}\right]_{(m,l)}. \tag{4.21}$$

For a square matrix A of order n and the identity matrix I_n, $AI_n = I_nA = A$.

The multiplication of matrices is associative. If

$$A = [a_{ik}]_{(m,n)}, \qquad B = [b_{kl}]_{(n,p)}, \qquad C = [c_{lr}]_{(p,q)},$$

then

$$\begin{aligned} (AB)C &= \left[\sum_{k=1}^{n} (a_{ik})(b_{kl})\right]_{(m,p)} \cdot [c_{lr}]_{(p,q)} \\ &= \left[\sum_{l=1}^{p}\left(\sum_{k=1}^{n} a_{ik}b_{kl}\right)c_{lr}\right]_{(m,q)} \\ &= \left[\sum_{l=1}^{p}\left(\sum_{k=1}^{n} a_{ik}b_{kl}c_{lr}\right)\right]_{(m,q)}. \end{aligned} \tag{4.22}$$

Similarly,

$$A(BC) = \left[\sum_{k=1}^{n}\left(\sum_{l=1}^{p} a_{ik}b_{kl}c_{lr}\right)\right]_{(m,q)}, \tag{4.23}$$

and since the order of summation is arbitrary,

$$(AB)C = A(BC). \tag{4.24}$$

4.4 Linear Equations

A system of n linear equations in n unknowns, such as

$$\begin{aligned} a_{11}x_1 + a_{12}x_2 + \cdots + a_{1n}x_n &= b_1 \\ a_{21}x_1 + a_{22}x_2 + \cdots + a_{2n}x_n &= b_2 \\ \cdot \quad \cdot \quad \cdot \quad & \cdot \quad \cdot \\ a_{n1}x_1 + a_{n2}x_2 + \cdots + a_{nn}x_n &= b_n, \end{aligned} \tag{4.25}$$

may be expressed as a matrix equation of the form

$$\begin{bmatrix} a_{11} & a_{12} & \cdots & a_{1n} \\ a_{21} & a_{22} & \cdots & a_{2n} \\ \cdot & \cdot & \cdot & \cdot \\ \cdot & \cdot & \cdot & \cdot \\ \cdot & \cdot & \cdot & \cdot \\ a_{n1} & a_{n2} & \cdots & a_{nn} \end{bmatrix} \cdot \begin{bmatrix} x_1 \\ x_2 \\ \cdot \\ \cdot \\ \cdot \\ x_n \end{bmatrix} = \begin{bmatrix} b_1 \\ b_2 \\ \cdot \\ \cdot \\ \cdot \\ b_n \end{bmatrix}. \tag{4.26}$$

This is true by definition of the multiplication of matrices. Let

$$A = [a_{ij}]_{(n)}, \qquad X = [x_j]_{(n,1)}, \qquad B = [b_i]_{(n,1)},$$

then Eq. 4.26 may be written as $AX = B$.[3]

4.5 Determinants

Associated with every square matrix A, there is a number or a function called the *determinant* of A, which is formally defined by the following expression:[4]

$$\det A = \sum_{(j)} \epsilon_{j_1 j_2 \ldots j_n} a_{1j_1} a_{2j_2} \cdots a_{nj_n} \tag{4.27}$$

where $j_1 j_2 \ldots j_n$ represents a permutation of the integers $1, 2, \ldots, n$, and

[3] A single column matrix such as X or B is called a vector, and its elements are called the components of the vector. The vector X may also be written as $\{x_1, x_2, \ldots, x_n\}$ in order to save space. The vector $X = \{x_1, x_2, \ldots, x_n\}$ should not be confused with $X^T = [x_1, x_2, \ldots, x_n]$.

[4] For a complete explanation see Franz E. Hohn, *Elementary Matrix Algebra*, 2d ed. (New York: The Macmillan Company, 1964), Ch. 2.

$$\epsilon_{j_1 j_2 \ldots j_n} = \begin{cases} -1 & \text{if } j_1, j_2, \ldots, j_n \text{ is an odd permutation,} \\ 0 & \text{if two } j_k \text{ are equal,} \\ 1 & \text{if } j_1 j_2 \ldots j_n \text{ is an even permutation.} \end{cases} \quad (4.28)$$

4.5.1 Cofactor of an Element of a Determinant—Minors

The cofactor A_{ij} of an element a_{ij} in det A is defined as $(-1)^{i+j}$ times the determinant (called a minor determinant) of the submatrix of order $n - 1$ obtained by deleting the ith row and the jth column from A, and[5]

$$\det A = \sum_{k=1}^{n} a_{ik} A_{ik}.$$

A square submatrix of order r ($r < n$) may be found by striking out $n - r$ rows and $n - r$ columns. The determinant of such a square submatrix is called a *minor determinant.* If the eliminated rows and columns have the same indices, the minor determinant of the remaining submatrix is called a *principal* minor determinant. Minor determinants are usually called minors (omitting the word determinant). If A is a matrix of order n and A_{ij} is the cofactor of a_{ij} in the determinant of A, then

$$a = [A_{ij}]^T \quad (4.29)$$

is called the *adjoint* matrix of A.

4.5.2 Inverse of a Square Matrix

Let $A = [a_{ij}]_{(n)}$ and det $A \neq 0$. Then the inverse of A is defined by the equation

$$A^{-1} = \left[\frac{A_{ij}}{\det A}\right]^T, \quad (4.30)$$

and it follows that

$$A^{-1}A = AA^{-1} = I. \quad (4.31)$$

Theorem: A square matrix A has an inverse if and only if det $A \neq 0$.

A square matrix A whose determinant is not equal to zero is called a *nonsingular* matrix, whereas if the determinant of $A = 0$, the matrix A

[5] See Hohn, *Elementary Matrix Algebra,* Ch. 2.

is called a *singular* matrix. Thus, the above theorem states that the matrix A has an inverse if and only if A is nonsingular.

4.5.3 Rank of a Matrix

If, in a matrix A of order m by n, determinants of all submatrices[6] of A of order $r + 1$ or greater are zero, and if the determinant of at least one submatrix of order r is not zero, then the matrix A is said to have rank r.

Operations on matrices that do not alter the rank of a matrix are called *elementary transformations* of a matrix. These transformations are:

1. The interchange of the elements of any two rows (columns)
2. The multiplication of the elements of any row (column) by a nonzero constant
3. The addition of a multiple of the elements of any row (column) to the corresponding elements of another row (column)

4.6 Cramer's Rule

A system of n linear equations in n unknowns (Eq. 4.25) may be written as

$$AX = B, \tag{4.32}$$

where A is a nonsingular matrix, and X and B are column matrices—i.e., each consists of one column. Multiplying (4.32) by A^{-1},

$$A^{-1}AX = A^{-1}B \tag{4.33}$$

or

$$X = A^{-1}B. \tag{4.34}$$

Since

$$A^{-1} = \left[\frac{A_{ij}}{\det A}\right]^T, \tag{4.35}$$

then

[6] A submatrix of a matrix A is an array remaining when rows and/or columns are deleted.

$$X = \left[\frac{A_{ji}}{\det A}\right]^B \tag{4.36}$$

or

$$\begin{bmatrix} x_1 \\ x_2 \\ \cdot \\ \cdot \\ \cdot \\ x_n \end{bmatrix} = \frac{\begin{bmatrix} b_1A_{11} + b_2A_{21} + \cdots + b_nA_{n1} \\ b_1A_{12} + b_2A_{22} + \cdots + b_nA_{n2} \\ \cdot \quad \cdot \quad \cdot \quad \cdot \\ \cdot \quad \cdot \quad \cdot \quad \cdot \\ \cdot \quad \cdot \quad \cdot \quad \cdot \\ b_1A_{1n} + b_2A_{2n} + \cdots + b_nA_{nn} \end{bmatrix}}{\det A}. \tag{4.37}$$

Thus,

$$\begin{aligned} x_1 &= \frac{b_1A_{11} + b_2A_{21} + \cdots + b_nA_{n1}}{\det A} \\ &\cdot \quad \cdot \quad \cdot \quad \cdot \quad \cdot \quad \cdot \quad \cdot \\ x_j &= \frac{b_1A_{1j} + b_2A_{2j} + \cdots + b_nA_{nj}}{\det A} \\ &\cdot \quad \cdot \quad \cdot \quad \cdot \quad \cdot \quad \cdot \quad \cdot \\ x_n &= \frac{b_1A_{1n} + b_2b_{2n} + \cdots + b_nA_{nn}}{\det A}. \end{aligned} \tag{4.38}$$

Using the concept of cofactor, (Sec. 4.5.1), Eqs. 4.38 become

$$x_1 = \frac{\begin{vmatrix} b_1 & a_{12} & \cdots & a_{1n} \\ b_2 & a_{22} & \cdots & a_{2n} \\ \cdot & \cdot & \cdots & \cdot \\ b_n & a_{n2} & \cdots & a_{nn} \end{vmatrix}}{\det A}, \tag{4.39}$$

$$x_j = \frac{\begin{vmatrix} a_{11} & a_{12} & \cdots & a_{1,j-1} & b_1 & a_{1,j+1} & \cdots & a_{1n} \\ a_{21} & a_{22} & \cdots & a_{2,j-1} & b_2 & a_{2,j+1} & \cdots & a_{2n} \\ \cdot & \cdot & \cdots & \cdot & \cdot & \cdot & \cdots & \cdot \\ a_{n1} & a_{n2} & \cdots & a_{n,j-1} & b_n & a_{n,j+1} & \cdots & a_{nn} \end{vmatrix}}{\det A}, \tag{4.40}$$

$$x_n = \frac{\begin{vmatrix} a_{11} & a_{12} & \cdots & a_{1,n-1} & b_1 \\ a_{21} & a_{22} & \cdots & a_{2,n-1} & b_2 \\ \cdot & \cdot & \cdots & \cdot & \cdot \\ a_{n1} & a_{n2} & \cdots & a_{n,n-1} & b_n \end{vmatrix}}{\det A}. \tag{4.41}$$

Later in this chapter, other methods of solving systems of equations will be given.[7] Cramer's rule is not recommended as a computer method.

4.7 Some Simple Programming Methods

Let

$$U = [u_{ij}]_{(m,n)}. \tag{4.42}$$

In all of the following exercises, it is assumed that the elements u_{ij} and m and n have been stored in the computer.

These exercises are not programs; they are simple routines and are given here to acquaint the reader with programming procedures involved in using subscripted variables.

EXERCISE 1

Write a flow chart to sum all elements of U. From Eq. 4.6, the sum of all elements of U can be expressed as

$$\sum_{i=1}^{m}\left(\sum_{j=1}^{n} u_{ij}\right) \quad \text{or} \quad \sum_{j=1}^{n}\left(\sum_{i=1}^{m} u_{ij}\right).$$

From the first of these, the sum is expressed as

$$SUM = \sum_{j=1}^{n} u_{1j} + \sum_{j=1}^{n} u_{2j} + \cdots + \sum_{j=1}^{n} u_{mj}.$$

Then the flow chart for this routine can be written as shown on page 129.

Write a flow chart to compute the sum of all u_{ij} by using the formula

$$\sum_{j=1}^{n}\sum_{i=1}^{m} u_{ij}.$$

[7] This brief treatment sets forth only an elementary description of the basic principles and ideas in matrix algebra. Any text on matrix algebra will serve as a reference; Hohn's *Elementary Matrix Algebra* is suggested.

FLOW CHART for Exercise 1

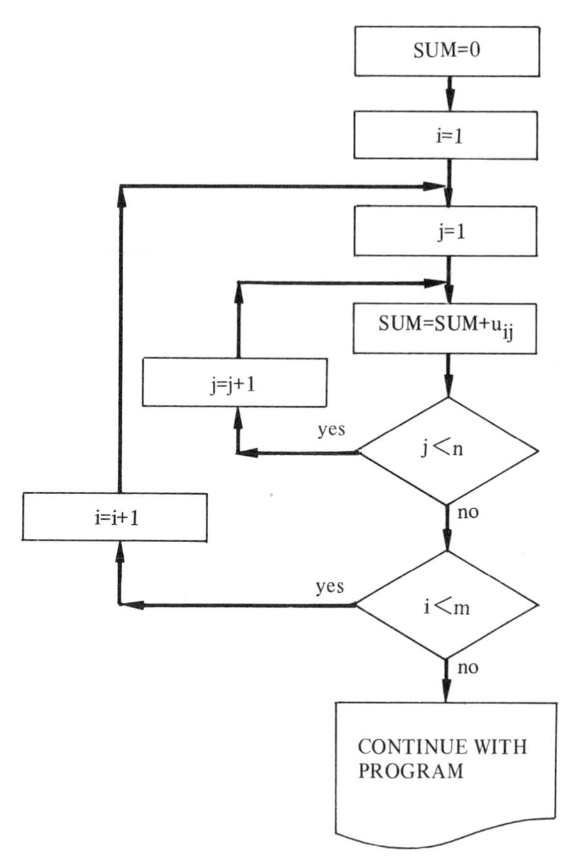

EXERCISE 2

The sum of all $x_i x_j$ ($j \neq i$; $i = 1, 2, \ldots, m$; $j = 1, 2, \ldots, m$) is either

$$\sum_{i,j=1}^{m} x_i x_j, \qquad (i \neq j)$$

or

$$2 \sum_{i,j=1}^{m} x_i x_j, \qquad (i < j).$$

The following flow chart forms the sum of all these products based upon the first of these formulas. It is left as an exercise for the reader to compute the same sum based upon the second formula.

Referring to the flow chart, for each time j is either less than or equal to m, the test of whether or not j is equal to i must be made so that the sum box will be bypassed if $j = i$.

The level chart (Table 4.1) for

$$\sum_{i,j=1}^{4} x_i x_j, \qquad (i \neq j)$$

shows that there are twenty levels or steps in forming the sum.

TABLE 4.1 Level Chart for Exercise 2.

Level	*Sum*	i	j	$j < 4$	$j = i?$	$i < 4$
1	0	1	1	yes	yes	
2			2	yes	no	
3	$+x_1x_2$		3	yes	no	
4	$+x_1x_3$		4	yes	no	
5	$+x_1x_4$		5	no		yes
6		2	1	yes	no	
7	$+x_2x_1$		2	yes	yes	
8			3	yes	no	
9	$+x_2x_3$		4	yes	no	
10	$+x_2x_4$		5	no		yes
11		3	1	yes	no	
12	x_3x_1		2	yes	no	
13	x_3x_2		3	yes	yes	
14	x_3x_4		4	yes	no	
15			5	no		yes
16		4	1	yes	no	
17	$+x_4x_1$		2	yes	no	
18	$+x_4x_2$		3	yes	no	
19	x_4x_3		4	yes	yes	
20			5	no		no

Construct a level chart for

$$2 \sum_{i,j=1}^{4} x_i x_j, \qquad (i < j).$$

How many steps are there for this method?

FLOW CHART for Exercise 2

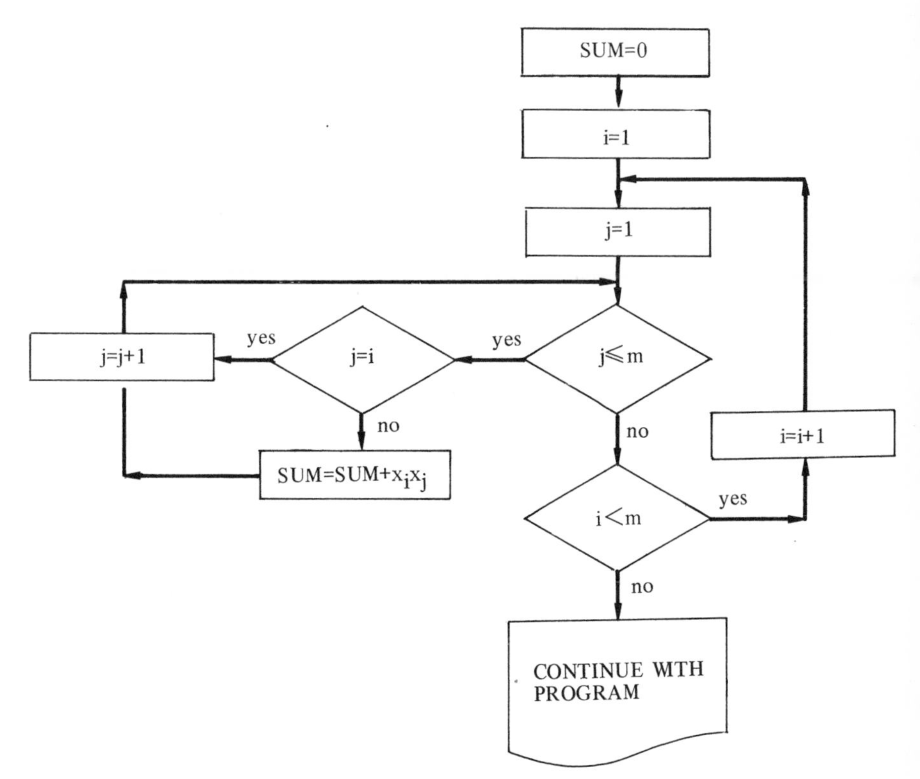

EXERCISE 3

Write a flow chart to compute the product of all elements of the array $[u_{ij}]_{(m,n)}$. Using the first of the two formulas (4.11), the product is expressed as

$$PROD = \prod_{i=1}^{m} \prod_{j=1}^{n} u_{ij}.$$

Initializing *PROD* as 1, then *PROD* takes on the values

$$u_{11}u_{12} \cdots u_{1n},$$

$$(u_{11}u_{12} \cdots u_{1n})(u_{21}u_{22} \cdots u_{2n}),$$

and finally

$$(u_{11}u_{12} \cdots u_{1n})(u_{21}u_{22} \cdots u_{2n}) \cdots (u_{m1}u_{m2} \cdots u_{mn}).$$

FLOW CHART for Exercise 3

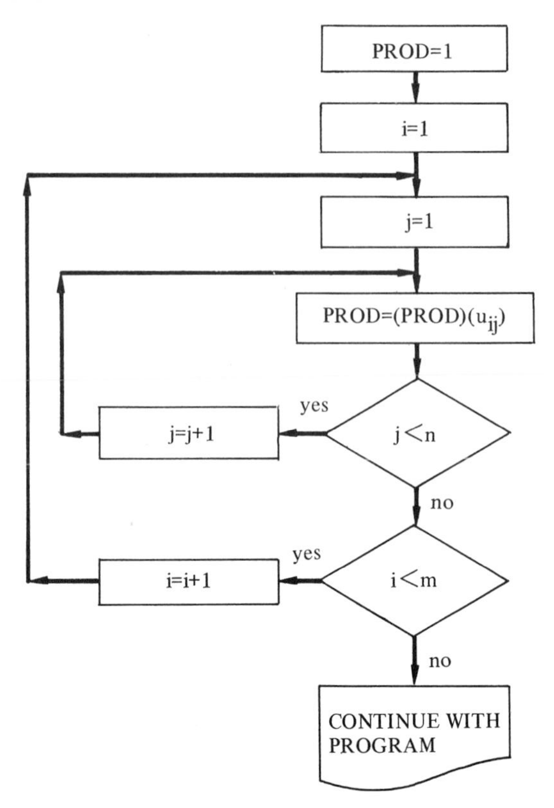

Write a flow chart to compute the product of all elements u_{ij}, by applying the formula

$$PROD = \prod_{j=1}^{n} \prod_{i=1}^{m} u_{ij}.$$

EXERCISE 4

Write a flow chart to compute the product of all row sums of $U = [u_{ij}]_{(m,n)}$. A formula must first be developed. From

$$\begin{bmatrix} u_{11} & u_{12} & \cdots & u_{1n} \\ u_{21} & u_{22} & \cdots & u_{2n} \\ \cdot & \cdot & \cdots & \cdot \\ u_{m1} & u_{m2} & \cdots & u_{mn} \end{bmatrix}$$

the product becomes

$$(u_{11} + u_{12} + \cdots + u_{1n})(u_{21} + u_{22} + \cdots + u_{2n})(u_{m1} + u_{m2} + \cdots + u_{mn});$$

expressing this product symbolically,

$$PROD = \left(\sum_{j=1}^{n} u_{1j}\right)\left(\sum_{j=1}^{n} u_{2j}\right) \cdots \left(\sum_{j=1}^{n} u_{mj}\right)$$

or

$$PROD = \prod_{i=1}^{m} \left(\sum_{j=1}^{n} u_{ij}\right).$$

Writing the flow chart is left as an exercise for the reader.

EXERCISE 5

Write a flow chart to compute the sum and the product of all elements of a square matrix A that are on and above the main diagonal. Let

$$A = \begin{bmatrix} a_{11} & a_{12} & \cdots & a_{1n} \\ a_{21} & a_{22} & \cdots & a_{2n} \\ \cdot & \cdot & \cdots & \cdot \\ a_{n1} & a_{n2} & \cdots & a_{nn} \end{bmatrix}.$$

The sum of all a_{ij} on and above the main diagonal is

$$SUM = \sum_{i=1}^{n} \sum_{j=i}^{n} a_{ij}$$

or

$$SUM = \sum_{j=1}^{n} \sum_{i=1}^{j} a_{ij}.$$

Similarly, the product of all elements on and above the main diagonal is

$$PROD = \prod_{i=1}^{n} \prod_{j=i}^{n} a_{ij}$$

or

$$PROD = \prod_{j=1}^{n} \prod_{i=1}^{j} a_{ij}.$$

Using the left-hand formulas for both sum and product, the following flow chart computes simultaneously the sum and product.

FLOW CHART for Exercise 5

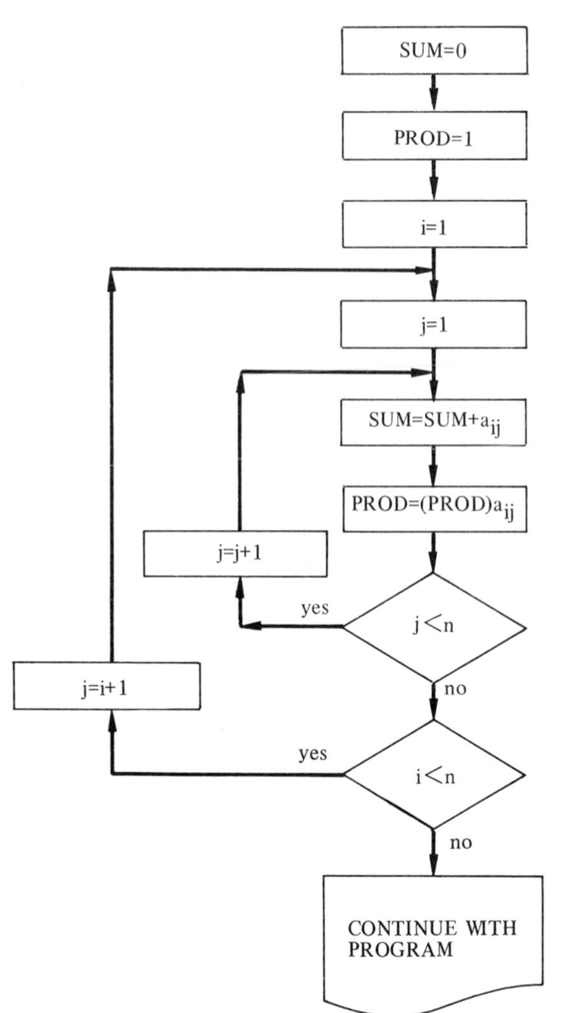

PROBLEMS

4-1. Given

$$A = \begin{bmatrix} a_{11} & a_{12} & \cdots & a_{1n} \\ a_{21} & a_{22} & \cdots & a_{2n} \\ \cdot & \cdot & \cdots & \cdot \\ a_{n1} & a_{n2} & \cdots & a_{nn} \end{bmatrix},$$

the sum of all elements on and above the main diagonal is

$$SUMA = \sum_{i=1}^{n} \sum_{j=i}^{n} a_{ij}.$$

Also, the product of all elements on and above the main diagonal is

$$PRODA = \prod_{i=1}^{n} \prod_{j=i}^{n} a_{ij}.$$

Similarly, the sum and product of all elements on and below the diagonal are

$$SUMB = \sum_{j=1}^{n} \sum_{i=j}^{n} a_{ij} = \sum_{i=1}^{n} \sum_{j=i}^{n} a_{ji},$$

$$PRODB = \prod_{j=1}^{n} \prod_{i=j}^{n} a_{ij} = \prod_{i=1}^{n} \prod_{j=i}^{n} a_{ji}.$$

Write a flow chart to compute *SUMA*, *SUMB*, *PRODA*, and *PRODB* simultaneously.

4-2. Let $\{x_i\} = \{x_1, x_2, \ldots, x_n\}$ be a set of known values of x.

(a) Write a flow chart to compute

$$\left(\sum_{i=1}^{n} x_i\right)^2 - \sum_{i=1}^{n} x_i^2.$$

(b) Simplify this expression to one formula and write a flow chart.

4-3. Given a set of x,y coordinates,

$$(x_1,y_1), (x_2,y_2), (x_3,y_3), \ldots, (x_n,y_n),$$

write a flow chart to form the following sums:

$$SUMX = \sum_{i=1}^{n} x_i, \quad SUMY = \sum_{i=1}^{n} y_i, \quad SUMXSQ = \sum_{i=1}^{n} x_i^2, \quad SUMCPR = \sum_{i=1}^{n} x_i y_i.$$

4-4. From the table of x and y values below:

y	76.30	77.80	79.75	80.80	82.35	83.90	85.10
x	19.1	25.0	30.1	36.0	40.0	45.1	50.0

write a program to compute *SUMX*, *SUMY*, *SUMXSQ*, *SUMCPR* and also to compute the values of a and b by Cramer's rule for the set of equations:

$$7a + b\sum_{i=1}^{7} x_i = \sum_{i=1}^{7} y_i,$$

$$a\sum_{i=1}^{7} x_i + b\sum_{i=1}^{7} x_i^2 = \sum_{i=1}^{7} x_i y_i.$$

Note: This is a simple example of the least squares method for a best-fitting curve for a given set of data. In this example, it is assumed that $y = a + bx$ is a best fit (see Chap. 5).

Answers: $a = 70.76$, $b = 0.288$, $y = 70.76 + 0.288x$.

4-5. Let $A = [a_{ik}]_{(m,l)}$ and $B = [b_{kj}]_{(l,n)}$. Write a flow chart to form

$$C = [c_{ij}]_{(m,n)} = [a_{ik}]_{(m,l)} \cdot [b_{kj}]_{(l,n)}$$

$$= \left[\sum_{k=1}^{l} (a_{ik})(b_{kj})\right]_{(m,n)}.$$

4-6. (a) Write a flow chart to form

$$PROD = \pi(x_i - x_j), \qquad (i, j = 1, 2, \ldots, n; i \neq j).$$

(See Exercise 2.)
(b) Write a flow chart to form

$$PROD = (-1)^{n(n-1)/2}[\pi(x_i - x_j)]^2, \qquad (i, j = 1, 2, \ldots, n; \text{i} < j \leq n).$$

4-7. Write a flow chart to form

$$SUM = \sum_{i=1}^{n}\left\{y_i \cdot \pi\left(\frac{x - x_j}{x_i - x_j}\right)\right\}, \qquad (1 \leq j \leq n, j \neq i)$$

where x is a known value. This is the Lagrange interpolation formula (see Ch. 5).

4.8 Evaluation of a Determinant

Let matrix $A = [a_{ij}]_n$; then

$$\det A = \begin{vmatrix} a_{11} & a_{12} & \cdots & a_{1n} \\ a_{21} & a_{22} & \cdots & a_{2n} \\ \cdot & \cdot & \cdots & \cdot \\ a_{n1} & a_{n2} & \cdots & a_{nn} \end{vmatrix}. \tag{4.43}$$

The following theorem will be the basis for the computation of det A: Any multiple of one row (column) added to any other row (column) will not alter the value of the determinant of A.

Using this theorem, the determinant of A will become

$$\det A = \begin{vmatrix} b_{11} & b_{12} & \cdots & b_{1n} \\ 0 & b_{22} & \cdots & b_{2n} \\ \cdot & \cdot & \cdots & \cdot \\ 0 & 0 & \cdots & b_{nn} \end{vmatrix}, \tag{4.44}$$

where all b_{ij} are computed by using the above theorem. Then employing the concept of a cofactor (Sec. 4.5.1):

$$\det A = b_{11} \begin{vmatrix} b_{22} & b_{23} & \cdots & b_{2n} \\ 0 & b_{33} & \cdots & b_{3n} \\ \cdot & \cdot & \cdot & \cdot \\ 0 & 0 & \cdots & b_{nn} \end{vmatrix}. \tag{4.45}$$

Continuing,

$$\det A = b_{11} \cdot b_{22} \begin{vmatrix} b_{33} & b_{34} & \cdots & b_{3n} \\ 0 & b_{44} & \cdots & b_{4n} \\ \cdot & \cdot & \cdots & \cdot \\ 0 & 0 & \cdots & b_{nn} \end{vmatrix}$$

$$= b_{11} \cdot b_{22} \cdots b_{n-2} \begin{vmatrix} b_{n-1,n-1} & b_{n-1,n} \\ 0 & b_{nn} \end{vmatrix} \tag{4.46}$$

$$= b_{11} \cdot b_{22} \cdots b_{n-2} \cdot b_{n-1,n-1} \cdot b_{nn}.$$

Considering the first two rows of det A:

$$\begin{matrix} a_{11} & a_{12} & \cdots & a_{1n} \\ a_{21} & a_{22} & \cdots & a_{2n}, \end{matrix}$$

a multiple of the first row added to the second row must be such that $b_{21} = 0$. Hence

$$b_{21} = a_{21} - \frac{(a_{21})(a_{11})}{a_{11}} \equiv 0. \tag{4.47}$$

The multiplier of row one then is $-(a_{21}/a_{11})$. Hence,

$$\begin{aligned} b_{22} &= a_{22} - \frac{(a_{21})(a_{12})}{a_{11}} \\ b_{23} &= a_{23} - \frac{(a_{21})(a_{13})}{a_{11}} \\ &\cdot \\ &\cdot \\ &\cdot \\ b_{2j} &= a_{2j} - \frac{(a_{21})(a_{1j})}{a_{11}} \\ &\cdot \\ &\cdot \\ &\cdot \\ b_{2n} &= a_{2n} - \frac{(a_{21})(a_{1n})}{a_{11}}. \end{aligned} \tag{4.48}$$

Each of these may be expressed as

$$b_{2j} = a_{2j} - \frac{(a_{21})(a_{1j})}{a_{11}}, \qquad (j = 1, 2, \ldots, n). \tag{4.49}$$

Again, the theorem may be used with row 1 and row 3 so that

$$b_{31} = a_{31} - \frac{(a_{31})(a_{11})}{a_{11}} \equiv 0, \tag{4.50}$$

and all elements in the third row will become

$$b_{3j} = a_{3j} - \frac{(a_{31})(a_{1j})}{a_{11}}, \qquad (j = 1, 2, \ldots, n). \tag{4.51}$$

Or, in general, operating on each row in succession, for the ith row,

$$b_{ij} = a_{ij} - \frac{(a_{i1})(a_{1j})}{a_{11}}, \qquad (j = 1, 2, \ldots, n). \tag{4.52}$$

Thus, at this point,

$$\det A = \begin{vmatrix} a_{11} & a_{12} & \cdots & a_{1n} \\ 0 & b_{22} & \cdots & b_{2n} \\ \cdot & \cdot & \cdots & \cdot \\ 0 & b_{n2} & \cdots & b_{nn} \end{vmatrix} = a_{11} \begin{vmatrix} b_{22} & b_{23} & \cdots & b_{2n} \\ b_{32} & b_{33} & \cdots & b_{3n} \\ \cdot & \cdot & \cdots & \cdot \\ b_{n2} & b_{n3} & \cdots & b_{nn} \end{vmatrix}. \tag{4.53}$$

Repeating the same procedure on this reduced determinant,

$$\det A = a_{11} \begin{vmatrix} b_{22} & b_{23} & \cdots & b_{2n} \\ 0 & c_{33} & \cdots & c_{3n} \\ \cdot & \cdot & \cdots & \cdot \\ 0 & c_{n3} & \cdots & c_{nn} \end{vmatrix}, \tag{4.54}$$

where in the ith row,

$$c_{ij} = b_{ij} - \frac{(b_{i2})(b_{2j})}{b_{22}}, \qquad (j = 2, 3, \ldots, n). \tag{4.55}$$

This procedure may be continued until all elements below the main diagonal are zero.

Instead of using notation such as b_{ij} and c_{ij}, a simpler notation is to use the following:

$$a_{ij}^{(l)} = a_{ij}^{(l-1)} - \frac{a_{il}^{(l-1)} a_{lj}^{(l-1)}}{a_{ll}^{(l-1)}}, \tag{4.56}$$

where $l = 1, \ldots, n - 1,$
$j = l + 1, \ldots, n,$
$i = l + 1, \ldots, n.$

It is assumed that all $a_{ll}^{(l-1)}$ are nonzero. Section 4.9 will consider the possibility of $a_{ll}^{(l-1)}$ being zero.

For example, in the first application, where $l = 1$, $i = 2$, $j = 2, 3, \ldots, n$,

$$
\begin{aligned}
a_{22}^{(1)} &= a_{22} - \frac{(a_{21})(a_{12})}{a_{11}} \\
&\;\;\vdots \\
a_{2k}^{(1)} &= a_{2k} - \frac{(a_{21})(a_{1k})}{a_{11}} \\
&\;\;\vdots \\
a_{2n}^{(1)} &= a_{2n} - \frac{(a_{21})(a_{1n})}{a_{11}}.
\end{aligned}
\tag{4.57}
$$

Thus, det A is finally transformed into

$$
\det A = \begin{vmatrix} a_{11} & a_{12} & \cdots & a_{1n} \\ 0 & a_{22}^{(1)} & \cdots & a_{2n}^{(1)} \\ 0 & 0 & a_{33}^{(2)} & a_{3n}^{(2)} \\ \cdot & \cdot & \cdots & \cdot \\ 0 & 0 & 0 & a_{nn}^{(n-1)} \end{vmatrix} = a_{11} \cdot a_{22}^{(1)} \cdot a_{33}^{(2)} \cdots a_{nn}^{(n-1)}. \tag{4.58}
$$

Assuming that all a_{ij} have been stored in the computer, the following steps outline the program to compute the determinant of matrix A of order n, assuming that $a_{ll}^{(l-1)} \neq 0$, $l = 1, 2, \ldots, n-1$.

Steps

1. Set $l = 1$.
2. Set $n1 = 2$.
3. Set $i = n1$.
4. Set $j = n1$.
5. Calculate

   $$\frac{a_{ij}^{(l-1)} - (a_{il}^{(l-1)})(a_{lj}^{(l-1)})}{a_{ll}^{(l-1)}}$$

   and set the result equal to a_{ij}.
6. If j is less than n, continue with step 7; otherwise transfer to step 8.
7. Replace j by $j + 1$ and transfer to step 5.
8. If i is less than n, continue with step 9; otherwise transfer to step 10.
9. Replace i by $i + 1$ and transfer to step 4.

FLOW CHART 4.8.1 Evaluation of a Determinant *A*

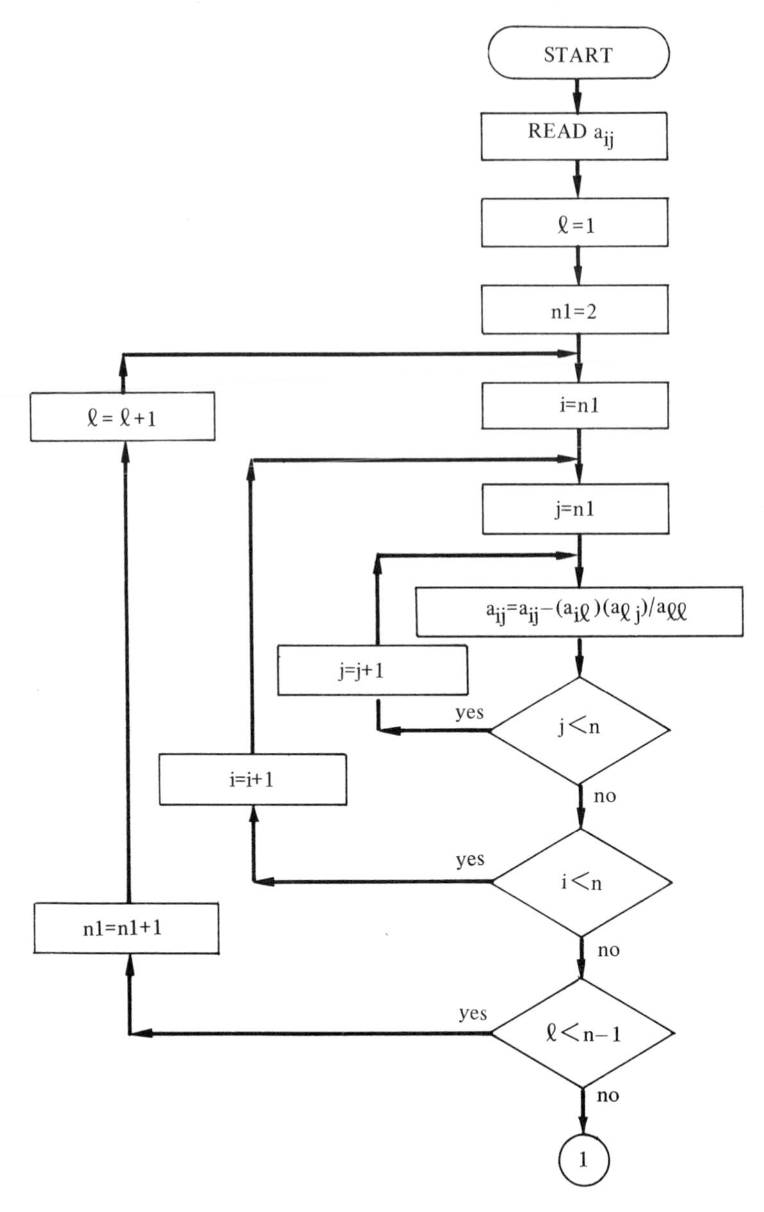

10. If l is less than $(n - 1)$, replace l by $l + 1$ and continue with step 11; otherwise transfer to step 12.
11. Replace $n1$ by $n1 + 1$ and transfer to step 3.
12. Set DET = 1.
13. Set $i = 1$.
14. Calculate $(\text{DET})a_{ii}^{(i-1)}$ and set the result equal to DET.
15. If i is less than n, replace i by $i + 1$ and transfer to step 14; otherwise continue with step 16.
16. Print DET.
17. Stop.

4.8.1 Flow Chart

To compute the determinant of

$$A = \begin{bmatrix} a_{11} & a_{12} & \cdots & a_{1n} \\ a_{21} & a_{22} & \cdots & a_{2n} \\ \cdot & \cdot & \cdots & \cdot \\ a_{n1} & a_{n2} & \cdots & a_{nn} \end{bmatrix}.$$

Flow Chart 4.8.1 (*Continued*)

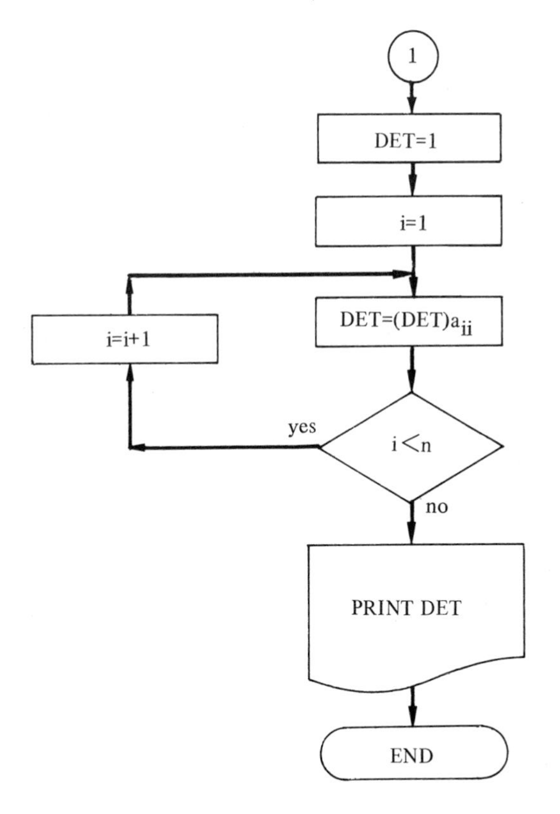

4.8.2 Program

To evaluate:

$$\det A \begin{vmatrix} 1 & 3 & 1 \\ 2 & 4 & 6 \\ 7 & 9 & 11 \end{vmatrix}.$$

```
/ID
/JOB
/FTC
        DIMENSION A(10,10)
      1 FORMAT(I2)
      2 FORMAT(1H1,'THE MATRIX A IS',//)
      3 FORMAT(//,'THE TRIANGULAR MATRIX IS',//)
      4 FORMAT(5F10.4)
      5 FORMAT(//,5X,'THE VALUE OF DETERMINANT OF A IS',F14.6)
        READ(5,1)N
        READ(5,4)((A(I,J),J=1,N),I=1,N)
        WRITE(6,2)
        WRITE(6,4)((A(I,J),J=1,N),I=1,N)
        DET=1.0
        NL=N-1
        N1=2.0
        DO 30 L=1,NL
        CLL=A(L,L)
        DO 20 I=N1,N
        DO 10 J=N1,N
     10 A(I,J)=A(I,J)-A(I,L)*A(L,J)/CLL
     20 CONTINUE
     30 N1=N1+1
        WRITE(6,3)
        WRITE(6,4)((A(I,J),J=1,N)I=1,N)
        DO 40 I=1,N
     40 DET=DET*A(I,I)
        WRITE(6,5)DET
        STOP
        END

        THE RESULT IS

        DET=40
```

4.8.3 Explanation

The READ and WRITE statements for $A(I,J)$ can be interpreted in terms of DO loops. The READ statement

```
READ(5,4)((A(I,J),J=1,N),I=1,N)
```

is interpreted by the computer as a set of nested DO loops, each set of parentheses being the equivalent of a DO loop.

The above READ statement in effect is the same as

```
 4 FORMAT(5F10.4)
   DO 10 I=1,N
   DO 20 J=1,N
20 READ(5,4)A(I,J)
10 CONTINUE
```

The innermost set of parentheses is equivalent to the innermost DO loop. In this READ statement, $A(I,J)$ are read in row by row. The statement

```
READ(5,4)((A(I,J),I=1,N),J=1,N)
```

would cause the matrix A to be read in column by column. The READ statement

```
READ(5,4)(((A(I,J,K),I=1,M),J=1,N),K=1,L)
```

would cause the array $A(M,N,L)$ to be read in as:

$$
\begin{array}{llll}
A(1,1,1) & A(2,1,1) & \cdots & A(M,1,1) \\
A(1,2,1) & A(2,2,1) & \cdots & A(M,2,1) \\
\cdot & \cdot & \cdots & \cdot \\
A(1,N,1) & A(2,N,1) & \cdots & A(M,N,1) \\
A(1,1,2) & A(2,1,2) & \cdots & A(M,1,2) \\
\cdot & \cdot & \cdots & \cdot \\
A(1,1,L) & A(2,1,L) & \cdots & A(M,1,L) \\
\cdot & \cdot & \cdots & \cdot \\
A(1,N,L) & A(2,N,L) & \cdots & A(M,N,L).
\end{array}
$$

In how many different ways may the array $A(I,J,K)$ be read into the computer? A useful rule of thumb for nested sets of parentheses is illustrated by the following:

$$
\begin{array}{cccccccc}
(& (& (& (&) &) &) &) \\
1 & 2 & 3 & 4 & 3 & 2 & 1 & 0
\end{array}
$$

Number all left-hand parentheses beginning at the extreme left as 1, 2, . . . , decreasing by one for every right-hand parenthesis. If the sets are nested correctly, the sets will be matched as follows:

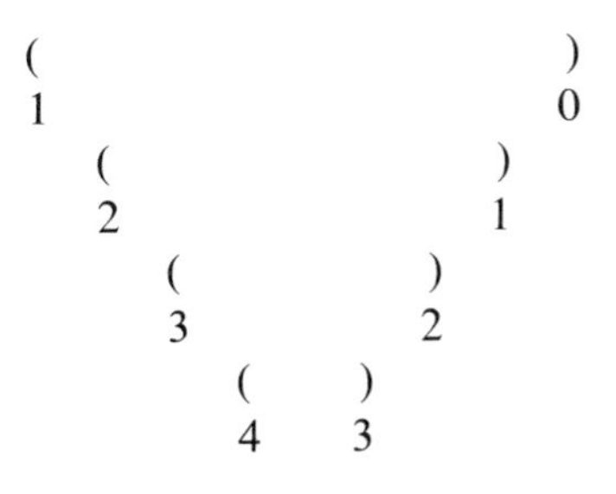

A left-hand parenthesis numbered n is matched with nearest right-hand parenthesis numbered $n - 1$.

4.9 More on the Evaluation of a Determinant

In Sec. 4.8, no consideration was given to the fact that the value of the determinant may be zero, due to the possibility that all elements in a row or column may be zero. A more ambitious routine would be to test row with row or column with column to determine if the corresponding elements of any two rows or any two columns are in proportion. And if this is true, the value of the determinant would be zero.[8] But such a routine would defeat the purpose; it would consume too much computer time.

Another important consideration is that in computing each $a_{ij}^{(l)}$ by the formula

$$a_{ij}^{(l)} = a_{ij}^{(l-1)} - (a_{il}^{(l-1)})(a_{lj}^{(l-1)})/a_{ll}^{(l-1)},$$

$a_{ll}^{(l-1)}$ should be the largest number in absolute value for each value of l. The purpose behind this choice is to avoid division by a small number, thereby causing too much round off. Note: the range of a real constant is approximately 10^{-75} to 10^{75}.

Specifically, the following operations should be performed:

1. For a fixed l and $k = l, l + 1, \ldots, n$, the largest $a_{kl}^{(l-1)}$ is chosen as $a_{ll}^{(l-1)}$.
2. If $a_{kl}^{(l-1)} = 0$, for $k = l, l + 1, \ldots, n$, a transfer is made to a statement DET = 0. Subsequently, another transfer could be made to an output statement stating that the value of the determinant is zero.
3. If $a_{kl}^{(l-1)} \neq 0$, the lth row is interchanged with the kth row, thereby guaranteeing that $a_{ll}^{(l-1)}$ of greatest magnitude will be used in

$$\frac{a_{ij}^{(l)} = a_{ij}^{(l-1)} - (a_{il}^{(l-1)})(a_{lj}^{(l-1)})}{a_{ll}^{(l-1)}}.$$

4. If an actual interchange of rows occurs, the last operation to be executed is that of changing the sign of the determinant.[9]

The following set of statements, if inserted appropriately within the

[8] A theorem from matrix algebra states: If all elements of a row (column) of a square matrix A are zero, or if the elements of one row (column) are in proportion to corresponding elements of another row (column), then the determinant $A = 0$.

[9] If any two rows (columns) of a matrix A are interchanged, the value of the determinant of the resulting matrix is $-\det A$.

determinant evaluation program, will cause the above operations to be performed in evaluating a determinant.

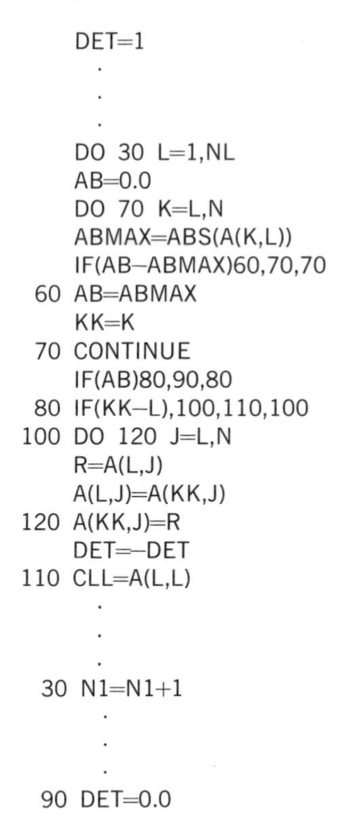

```
        DET=1
        .
        .
        .
        DO 30 L=1,NL
        AB=0.0
        DO 70 K=L,N
        ABMAX=ABS(A(K,L))
        IF(AB-ABMAX)60,70,70
    60  AB=ABMAX
        KK=K
    70  CONTINUE
        IF(AB)80,90,80
    80  IF(KK-L),100,110,100
   100  DO 120 J=L,N
        R=A(L,J)
        A(L,J)=A(KK,J)
   120  A(KK,J)=R
        DET=-DET
   110  CLL=A(L,L)
        .
        .
        .
    30  N1=N1+1
        .
        .
        .
    90  DET=0.0
```

4.10 A Search Routine

The following routine is a subprogram to search for and select a_{kl} of greatest magnitude of all a_{ij} of a matrix $A_{(m,n)}$. Further, it is designed to interchange rows and columns so that the first and kth rows are interchanged; also in the resulting matrix, the first and lth columns are interchanged. Hence the max $|a_{kl}|$ will become the pivotal value, replacing a_{11}. Specifically, for

$$A = \begin{bmatrix} a_{11} & a_{12} & \cdots & a_{1l} & \cdots & a_{1n} \\ a_{21} & a_{22} & \cdots & a_{2l} & \cdots & a_{2n} \\ \cdot & \cdot & \cdots & \cdot & \cdots & \cdot \\ a_{k1} & a_{k2} & \cdots & a_{kl} & \cdots & a_{kn} \\ \cdot & \cdot & \cdots & \cdot & \cdots & \cdot \\ a_{m1} & a_{m2} & \cdots & a_{ml} & \cdots & a_{mn} \end{bmatrix},$$

1. A comparison test to find a_{kl} of greatest magnitude of all mn a_{ij} is made.
2. The kth row elements are interchanged with the corresponding first row elements.
3. The lth column elements are interchanged with the current corresponding first column elements.

Hence, the rearranged matrix A appears as

$$\begin{bmatrix} a_{kl} & a_{k2} & \cdots & a_{k1} & \cdots & a_{kn} \\ a_{2l} & a_{22} & \cdots & a_{21} & \cdots & a_{2n} \\ \cdot & \cdot & \cdots & \cdot & \cdots & \cdot \\ a_{1l} & a_{12} & \cdots & a_{11} & \cdots & a_{1n} \\ \cdot & \cdot & \cdots & \cdot & \cdots & \cdot \\ a_{ml} & a_{m2} & \cdots & a_{m1} & \cdots & a_{mn} \end{bmatrix}.$$

4.10.1 Flow Chart

To search for and select the largest $|a_{kl}|$.
To interchange rows and columns so that the kth row is interchanged with the first row, and in the resulting matrix, the lth column is interchanged with the first column.

FLOW CHART 4.10.1 Search Routine

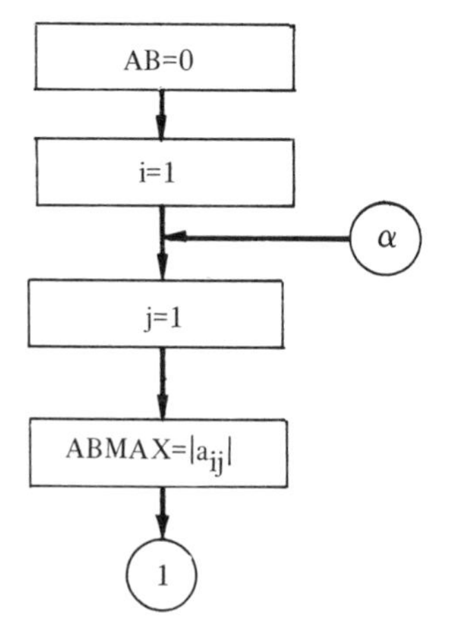

Flow Chart 4.10.1 (*Continued*)

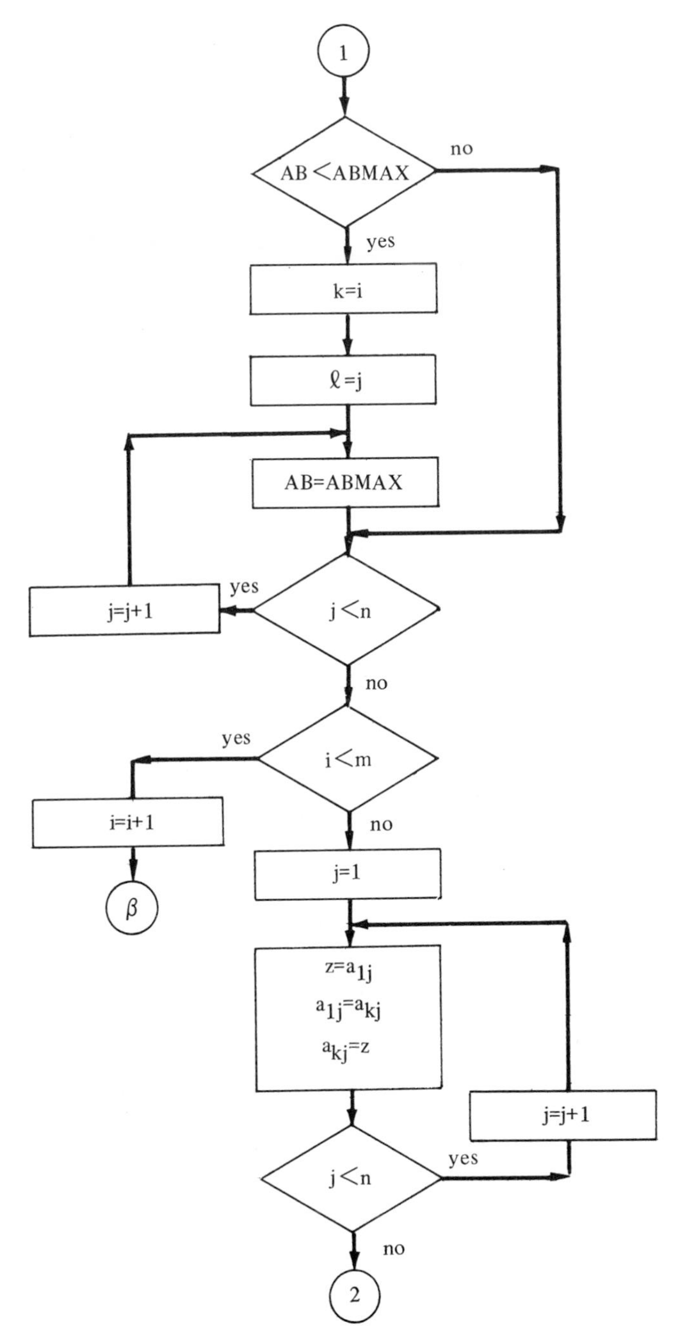

Flow Chart 4.10.1 (*Continued*)

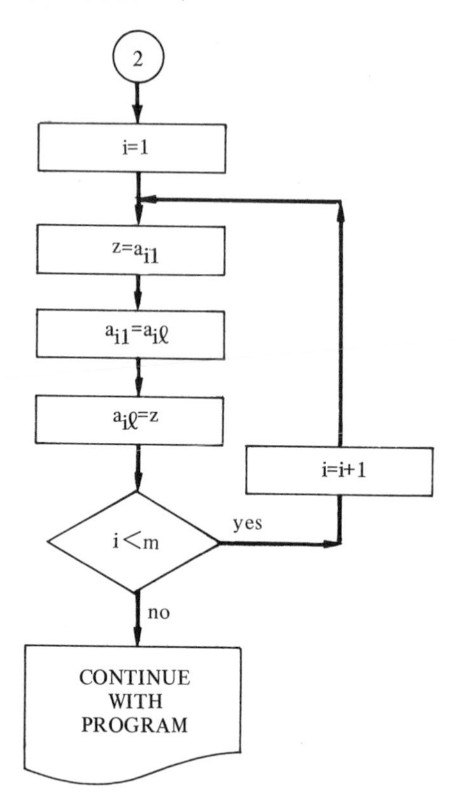

This partial flow chart, when used in the evaluation of a determinant, can be made more general by considering the following points:

1. The letters i and j should be set equal to the current value of l.
2. If after the search is made, AB is still zero, then the value of the determinant is zero.
3. If after the current search, a test shows that $k = l$, then rows do not have to be interchanged. Also, columns need not be interchanged if $jk = j$.

It is left as an exercise for the reader to incorporate these points in a flow chart and a program.

EXERCISE

Write a flow chart and a program to evaluate the determinants of the matrices

(a)
$$\begin{bmatrix} 2 & 1 & 0 & 3 \\ 3 & 2 & 1 & 4 \\ 6 & 4 & 2 & 8 \\ 1 & 3 & 0 & 5 \end{bmatrix}$$
whose determinant = 0.0,

(b)
$$\begin{bmatrix} 1 & 2 & 3 \\ 0 & 0 & -1 \\ 4 & -2 & 0 \end{bmatrix}$$
whose determinant = −10,

first by the method of Secs. 4.8 and 4.9, and second by the method of Secs. 4.8 and 4.10.

4.11 The Inverse of a Matrix—An Elimination Method

The inverse of a square matrix was defined in Sec. 4.5.2 as

$$A^{-1} = \frac{[A_{ij}]^T}{\det A}, \qquad (\det A \neq 0) \tag{4.59}$$

such that $AA^{-1} = A^{-1}A = I$.

Example

Determine A^{-1} if

$$A = \begin{bmatrix} 0 & 1 & 3 \\ -2 & 3 & 9 \\ 1 & -2 & -5 \end{bmatrix}. \tag{4.60}$$

Step 1.

$$\det A = \begin{vmatrix} 0 & 1 & 3 \\ -2 & 3 & 9 \\ 1 & -2 & -5 \end{vmatrix} = 2. \tag{4.61}$$

Step 2.

$$[A_{ij}] = \begin{bmatrix} 3 & -1 & 1 \\ -1 & -3 & 1 \\ 0 & -6 & 2 \end{bmatrix}. \tag{4.62}$$

Step 3.

$$[A_{ij}]^T = \begin{bmatrix} 3 & -1 & 0 \\ -1 & -3 & -6 \\ 1 & 1 & 2 \end{bmatrix}. \tag{4.63}$$

Step 4.

$$A^{-1} = \frac{[A_{ij}]^T}{\det A} = \begin{bmatrix} 3/2 & -1/2 & 0 \\ -1/2 & -3/2 & -3 \\ 1/2 & 1/2 & 1 \end{bmatrix}. \tag{4.64}$$

Hence,

$$AA^{-1} = \begin{bmatrix} 0 & 1 & 3 \\ -2 & 3 & 9 \\ 1 & -2 & -5 \end{bmatrix} \cdot \begin{bmatrix} 3/2 & -1/2 & 0 \\ -1/2 & -3/2 & -3 \\ 1/2 & 1/2 & 1 \end{bmatrix} = \begin{bmatrix} 1 & 0 & 0 \\ 0 & 1 & 0 \\ 0 & 0 & 1 \end{bmatrix}. \tag{4.65}$$

However, this method as applied to any matrix of order greater than 3 would entail entirely too many operations, and therefore would be too lengthy and costly. A simpler method, more adaptable to machine methods, is based upon the three elementary transformations and their inverses as defined in Sec. 4.5.3.

If instead of only considering matrix A, a combined matrix of A and I is considered, as shown below

$$\begin{bmatrix} a_{11} & a_{12} & \cdots & a_{1n} & 1 & 0 & \cdots & 0 \\ a_{21} & a_{22} & \cdots & a_{2n} & 0 & 1 & \cdots & 0 \\ \cdot & \cdot & \cdots & \cdot & \cdot & \cdot & \cdots & \cdot \\ a_{n1} & a_{n2} & \cdots & a_{nn} & 0 & 0 & \cdots & 1 \end{bmatrix} \tag{4.66}$$

and elementary transformations are performed on the rows of $[A,I]$ in such a way that the result is

$$\begin{bmatrix} 1 & 0 & \cdots & 0 & c_{1,n+1} & c_{1,n+2} & \cdots & c_{1,2n} \\ 0 & 1 & \cdots & 0 & c_{2,n+1} & c_{2,n+2} & \cdots & c_{2,2n} \\ \cdot & \cdot & \cdots & \cdot & \cdot & \cdot & \cdots & \cdot \\ 0 & 0 & \cdots & 1 & c_{n,n+1} & c_{n,n+2} & \cdots & c_{n,2n} \end{bmatrix}, \tag{4.67}$$

then the matrix

$$C = \begin{bmatrix} c_{1,n+1} & c_{1,n+2} & \cdots & c_{1,2n} \\ c_{2,n+1} & c_{2,n+2} & \cdots & c_{2,2n} \\ \cdot & \cdot & \cdots & \cdot \\ c_{n,n+1} & c_{n,n+2} & \cdots & c_{n,2n} \end{bmatrix} = A^{-1}. \tag{4.68}$$

In the evaluation of a determinant, the formula

$$a_{ij}^{(l)} = \frac{a_{ij}^{(l-1)} - (a_{il}^{(l-1)})(a_{lj}^{(l-1)})}{a_{ll}^{(l-1)}} \tag{4.69}$$

was applied repeatedly so that all elements below the principal diagonal become zero. However, in finding the inverse of A it is first necessary to divide all elements of each row l by $a_{ll}^{(l-1)}$ from the lth column to the $(l + n)n$th column, and then to operate on all rows above and below the lth row so that all elements in the lth column except $a_{ll}^{(l-1)}$ will vanish. Thus, by dividing the first row by a_{11},

$$a_{1j} = \frac{a_{1j}}{a_{11}}, \qquad (j = 1, 2, \ldots, n + 1), \tag{4.70}$$

the result is

$$\begin{bmatrix} 1 & a_{1,2/a_{11}} & \cdots & a_{1,n/a_{11}} & 1/a_{11} & 0 & \cdots & 0 \\ a_{21} & a_{22} & \cdots & a_{2n} & 0 & 1 & \cdots & 0 \\ \cdot & \cdot & \cdots & \cdot & \cdot & \cdot & \cdots & \cdot \\ a_{n1} & a_{n2} & \cdots & a_{nn} & 0 & 0 & \cdots & 1 \end{bmatrix}. \tag{4.71}$$

In general, this formula is

$$a_{lj}^{(l)} = a_{lj}^{(l-1)}/a_{ll}^{(l-1)} \qquad (l = 1, 2, \ldots, n, j = l, l + 1, \ldots, l + n). \tag{4.72}$$

The second step then is to effect zeros in the lth column above and below the diagonal element $a_{ll}^{(l)}$. For example, by multiplying the elements of the first row by $-a_{21}$ and adding these results to the corresponding elements of the second row, the result is:

$$\begin{bmatrix} 1 & a_{12/a_{11}} & \cdots & a_{1n/a_{11}} & 1/a_{11} & 0 & \cdots & 0 \\ 0 & a_{22}^{(1)} & \cdots & a_{2n}^{(1)} & a_{2,n+1}^{(1)} & 1 & \cdots & 0 \\ \cdot & \cdot & \cdots & \cdot & \cdot & \cdot & \cdots & \cdot \\ a_{n1} & a_{n2} & \cdots & a_{nn} & 0 & 0 & \cdots & 1 \end{bmatrix}, \tag{4.73}$$

where now

$$a_{22}^{(1)} = a_{22} - (a_{21})\{a_{12}/a_{11}\},$$

and, in general,

$$a_{2j}^{(1)} = a_{2j}^{(1)} - (a_{21})\{a_{1j}/a_{11}\}, \qquad (j = 2, 3, \ldots, n + 1). \tag{4.74}$$

This method can again be applied to the third, fourth, . . . , nth rows, so that in effect, $a_{31}, a_{41}, \ldots, a_{n1}$ become zero.

Hence, for any row i,

$$a_{ij}^{(1)} = a_{ij} - (a_{i1})\{a_{1j}/a_{11}\}, \qquad (j = 1, 2, 3, \ldots, 1 + n). \tag{4.75}$$

Now consider that the matrix has been developed in this process to the point where it appears as shown below:

$$\begin{bmatrix} 1 & 0 & \cdots & a_{1l}^{(l-1)} & \cdots & a_{1n}^{(l-1)} & a_{1,n+1}^{(l-1)} & a_{1,n+2}^{(l-1)} & \cdots & 0 \\ 0 & 1 & \cdots & a_{2l}^{(l-1)} & \cdots & a_{2n}^{(l-1)} & a_{2,n+1}^{(l-1)} & a_{2,n+2}^{(l-1)} & \cdots & 0 \\ \cdot & \cdot & \cdots & \cdot & \cdots & \cdot & \cdot & \cdot & \cdots & \cdot \\ 0 & 0 & \cdots & a_{ll}^{(l-1)} & \cdots & a_{ln}^{(l-1)} & a_{l,n+1}^{(l-1)} & a_{l,n+2}^{(l-1)} & \cdots & 0 \\ 0 & 0 & \cdots & a_{l+1,l}^{(l-1)} & \cdots & a_{l+1,n}^{(l-1)} & a_{l+1,n+1}^{(l-1)} & a_{l,n+2}^{(l-1)} & \cdots & 0 \\ \cdot & \cdot & \cdots & \cdot & \cdots & \cdot & \cdot & \cdot & \cdots & \cdot \\ 0 & 0 & \cdots & a_{nl}^{(l-1)} & \cdots & a_{nn}^{(l-1)} & a_{n,n+1}^{(l-1)} & a_{n,n+2}^{(l-1)} & \cdots & 1 \end{bmatrix}. \tag{4.76}$$

It now becomes apparent that all elements in the lth row must be divided by $a_{ll}^{(l-1)}$ from the lth column to the $(l + n)$th column. Hence, all $a_{lj}^{(l-1)}$ will be replaced by $a_{lj}^{(l-1)}/a_{ll}^{(l-1)}$ where $j = l, l + 1, \ldots, l + n$.

With $a_{ll}^{(l)}$ now equal to 1, it is necessary to multiply the elements of row l by $-a_{1l}^{(l)}$ and to add the results to the corresponding elements of the first row. Thus, $a_{1l}^{(l-1)}$ becomes $a_{1l}^{(l-1)} - (a_{1l})^{(l-1}\{a_{ll}/a_{ll}\} = 0$.

Hence, any element $a_{1j}^{(l-1)}$ in the first row is replaced by

$$a_{1j}^{(l-1)} - a_{1l}^{(l-1)}\{a_{lj}^{(l-1)}/a_{ll}^{(l-1)}\}, \qquad (j = l, l + 1, \ldots, l + n).$$

And, for the ith row $(i \neq l)$, $a_{ij}^{(l-1)}$ becomes

$$a_{ij}^{(l-1)} - a_{il}^{(l-1)}\{a_{lj}^{(l-1)}/a_{ll}^{(l-1)}\}, \qquad (j = l, l + 1, \ldots, l + n).$$

Thus, the two principal steps in the process are:

1. For each row l, divide all $a_{lj}^{(l-1)}$ by $a_{ll}^{(l-1)}$, $j = l, l + 1, \ldots, l + n$.
2. For $i = 1, 2, \ldots, n$, $i \neq l$, replace $a_{ij}^{(l-1)}$ by

$$a_{ij}^{(l-1)} - a_{il}^{(l-1)}\{a_{lj}^{(l-1)}/a_{ll}^{(l-1)}\}, \qquad (j = l, l + 1, \ldots, l + n).$$

Thus, the equations to find A^{-1} become:

$$a_{lj}^{(l)} = a_{lj}^{(l-1)}/a_{ll}^{(l-1)}, \qquad l = 1, 2, \ldots, n, \quad j = l, \ldots, l + n)$$

and (4.77)

$$a_{ij}^{(l)} = a_{ij}^{(l-1)} - a_{il}^{(l-1)}a_{lj}^{(l)}, \qquad (i = 1, 2, \ldots, l - 1, l + 1, \ldots, n, \; j = l, \ldots, l + n).$$

4.11.1 Flow Chart

As usual, the letter i denotes the current row, and the letter j denotes the current column. The letter l initially set equal to zero but immediately replaced by $l + 1$ is the subscript of the current diagonal element.[10] It is necessary to place a_{ll} in another location CLL for each value of l, so that all elements in row l will be divided by a_{ll} and not by one. For, if a_{ll} were not stored in CLL, then a_{ij} for $i = l$ and $j = l$ would become $a_{ij} = a_{ll}/a_{ll} = 1$, and all subsequent a_{ij} for $j = l$, $l + 1, \ldots$ would remain as they were; they would simply be divided by 1.

In the first loop on $j < (l + n)$, when j equals $l + n$, i must be reset to one and j reset to the current value of l. However, when $i = l$, the element a_{ll} must be bypassed since a_{ll} is the diagonal element previously computed to be one. Then, as long as i is less than n, a_{ij} is computed and replaces the current a_{ij}; i.e., a_{ij} is replaced by $a_{ij} - (a_{il})(a_{lj})$ for $j = l, l + 1, \ldots, 2n$.

The test of i greater than n insures that $a_{n+1,j}$ will not be computed when the last test of i less than n is not satisfied. Control is transferred to the statement incrementing l to $l + 1$, and hence a new diagonal element a_{ll} is chosen. Thus, the process is repeated. When the test $i > n$ is satisfied, then transfer is made to the print statement.

FLOW CHART 4.11.1 Inverse of a Square Matrix

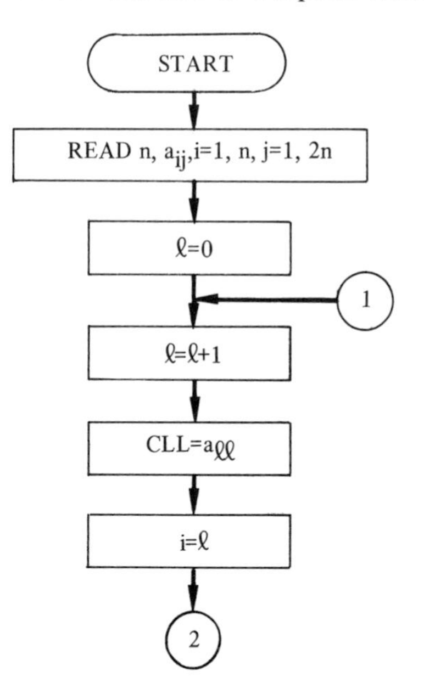

[10] There is no need to use a superscript in a flow chart.

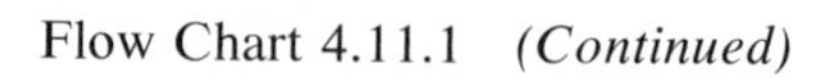
Flow Chart 4.11.1 *(Continued)*

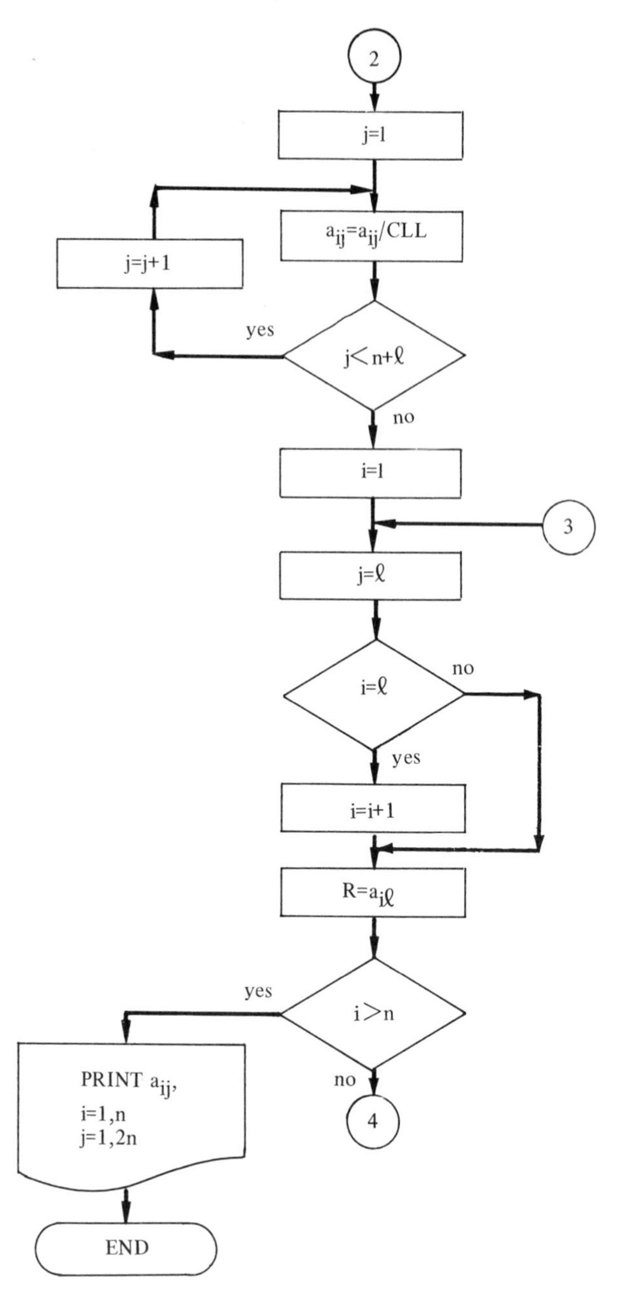

Flow Chart 4.11.1 *(Continued)*

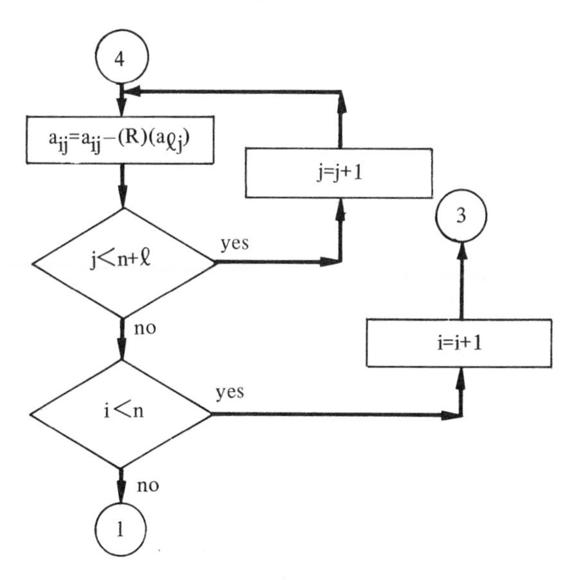

4.11.2 Program

Given: $A = \begin{bmatrix} 2 & 3 & 1 \\ -1 & 2 & -1 \\ 3 & 0 & 2 \end{bmatrix}.$

To find: A^{-1}.

```
/JOB GO, MAP
/FTC LIST,REF
BPS FORTRAN D COMPILER
      DIMENSION A(20,40)
   10 FORMAT(3I4)
   11 FORMAT(7F10.0)
   16 FORMAT(1H1,T57,'INVERSE'/)
   17 FORMAT(6F19.5)
      READ(5,10)N,M
      READ(5,11)((A(I,J),J=1,M),I=1,N)
      L=0
  100 L=L+1
      I=L
```

```
      J=L
      C1=A(L,L)
  110 A(I,J)=A(I,J)/C1
      IF(J-(L+N))120,130,130
  120 J=J+1
      GO TO 110
  130 I=1
  220 J=L
      IF(I-L)140,150,140
  150 I=I+1
  140 C2=A(I,L)
      IF(I-N)160,160,170
  160 A(I,J)=A(I,J)-C2*A(L,J)
      IF(J-(L+N))180,190,190
  180 J=J+1
      GO TO 160
  190 IF(I-N)200,100,100
  200 I=I+1
      GO TO 220
  170 WRITE(6,16)
      WRITE(6,17)((A(I,J),J=1,M),I=1,N)
      STOP
      END
```

```
                              INVERSE
1.00000  0.0      0.0      -4.00000   6.00000   5.00000
0.0      1.00000  0.0       1.00000  -1.00000  -1.00000
0.0      0.0      1.00000   6.00000  -9.00000  -7.00000
```

EXERCISE

In Flow Chart 4.11.1, the READ statement requires that all elements of the rectangular matrix should be read in. Since in the matrix $[A\,\vdots\,I]$, I has zeros everywhere except on the diagonal where they are unity, a more efficient method of designating these elements as zero or one can be applied.

Write a flow chart to compute A^{-1} with the following changes by use of two DO loops:

1. Read in a_{ij}, $i = 1, 2, \ldots, n$; $j = 1, 2, \ldots, n$.
2. Form a_{ij}, $i = 1, 2, \ldots, n$; $j = n + 1, \ldots, 2n$.

4.12 Some Remarks on the Solution of Simultaneous Linear Equations

For the system of equations (4.32), namely $AX = B$, there are two kinds of methods of solution—direct and iterative. A *direct method,* based upon the Gauss elimination method, is one whereby the true solution is derived in one unrepeated sequence of steps, provided that all computations are executed without roundoff error.

An *iterative method* is any method that assumes some initial values of the components of the vector X, and by a repeating process—an iteration—approximates the true values. However, before considering methods of solution, it is well to look at least briefly at ill-conditioned equations.

Given: the two systems of equations,

$$\begin{aligned} 3x + 8y &= 11 \\ 3x + 8.0001y &= 11.0001, \end{aligned} \tag{4.78}$$

with the solution $x = 1$, $y = 1$, and

$$\begin{aligned} 3x + 8y &= 11 \\ 3x + 7.9999y &= 11.0002, \end{aligned} \tag{4.79}$$

with the solution $x = 9$, $y = -2$. Relating each of these systems to the form

$$\begin{aligned} a_{11}x + a_{12}y &= b_1 \\ a_{21}x + a_{22}y &= b_2, \end{aligned}$$

it is seen that a change of $-.0002$ in a_{22} and a change of $+.0001$ in b_2 cause a large change in the solution. When such a slight change in coefficients causes a large change in the solution, the system is said to be ill-conditioned. Hence, regardless of the extreme accuracy of a method, the solution may be completely erroneous.[11]

DIRECT METHODS

4.13 Solution by an Elimination Method

The method of finding the inverse of a square matrix (Sec. 4.11) can be applied to solve a system of n linear nonhomogeneous equations in n unknowns with only the added step of finding all x_i. This method accomplishes two things:

1. The inverse of A is determined.
2. The solution of $AX = B$ is found.

[11] See Anthony Ralston, *A First Course in Numerical Analysis* (New York: McGraw-Hill Book Company, Inc., 1965).

The set of equations $AX = B$ may be written as

$$\begin{bmatrix} a_{11} & a_{12} & \cdots & a_{1n} \\ a_{21} & a_{22} & \cdots & a_{2n} \\ \cdot & \cdot & \cdot & \cdot \\ a_{n1} & a_{n2} & \cdots & a_{nn} \end{bmatrix} \begin{bmatrix} x_1 \\ x_2 \\ \cdots \\ x_n \end{bmatrix} = \begin{bmatrix} b_1 \\ b_2 \\ \cdots \\ b_n \end{bmatrix}.$$

If A^{-1} exists, then $A^{-1}AX = A^{-1}B$ or $X = A^{-1}B$.

Thus, by performing elementary transformations on the matrix $[A,I]$, i.e., on

$$\begin{bmatrix} a_{11} & a_{12} & \cdots & a_{1n} & 1 & 0 & \cdots & 0 \\ a_{21} & a_{22} & \cdots & a_{2n} & 0 & 1 & \cdots & 0 \\ \cdot & \cdot & \cdots & \cdot & \cdot & \cdot & \cdots & \cdot \\ a_{n1} & a_{n2} & \cdots & a_{nn} & 0 & 0 & \cdots & 1 \end{bmatrix},$$

the resulting matrix is

$$\begin{bmatrix} 1 & 0 & \cdots & 0 & a'_{1,n+1} & a'_{1,n+2} & \cdots & a'_{12n} \\ 0 & 1 & \cdots & 0 & a'_{2,n+1} & a'_{2,n+2} & \cdots & a'_{22n} \\ \cdot & \cdot & \cdots & \cdot & \cdot & \cdot & \cdots & \cdot \\ 0 & 0 & \cdots & 1 & a'_{n,n+1} & a'_{n,n+2} & \cdots & a'_{n2n} \end{bmatrix}$$

where

$$\begin{bmatrix} a'_{1,n+1} & a'_{1,n+2} & \cdots & a'_{12n} \\ a'_{2,n+1} & a'_{2,n+2} & \cdots & a'_{22n} \\ \cdot & \cdot & \cdots & \cdot \\ a'_{n,n+1} & a'_{n,n+2} & \cdots & a'_{n2n} \end{bmatrix} = A^{-1}.$$

Hence, from $AX = B$, the solution may be stated as $X = A^{-1}B$; i.e.,

$$\begin{bmatrix} x_1 \\ x_2 \\ \cdots \\ x_n \end{bmatrix} = \begin{bmatrix} a'_{1,n+1} & a'_{1,n+2} & \cdots & a'_{12n} \\ a'_{2,n+1} & a'_{2,n+2} & \cdots & a'_{22n} \\ \cdot & \cdot & \cdot & \cdot \\ a'_{n,n+1} & a'_{n,n+2} & \cdots & a'_{n2n} \end{bmatrix} \begin{bmatrix} b_1 \\ b_2 \\ \cdots \\ b_n \end{bmatrix}. \tag{4.80}$$

Thus,

$$\begin{aligned} x_1 &= a'_{1,n+1}b_1 + a'_{1,n+2}b_2 + \cdots + a'_{12n}b_n \\ &\cdot \\ x_i &= a'_{i,n+1}b_1 + a'_{i,n+2}b_2 + \cdots + a'_{i2n}b_n \\ &\cdot \\ x_n &= a'_{n,n+1}b_1 + a'_{n,n+2}b_2 + \cdots + a'_{n2n}b_n, \end{aligned} \tag{4.81}$$

or, for $i = 1, 2, \ldots, n$,

$$x_i = \sum_{j=1}^{n} a'_{i,n+j}b_j. \tag{4.81a}$$

Hence, the principal steps to solve $AX = B$ and to find A^{-1} are:

1. Equations 4.77 are used to find A^{-1}.
2. The solution then is found by using

$$x_i = \sum_{j=1}^{n} a_{i,n+j}^{(n-1)} b_j, \qquad (i = 1, \ldots, n). \tag{4.82}$$

4.13.1 Flow Chart

To find the inverse of the coefficient matrix A, using the elimination method for solving a system of linear equations.
Given $AX = B$:

Let n = order of matrix A.
Let i represent the current row.
Let j represent the current column.
Let l represent the current pivotal element on the diagonal.

FLOW CHART 4.13.1 Elimination Method

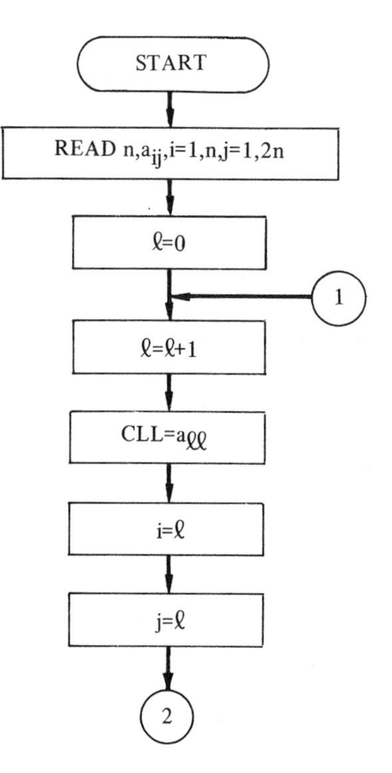

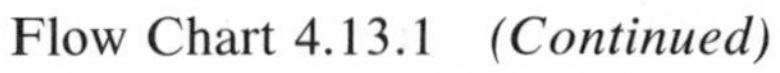
Flow Chart 4.13.1 *(Continued)*

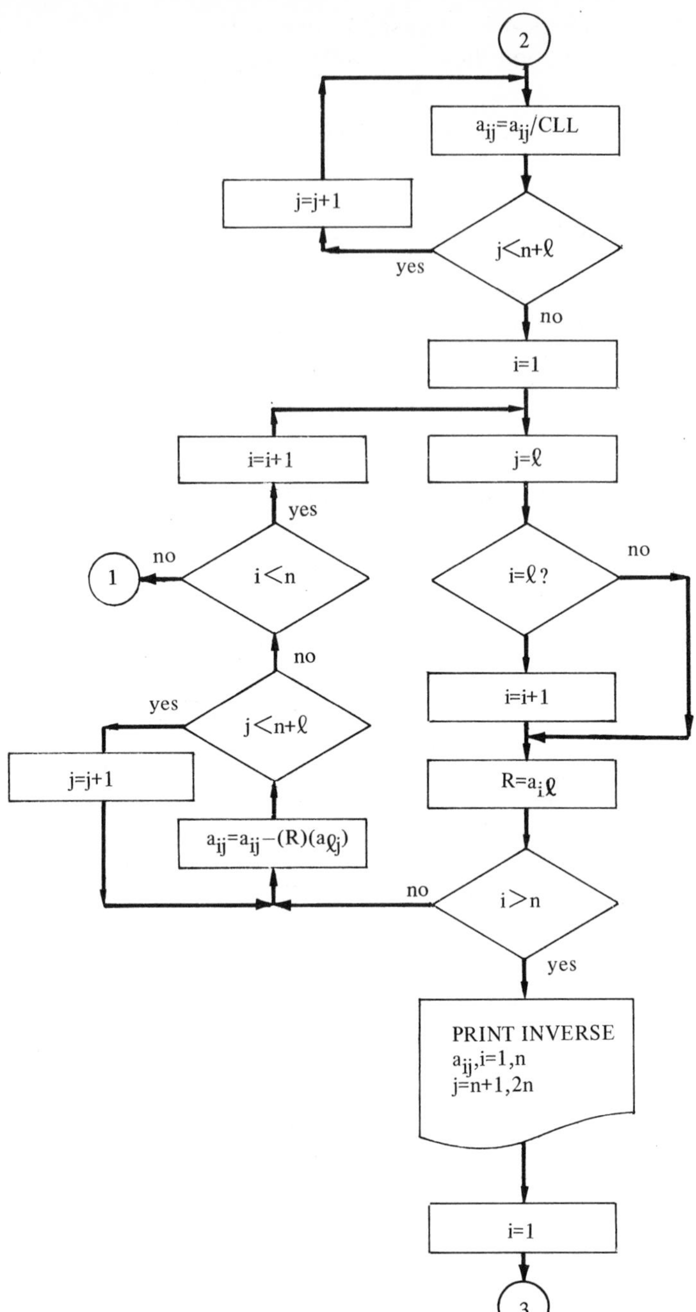

Flow Chart 4.13.1 *(Continued)*

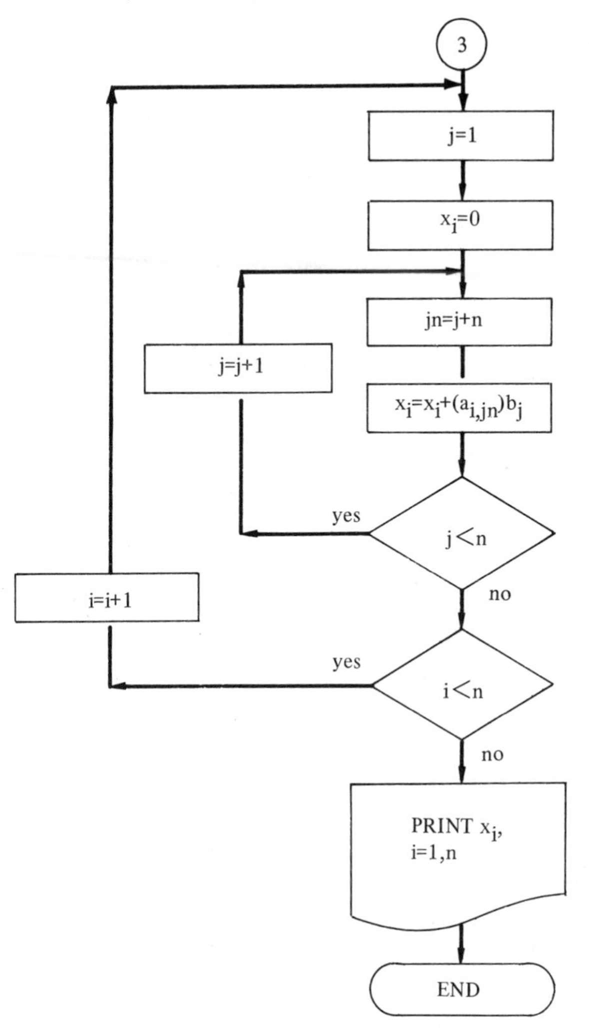

4.13.2 Gaussian Elimination

The system (4.25) may be expressed in the form

$$\begin{aligned} a_{11}x_1 + a_{12}x_2 + \cdots + a_{1n}x_n &= a_{1,n+1} \\ a_{21}x_1 + a_{22}x_2 + \cdots + a_{2n}x_n &= a_{2,n+1} \\ \cdot\ \cdot\ \cdot\ \cdot\ \cdot\ \cdot\ \cdot\ \cdot\ \cdot\ \cdot\ \cdot\ &\cdot\ \cdot\ \cdot\ \cdot \\ a_{n1}x_1 + a_{n2}x_2 + \cdots + a_{nn}x_n &= a_{n,n+1}, \end{aligned} \tag{4.83}$$

where b_i is replaced by $a_{i,n+1}$.

Suppose $a_{11} \neq 0$. Then by using Eqs. 4.56 for $l = 1$,

$$a_{ij}^{(1)} = a_{ij} - \frac{(a_{il})(a_{lj})}{a_{ll}}, \qquad (i = 2, \ldots, n, \quad j = 1, \ldots, n+1). \tag{4.84}$$

The following system is derived from the system (4.83):

$$\begin{aligned} a_{11}x_1 + a_{12}x_2 + \cdots + a_{1n}x_n &= a_{1,n+1} \\ a_{22}^{(1)}x_2 + \cdots + a_{2n}^{(1)}x_n &= a_{2,n+1}^{(1)} \\ \cdots\cdots\cdots\cdots \\ a_{n2}^{(1)}x_2 + \cdots + a_{nn}^{(1)}x_n &= a_{n,n+1}^{(1)}. \end{aligned} \tag{4.85}$$

Again, if $a_{22}^{(1)} \neq 0$ (assumed here), then for $l = 2$, $i = 3, \ldots, n$, and $j = 2, \ldots, n + 1$, a second system of equations is derived:

$$\begin{aligned} a_{11}x_1 + a_{12}x_2 + \cdots + a_{1n}x_n &= a_{1,n+1} \\ a_{22}^{(1)}x_2 + \cdots + a_{2n}^{(1)}x_n &= a_{2,n+1}^{(1)} \\ a_{33}^{(2)}x_2 + \cdots + a_{3n}^{(2)}x_n &= a_{3,n+1}^{(2)} \\ \cdots\cdots\cdots\cdots \\ a_{n3}^{(2)}x_2 + \cdots + a_{nn}^{(2)}x_n &= a_{n,n+1}^{(2)}. \end{aligned} \tag{4.86}$$

If this process is repeated $n - 1$ times, the final derived system of equations becomes

$$\begin{aligned} a_{11}x_1 + a_{12}x_2 + \cdots\cdots\cdots + a_{1n}x_n &= a_{1,n+1} \\ a_{22}^{(1)}x_2 + \cdots\cdots\cdots + a_{2n}^{(1)}x_n &= a_{2,n+1}^{(1)} \\ a_{33}^{(2)}x_2 + \cdots + a_{3n}^{(2)}x_n &= a_{3,n+1}^{(2)} \\ \cdots\cdots\cdots\cdots \\ a_{nn}^{(n-1)}x_n &= a_{n,n+1}^{(n-1)}, \end{aligned} \tag{4.87}$$

where diagonal elements $a_{ii}^{(i-1)} \neq 0$, and

$$a_{ij}^{(l)} = a_{ij}^{(l-1)} - \frac{a_{il}^{(l-1)} \cdot a_{lj}^{(l-1)}}{a_{ll}^{(l-1)}}, \quad \begin{aligned} &l = 1, \ldots, n-1, j = l+1, \ldots, n+1, \\ &i = l+1, \ldots, n, \; a_{ij}^{(0)} = a_{ij}. \end{aligned} \tag{4.88}$$

Now the solution of (4.87) can be found by *back substitution*, i.e.,

$$\begin{aligned} x_n &= \frac{a_{n,n+1}^{(n-1)}}{a_{n,n}^{(n-1)}} \\ x_{n-1} &= \frac{1}{a_{n-1,n-1}^{(n-2)}}\{a_{n-1,n+1}^{(n-2)} - a_{n-1,n}^{(n-1)}x_n\} \\ &\cdots\cdots\cdots\cdots \\ x_1 &= \frac{1}{a_{11}}\left\{a_{1,n+1} - \sum_{j=2}^{n} a_{1j}x_j\right\}. \end{aligned} \tag{4.89}$$

Thus,

$$x_i = \frac{1}{a_{ii}^{(i-1)}}\left\{a_{i,n+1}^{(i-1)} - \sum_{j=i+1}^{n} a_{ij}^{(i-1)}x_j\right\}, \qquad (i = n, \ldots, 1). \tag{4.90}$$

The process leading to the system (4.87) is called Gaussian elimination. Calculation of x_i by (4.90) is called back substitution.

If in the elimination method of Sec. 4.13, the calculation of the inverse of A is omitted and only the solution of the system is considered, the process resulting from this change leads to the following system of equations:

$$\begin{aligned} x_1 \quad\quad\quad &= a_{1,n+1}^{(n-1)} \\ x_2 \quad\quad &= a_{2,n+1}^{(n-1)} \\ \cdot \quad\quad & \\ \cdot \quad & \\ \cdot & \\ x_n &= a_{n,n+1}^{(n-1)}, \end{aligned} \tag{4.91}$$

and the solution of (4.91) is

$$x_i = a_{i,n+1}^{(n-1)}. \tag{4.92}$$

Thus, by using Eqs. 4.77 where $j = l, \ldots, n+1$ and Eq. 4.92, a variation of the Gauss process called the Gauss-Jordan method is derived.

Of the three methods discussed, the Gauss method is the most efficient for one system of equations. For many choices of B in $AX = B$, it may be more efficient to find A^{-1} and then calculate $A^{-1}B$ for each B. In this case, the elimination method of Sec. 4.11 could be used with advantage. Section 4.14 will consider several sets of systems of equations based upon the fact that there are many choices of B but A is fixed.

4.13.3 Program

To solve $AX = B$ by the Gaussian elimination method with back substitution.

Given the system of equations:

$$\begin{aligned} 2x_1 + 3x_2 + x_3 &= 11 \\ -x_1 + 2x_2 - x_3 &= 0 \\ 3x_1 + 2x_3 &= 9. \end{aligned} \tag{4.93}$$

The following program consists of two subroutines. The first, SUBROUTINE MATRIX, transforms (4.93) into a system

$$\begin{aligned} a_{11}x_1 + a_{12}x_2 + a_{13}x_3 &= a_{14} \\ a_{22}^{(1)}x_2 + a_{23}^{(1)}x_3 &= a_{24}^{(1)} \\ a_{33}^{(2)}x_3 &= a_{34}^{(2)}. \end{aligned} \tag{4.94}$$

The second one, SUBROUTINE SOLUTS, solves (4.94).

```
/JOB GO,MAP
/FTC LIST,REF
BPS FORTRAN D COMPILER
        CALL MATRIX
        CALL SOLUTS
        END
        SUBROUTINE MATRIX
C       GAUSS ELIMINATION METHOD PART I
        DOUBLE PRECISION A(30,31)
        COMMON A,N,M,N1
    10  FORMAT(2I5,7F10.0/(10X,7F10.0))
    21  FORMAT(1H1,T10, 'ORIGINAL MATRIX',6X,I6)
    22  FORMAT(/7F15.5)
    23  FORMAT(1H1,T10,'NEW MATRIX')
        READ(5,10)N,M,((A(I,J),J=1,M),I=1,N)
        WRITE(6,21)N
        DO 100 I=1,N
   100  WRITE(6,22)(A(I,J),J=1,M)
        N1=N-1
        DO 200 L=1,N1
        I1=L+1
        DO 200 I=I1,N
        J1=L+1
        DO 200 J=J1,M
   200  A(I,J)=A(I,J)-A(I,L)*A(L,J)/A(L,L)
        WRITE(6,23)
        DO 300 I=1,N
   300  WRITE(6,22)(A(I,J),J=1,M)
        RETURN
        END
        SUBROUTINE SOLUTS
C       GAUSS ELIMINATION METHOD PART 2, SOLUTION
        DOUBLE PRECISION A(30,31),X(30)
        COMMON A,N,M,N1
    10  FORMAT(1H1,T10,'SOLUTION')
    11  FORMAT(F20.10/)
        X(N)=A(N,M)/A(N,N)
        I=N1
        J=N
```

```
100 SUM=0.0
200 SUM=SUM-A(I,J)*X(J)
    IF(J-N)300,400,400
300 J=J+1
    GO TO 200
400 X(I)=SUM+A(I,M)/A(I,I)
    IF(I-1)600,600,500
500 J=I
    I=I-1
    GO TO 100
600 WRITE(6,10)
    WRITE(6,11)(X(I),I=1,N)
    RETURN
    END
```

```
ORIGINAL MATRIX
  2.00000  3.00000   1.00000  11.00000
 -1.00000  2.00000  -1.00000   0.0
  3.00000  0.0       2.00000   9.00000

NEW MATRIX
2.00000  3.00000   1.00000  11.00000
         3.50000  -0.50000   5.50000
                  -0.14286  -0.42857

SOLUTION
1.0000000000
2.0000000000
3.0000000000
```

4.14 Solution of Linear Equations XA = B

First, notation must be explained. X in this case is a row matrix, i.e.,

$$X = [x_1 \quad x_2 \quad \cdots \quad x_n].$$

Also, B is a row matrix, i.e.,

$$B = [b_1 \quad b_2 \quad \cdots \quad b_n]$$

and

$$A = \begin{bmatrix} a_{11} & a_{12} & \cdots & a_{1n} \\ a_{21} & a_{22} & \cdots & a_{2n} \\ \cdot & \cdot & \cdots & \cdot \\ a_{n1} & a_{n2} & \cdots & a_{nn} \end{bmatrix}. \tag{4.95}$$

Thus, $XA = B$ may be expressed as

$$[x_1 \quad x_2 \quad \cdots \quad x_n]\begin{bmatrix} a_{11} & a_{12} & \cdots & a_{1n} \\ a_{21} & a_{22} & \cdots & a_{2n} \\ \cdot & \cdot & \cdots & \cdot \\ a_{n1} & a_{n2} & \cdots & a_{nn} \end{bmatrix} = [b_1 \quad b_2 \quad \cdots \quad b_n] \tag{4.96}$$

or

$$\begin{aligned}[a_{11}x_1 + a_{21}x_2 + \cdots + a_{n1}x_n,\ a_{12}x_1 + a_{22}x_2 + \cdots + a_{n2}x_n, \ldots, \\ a_{1n}x_1 + a_{2n}x_n + \cdots + a_{nn}x_n] = [b_1 \quad b_2 \quad \cdots \quad b_n].\end{aligned} \tag{4.97}$$

That is,

$$\begin{aligned} a_{11}x_1 + a_{21}x_2 + \cdots + a_{n1}x_n &= b_1 \\ a_{12}x_1 + a_{22}x_2 + \cdots + a_{n2}x_n &= b_2 \\ \cdots\cdots\cdots\cdots &\cdots \\ a_{1n}x_n + a_{2n}x_n + \cdots + a_{nn}x_n &= b_n . \end{aligned} \tag{4.98}$$

If there are several choices of B for the same A, then the following method may be used to find solutions of $XA = B$ for the several choices of B:

Step 1. Find A^{-1}. Then

$$X = BA^{-1}. \tag{4.99}$$

Step 2 (a). Since B is a row matrix,

$$\begin{aligned} x_1 &= \sum_{i=1}^{n} b_i a'_{i1} \\ &= b_1 a'_{11} + b_2 a'_{21} + b_3 a'_{31} + \cdots + b_n a'_{n1} \\ &\cdots\cdots\cdots \\ x_k &= \sum_{i=1}^{n} b_i a'_{ik} \\ &\cdots\cdots\cdots \\ x_n &= \sum_{i}^{n} b_i a'_{in} \end{aligned} \tag{4.100}$$

where $[a'_{ij}] = A^{-1}$.

Step 2 (b). If there are several choices of B, then let the composite matrix B represent these choices—that is,

$$B = \begin{bmatrix} b_{11} & b_{12} & \cdots & b_{1n} \\ b_{21} & b_{22} & \cdots & b_{2n} \\ \cdot & \cdot & \cdots & \cdot \\ b_{m1} & b_{m2} & \cdots & b_{mn} \end{bmatrix}. \tag{4.101}$$

Then, for the first choice of B, namely $b_{11}b_{12} \cdots b_{1n}$,

$$\begin{aligned} x_1 &= \sum_{i=1}^{n} b_{1i}a'_{i1} \\ x_2 &= \sum_{i=1}^{n} b_{1i}a'_{i2} \\ &\cdots\cdots \\ x_n &= \sum_{i=1}^{n} b_{1i}a'_{in}. \end{aligned} \tag{4.102}$$

For the second choice of B, namely $b_{21}b_{22} \cdots b_{2n}$,

$$\begin{aligned} x_1 &= \sum_{i=1}^{n} b_{2i}a'_{i1} \\ x_2 &= \sum_{i=1}^{n} b_{2i}a'_{i2} \\ &\cdots\cdots \\ x_n &= \sum_{i=1}^{n} b_{2i}a'_{in}, \end{aligned} \tag{4.103}$$

and for the kth choice of B, namely $b_{k1}b_{k2} \cdots b_{kn}$,

$$\begin{aligned} x_1 &= \sum_{i=1}^{n} b_{ki}a'_{i1} \\ x_2 &= \sum_{i=1}^{n} b_{ki}a'_{i2} \\ &\cdots\cdots \\ x_n &= \sum_{i=1}^{n} b_{ki}a'_{in}. \end{aligned} \tag{4.104}$$

Hence, in this case (several choices of B), it would be better to consider the X vector as several row vectors, i.e.,

$$X = \begin{bmatrix} x_{11} & x_{12} & \cdots & x_{1n} \\ x_{21} & x_{22} & \cdots & x_{2n} \\ \cdot & \cdot & \cdots & \cdot \\ x_{m1} & x_{m2} & \cdots & x_{mn} \end{bmatrix}. \tag{4.105}$$

Then $X = BA^{-1}$ would appear as:

$$\begin{bmatrix} x_{11} & x_{12} & \cdots & x_{1n} \\ x_{21} & x_{22} & \cdots & x_{2n} \\ \cdot & \cdot & \cdots & \cdot \\ x_{m1} & x_{m2} & \cdots & x_{mn} \end{bmatrix} = \begin{bmatrix} b_{11} & b_{12} & \cdots & b_{1n} \\ b_{21} & b_{22} & \cdots & b_{2n} \\ \cdot & \cdot & \cdots & \cdot \\ b_{m1} & b_{m2} & \cdots & b_{mn} \end{bmatrix} \begin{bmatrix} a'_{11} & a'_{12} & \cdots & a'_{1n} \\ a'_{21} & a'_{22} & \cdots & a'_{2n} \\ \cdot & \cdot & \cdots & \cdot \\ a'_{n1} & a'_{n2} & \cdots & a'_{nn} \end{bmatrix}. \tag{4.106}$$

Thus

$$
\begin{aligned}
x_{11} &= \sum_{i=1}^{n} b_{1i}a'_{i1} \\
x_{12} &= \sum_{i=1}^{n} b_{1i}a'_{i2} \\
\cdot\ \ &\cdot\ \ \cdot\ \ \cdot\ \ \cdot \\
x_{1n} &= \sum_{i=1}^{n} b_{1i}a'_{in}
\end{aligned}
\tag{4.107}
$$

represent the solution of $XA = [b_{11} \quad b_{12} \quad \cdots \quad b_{1n}]$ where $X = [x_{11} \quad x_{12} \quad \cdots \quad x_{1n}]$, and similarly,

$$
\begin{aligned}
x_{21} &= \sum_{i=1}^{n} b_{2i}a'_{i1} \\
\cdot\ \ &\cdot\ \ \cdot\ \ \cdot\ \ \cdot \\
x_{2n} &= \sum_{i=1}^{n} b_{2i}a'_{in}
\end{aligned}
\tag{4.108}
$$

represent the solution of

$$XA = [b_{21} \quad b_{22} \quad \cdots \quad b_{2n}], \qquad X = [x_{21} \quad x_{22} \quad \cdots \quad x_{2n}].$$

So, as a general expression of the solution of

$$
\begin{aligned}
XA &= [b_{k1} \quad b_{k2} \quad \cdots \quad b_{kn}], \\
x_{k1} &= \sum_{i=1}^{n} b_{ki}a'_{i1} \\
\cdot\ \ &\cdot\ \ \cdot\ \ \cdot\ \ \cdot \\
x_{kn} &= \sum_{i=1}^{n} b_{ki}a'_{in}, \qquad (k = 1, \ldots, m)
\end{aligned}
\tag{4.109}
$$

are the solutions for the several choices of B.

4.14.1 Flow Chart

To solve: $XA = B$.
To find: A^{-1}.
Let

$$
X = \begin{bmatrix}
x_{11} & x_{12} & \cdots & x_{1n} \\
x_{21} & x_{22} & \cdots & x_{2n} \\
\cdot & \cdot & \cdots & \cdot \\
x_{n1} & x_{n2} & \cdots & x_{nn}
\end{bmatrix},
\tag{4.110}
$$

$$A = \begin{bmatrix} a_{11} & a_{12} & \cdots & a_{1n} \\ a_{21} & a_{22} & \cdots & a_{2n} \\ \cdot & \cdot & \cdots & \cdot \\ a_{n1} & a_{n2} & \cdots & a_{nn} \end{bmatrix}, \tag{4.111}$$

and

$$B = \begin{bmatrix} b_{11} & b_{12} & \cdots & b_{1n} \\ b_{21} & b_{22} & \cdots & b_{2n} \\ \cdot & \cdot & \cdots & \cdot \\ b_{m1} & b_{m2} & \cdots & b_{mn} \end{bmatrix}. \tag{4.112}$$

The following flow chart is abridged.

FLOW CHART 4.14.1

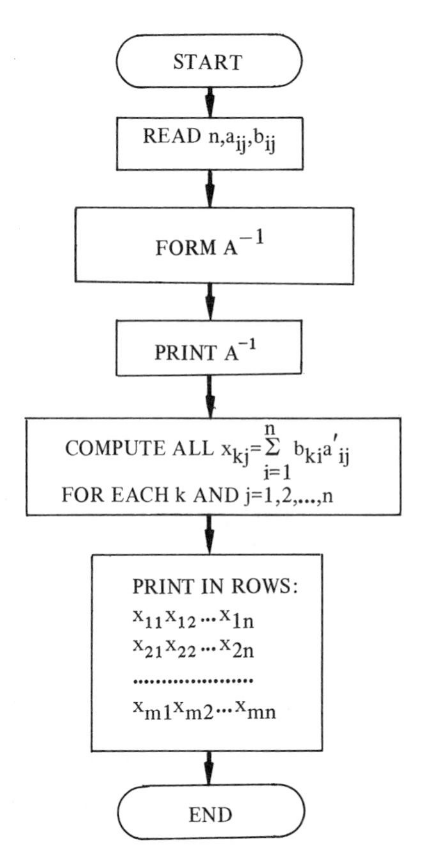

4.15 Cholesky's Method

Under certain conditions, the linear system of equations

$$AX = B \tag{4.113}$$

can be solved by the technique known as Cholesky's method.

The conditions are:

1. If all principal minors of A are nonsingular, i.e., if $a_{11} \neq 0$,

$$\begin{vmatrix} a_{11} & a_{12} \\ a_{21} & a_{22} \end{vmatrix} \neq 0, \begin{vmatrix} a_{11} & a_{12} & a_{13} \\ a_{21} & a_{22} & a_{23} \\ a_{31} & a_{32} & a_{33} \end{vmatrix} \neq 0, \quad \ldots, \quad |A| \neq 0, \tag{4.114}$$

then the matrix A may be uniquely factored into the product $A = LU$, where L is a lower triangular matrix, namely

$$L = \begin{bmatrix} l_{11} & 0 & 0 & \cdots & 0 \\ l_{21} & l_{22} & 0 & \cdots & 0 \\ l_{31} & l_{32} & l_{33} & \cdots & 0 \\ \cdot & \cdot & \cdot & \cdots & \cdot \\ l_{n1} & l_{n2} & l_{n3} & \cdots & l_{nn} \end{bmatrix}. \tag{4.115}$$

2. U is an upper triangular matrix, namely

$$U = \begin{bmatrix} 1 & u_{12} & u_{13} & \cdots & & u_{1n} \\ 0 & 1 & u_{23} & \cdots & & u_{2n} \\ 0 & 0 & 1 & u_{34} & \cdots & u_{3n} \\ \cdot & \cdot & \cdot & \cdots & & \cdot \\ 0 & 0 & 0 & 0 & & 1 \end{bmatrix}. \tag{4.116}$$

Provided that the above conditions are satisfied, then the system $AX = B$ becomes $LUX = B$; assuming for the moment that A has been factored and all elements of L and U are known, the system can be solved as follows: Let $UX = Y$; then $LUX = B$ becomes $LY = B$.

Thus, there are two systems to be solved. First, $LY = B$, i.e.,

$$\begin{bmatrix} l_{11} & 0 & 0 & \cdots & 0 \\ l_{21} & l_{22} & 0 & \cdots & 0 \\ \cdot & \cdot & \cdot & \cdots & \cdot \\ l_{n1} & l_{n2} & l_{n3} & \cdots & l_{nn} \end{bmatrix} \begin{bmatrix} y_1 \\ y_2 \\ \cdots \\ y_n \end{bmatrix} = \begin{bmatrix} b_1 \\ b_2 \\ \cdots \\ b_n \end{bmatrix} \tag{4.117}$$

or

$$\begin{aligned} l_{11}y_1 \qquad\qquad\qquad\qquad &= b_1 \\ l_{21}y_1 + l_{22}y_2 \qquad\qquad &= b_2 \\ \cdots\cdots\cdots\cdots\cdots & \\ l_{n1}y_1 + l_{n2}y_2 + \cdots + l_{nn}y_n &= b_n \end{aligned} \tag{4.118}$$

is to be solved. The solution for this system is

$$y_i = \frac{l}{l_{ii}}\left\{b_i - \sum_{j=1}^{i-1} l_{ij}y_j\right\}, \qquad (i = 1, 2, \ldots, n). \tag{4.119}$$

Second, $UX = Y$ or

$$\begin{aligned} x_1 + u_{12}x_2 + u_{13}x_3 + \cdots + u_{1n}x_n &= y_1 \\ x_2 + u_{23}x_3 + \cdots + u_{2n}x_n &= y_2 \\ \cdots\cdots\cdots\cdots\cdots & \\ x_{n-1} + u_{n-1,n}x_n &= y_{n-1} \\ x_n &= y_n \end{aligned} \tag{4.120}$$

is to be solved. The solution is

$$x_i = y_i - \sum_{j=i+1}^{n} u_{ij}x_j, \qquad (i = n, n-1, \ldots, 1 \text{ in this order}). \tag{4.121}$$

Note: for any positive integer k,

$$\sum_{i=k}^{k-1} A_i = 0.$$

Now to find the matrices L and U, such that $LU = A$—that is,

$$\begin{bmatrix} l_{11} & 0 & 0 & \cdots & 0 \\ l_{21} & l_{22} & 0 & \cdots & 0 \\ \cdot & \cdot & \cdot & \cdot & \cdot \\ l_{n1} & l_{n2} & l_{n3} & \cdots & l_{nn} \end{bmatrix} \cdot \begin{bmatrix} 1 & u_{12} & u_{13} & \cdots & u_{1n} \\ 0 & 1 & u_{23} & \cdots & u_{2n} \\ \cdot & \cdot & \cdot & \cdot & \cdot \\ 0 & 0 & 0 & \cdots & 1 \end{bmatrix} = \begin{bmatrix} a_{11} & a_{12} & a_{13} & \cdots & a_{1n} \\ a_{21} & a_{22} & a_{23} & \cdots & a_{2n} \\ \cdot & \cdot & \cdot & \cdot & \cdot \\ a_{n1} & a_{n2} & a_{n3} & \cdots & a_{nn} \end{bmatrix}. \tag{4.122}$$

It should be seen that by the operation of matrix multiplication and the definition of the equality of matrices,

$$l_{i1} = a_{i1}, \quad (i = 1, 2, \ldots, n).$$

That is, the first column of L equals the first column of A.

With the first column of L found, the first row of U can be found by the formula

$$l_{11}u_{1j} = a_{1j}, \qquad (j = 2, 3, \ldots, n)$$

or

$$u_{1j} = a_{1j}/l_{11} = a_{1j}/a_{11}, \qquad (a_{11} \neq 0), \qquad (j = 2, 3, \ldots, n).$$

With the first column of L and the first row of U found, the second column of L can now be determined by the formula

$$l_{i1}u_{12} + l_{i2} = a_{i2} \quad \text{or} \quad l_{i2} = a_{i2} - l_{i1}u_{12}, \qquad (i = 2, 3, \ldots, n).$$

Now the second row of U can be found using the above-determined values of the first and second columns of L and the first row of U. The second row of U is found by using the formula

$$l_{21}u_{1j} + l_{22}u_{2j} = a_{2j} \quad \text{or} \quad u_{2j} = \frac{l}{l_{22}}(a_{2j} - l_{21}u_{1j}), \qquad (j = 3, 4, \ldots, n).$$

Now the first column of L, the first row of U, the second column of L, and the second row of U have been found. The next step is to find the third column of L, using the values already determined. For the third column of L, the formula is

$$l_{i1}u_{13} + l_{i2}u_{23} + l_{i3} = a_{i3}, \qquad (i = 3, 4, \ldots, n),$$

$$l_{i3} = a_{i3} - (l_{i1}u_{13} + l_{i2}u_{23}) \text{ or } l_{i3} = a_{i3} - \sum_{k=1}^{2} l_{ik}u_{k3}, \qquad (i = 3, 4, \ldots, n).$$

The process of finding the jth column $(i \geq j)$ of L, and then finding the ith row $(i < j)$ of U can be repeated until l_{nn} is found. Thus, if the above order is preserved, the recursive formulas for finding all l_{ij} and u_{ij} are

$$l_{ij} = a_{ij} - \sum_{k=1}^{j-1} l_{ik}u_{kj}, \qquad (i \geq j) \tag{4.123}$$

and

$$u_{ij} = \frac{1}{l_{ii}}\left[a_{ij} - \sum_{k=1}^{i-1} l_{ik}u_{kj}\right], \qquad (i < j). \tag{4.124}$$

The order of computing the elements of L and U can be stated as follows:

1. Compute l_{i1}, $i = 1, 2, \ldots, n$;
   Compute u_{1j}, $j = 2, 3, \ldots, n$.

$$\begin{aligned}
&2.\ \text{Compute } l_{i2},\ i = 2, 3, \ldots, n;\\
&\quad\ \text{Compute } u_{2j},\ j = 3, 4, \ldots, n.\\
&\quad\ \cdot\ \cdot\ \cdot\ \cdot\ \cdot\ \cdot\ \cdot\ \cdot\ \cdot\ \cdot\ \cdot\\
&n-1.\ \text{Compute } l_{i,n-1},\ i = n-1, n;\\
&\quad\ \text{Compute } u_{n-1,j},\ j = n.\\
&n.\ \text{Compute } l_{n,n}.
\end{aligned} \tag{4.125}$$

When the values of the elements of L and U have been computed, the system of equations $AX = B$ can be solved by using the equations

$$LY = B \qquad \text{and} \qquad UX = Y,$$

for which the solutions are

$$y_i = \frac{1}{l_{ii}}\left[b_i - \sum_{j=1}^{i-1} l_{ij}y_j\right], \qquad (i = 1, 2, \ldots, n) \tag{4.126}$$

and

$$x_i = y_i - \sum_{j=i+1}^{n} u_{ij}x_j \tag{4.127}$$

where i takes on the values $n, n-1, n-2, \ldots, 1$ in this order.

4.15.1 Flow Chart

To solve the linear system of equations $AX = B$ by Cholesky's method, the following equations are required:

Part I

1. $l_{ij} = a_{ij} - \sum_{k=1}^{j-1} l_{ik}u_{kj}, \qquad (i \geq j,\ i = 1, 2, \ldots, n)$

2. $u_{ij} = \frac{1}{l_{ii}}\left[a_{ij} - \sum_{k=1}^{i-1} l_{ik}u_{kj}\right], \qquad (i < j,\ j = 2, 3, \ldots, n)$

Part II

3. $y_i = \frac{1}{l_{ii}}\left\{b_i - \sum_{j=1}^{i-1} l_{ij}y_j\right\}, \qquad (i = 1, 2, \ldots, n)$

Part III

4. $x_i = y_i - \sum_{j=i+1}^{n} u_{ij}x_j, \qquad (i = n, n-1, \ldots, 1 \text{ in this order}).$

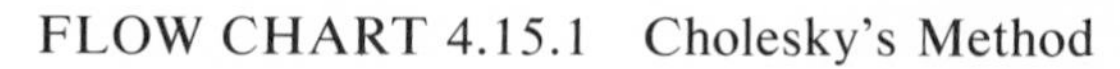

FLOW CHART 4.15.1 Cholesky's Method

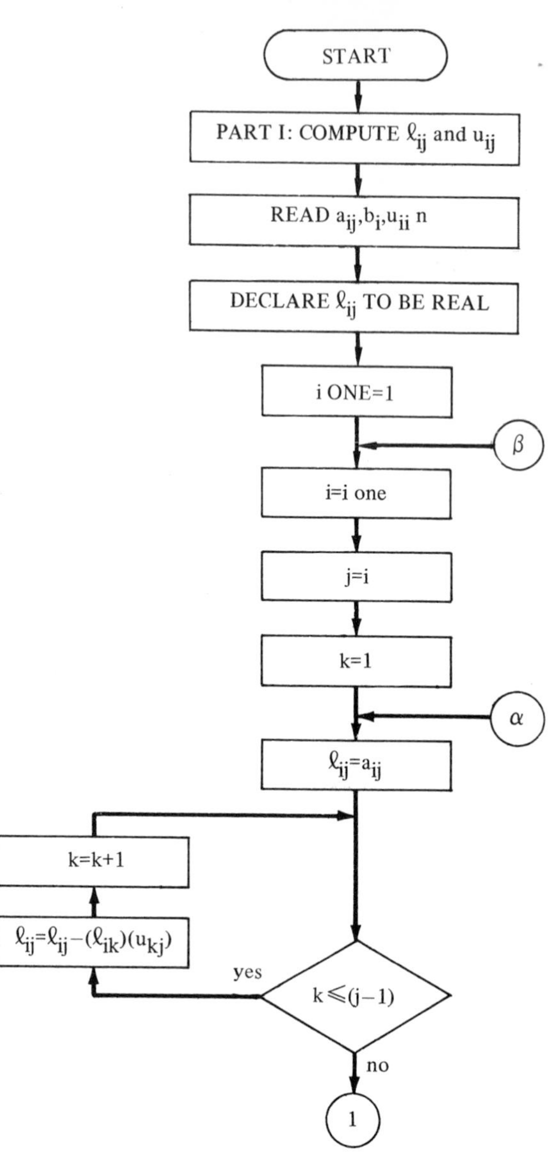

Flow Chart 4.15.1 *(Continued)*

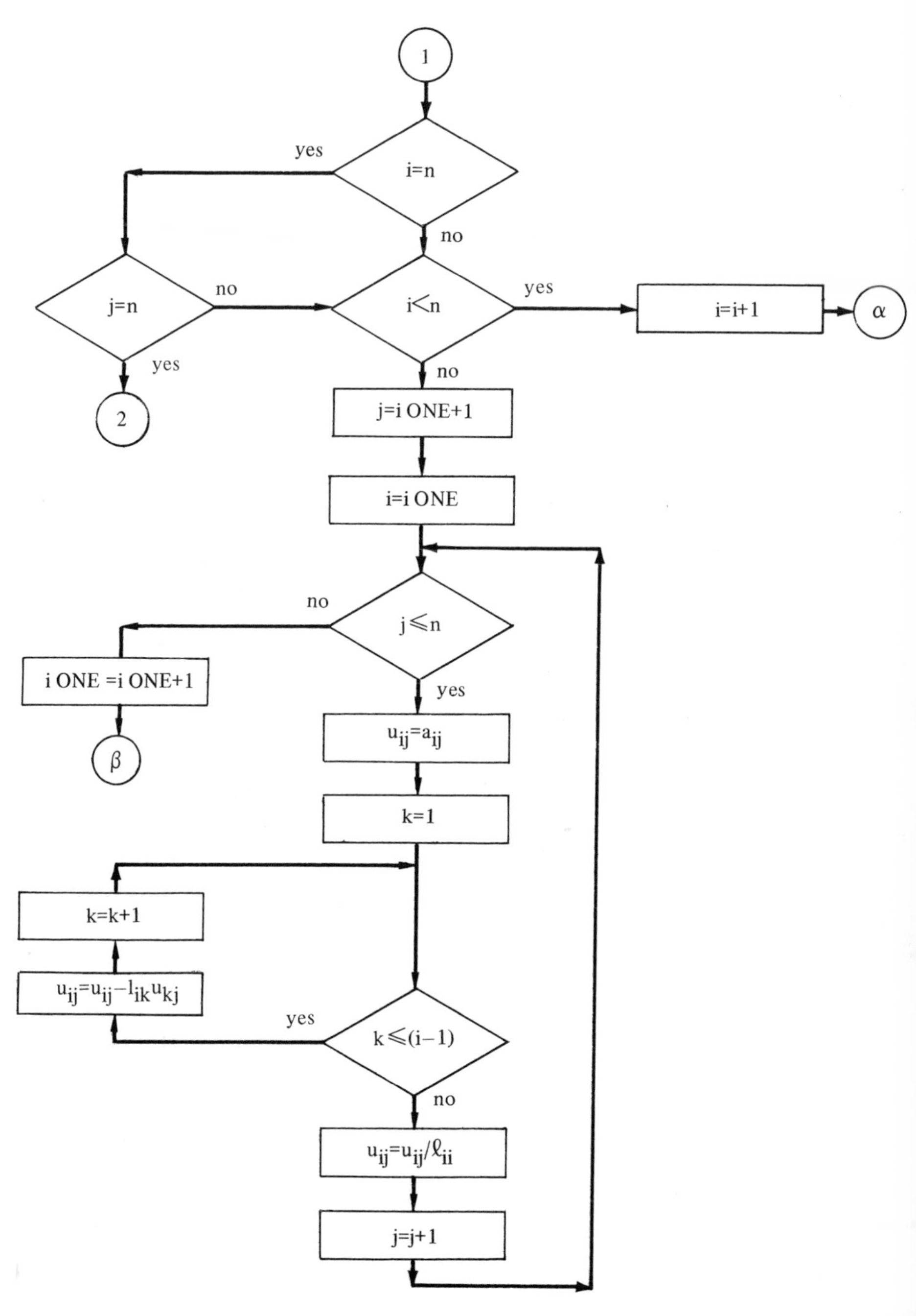

Flow Chart 4.15.1 *(Continued)*

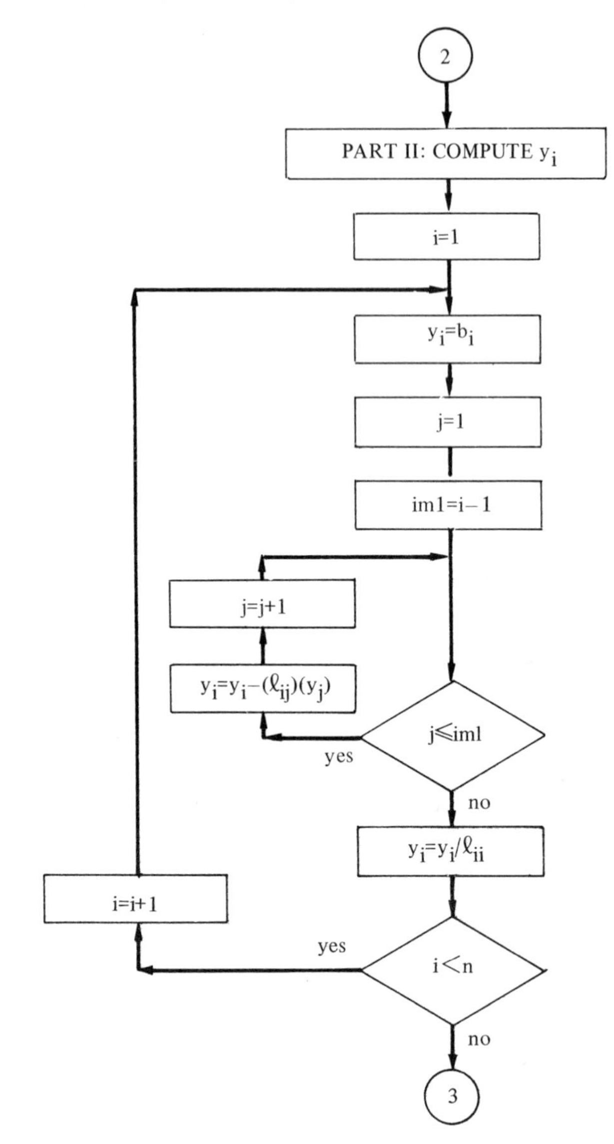

Flow Chart 4.15.1 *(Continued)*

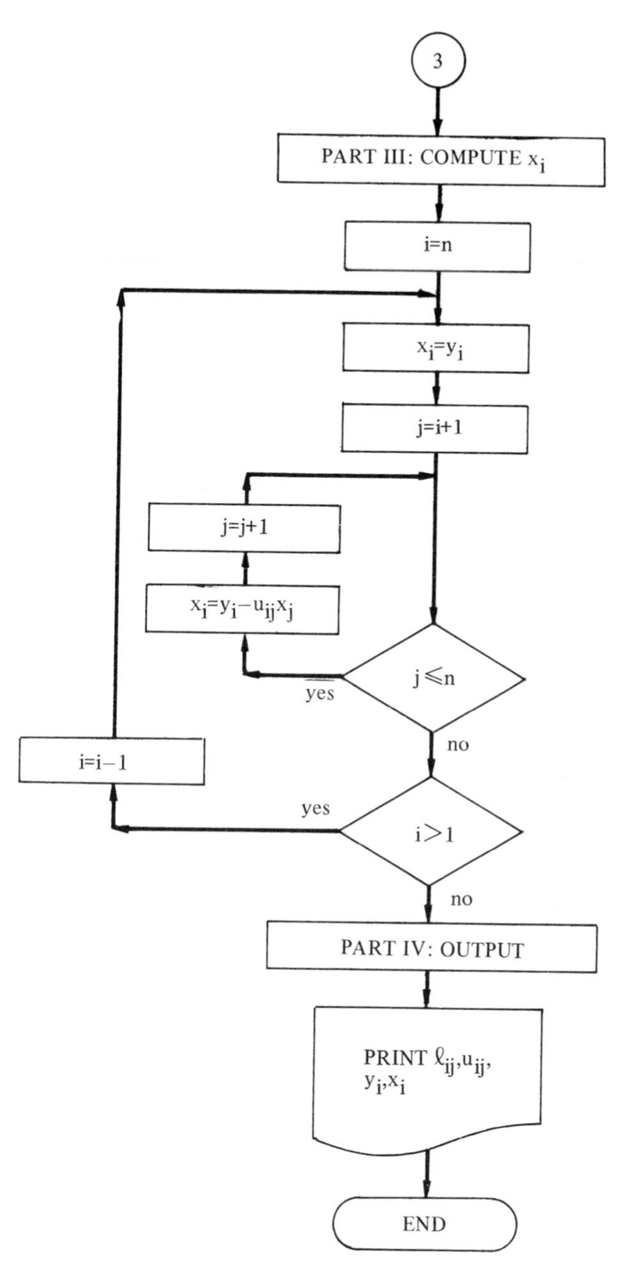

4.15.2 Band Type Systems

It seems appropriate at this time to consider systems of equations of the form $AX = B$ where A is a matrix having zero elements everywhere except along the main diagonal and some diagonals parallel to the main diagonal. For example, a tridiagonal matrix of order 5 is

$$A = \begin{bmatrix} a_{11} & a_{12} & 0 & 0 & 0 \\ a_{21} & a_{22} & a_{23} & 0 & 0 \\ 0 & a_{32} & a_{33} & a_{34} & 0 \\ 0 & 0 & a_{43} & a_{44} & a_{45} \\ 0 & 0 & 0 & a_{54} & a_{55} \end{bmatrix}. \tag{4.128}$$

Such a matrix A is called a *band type matrix.*

The reason for presenting Cholesky's method for a band type system is because of its use in solving boundary value differential equations by finite differences (Ch. 7). Using the method of matrix factorization, it should be apparent that both L and U are also band type. Thus, L becomes

$$L = \begin{bmatrix} l_{11} & 0 & 0 & 0 & 0 \\ l_{21} & l_{22} & 0 & 0 & 0 \\ 0 & l_{32} & l_{33} & 0 & 0 \\ 0 & 0 & l_{43} & l_{44} & 0 \\ 0 & 0 & 0 & l_{54} & l_{55} \end{bmatrix}, \tag{4.129}$$

and U becomes

$$U = \begin{bmatrix} 1 & u_{12} & 0 & 0 & 0 \\ 0 & 1 & u_{23} & 0 & 0 \\ 0 & 0 & 1 & u_{34} & 0 \\ 0 & 0 & 0 & 1 & u_{45} \\ 0 & 0 & 0 & 0 & 1 \end{bmatrix}. \tag{4.130}$$

Multiplying L by U, $LU = A$ becomes

$$\begin{bmatrix} l_{11} & l_{11}u_{12} & 0 & 0 & 0 \\ l_{21} & l_{21}u_{12} + l_{22} & l_{22}u_{23} & 0 & 0 \\ 0 & l_{32} & l_{32}u_{23} + l_{33} & l_{33}u_{34} & 0 \\ 0 & 0 & l_{43} & l_{43}u_{34} + l_{44} & l_{44}u_{45} \\ 0 & 0 & 0 & l_{54} & l_{54}u_{45} + l_{55} \end{bmatrix} = \begin{bmatrix} a_{11} & a_{12} & 0 & 0 & 0 \\ a_{21} & a_{22} & a_{23} & 0 & 0 \\ 0 & a_{32} & a_{33} & a_{34} & 0 \\ 0 & 0 & a_{43} & a_{44} & a_{45} \\ 0 & 0 & 0 & a_{54} & a_{55} \end{bmatrix}. \tag{4.131}$$

The same pattern used in Cholesky's method (without a band type matrix) is applied here. The first column of L is computed, then the first row of U is computed. This technique of computing first a column of L followed by a row of U is continued until l_{55} is found.

First, it is seen that for each column of L, only two values need be computed. These are

$$l_{kk} = a_{kk} - l_{k,k-1}u_{k-1,k}, \qquad (k = 1, 2, \ldots, 5) \tag{4.132}$$

where it is assumed that $l_{1,0}$ and $u_{0,1}$ are zero, and

$$l_{k+1,k} = a_{k+1,k}, \qquad (k = 1, 2, \ldots, 5). \tag{4.133}$$

Also, only one value, $u_{k,k+1}$ for each kth row of U needs to be computed. Thus

$$u_{k,k+1} = \frac{1}{l_{kk}}(a_{k,k+1}), \qquad (k = 1, 2, \ldots, 5). \tag{4.134}$$

The system $AX = B$ now becomes $LUX = B$; letting $UX = Y$, then $LY = B$. For $n = 5$, this becomes

$$\begin{aligned}
l_{11}y_1 \qquad\qquad\qquad\qquad\qquad\qquad &= b_1 \\
l_{21}y_1 + l_{22}y_2 \qquad\qquad\qquad\qquad &= b_2 \\
l_{32}y_2 + l_{33}y_3 \qquad\qquad\quad &= b_3 \\
l_{43}y_3 + l_{44}y_4 \qquad &= b_4 \\
l_{54}y_4 + l_{55}y_5 &= b_5.
\end{aligned} \tag{4.135}$$

The solutions of these equations are

$$y_k = \frac{1}{l_{kk}}(b_k - (l_{k,k-1})y_{k-1}), \qquad (k = 1, 2, \ldots, 5)$$

where $l_{1,0}$ and y_0 are assumed to be zero.

Then the solutions of the system of equations

$$\begin{aligned}
x_1 + u_{12}x_2 \qquad\qquad\qquad\qquad\qquad &= y_1 \\
x_2 + u_{23}x_3 \qquad\qquad\qquad &= y_2 \\
x_3 + u_{34}x_4 \qquad\quad &= y_3 \\
x_4 + u_{45}x_5 &= y_4 \\
x_5 &= y_5
\end{aligned} \tag{4.136}$$

are

$$x_k = y_k - u_{k,k+1}x_{k+1}, \qquad (k = 5, 4, \ldots, 1) \tag{4.137}$$

where $u_{5,6}$ and x_6 are assumed to be zero.

An application of this method involving a band type matrix will be considered in Ch. 7 in connection with the solution of a second-order differential equation with boundary conditions. However, it is suggested that the reader now write a flow chart for this method.

PROBLEMS

4-8. Write an unabridged flow chart to solve $XA = B$ where

$$X = [x_{ij}]_{(m,n)}$$
$$A = [a_{ij}]_{(n,n)}$$
$$B = [b_{ij}]_{(m,n)}.$$

The flow chart should include all principal parts of Flow Chart 4.14.1.

4-9. Write a program based on the flow chart of Prob. 4–8 to solve the following sets of equations and to find A inverse:

(a)
$$\begin{aligned} 5x_{11} - 3x_{12} - 4x_{13} &= 1 \\ 2x_{11} + 4x_{12} + x_{13} &= 3 \\ x_{11} + 2x_{12} - 2x_{13} &= 9 \end{aligned}$$

Answers: $x_{11} = -1$, $x_{12} = 2$, $x_{13} = -3$.

(b)
$$\begin{aligned} 5x_{21} - 3x_{22} - 4x_{23} &= 23 \\ 2x_{21} + 4x_{22} + x_{23} &= -9 \\ x_{21} + 2x_{22} - 2x_{23} &= -2 \end{aligned}$$

Answers: $x_{21} = 2$, $x_{22} = -3$, $x_{23} = -1$.

(c)
$$\begin{aligned} 5x_{31} - 3x_{32} - 4x_{33} &= -20 \\ 2x_{31} + 4x_{32} + x_{33} &= -8 \\ x_{31} + 2x_{32} - 2x_{33} &= -9 \end{aligned}$$

Answers: $x_{31} = -3$, $x_{32} = -1$, $x_{33} = 2$.

4-10. Write a flow chart and program to solve the sets of equations in 4-9(a), (b), and (c) by the method of Sec. 4.13.1. The following steps should be included:

(a) A main program. The purpose of this program would be administrative, i.e., it should contain control cards, input, identification of the problem, and call statements for the subprograms.

(b) Subprogram No. 1—evaluation of the determinant. Rows and columns should be interchanged so that the largest pivotal absolute value of $[a_{ij}]$ can be chosen for each value of l. Provision should be made for a transfer to the end of the program if this value is zero. All a_{ij} should be stored in other locations—for example, c_{ij}—so that a_{ij} will be left undisturbed for the evaluation of A inverse.

(c) Subprogram No. 2—evaluation of A inverse. The largest $|a_{ij}|$ should be chosen for each value of l.

(d) Subprogram No. 3—formation of all components of each l vector corresponding to the l column of B; i.e., for each l form

$$x_{k,l} = \sum_{j=1}^{n} a'_{kj} b_{jl}, \qquad (k = 1, 2, \ldots, n).$$

(e) Subprogram No. 4—Output. Output should be clearly defined. For example, if the determinant of $A = 0$, the output should state that det $A = 0$, and therefore no unique solution exists.

If a unique solution does exist, then output should state the value of the determinant, the A inverse, and values of all x_{kl}.

4-11. Write a program based upon Cholesky's method to solve the set of equations:

$$\begin{aligned} 3x_1 + 6x_2 + \ \ 9x_3 &= 42 \\ 2x_1 + 5x_2 + \ \ 8x_3 &= 36 \\ x_1 + 4x_2 + 10x_3 &= 39 \end{aligned}$$

Answers: $x_1 = 1$, $x_2 = 2$, $x_3 = 3$.

Include in the output the following

(a) $Y = UX$

(b) $LY = B$

The true expressions for (a) and (b) are, respectively:

$$\begin{aligned} 14 &= x_1 + 2x_2 + 3x_3 \\ 8 &= \quad\;\; x_2 + 2x_3 \\ 3 &= \qquad\quad\;\; x_3 \end{aligned} \qquad \text{and} \qquad \begin{aligned} 3y_1 \qquad\qquad &= 42 \\ 2y_1 + \ y_2 \qquad &= 36 \\ y_1 + 2y_2 + 3y_3 &= 39. \end{aligned}$$

ITERATIVE METHODS

4.16 Gauss-Seidel Method

If in the system

$$AX = B \tag{4.138}$$

the coefficient of a different unknown in each equation is greater in absolute value than the sum of the absolute values of all other coefficients in that equation, the iterative method called the Gauss-Seidel process may be applied. Its one great advantage is its simplicity; this method is particularly applicable to the solution of partial differentiable equations.

Let $AX = B$ be rewritten in the form

$$\begin{aligned} x_1 &= c_{12}x_2 + c_{13}x_3 + \cdots + c_{1n}x_n + b_1 \\ x_2 &= c_{21}x_1 + c_{23}x_3 + \cdots + c_{2n}x_n + b_2 \\ &\cdots\cdots\cdots\cdots\cdots\cdots\cdots\cdots \\ x_n &= c_{n1}x_1 + c_{n2}x_2 + \cdots + c_{n,n-1}x_{n-1} + b_n \end{aligned} \tag{4.139}$$

where $c_{ii} = 1$ for $i = 1, 2, \ldots, n$, and

$$1 > \sum_{j=1, j \neq k}^{n} |c_{kj}|$$

for $k = 1, 2, \ldots, n$. The method consists of the following steps:

1. Assign initial values to $x_1, x_2, x_3, \ldots, x_n$ and assign the same values to $z_1, z_2, z_3, \ldots, z_n$.
2. Compute new x_i from the given equations using the current values of x_i.
3. If $|z_i - x_i| < \epsilon$ for all i (ϵ a small positive number arbitrarily chosen), transfer to statement 6; otherwise, continue with statement 4.
4. Replace z_i with x_i.
5. Transfer to statement 2.
6. Print all x_i.
7. Stop.

Example

Given:

$$\begin{aligned} x_1 &= .2x_2 + .1x_3 + .3 \\ x_2 &= .1x_1 + .2x_3 + 1.3 \\ x_3 &= .2x_1 + .1x_2 + 2.6 \end{aligned} \tag{4.140}$$

let $x_2 = 0$, $x_3 = 0$. Then from the first equation, $x_1 = .3$. From the second equation $x_2 = .03 + 1.3 = 1.33$; from the third equation

$$\begin{aligned} x_3 &= .06 + .133 + 2.6 \\ &= 2.793 \\ &\cong 2.79. \end{aligned}$$

Repeating the process, the results are shown in box form in Table 4.2.

TABLE 4.2

$n =$	1	2	3
x_1	.3	.85	.99
x_2	1.33	1.95	1.99
x_3	2.79	2.97	3.0

Thus, on the third iteration, $x_1 = .99$, $x_2 = 1.99$, and $x_3 = 3.0$.

It can be also shown that if

$$A = \begin{bmatrix} a_{11} & a_{12} & \cdots & a_{1n} \\ a_{21} & a_{22} & \cdots & a_{2n} \\ \cdot & \cdot & \cdot & \cdot \\ a_{1n} & a_{2n} & \cdots & a_{nn} \end{bmatrix}$$

is positive definite, the Gauss–Seidel iteration converges regardless of the initial values of x_i.[12]

4.16.1 Flow Chart

For the set of equations (4.139), let n = order of A, and let x_i and z_i have the initial value 0. Let k represent the maximum allowable number of iterations and EPS be an arbitrarily chosen number for the test of convergence. The iteration is

$$x_i = \sum_{j=1, j\neq i}^{n} c_{ij}x_j + b_i, \qquad (i = 1, 2, \ldots, n).$$

FLOW CHART 4.16.1 Gauss–Seidel Process

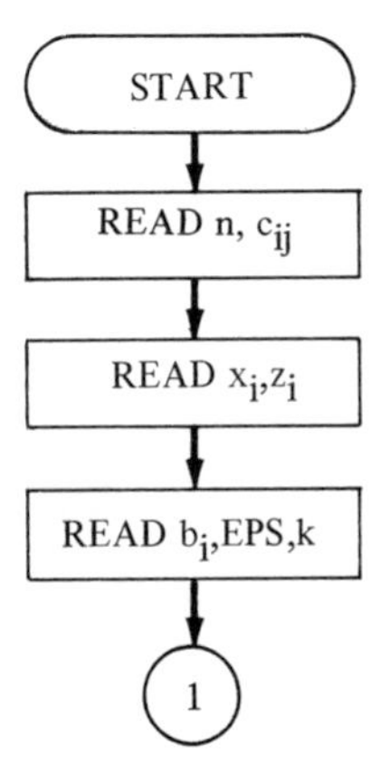

[12] A symmetric matrix A is called *positive definite* if the quadratic form

$$Q = X^TAX > 0, \qquad (X \neq 0).$$

For example,

$$A = \begin{bmatrix} 2 & 0 \\ 0 & 4 \end{bmatrix}$$

is positive definite, since

$$X^TAX = [x_1, x_2]\begin{bmatrix} 2 & 0 \\ 0 & 4 \end{bmatrix}\begin{bmatrix} x_1 \\ x_2 \end{bmatrix} = 2x_1^2 + 4x_2^2 > 0$$

except when $x_1 = x_2 = 0$.

Flow Chart 4.16.1 *(Continued)*

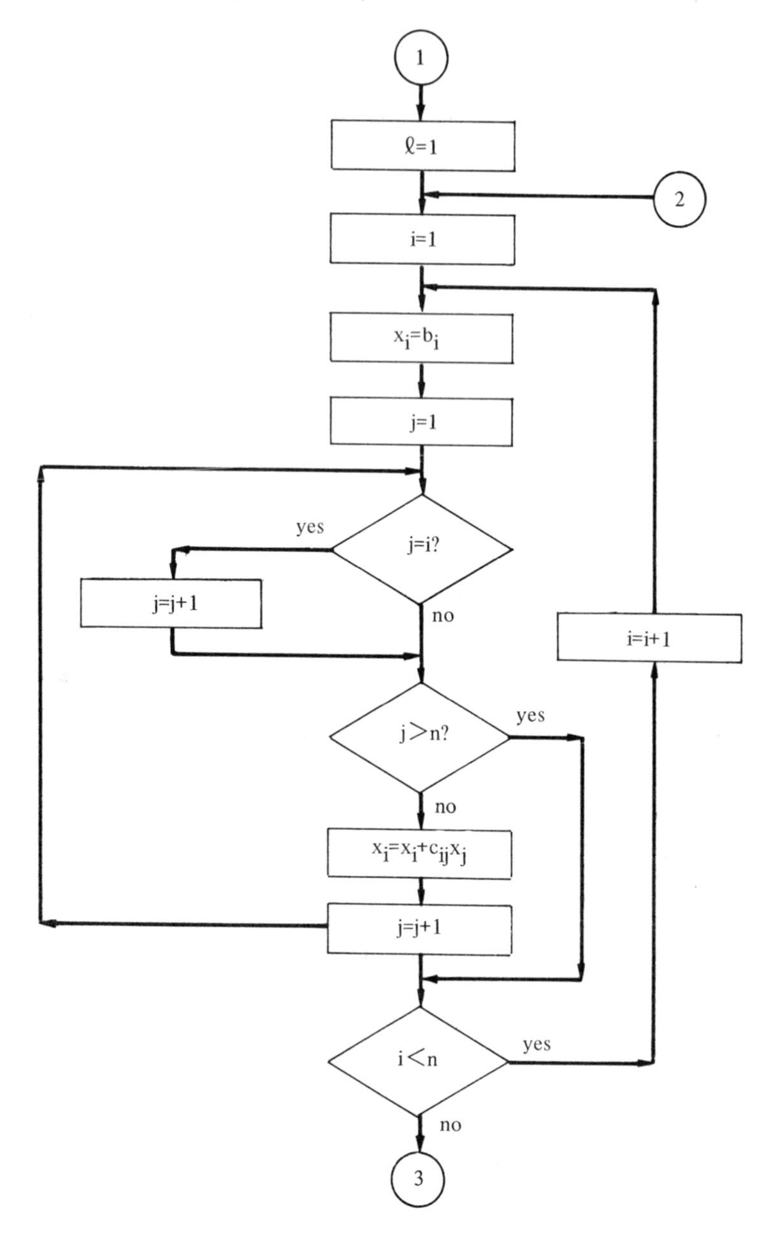

Flow Chart 4.16.1 *(Continued)*

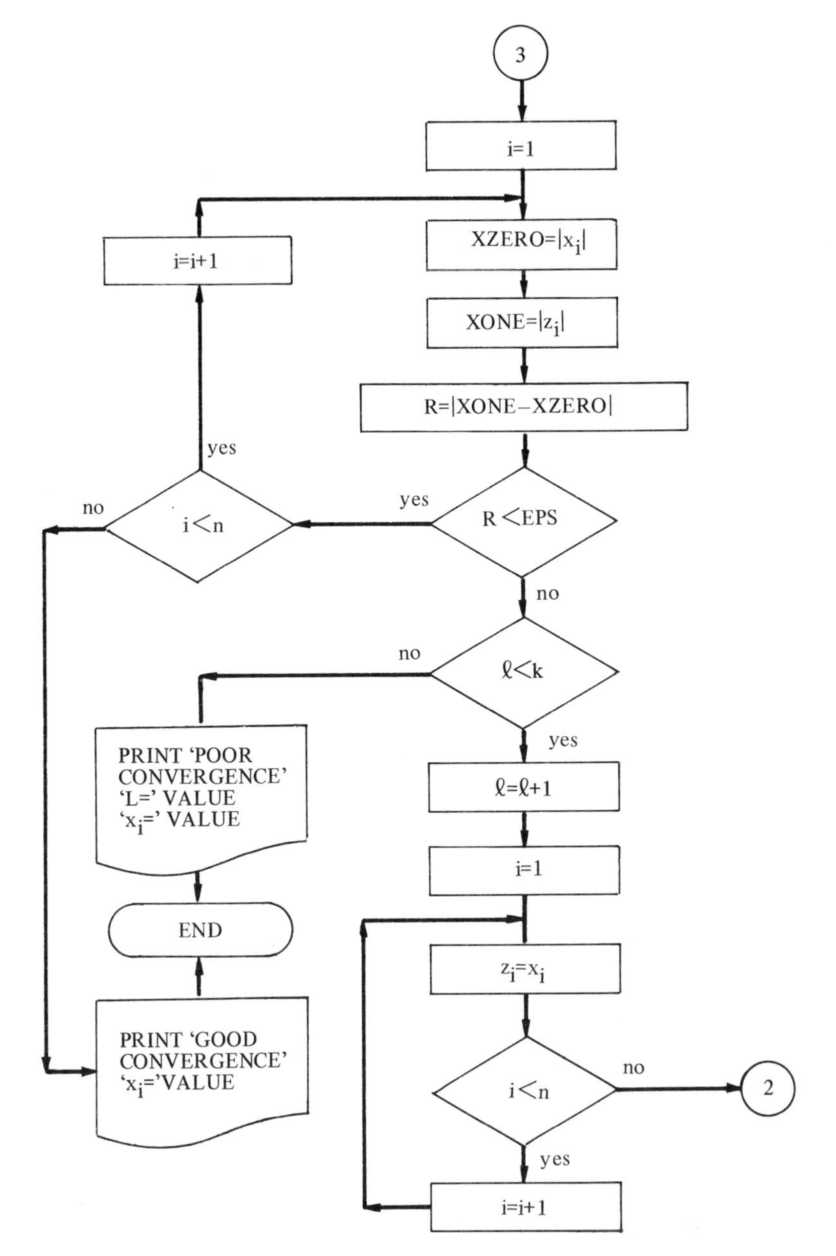

4.16.2 Program

The following program is for Eqs. 4.140. The matrix A is read in and also is printed as output in the form of

$$\begin{bmatrix} -1 & a_{12} & \cdots & a_{1n} \\ a_{21} & -1 & \cdots & a_{2n} \\ \cdot & \cdot & \cdot & \cdot \\ a_{n1} & a_{n2} & \cdots & -1 \end{bmatrix}.$$

```
/ID
/JOB GO,MAP
/FTC LIST,REF
      DIMENSION A(10,10),B(10),Z(10),X(10)
    1 FORMAT(2I2,F10.4)
    2 FORMAT(10F7.4)
    4 FORMAT(///5X,'THE MATRIX B IS',/)
    5 FORMAT(///5X,'THERE IS NO CONVERGENCE',/)
    6 FORMAT(///5X,'THE MATRIX A IS ',/)
    7 FORMAT(///5X,'THE SOLUTIONS ARE',/)
      READ(5,1)N,L,EPS
      DO 10 I=1,N
      DO 11 J=1,N
   11 READ(5,2)A(I,J)
   10 CONTINUE
      READ(5,2)(Z(I),I=1,N),(X(I),I=1,N)
      READ(5,2)(B(I),I=1,N)
      WRITE(6,6)
      DO 55 I=1,N
      WRITE(6,2)(A(I,J),J=1,N)
   55 CONTINUE
      WRITE(6,4)
      DO 56 J=1,N
   56 WRITE(6,2)B(J)
      K=1
   13 DO 14 I=1,N
      X(I)=B(I)
      DO 15 J=1,N
      IF(I-J)16,15,16
   16 X(I)=X(I)+A(I,J)*Z(J)
   15 CONTINUE
   14 CONTINUE
      DO 17 I=1,N
      XZERO=ABS(X(I))
      XONE=ABS(Z(I))
      R=ABS(XONE-XZERO)
      IF(R-EPS)17,18,18
   17 CONTINUE
```

```
      WRITE(6,7)
      DO 20 I=1,N
   20 WRITE(6,2)X(I)
      GO TO 25
   18 DO 21 I=1,N
      Z(I)=X(I)
   21 CONTINUE
      IF(K-L)22,23,23
   22 K=K+1
      GO TO 13
   23 WRITE(6,5)
      DO 24 I=1,N
   24 WRITE(6,2)X(I)
   25 CONTINUE
      STOP
      END
/DATA
```

```
        THE MATRIX A IS
      -1.000      0.200    0.100
       0.1000   -1.0000   0.2000
       0.2000    0.1000  -1.0000
        THE MATRIX B IS
      0.3000
      1.3000
      2.6000
        THE SOLUTIONS ARE
      1.0000
      2.0000
      3.0000
      STOP
```

4.17 The Jacobi Iteration

For the system of equations $AX = B$ (Eq. 4.138), where

$$A = \begin{bmatrix} a_{11} & a_{12} & \cdots & a_{1n} \\ a_{21} & a_{22} & \cdots & a_{2n} \\ \cdot & \cdot & \cdot & \cdot \\ a_{n1} & a_{n2} & \cdots & a_{nn} \end{bmatrix}, \tag{4.141}$$

the matrix A can be written as $D + L + U$ where

$$D = \begin{bmatrix} a_{11} & 0 & \cdots & 0 \\ 0 & a_{22} & \cdots & 0 \\ \cdot & \cdot & \cdot & \cdot \\ 0 & 0 & \cdots & a_{nn} \end{bmatrix}, \tag{4.142}$$

$$L = \begin{bmatrix} 0 & 0 & \cdots & 0 \\ a_{21} & 0 & \cdots & 0 \\ \cdot & \cdot & \cdot & \cdot \\ a_{n1} & a_{n2} & a_{n,n-1} & 0 \end{bmatrix}, \tag{4.143}$$

$$U = \begin{bmatrix} 0 & a_{12} & \cdots & a_{1n} \\ 0 & 0 & a_{23} & a_{2n} \\ \cdot & \cdot & \cdot & \cdot \\ 0 & 0 & \cdots & a_{n-1,n} \\ 0 & 0 & \cdots & 0 \end{bmatrix}. \tag{4.144}$$

That is, D is a diagonal matrix, with zeros everywhere except on the diagonal where the elements are a_{ii}. L is a lower triangle matrix, where the elements below the main diagonal are a_{ij}, and on and above the main diagonal the elements are zero. U is an upper triangle matrix, where the elements above the main diagonal are a_{ij}, and on and below the main diagonal are zero.

Thus, Eq. 4.138 can be written as

$$(D + L + U)X = B \tag{4.145}$$

or

$$DX = -(L + U)X + B; \tag{4.146}$$

hence,

$$X = -D^{-1}(L + U)X + D^{-1}B. \tag{4.147}$$

If all diagonal elements of A are assumed to be nonzero, then D inverse is

$$D^{-1} = \begin{bmatrix} 1/a_{11} & 0 & \cdots & 0 \\ 0 & 1/a_{22} & \cdots & 0 \\ \cdot & \cdot & \cdot & \cdot \\ 0 & 0 & \cdots & 1/a_{nn} \end{bmatrix}. \tag{4.148}$$

Also, $L + U$ can be stated as

$$L + U = \begin{bmatrix} 0 & a_{12} & \cdots & a_{1n} \\ a_{21} & 0 & \cdots & a_{2n} \\ \cdot & \cdot & \cdot & \cdot \\ a_{n1} & a_{n2} & \cdots & 0 \end{bmatrix}, \tag{4.149}$$

and $D^{-1}B$ may be stated as

$$D^{-1}B = \begin{bmatrix} b_1/a_{11} \\ b_2/a_{22} \\ \cdot \\ \cdot \\ \cdot \\ b_n/a_{nn} \end{bmatrix}. \tag{4.150}$$

Thus Eq. 4.147 becomes

$$X = -\begin{bmatrix} 0 & a_{12}/a_{11} & \cdots & a_{1n}/a_{11} \\ a_{21}/a_{22} & 0 & \cdots & a_{2n}/a_{22} \\ \cdot & \cdot & \cdots & \cdot \\ a_{n1}/a_{nn} & a_{n2}/a_{nn} & \cdots & 0 \end{bmatrix} \begin{bmatrix} x_1 \\ x_2 \\ \cdot \\ \cdot \\ \cdot \\ x_n \end{bmatrix} + \begin{bmatrix} b_1/a_{11} \\ b_2/a_{22} \\ \cdot \\ \cdot \\ \cdot \\ b_n/a_{nn} \end{bmatrix}. \tag{4.151}$$

With given initial values of x_j, computed values x_i become

$$x_i = \frac{1}{a_{ii}}\left(b_i - \sum_{j=1, j \neq i}^{n} a_{ij}x_j\right). \tag{4.152}$$

This method appears to be the same process as the Gauss–Seidel. The difference between the two methods occurs in the fact that the Jacobi process requires that every element x_i of the vector X is changed simultaneously before any new elements are used in the iteration. In the Gauss–Seidel method, as each new element x_i is computed, it is used immediately in the next iteration.

For these reasons, the Jacobi method is sometimes called the method of *simultaneous displacements,* and the Gauss–Seidel method is referred to as the method of *successive displacements.*

As stated in Sec. 4.16, it can be shown that if A is positive definite, the Gauss–Seidel method converges regardless of initial values of x_i. That is, for A a symmetric matrix, the quadratic form

$$X^T A X = \sum_{i,j=1}^{n} a_{ij}x_i x_j > 0 \tag{4.153}$$

for x_i, $x_j \neq 0$, then the Gauss–Seidel method converges regardless of initial values of x_i.

From other theorems beyond the scope of this text, a conclusion is drawn that if the Gauss–Seidel method converges, the Jacobi method also converges, but the Gauss–Seidel method is faster except in the trivial case.[13]

[13] See Ralston, *A First Course in Numerical Analysis.*

Example

Multiplying each equation of (4.140) by 10, and transposing terms, the system becomes

$$\begin{aligned} 10x_1 - 2x_2 - x_3 &= 3 \\ -x_1 + 10x_2 - 2x_3 &= 13 \\ -2x_1 - x_2 + 10x_3 &= 26. \end{aligned} \tag{4.154}$$

Let $x_1 = x_2 = x_3 = 0$, and using Eq. 4.152, that is,

$$x1_i = 1/a_{ii}\left(b_i - \sum_{j=1,\, j\neq i}^{n} a_{ij}x_j\right), \qquad (i = 1, 2, \ldots, n),$$

the first iteration yields:

$$x1_1 = 3/10, \qquad x1_2 = 13/10, \qquad x1_3 = 26/10;$$

the second iteration yields:

$$\begin{aligned} x2_1 &= 1/10(3 - (-2(13/10) - 26/10)) = 82/100, \\ x2_2 &= 1/10(13 - (-3/10 - 52/10)) = 185/100, \\ x2_3 &= 1/10(26 - (-6/10 - 13/10)) = 279/100; \end{aligned}$$

and the third iteration yields:

$$\begin{aligned} x3_1 &= 1/10(3 - (370/100 - 279/100) = 949/1000, \\ x3_2 &= 1/10(13 - (-82/100 - 558/100) = 194/100, \\ x3_3 &= 1/10(26 - (164/100) - 185/100) = 2949/1000. \end{aligned}$$

Compared with Table 4.2, convergence of the Jacobi method is seen to be slower than that of the Gauss–Seidel process.

4.17.1 Flow Chart

Let $AX = B$.
Let n = order of A.
Let k, an arbitrary number, represent the maximum number of allowed iterations.
Assume that all $a_{ii} \neq 0$.
Let all $x_i = 0$.
Let $x1_i$ represent computed values of the elements of X.
Let EPS be an arbitrary small positive number. The test $|x1_i - x_i| < \epsilon$ will be made for convergence.

FLOW CHART 4.17.1 Jacobi Method

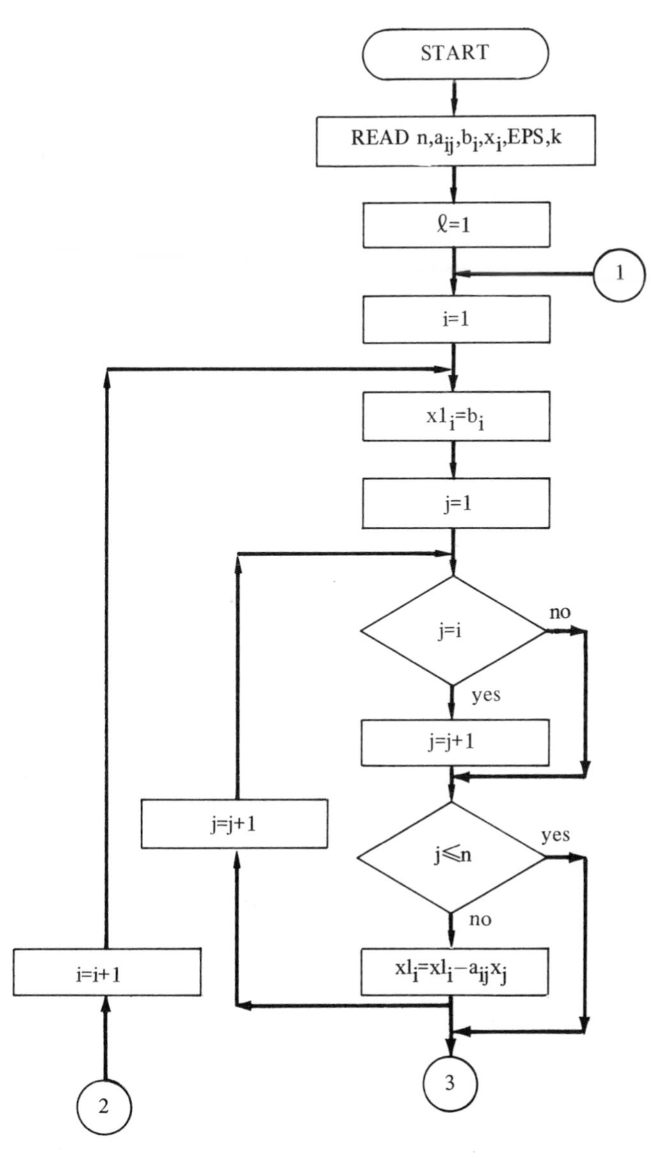

Flow Chart 4.17.1 *(Continued)*

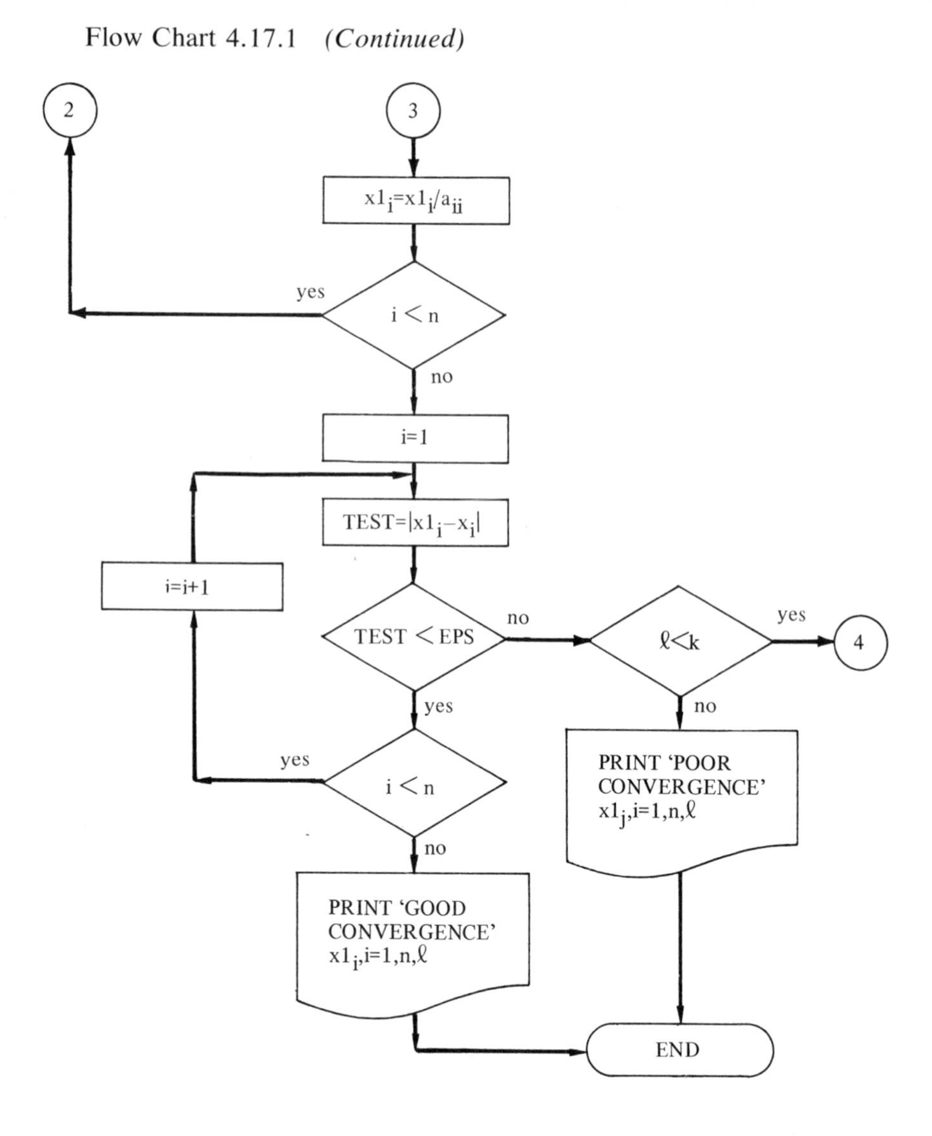

Flow Chart 4.17.1 *(Continued)*

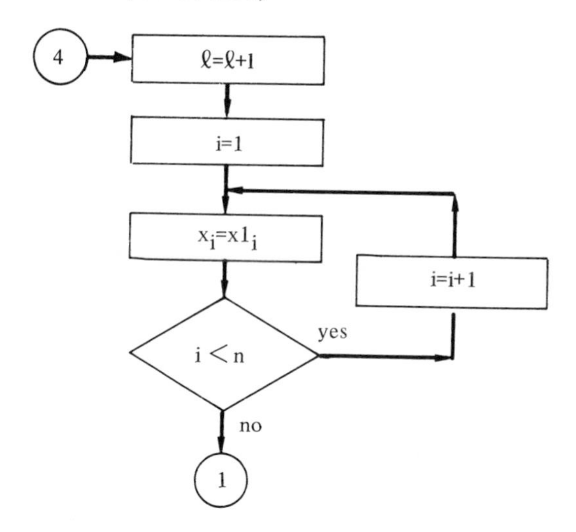

A comparison of the Gauss–Seidel Flow Chart 4.16.1 and the Jacobi Flow Chart 4.17.1 shows the essential difference is that in the Gauss–Seidel method, newly computed values of x_i are used immediately in the next iteration.

4.18 Relaxation Method

In the Gauss–Seidel and Jacobi methods, the principal idea was to assume initial values x_i of the vector X, and that by repeatedly changing one or more values of x_i, AX approximated B, that is, $AX \cong B$, or the residual $R = B - AX \cong 0$.

Those methods whereby values of x_i are relaxed are called *relaxation* methods. In the relaxation method, it is assumed that the system is already written in a form convenient for relaxation. Thus $AX = B$ is assumed to be in the form

$$\begin{aligned} -x_1 + a_{12}x_2 + \cdots + a_{1n}x_n + b_1 &= 0 \\ a_{21}x_1 - x_2 + \cdots + a_{2n}x_n + b_2 &= 0 \\ \cdots\cdots\cdots\cdots\cdots\cdots\cdots\cdots\cdots\cdots \\ a_{n1}x_1 + a_{n2}x_2 + \cdots - x_n + b_n &= 0. \end{aligned} \tag{4.155}$$

Now let x_i be the initial values of the components of the vector X. Indicate by R_i the residual of each equation. Then

$$\begin{array}{c} -x_1 + a_{12}x_2 + \cdots + a_{1n}x_n + b_1 = R_1 \\ a_{21}x_1 - x_2 + \cdots + a_{2n}x_n + b_2 = R_2 \\ \cdots\cdots\cdots\cdots\cdots\cdots \\ a_{n1}x_1 + a_{n2}x_2 + \cdots - x_n + b_n = R_n. \end{array} \tag{4.156}$$

One of these residuals, say R_k, is at least as large or larger than any other residual. If x_k is changed by $\Delta x_k = R_k$, then R_k becomes zero and all other x_i are changed by $a_{ik}\,\Delta x_k$. This process of repeatedly seeking the largest R_k, setting $\Delta x_k = R_k$, and adjusting all other x_i by an amount $a_{ik}\,\Delta x_k$ will cause all R_i to become approximately zero within the desired degree of accuracy, dependent on whether or not the method is convergent.

More specifically, the steps in the method are as follows:

1. Choose initial values of all x_i.
2. Calculate all $R_i = a_{i1}x_1 + a_{i2}x_2 + \cdots - x_i + \cdots a_{in}x_n + b_i$.
3. Choose the residual of greatest magnitude, say R_k.
4. Let $\Delta x_k = R_k$. Then x_k becomes $x_k + \Delta x_k$.
5. Calculate new R_i by adding $a_{ik}\,\Delta x_k$ to each R_i. R_k now becomes zero since $-\Delta k = -R_k$ is added to R_k.
6. Repeat steps 3, 4, and 5 until desired accuracy is attained.
7. Stop.

Example

Equations 4.140 written for the relaxation method become:

$$\begin{aligned} R_1 &= -x_1 + .2x_2 + .1x_3 + .3 \\ R_2 &= .1x_1 - x_2 + .2x_3 + 1.3 \\ R_3 &= .2x_1 + .1x_2 - x_3 + 2.6. \end{aligned}$$

Let $x_1 = x_2 = x_3 = 0$. Then

$$R_1 = .3, \qquad R_2 = 1.3, \qquad R_3 = 2.6.$$

Choosing $R_3 = 2.6$ and setting $\Delta x_3 = 2.6$, the new residuals become

$$\begin{aligned} R_1 &= .3 + .26 = .56 & & x_1 = 0 \\ R_2 &= 1.3 + .52 = 1.82 & \text{and} \quad & x_2 = 0 \\ R_3 &= 2.6 - 2.6 = 0, & & x_3 = 0 + 2.6. \end{aligned}$$

Again, choosing $R_2 = 1.82$ and setting $\Delta x_2 = 1.82$, the next residuals become

$$R_1 = .56 + .364 = .924 \qquad x_1 = 0$$
$$R_2 = 1.82 - 1.82 = 0 \qquad \text{and} \qquad x_2 = 0 + 1.82$$
$$R_3 = 0 + .182 = .182, \qquad x_3 = 2.6.$$

Repeating the process, by choosing $R_1 = .924$ and setting $\Delta x_1 = .924$, the residuals are

$$R_1 = .924 - .924 = 0 \qquad x_1 = .924$$
$$R_2 = 0 + .092 = .092 \qquad \text{and} \qquad x_2 = 1.82$$
$$R_3 = .182 + .185 = .367, \qquad x_3 = 2.6.$$

This can be repeated until convergence is assured. However, the form of Table 4.3 shows the process more clearly.

TABLE 4.3 Process of the Relaxation Method

x_1	R_1	x_2	R_2	x_3	R_3
0	.3 .26	0	1.3 .52	0 2.6	2.6 −2.6
0	.56 .364	0 1.82	1.82 −1.82	2.6	0 .182
0 .924	.924 −.924	1.82	0 .092	2.6	.182 .185
.924	0 .037	1.82	.092 .073	2.6 .367	.367 − .367
.942	.037 .033	1.82 .165	.165 − .165	2.967	0 .016
.924 .07	.070 −.07	1.985	0 .007	2.967	.016 .014
.994	0	1.985	.007	2.967	.030

4.18.1 Flow Chart

Assume that $AX = B$ is written in the form of Eq. 4.155.
N = order of A.
l = maximum number of iterations.
k is the count of iterations.
EPS is an arbitrary small positive number to test the largest $|R_i|$. When $|R_i| < EPS$, the desired degree of accuracy has been obtained.

AB initially set equal to zero is used for the purpose of selecting the largest $|R_i|$.
ABMAX is also used for the purpose of selecting the largest $|R_i|$.

FLOW CHART 4.18.1 Relaxation Method

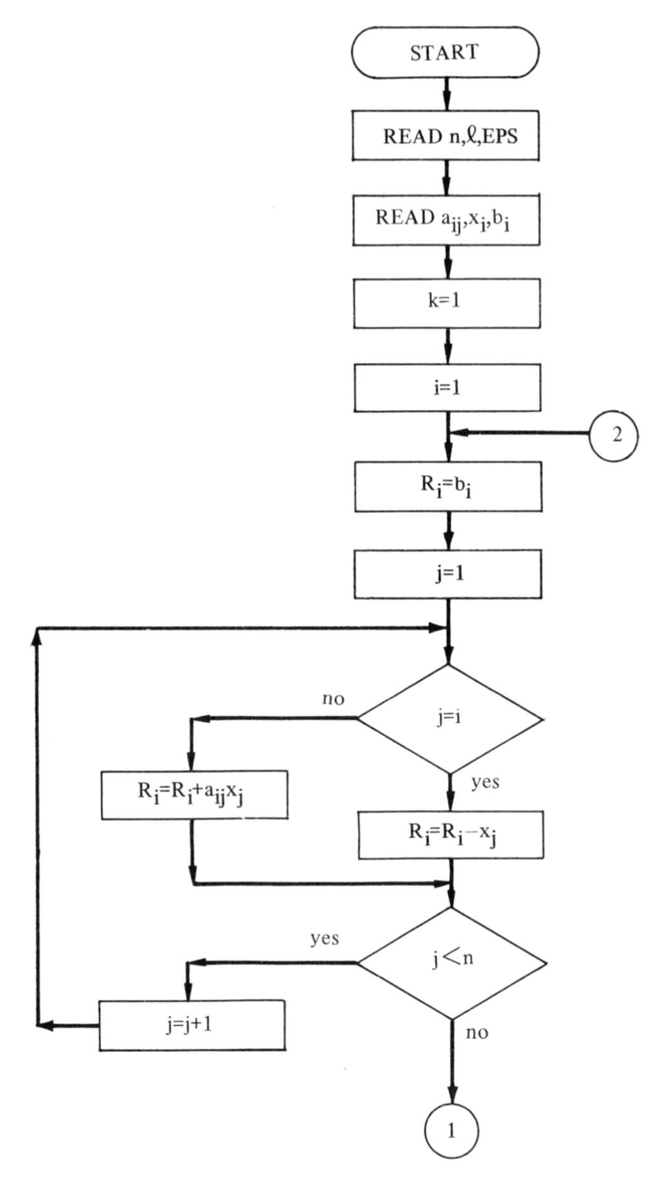

Flow Chart 4.18.1 *(Continued)*

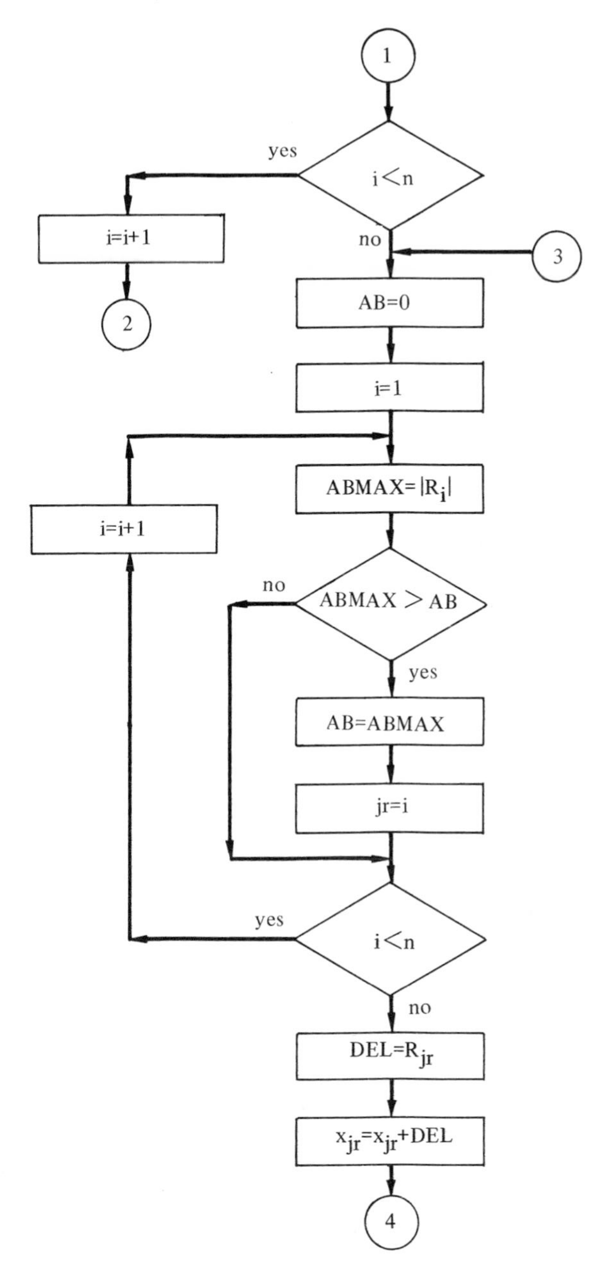

Flow Chart 4.18.1 *(Continued)*

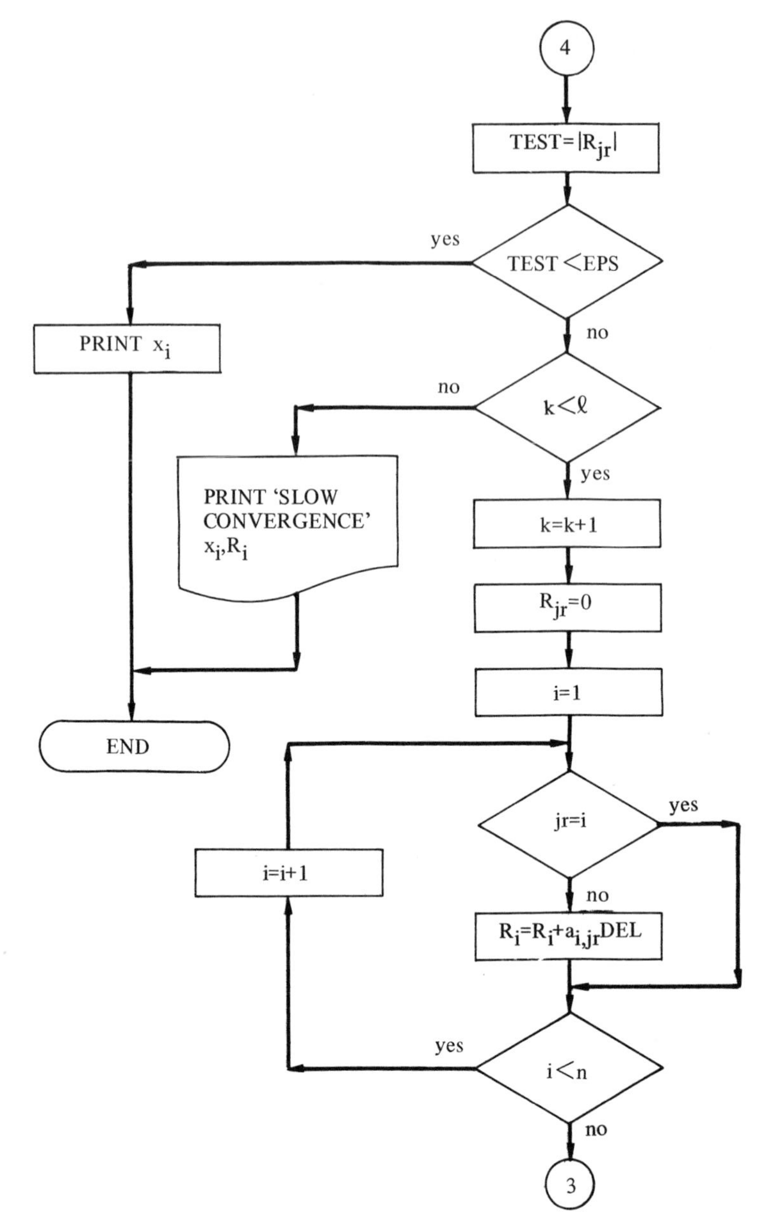

4.18.2 Program

To solve the set of equations (4.140) by the relaxation method. Starting values of x_i ($i = 1, 2, 3$) are zero.

```
/ID
/JOB GO,MAP
/FTC LIST,REF
      DIMENSION A(10,10),B(10),R(10),X(10)
    1 FORMAT(2I2,F10.4)
    2 FORMAT(10F7.4)
    4 FORMAT(///5X,'THE MATRIX X IS',/)
    5 FORMAT(///5X,'THE MATRIX B IS',/)
    6 FORMAT(///5X,'THERE IS NO CONVERGENCE',/)
    7 FORMAT(///5X,'THE MATRIX A IS',/)
    8 FORMAT(///5X,'THE SOLUTIONS ARE',/)
      READ(5,1)N,L,EPS
      DO 50 I=1,N
      DO 51 J=1,N
      READ(5,2)A(I,J)
   51 CONTINUE
   50 CONTINUE
      READ(5,2)(X(I),I=1,N)
      READ(5,2)(B(I),I=1,N)
      WRITE(6,7)
      DO 55 I=1,N
      WRITE(6,2)(A(I,J),J=1,N)
   55 CONTINUE
      WRITE(6,5)
      DO 56 J=1,N
   56 WRITE(6,2)B(J)
      WRITE(6,4)
      DO 57 J=1,N
   57 WRITE(6,2)X(J)
      K=1
      DO 10 I=1,N
      R(I)=B(I)
      DO 11 J=1,N
      R(I)=R(I)+A(I,J)*X(J)
   11 CONTINUE
   10 CONTINUE
   30 DO 12 I=1,N
      IF(ABS(R(I)-EPS)12,12,13
   12 CONTINUE
      WRITE(6,8)
      DO 14 I=1,N
   14 WRITE(6,2)X(I)
      GO TO 40
   13 IF(K-L)15,16,16
   16 WRITE(6,6)
```

```
      DO 17 I=1,N
   17 WRITE(6,2)X(I)
      GO TO 40
   15 K=K+1
      AB=0.0
      DO 20 I=1,N
      ABMAX=ABS(R(I))
      IF(AB-ABMAX)21,20,20
   21 AB=ABMAX
      KK=I
   20 CONTINUE
      DELX=R(KK)
      X(KK)=X(KK)+DELX
      R(KK)=0.0
      I=1
   35 IF(I-KK)25,26,25
   25 R(I)=R(I)+A(I,KK)*DELX
   26 IF(I-N)28,30,30
   28 I=I+1
      GO TO 35
   40 STOP
      END
/DATA

      THE MATRIX A IS
      -1.0000    0.2000    0.1000
       0.1000   -1.0000    0.2000
       0.2000    0.1000   -1.0000

      THE MATRIX B IS
      0.3000
      1.3000
      2.6000

      THE MATRIX X (STARTING VALUES) IS
      0.0
      0.0
      0.0

      THE SOLUTIONS ARE
      1.0000
      2.0000
      3.0000
```

4.19 Matrix Inversion by a Newton–Raphson Process

To solve the equation

$$f(x) = \frac{1}{x} - a = 0,$$

that is, to find the reciprocal of the nonzero number a, by the Newton–Raphson method, the iteration becomes

$$x_{i+1} = x_i(2 - ax_i).$$

In order for this iteration to converge, the relative error

$$\left| \frac{\frac{1}{a} - x_0}{\frac{1}{a}} \right|,$$

must be less than 1, where x_0 is the initial choice of $1/a$. Hence,

$$|1 - ax_0| < 1.$$

Corresponding to the pattern of finding the reciprocal of a number a by the Newton–Raphson method, a similar process can be applied to find the inverse of a matrix A. Let A be a non-singular matrix of order n and let X_0 be an arbitrary matrix of order n. Then by application of the Newton–Raphson process,

$$X_{i+1} = X_i(2I - AX_i), \qquad (i = 0, 1, 2, \ldots)$$

where I is the identity matrix.

X_i will approach A^{-1} if and only if $(I - AX_i)$ approaches the null matrix, and $(I - AX_i)$ will approach the null matrix if and only if each eigenvalue in absolute value of $(I - AX_0)$ is less than 1. (See Sec. 4.20 for a definition of eigenvalue.)

Example

Let

$$A = \begin{bmatrix} 4 & 3 \\ 1 & 1 \end{bmatrix}, \qquad A^{-1} = \begin{bmatrix} 1 & -3 \\ -1 & 4 \end{bmatrix}.$$

Choose

$$X_0 = \begin{bmatrix} .9 & -2.9 \\ -.9 & 3.9 \end{bmatrix}.$$

Then

$$I - AX_0 = \begin{bmatrix} 1 & 0 \\ 0 & 1 \end{bmatrix} - \begin{bmatrix} .9 & .1 \\ 0 & 1. \end{bmatrix} = \begin{bmatrix} .1 & -.1 \\ 0 & 0 \end{bmatrix}.$$

The eigenvalues are computed from

$$\begin{vmatrix} .1-\lambda & -.1 \\ 0 & -\lambda \end{vmatrix} = 0$$

or

$$\lambda^2 - .1\lambda = 0, \qquad \lambda_1 = 0, \qquad \lambda_2 = .1.$$

Hence, the conditions for convergence are satisfied, and X_i will approach A^{-1}, $i = 1, 2, \ldots$. Applying the iteration formula twice,

$$X_1 = \begin{bmatrix} .99 & -2.99 \\ -.99 & 3.99 \end{bmatrix} \quad \text{and} \quad X_2 = \begin{bmatrix} .9999 & -2.9999 \\ -.9999 & 3.9999 \end{bmatrix}.$$

The formula is simple enough to apply and the program is straightforward, although there are two matrix multiplications that can cause an excess of round-off error.

However, a particularly weak feature of the process is the initial choice of X. It is very difficult to find an X that will satisfy the necessary and sufficient condition. To circumvent this feature, the Gauss elimination method may first be applied to find an X_0. Then the Newton–Raphson method may be applied with X_0 as the first approximation to A^{-1}.

4.19.1 Flow Chart

Let

$$A = \begin{bmatrix} a_{11} & a_{12} & \cdots & a_{1n} \\ a_{21} & a_{22} & \cdots & a_{2n} \\ \cdot & \cdot & \cdot & \cdot \\ a_{n1} & a_{n2} & \cdots & a_{nn} \end{bmatrix},$$

and let

$$X_0 = \begin{bmatrix} x_{11} & x_{12} & \cdots & x_{1n} \\ x_{21} & x_{22} & \cdots & x_{2n} \\ \cdot & \cdot & \cdots & \cdot \\ x_{n1} & x_{n2} & \cdots & x_{nn} \end{bmatrix}$$

be the initial choice to approximate A^{-1}.

The iteration is

$$X_{i+1} = X_i(2I - AX_i).$$

FLOW CHART 4.19.1 *A* Inverse by Newton–Raphson Process

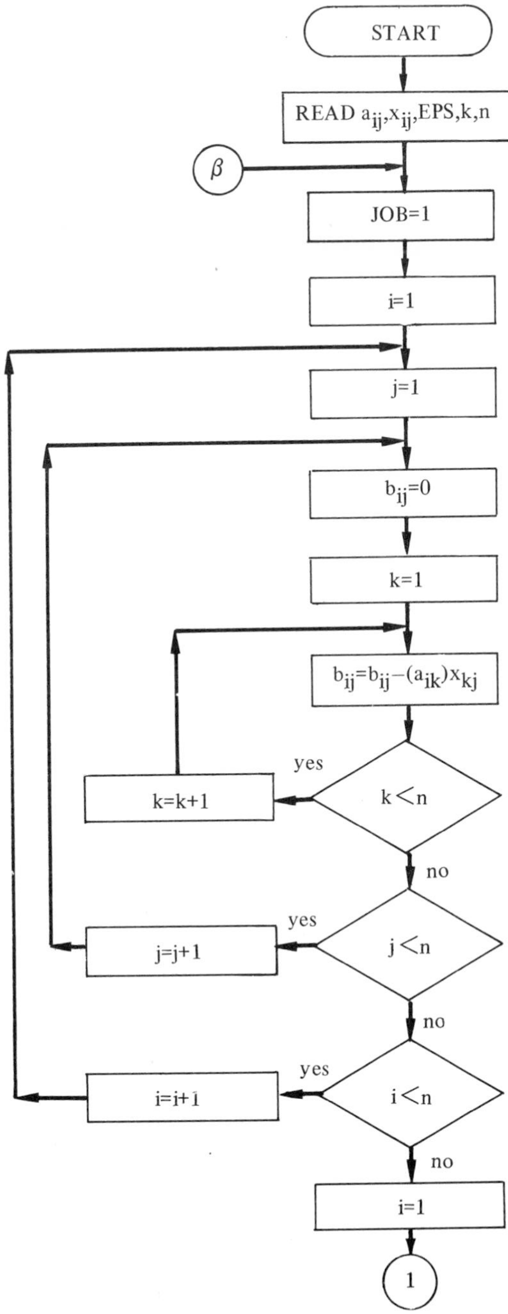

START

READ a_{ij}, x_{ij}, EPS, k, n

β

JOB=1

i=1

j=1

$b_{ij}=0$

k=1

$b_{ij}=b_{ij}-(a_{ik})x_{kj}$

$k<n$ — yes: k=k+1; no

$j<n$ — yes: j=j+1; no

$i<n$ — yes: i=i+1; no

i=1

1

Flow Chart 4.19.1 *(Continued)*

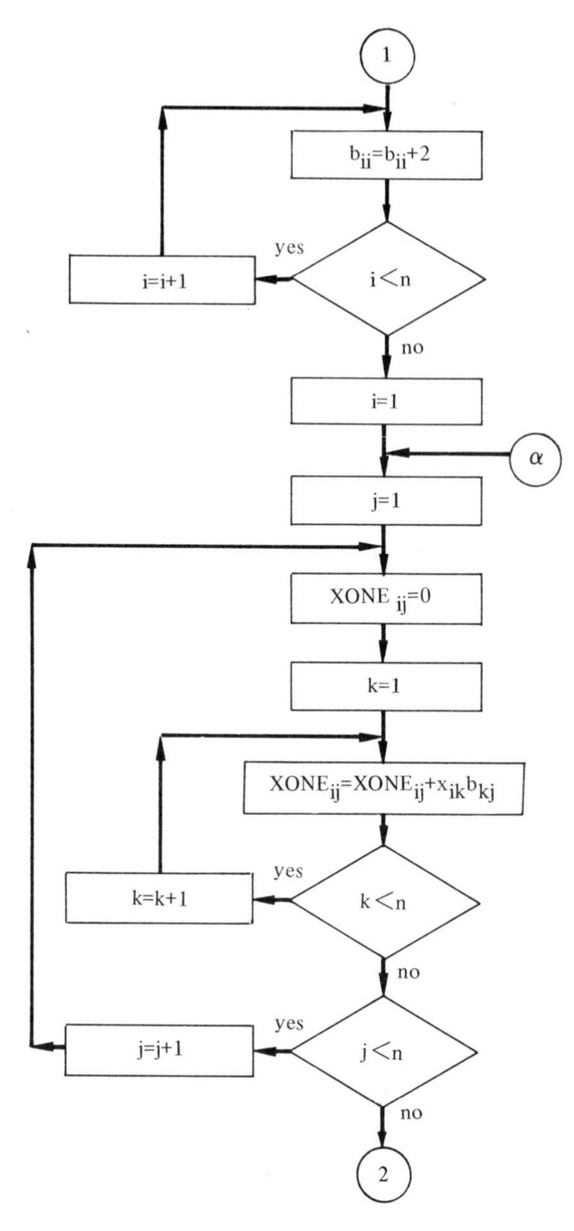

Flow Chart 4.19.1 *(Continued)*

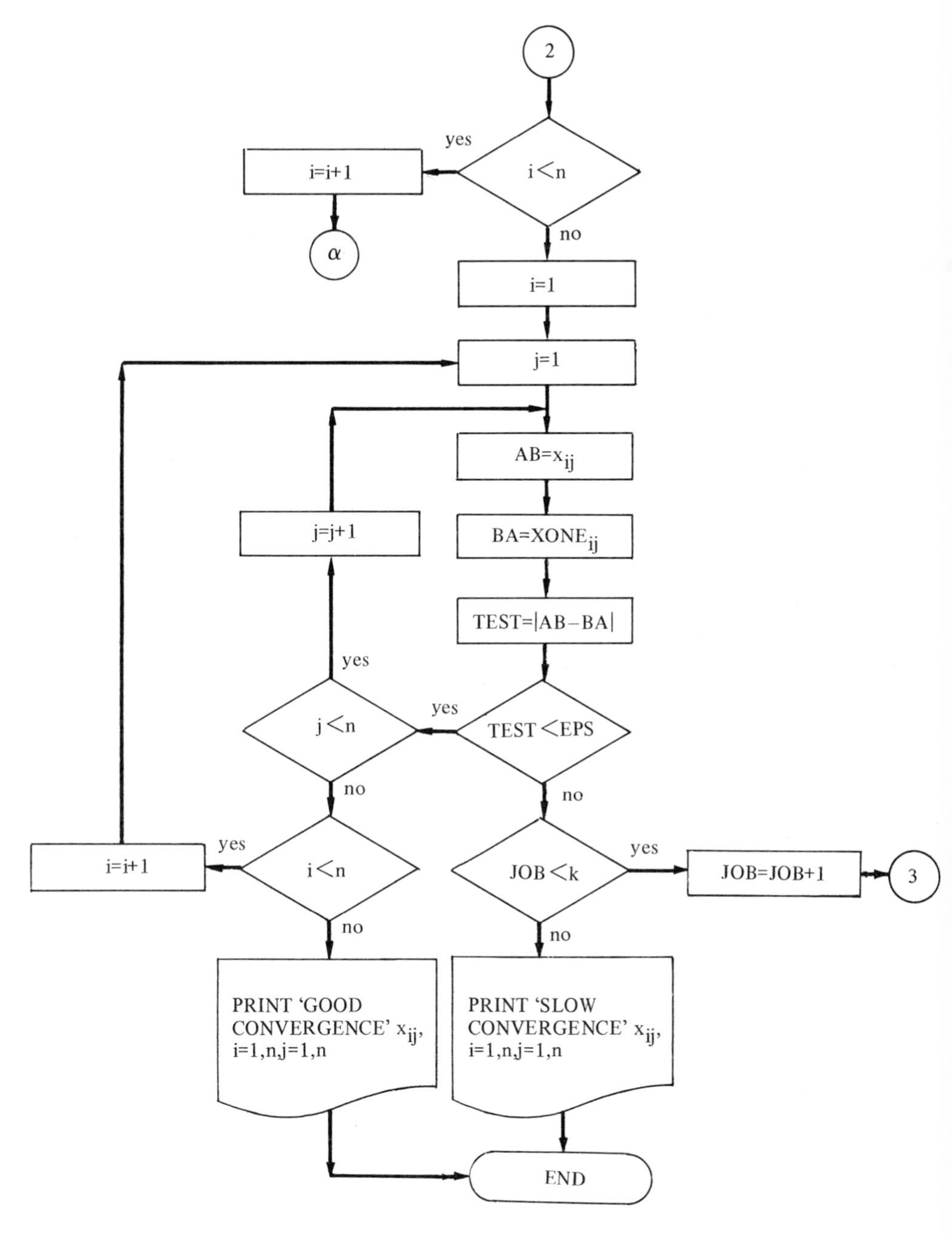

Flow Chart 4.19.1 *(Continued)*

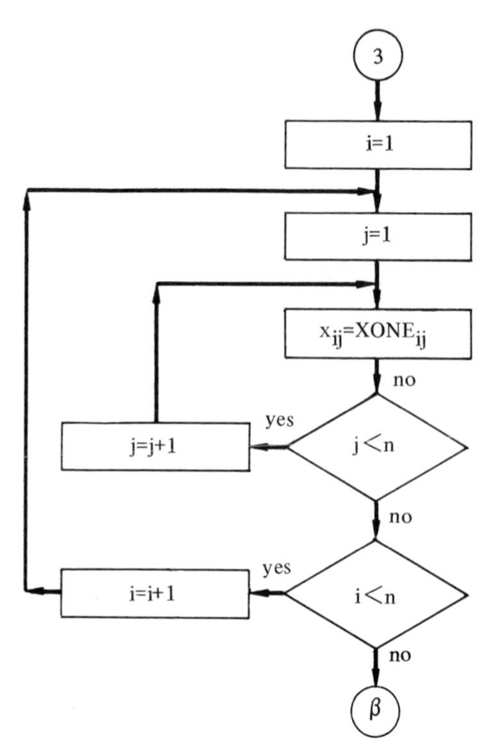

PROBLEMS

Write a flow chart and program to find the inverse of a square matrix A according to the procedures given in the following problems. Let

$$A = \begin{bmatrix} 0 & 1 & 3 \\ -2 & 3 & 9 \\ 1 & -2 & -5 \end{bmatrix}.$$

4-12. Use the method of Sec. 4.11.1 to find a first approximation X_0 to A^{-1}. The result,

$$A^{-1} = \begin{bmatrix} a_{1,n+1} & a_{1,n+2} & \cdots & a_{1,2n} \\ a_{2,n+1} & a_{2,n+2} & \cdots & a_{2,2n} \\ \cdot & \cdot & \cdots & \cdot \\ a_{n,n+1} & a_{n,n+2} & \cdots & a_{n,2n} \end{bmatrix}$$

may now be considered as the initial matrix X_0 of the Newton–Raphson process.

4-13. Use the Newton–Raphson method to improve the result in Prob. 4-12. In this part, it will not be necessary to compare $XONE_{ij}$ with x_{ij}. Instead, permit the iteration to be repeated three times.

4.20 Eigenvalues and Eigenvectors

The set of equations

$$\begin{aligned}(1-\lambda)x + 2y &= 0\\ 2x + (1-\lambda)y &= 0\end{aligned} \tag{4.157}$$

always has the solution $x = 0$ and $y = 0$. Such a solution, called a *trivial solution*, is usually of no consequence to the scientist—hence, its name.

But, an important question to the investigator is: For what values of the parameter λ will the set of equations have a nonzero solution, i.e., a nontrivial solution?

Borrowing a theorem from matrix algebra, it is known that a set of n homogeneous linear equations in n unknowns has a nontrivial solution if the determinant of the coefficient matrix equals zero. Hence, for Eqs. 4.157,

$$\begin{vmatrix}1-\lambda & 2\\ 2 & 1-\lambda\end{vmatrix} = \lambda^2 - 2\lambda - 3 = 0.$$

Thus, for $\lambda = 3, -1$, the set of equations has nontrivial solutions. For example, for $\lambda = 3$,

$$\begin{aligned}-2x + 2y &= 0\\ 2x - 2y &= 0\end{aligned}$$

or (4.158)

$$y = x.$$

The values $\lambda = 3, -1$ are called eigenvalues or characteristic values; and the solution $y = x$, which may be written as a vector, i.e.,

$$k\begin{bmatrix}1\\1\end{bmatrix}$$

where k is any real number, is called an eigenfunction, or more specifically in this case, an eigenvector.

From the above example, it can be seen that eigenvalues occur because of conditions placed upon the set of equations. The condition was that the set of equations would have a nontrivial solution.

Now consider a general problem, such as the solution of

$$
\begin{aligned}
(a_{11} - \lambda)x_1 + a_{12}x_2 + \cdots + a_{1n}x_n &= 0 \\
a_{21}x_1 + (a_{22} - \lambda)x_2 + \cdots + a_{2n}x_n &= 0 \\
\cdots\cdots\cdots\cdots\cdots\cdots\cdots\cdots \\
a_{n1}x_1 + a_{n2}x_2 + \cdots + (a_{nn} - \lambda)x_n &= 0.
\end{aligned}
\tag{4.159}
$$

For what values of λ will this set of equations have a nontrivial solution?

In matrix notation, Eqs. 4.159 may be written as

$$
\begin{bmatrix}
a_{11} - \lambda & a_{12} & \cdots & a_{1n} \\
a_{21} & a_{22} - \lambda & \cdots & a_{2n} \\
\cdot & \cdot & \cdot & \cdot \\
\cdot & \cdot & \cdot & \cdot \\
\cdot & \cdot & \cdot & \cdot \\
a_{n1} & a_{n2} & \cdots & a_{nn} - \lambda
\end{bmatrix}
\begin{bmatrix} x_1 \\ x_2 \\ \cdot \\ \cdot \\ \cdot \\ x_n \end{bmatrix}
=
\begin{bmatrix} 0 \\ 0 \\ \cdot \\ \cdot \\ \cdot \\ 0 \end{bmatrix}.
\tag{4.160}
$$

An answer to the above question may be found in the following way:

1. Expand

$$
\begin{vmatrix}
a_{11} - \lambda & a_{12} & \cdots & a_{1n} \\
a_{21} & a_{22} - \lambda & \cdots & a_{2n} \\
\cdot & \cdot & \cdots & \cdot \\
a_{n1} & a_{n2} & \cdots & a_{nn} - \lambda
\end{vmatrix}
$$

   into a polynomial, $f(\lambda)$.
2. Solve $f(\lambda) = 0$ for its roots $\lambda_1, \lambda_2, \ldots, \lambda_n$.
3. For each λ_i, solve the set of equations for the associated eigenvector. However, in most cases this method proves unsatisfactory. Instead, the methods described in the following sections are preferred.

4.21 The Power Method

From now on, only the matrix A is considered. The set of Eqs. 4.159 is implied but not stated. In the power method, the dominant eigenvalue, i.e., the largest λ in absolute value, is found, and with this value the associated eigenvector is determined.

The power method consists of the following steps:

1. Let L represent the dominant eigenvalue and let V represent the associated eigenvector.

2. Define $U = \{1, 0, \ldots, 0\}$ as the first guess to V.
   Note: There are other ways of choosing U—see Probs. 4-12 and 4-13 for other suggested ways. A vector such as U is said to be *normalized.*
3. Compute $W^{(1)} = AU = \{w_1^{(1)}, w_2^{(1)}, \ldots, w_n^{(1)}\}$ as a first approximation to V. Write $W^{(1)}$ as $w_1^{(1)}\{1, w_2^{(1)}/w_1^{(1)}, w_3^{(1)}/w_1^{(1)}, \ldots, w_n^{(1)}/w_1^{(1)}\}$. Then the first approximation to L is $w_1^{(1)}$.
4. Replace $U = \{1, 0, \ldots, 0\}$ by $\{1, w_2^{(1)}/w_1^{(1)}, w_3^{(1)}/w_1^{(1)}, \ldots, w_n^{(1)}/w_1^{(1)}\}$.
5. Repeat step 3 to find $W^{(2)}$ and $w_1^{(2)}$. When $w_1^{(i)} = w_1^{(i+1)}$ within the desired degree of accuracy, then $W^{(i+1)}$ is the eigenvector V and $w_1^{(i+1)}$ is the eigenvalue L within the desired degree of accuracy.

Example

Let

$$A = \begin{bmatrix} 1 & 2 \\ 2 & 1 \end{bmatrix} \quad \text{and} \quad U = \begin{bmatrix} 1 \\ 0 \end{bmatrix}.$$

Step 1. Then

$$W^{(1)} = \begin{bmatrix} 1 & 2 \\ 2 & 1 \end{bmatrix}\begin{bmatrix} 1 \\ 0 \end{bmatrix} = \begin{bmatrix} 1 \\ 2 \end{bmatrix},$$

thus $w_1^{(1)} = 1$ and

$$U^{(1)} = \begin{bmatrix} 1 \\ 2 \end{bmatrix}.$$

Step 2. Repeating the process,

$$W^{(2)} = \begin{bmatrix} 1 & 2 \\ 2 & 1 \end{bmatrix}\begin{bmatrix} 1 \\ 2 \end{bmatrix} = \begin{bmatrix} 5 \\ 4 \end{bmatrix} = 5\begin{bmatrix} 1 \\ 4/5 \end{bmatrix},$$

$$w_1^{(2)} = 5 \quad \text{and} \quad U^{(2)} = \begin{bmatrix} 1 \\ 4/5 \end{bmatrix}.$$

Successive iterations of the process show convergence:

Step 3.

$$W^{(3)} = \begin{bmatrix} 1 & 2 \\ 2 & 1 \end{bmatrix}\begin{bmatrix} 1 \\ 4/5 \end{bmatrix} = \begin{bmatrix} 13/5 \\ 14/5 \end{bmatrix} = 13/5\begin{bmatrix} 1 \\ 14/13 \end{bmatrix},$$

$$w_1^{(3)} = 13/5, \qquad U^{(3)} = \begin{bmatrix} 1 \\ 14/13 \end{bmatrix}.$$

Step 4.

$$W^{(4)} = \begin{bmatrix} 1 & 2 \\ 2 & 1 \end{bmatrix} \begin{bmatrix} 1 \\ 14/13 \end{bmatrix} = \begin{bmatrix} 41/13 \\ 40/13 \end{bmatrix} = 41/13 \begin{bmatrix} 1 \\ 40/41 \end{bmatrix},$$

$$w_1^{(4)} = 41/13, \qquad U^{(4)} = \begin{bmatrix} 1 \\ 40/41 \end{bmatrix}.$$

Step 5.

$$W^{(5)} = \begin{bmatrix} 1 & 2 \\ 2 & 1 \end{bmatrix} \begin{bmatrix} 1 \\ 40/41 \end{bmatrix} = \begin{bmatrix} 121/41 \\ 122/41 \end{bmatrix} = 121/41 \begin{bmatrix} 1 \\ 122/121 \end{bmatrix},$$

$$w_1^{(5)} = 121/41, \qquad U^{(5)} = \begin{bmatrix} 1 \\ 122/121 \end{bmatrix},$$

Thus, $w_1^{(5)} \cong 3 = L$, the dominant eigenvalue, and

$$W^{(5)} = \begin{bmatrix} 1 \\ 122/121 \end{bmatrix} \cong \begin{bmatrix} 1 \\ 1 \end{bmatrix} = V,$$

the characteristic eigenvector.

4.21.1 Flow Chart

To find the dominant eigenvalue L and its eigenvector V of a square matrix A by the power method.
Let

$$A = [a_{ij}]_n.$$

Let

$$U = \begin{bmatrix} u_1 \\ u_2 \\ \cdot \\ \cdot \\ \cdot \\ u_n \end{bmatrix} = \begin{bmatrix} 1 \\ 0 \\ \cdot \\ \cdot \\ \cdot \\ 0 \end{bmatrix}$$

be the initial eigenvector.
Let EPS be an arbitrary small positive number for the purpose of testing convergence.
Let K be an arbitrary number for the maximum number of iterations.
R_1 and R_2 indicate values of L. Then the approximation to the true vector is

$$V = AU = \left[\sum_{j=1}^{n} a_{ij}u_j\right] = \{v_1, v_2, \ldots, v_n\};$$

v_1 is the approximation to L, and U becomes $\{1, v_2/v_1, \ldots, v_n/v_1\}$.

FLOW CHART 4.21.1 Power Method

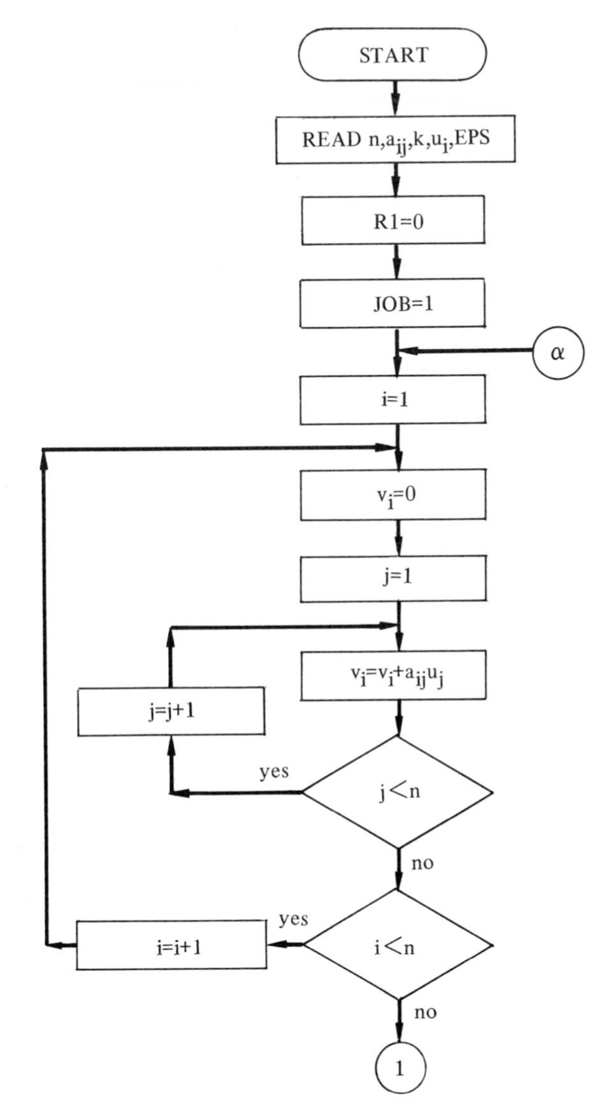

Flow Chart 4.21.1 *(Continued)*

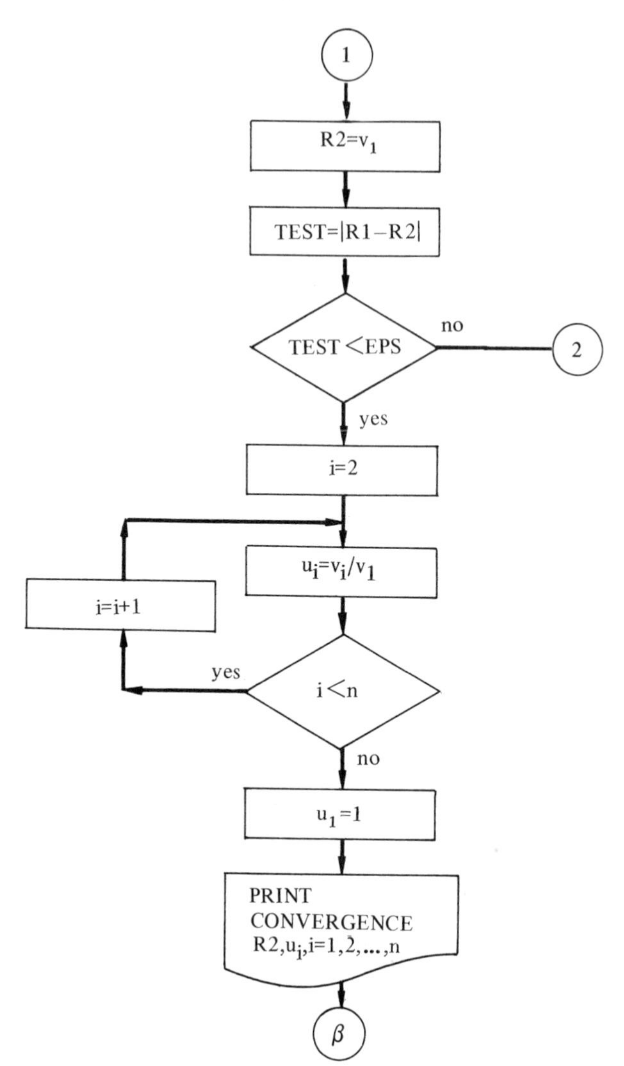

Flow Chart 4.21.1 *(Continued)*

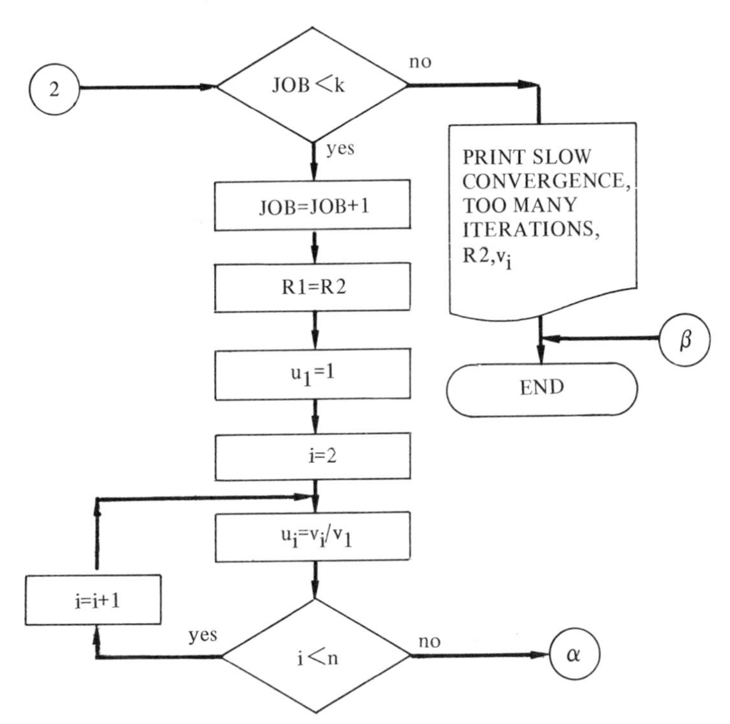

PROBLEMS

4-14. An initial vector U may be chosen so that the sum of the squares of its components equals unity. Write a flow chart and program to compute the dominant eigenvalue and its associated eigenvector for the matrix:

$$A = \begin{bmatrix} .2 & .9 & 1.32 \\ -11.2 & 22.28 & -10.72 \\ -5.8 & 9.45 & -1.94 \end{bmatrix}.$$

Choose the initial vector U such that

$$u_1^2 + u_2^2 + u_3^2 = 1.$$

4-15. The initial vector U may be chosen so that each component of U is less than unity. Write a flow chart and program based upon this choice of U. How do the results of Prob. 4-14 compare with this problem?

The exact answers are the eigenvector $V = \{1,10,5\}$ and the eigenvalue $\lambda = 15.8$.

4.22 Deflation

The power method is a simple way of finding the dominant eigenvalue and its associated eigenvector of a matrix A. Once this has been accomplished, the question of finding the remaining eigenvalues and associated eigenvectors can be answered by applying a combination of the power method and the following technique, provided that the eigenvalues are distinct.

Let λ_1 be an eigenvalue of A with its associated eigenvector X_1, which has been normalized so that the first component is unity. Define A_1 as the first row of A. Then define the matrix B as

$$B = A - X_1 A_1. \tag{4.161}$$

Expressing the matrix X_1 as

$$\begin{bmatrix} 1 \\ x_{21} \\ x_{31} \\ \cdot \\ \cdot \\ \cdot \\ x_{n1} \end{bmatrix}, \tag{4.162}$$

then

$$B = \begin{bmatrix} a_{11} & a_{12} & \cdots & a_{1n} \\ a_{21} & a_{22} & \cdots & a_{2n} \\ \cdot & \cdot & \cdots & \cdot \\ a_{n1} & a_{n2} & \cdots & a_{nn} \end{bmatrix} - \begin{bmatrix} a_{11} & a_{12} & \cdots & a_{1n} \\ x_{21}a_{11} & x_{21}a_{12} & \cdots & x_{21}a_{1n} \\ \cdot & \cdot & \cdots & \cdot \\ x_{n1}a_{11} & x_{n1}a_{12} & \cdots & x_{n1}a_{1n} \end{bmatrix} \tag{4.163}$$

or

$$B = \begin{bmatrix} 0 & 0 & \cdots & 0 \\ b_{21} & b_{22} & \cdots & b_{2n} \\ b_{31} & b_{32} & \cdots & b_{3n} \\ \cdot & \cdot & \cdots & \cdot \\ b_{n1} & b_{n2} & \cdots & b_{nn} \end{bmatrix}$$

where

$$b_{ij} = a_{ij} - x_{i1}a_{1j}, \qquad \begin{pmatrix} i = 2, 3, \ldots, n \\ j = 1, 2, \ldots, n \end{pmatrix}. \tag{4.164}$$

Let λ_2 be another eigenvalue of A distinct from λ_1. Let X_2 be a normalized eigenvector (first component being unity) associated with

λ_2. Then λ_2 is an eigenvalue of B and its associated eigenvector is $X_1 - X_2$; that is,

$$B(X_1 - X_2) = \lambda_2(X_1 - X_2). \tag{4.165}$$

A sketch of the proof follows:

$$B(X_1 - X_2) = (A - X_1A_1)(X_1 - X_2) = AX_1 - AX_2 - X_1A_1X_1 + X_1A_1X_2. \tag{4.166}$$

Since

$$A_1X_1 = [a_{11} \quad a_{12} \quad \cdots \quad a_{1n}]\begin{bmatrix} 1 \\ x_{21} \\ \cdot \\ \cdot \\ \cdot \\ x_{n1} \end{bmatrix} \tag{4.167}$$

$$= |1 + a_{12}x_{21} + a_{13}x_{31} + \cdots + a_{1n}x_{n1}|$$

or

$$A_1X_1 = \lambda_1 x_{11} = \lambda_1,$$

and similarly,

$$A_1X_2 = \lambda_2, \tag{4.168}$$

Eq. 4.166 becomes

$$B(X_1 - X_2) = AX_1 - AX_2 - \lambda_1X_1 + \lambda_2X_1$$

or (4.169)

$$B(X_1 - X_2) = \lambda_2(X_1 - X_2).$$

Example 1

As an example, consider the eigenvalue problem:

$$\begin{aligned} 3x + y - z &= \lambda x \\ x + z &= \lambda y \\ x + y + z &= \lambda z. \end{aligned} \tag{4.170}$$

The true values of λ are:

(a) $\lambda_1 = 1 + \sqrt{3}$, for which

$$X_1 = \begin{bmatrix} 1 \\ -1+\sqrt{3} \\ 1 \end{bmatrix},$$

(b) $\lambda_2 = 2$, for which

$$X_2 = \begin{bmatrix} 1 \\ 2 \\ 3 \end{bmatrix},$$

(c) $\lambda_3 = 1 - \sqrt{3}$, for which

$$X_3 = \begin{bmatrix} 1 \\ -1 \quad -\sqrt{3} \\ 1 \end{bmatrix}.$$

To show that Eq. 4.169 is true,

$$X_1 - X_2 = \begin{bmatrix} 0 \\ -3 + \sqrt{3} \\ -2 \end{bmatrix} \tag{4.171}$$

and

$$\lambda_2(X_1 - X_2) = \begin{bmatrix} 0 \\ -6 + 2\sqrt{3} \\ -4 \end{bmatrix}. \tag{4.172}$$

Also, $B = A - X_1 A_1$, or

$$B = \begin{bmatrix} 3 & 1 & -1 \\ 1 & 0 & 1 \\ 1 & 1 & 1 \end{bmatrix} - \begin{bmatrix} 1 \\ -1 + \sqrt{3} \\ 1 \end{bmatrix} [3 \quad 1 \quad -1] = \begin{bmatrix} 0 & 0 & 0 \\ 4 - 3\sqrt{3} & 1 - \sqrt{3} & \sqrt{3} \\ -2 & 0 & 2 \end{bmatrix}. \tag{4.173}$$

Thus, Eq. 4.169, $B(X_1 - X_2) = \lambda_2(X_1 - X_2)$, becomes

$$\begin{bmatrix} 0 & 0 & 0 \\ 4 - \sqrt{3} & 1 - \sqrt{3} & \sqrt{3} \\ -2 & 0 & 2 \end{bmatrix} \begin{bmatrix} 0 \\ -3 + \sqrt{3} \\ -2 \end{bmatrix} = \begin{bmatrix} 0 \\ -6 + 2\sqrt{3} \\ -4 \end{bmatrix} \tag{4.174}$$

or

$$\begin{bmatrix} 0 \\ -6 + 2\sqrt{3} \\ -4 \end{bmatrix} = \begin{bmatrix} 0 \\ -6 + 2\sqrt{3} \\ -4 \end{bmatrix}. \tag{4.175}$$

Thus $\lambda_2 = 2$ is an eigenvalue of B and $X_1 - X_2$ is the associated eigenvector.

It is now necessary to develop a method whereby $\lambda_i (i \neq 1)$, an eigenvalue of A, and its associated eigenvector are approximated.

First, it is seen that

$$B = \begin{bmatrix} 0 & 0 & \cdots & 0 \\ b_{21} & b_{22} & \cdots & b_{2n} \\ \cdot & \cdot & \cdots & \cdot \\ b_{n1} & b_{n2} & \cdots & b_{nn} \end{bmatrix} \tag{4.176}$$

has the same eigenvalues as A, except that λ_1 becomes zero. Why?

Since the elements of the first row of B are all zero, the matrix B can be deflated by striking out the first row and the first column, to become

$$B' = \begin{bmatrix} b_{22} & b_{23} & \cdots & b_{2n} \\ b_{32} & b_{33} & \cdots & b_{3n} \\ \cdot & \cdot & \cdots & \cdot \\ b_{n2} & b_{n3} & \cdots & b_{nn} \end{bmatrix}. \tag{4.177}$$

B' has the same eigenvalue λ_2 as B and therefore as A. B' will also have the same corresponding eigenvectors that B has with the first component removed.

The dominant eigenvalue λ_2 of B' can now be approximated by the power method. Since B' is of order $n - 1$, a trial eigenvector by the power method is of dimension $n - 1$. Let

$$Z' = \begin{bmatrix} z_2 \\ \cdot \\ \cdot \\ \cdot \\ z_n \end{bmatrix} \tag{4.178}$$

represent an eigenvector of B' corresponding to λ_2; then

$$Z = \begin{bmatrix} 0 \\ z_2 \\ \cdot \\ \cdot \\ \cdot \\ z_n \end{bmatrix} \tag{4.179}$$

is an eigenvector of B. The eigenvector X of A corresponding to λ_2 may be expressed as

$$X = (\lambda_2 - \lambda_1)Z + (A_1 Z)X_1, \qquad (\lambda_2 \neq \lambda_1). \tag{4.180}$$

It can be shown that X is an eigenvector of A corresponding to the eigenvalue λ_2. Due to round-off error, however, the deflation method is usually not used more than three times.

Example 2

From Example 1,

$$\lambda_1 = 1 + \sqrt{3}, \qquad \lambda_2 = 2;$$

$$X_1 = \begin{bmatrix} 1 \\ -1 + \sqrt{3} \\ 1 \end{bmatrix}, \qquad X_2 = \begin{bmatrix} 1 \\ 2 \\ 3 \end{bmatrix};$$

$$X_1 - X_2 = Z = \begin{bmatrix} 0 \\ -3 + \sqrt{3} \\ -2 \end{bmatrix}, \qquad A_1 = [3 \quad 1 \quad -1].$$

Equation 4.180 becomes

$$X = (1 - \sqrt{3}) \begin{bmatrix} 0 \\ -3 + \sqrt{3} \\ -2 \end{bmatrix} + [3\ 1\ -1] \begin{bmatrix} 0 \\ -3 + \sqrt{3} \\ -2 \end{bmatrix} \begin{bmatrix} 1 \\ -1 + \sqrt{3} \\ 1 \end{bmatrix} \tag{4.181}$$

or

$$X = \begin{bmatrix} 1 - \sqrt{3} \\ 2 - 2\sqrt{3} \\ -3 + 3\sqrt{3} \end{bmatrix} = -1 + \sqrt{3} \begin{bmatrix} 1 \\ 2 \\ 3 \end{bmatrix}; \tag{4.182}$$

that is, $X = (-1 + \sqrt{3})X_2$.

Also, for $\lambda_3 = 1 - \sqrt{3}$, the corresponding eigenvector is

$$X = (\lambda_3 - \lambda_1)Z + (A_1 Z)X_1, \qquad \text{where } Z = X_1 - X_3 = \begin{bmatrix} 0 \\ 2\sqrt{3} \\ 0 \end{bmatrix}.$$

Thus,

$$X = -2\sqrt{3} \begin{bmatrix} 0 \\ 2\sqrt{3} \\ 0 \end{bmatrix} + [3 \quad 1 \quad -1] \begin{bmatrix} 0 \\ 2\sqrt{3} \\ 0 \end{bmatrix} \begin{bmatrix} 1 \\ -1 + \sqrt{3} \\ 1 \end{bmatrix}$$

or

$$X = 2\sqrt{3} \begin{bmatrix} 1 \\ -1 - \sqrt{3} \\ 1 \end{bmatrix};$$

that is, $X = 2\sqrt{3}X_3$.

Although the examples given were for a nonsymmetric matrix, this section will now consider only symmetric matrices.[14] The generalized steps of the deflation method to find all eigenvalues and their associated eigenvectors of a symmetric matrix are:

1. Apply the power method to find λ_1 (the dominant eigenvalue) and X(the associated eigenvector).
2. Deflate the matrix A to B.
3. Apply the power method to matrix B to find the dominant eigenvalue of B.
4. Find the associated eigenvector of A for the dominant eigenvalue of B.

   This implies the application of the formula

$$X = (\lambda_i - \lambda_1)Z + (A_1 Z)X_1, \qquad (i \neq 1), \qquad (4.183)$$

which in turn implies that as the matrix B' of order $n - 1$ is deflated to the matrix B'' of order $n - 2$, Eq. 4.183 is used for a dominant eigenvalue of B'', and subsequently Eq. 4.183 is used in reference to matrix A.

Suppose, for example, that $A = [a_{ij}]_{(4)}$, and suppose also that the first and second dominant eigenvalues of A and the corresponding eigenvectors have been found. By applying Eq. 4.161, a matrix B'' of order 2 is derived; that is,

$$B'' = \begin{bmatrix} b_{33} & b_{34} \\ b_{43} & b_{44} \end{bmatrix}.$$

By applying the power method to B'', λ_3 can be found and an eigenvector of B',

$$X_3 = \begin{bmatrix} 0 \\ x_{33} \\ x_{43} \end{bmatrix},$$

is also found. Now it is necessary to find

$$X_3 = \begin{bmatrix} x_{23} \\ x_{33} \\ x_{43} \end{bmatrix}$$

as an eigenvector of B'. Thus, the formula (4.183) used to find X_3 is

[14] Further questions beyond the scope of this text can also be raised; for example, nonlinear divisors of a matrix A are discussed fully in Ralston, *A First Course in Numerical Analysis*.

$$X = (\lambda_3 - \lambda_2)Z + (B_1'Z)X_2,$$

where Z has been approximated by the power method and X_2 (first component equal to 1) is the eigenvector (dimension 3) associated with λ_2. Finally, Eq. 4.183 is used to find X_3 of four dimensions; that is, $X = (\lambda_3 - \lambda_1)Z + (A_1Z)X_1$.

5. Repeat steps 2, 3, and 4, each time deflating the preceding matrix B until all eigenvalues and corresponding eigenvectors have been found.

4.22.1 Procedure

The following example will illustrate the above steps.

Problem: To find all eigenvalues and eigenvectors of

$$A = \begin{bmatrix} 3 & 1 & -1 \\ 1 & 0 & 1 \\ 1 & 1 & 1 \end{bmatrix}.$$

1. By the power method, it is found that the largest eigenvalue is $\lambda_1 = 1 + \sqrt{3}$, and the associated eigenvector is

$$X_1 = \begin{bmatrix} 1 \\ -1 + \sqrt{3} \\ 1 \end{bmatrix}.$$

2. The matrix A is deflated to the matrix B, where $B = A - X_1A_1$; that is,

$$B = \begin{bmatrix} 0 & 0 & 0 \\ 4 - \sqrt{3} & 1 - \sqrt{3} & \sqrt{3} \\ -2 & 0 & 2 \end{bmatrix},$$

then

$$B' = \begin{bmatrix} 1 - \sqrt{3} & \sqrt{3} \\ 0 & 2 \end{bmatrix}.$$

Thus $(1 - \sqrt{3} - \lambda)(2 - \lambda) = 0$, or $\lambda_2 = 2$, $\lambda_3 = 1 - \sqrt{3}$.

3. Therefore, for $\lambda_2 = 2$,

$$(1 - \sqrt{3} - 2)x_2 + \sqrt{3}x_3 = 0, \qquad x_3 = \frac{1 + \sqrt{3}}{\sqrt{3}}x_2.$$

Let $x_2 = \sqrt{3}$; then $x_3 = 1 + \sqrt{3}$. Thus,

$$Z_2 = \begin{bmatrix} 0 \\ \sqrt{3} \\ 1 + \sqrt{3} \end{bmatrix}.$$

4. Using Eq. 4.183,

$$X_2 = [2 - (1 + \sqrt{3})]\begin{bmatrix} 0 \\ \sqrt{3} \\ 1 + \sqrt{3} \end{bmatrix} + [3 \quad 1 \quad -1]\begin{bmatrix} 0 \\ \sqrt{3} \\ 1 + \sqrt{3} \end{bmatrix}\begin{bmatrix} 1 \\ -1 + \sqrt{3} \\ 1 \end{bmatrix}$$

or

$$X_2 = \begin{bmatrix} -1 \\ -2 \\ -3 \end{bmatrix}.$$

Also for $\lambda_3 = 1 - \sqrt{3}$, the system of equations reduces to

$$\sqrt{3}x_3 = 0$$
$$(1 + \sqrt{3})x_3 = 0.$$

Hence, $x_3 = 0$ and x_2 may be chosen as 1. Then

$$Z_3 = \begin{bmatrix} 0 \\ 1 \\ 0 \end{bmatrix}.$$

and by Eq. 4.183,

$$X_3 = -2\sqrt{3}\begin{bmatrix} 0 \\ 1 \\ 0 \end{bmatrix} + [3 \quad 1 \quad -1]\begin{bmatrix} 0 \\ 1 \\ 0 \end{bmatrix}\begin{bmatrix} 1 \\ -1 + \sqrt{3} \\ 1 \end{bmatrix} \text{ or } X_3 = \begin{bmatrix} 1 \\ -1 - \sqrt{3} \\ 1 \end{bmatrix}.$$

4.22.2 Flow Chart

To compute all eigenvalues and eigenvectors of a square matrix of order 3 by the deflation method, given:

$$A = \begin{bmatrix} 3 & 1 & -1 \\ 1 & 0 & 1 \\ 1 & 1 & 1 \end{bmatrix}, \qquad U = \begin{bmatrix} 1 \\ 1 \\ 1 \end{bmatrix}, \qquad N = 3.$$

The eigenvalues and eigenvectors are

$$RL_1, \begin{bmatrix} x_{11} \\ x_{21} \\ x_{31} \end{bmatrix}; \qquad RL_2, \begin{bmatrix} x_{12} \\ x_{22} \\ x_{32} \end{bmatrix}; \qquad RL_3, \begin{bmatrix} x_{13} \\ x_{23} \\ x_{33} \end{bmatrix}.$$

FLOW CHART 4.22.2 Deflation Method for a Square Matrix of Order 3

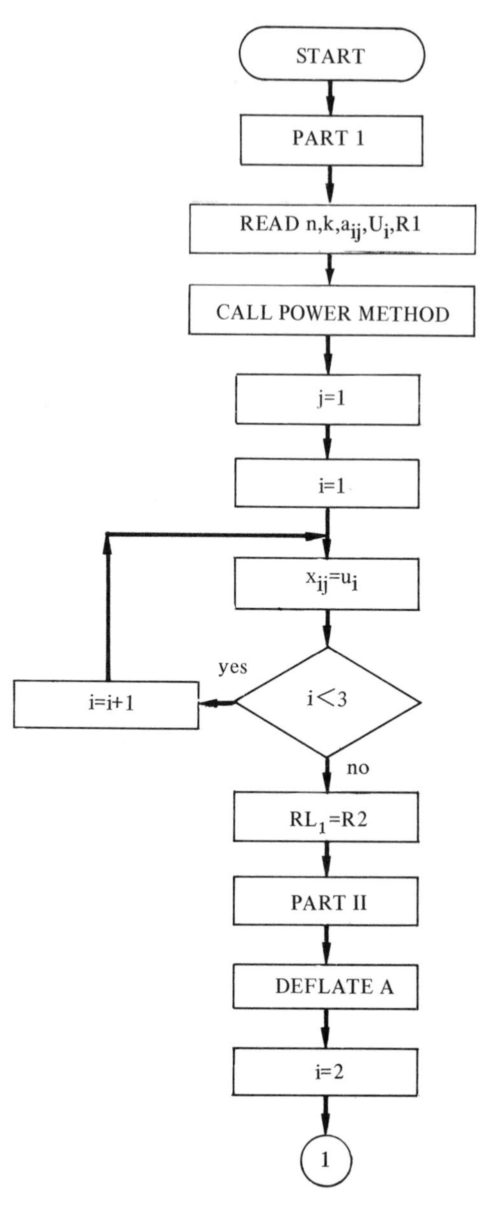

Flow Chart 4.22.2 *(Continued)*

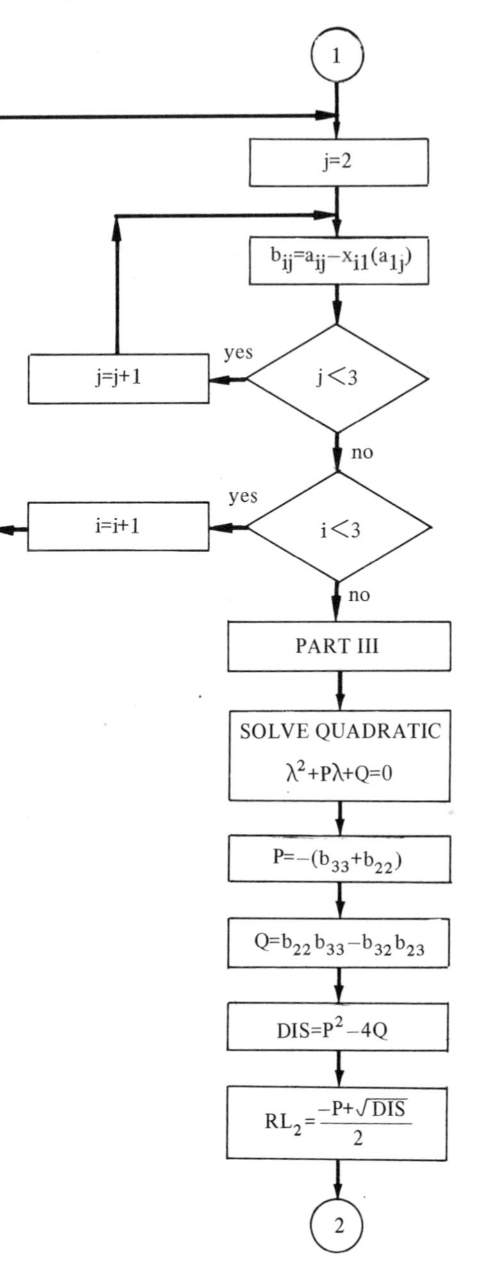

Flow Chart 4.22.2 *(Continued)*

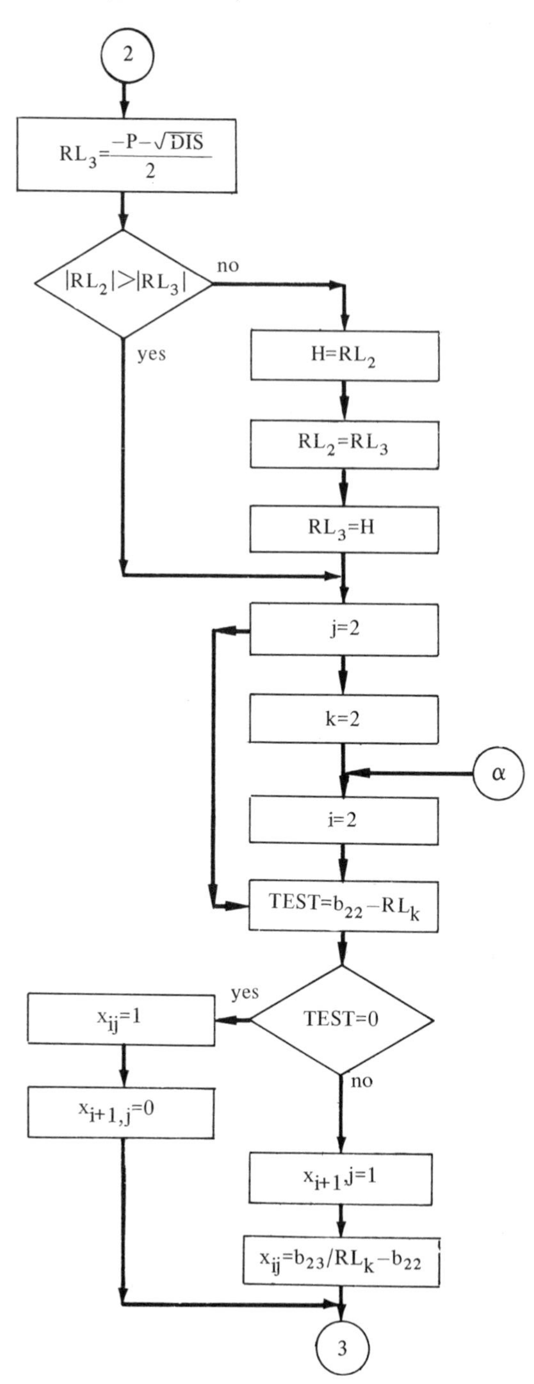

Flow Chart 4.22.2 *(Continued)*

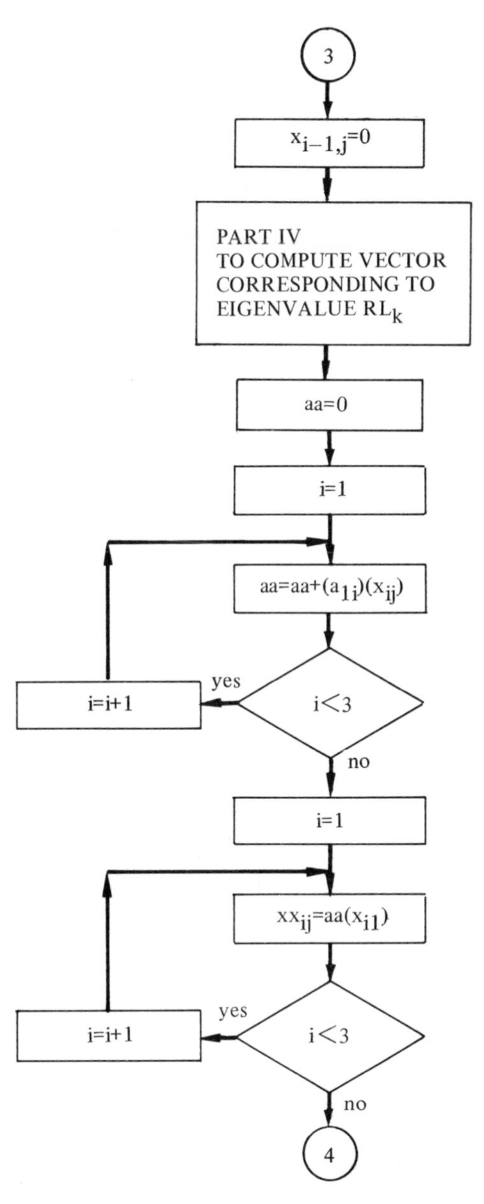

Flow Chart 4.22.2 *(Continued)*

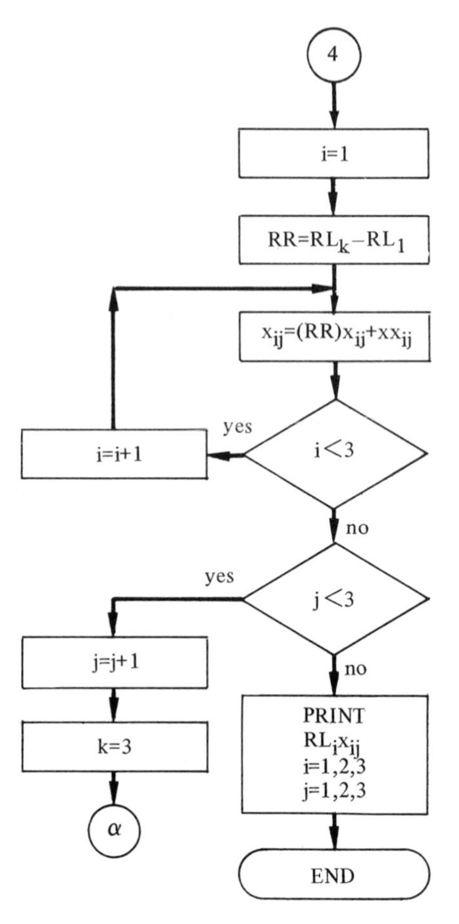

4.22.3 Program

```
C         PROGRAM TO COMPUTE ALL EIGENVALUES AND
C         EIGENVECTORS OF A SQUARE MATRIX OF ORDER 3
C
C         PART ONE   POWER METHOD
C
        DIMENSION A(3,3),X(3,3),U(3),RL(3),B(3,3),XX(3,3)
        READ(5,100)N
        READ(5,101)((A(I,J),J=1,N),I=1,N)
        READ(5,101)(U(I),I=1,N)
```

```
      K=10
      CALL POWER(A,U,K,N,R2)
      J=1
      DO 1 I=1,N
    1 X(I,J)=U(I)
      RL(1)=R2
C
C       PART TWO    DEFLATE A
C
      DO 3 I=2,3
      DO 2 J=2,3
    2 B(I,J)=A(I,J)-X(I,1)*A(1,J)
    3 CONTINUE
C
C       PART THREE    SOLVE QUADRATIC L**2+P*L+Q=0
C
      P=-(B(3,3)+B(2,2))
      Q=B(2,2)*B(3,3)-B(3,2)*B(2,3)
      DIS=P**2-4*Q
      RL(2)=(-P+SQRT(DIS))/2
      RL(3)=(-P-SQRT(DIS))/2
      IF(ABS(RL(2))-ABS(RL(3)))4,4,5
    4 H=RL(2)
      RL(2)=RL(3)
      RL(3)=H
    5 J=2
      K=2
    6 I=2
      TEST=B(2,2)-RL(K)
      IF(ABS(TEST)-.01)7,7,8
    7 X(I,J)=1
      X(I+1,J)=0
      GO TO 11
    8 X(I+1,J)=1
      X(I,J)=B(2,3)/(RL(K)-B(2,2))
   11 X(I-1,J)=0
C
C       PART FOUR  TO COMPUTE THE VECTOR CORRESPONDING
        TO EIGENVALUE RL(K)
C
      AA=0
      DO 12 I=1,3
   12 AA=AA+A(1,I)*X(I,J)
      DO 13 I=1,3
   13 XX(I,J)=AA*X(I,1)
      RR=RL(K)-RL(1)
      DO 14 I=1,3
   14 X(I,J)=RR*X(I,J)+XX(I,J)
      IF(J-3)15,16,16
   15 J=J+1
```

```
      K=3
      GO TO 6
   16 WRITE(6,102)(RL(I),I=1,3)
      WRITE(6,103)((X(I,J),I=1,3),J=1,3)
      STOP
  100 FORMAT(I2)
  101 FORMAT(16F5.2)
  102 FORMAT('1','EIGENVALUES',10X,F10.4,20X,F10.4,20X,F10.4)
  103 FORMAT(/,'EIGENVECTORS',10X,9F10.4)
      END
      SUBROUTINE POWER(A,U,K,N,R2)
      DIMENSION A(3,3),U(3),V(3)
      R1=0
      JOB=1
   29 DO 21 I=1,N
      V(I)=0
      DO 22 J=1,N
   22 V(I)=V(I)+A(I,J)*U(J)
   21 CONTINUE
      R2=V(1)
      TEST=ABS(R1-R2)
      IF(TEST-.0001)23,24,24
   23 DO 25 I=2,N
   25 U(I)=V(I)/V(1)
      U(1)=1
   27 RETURN
   24 IF(JOB-K)26,27,27
   26 JOB=JOB+1
      R1=R2
      DO 28 I=2,N
   28 U(I)=V(I)/V(1)
      U(1)=1
      GO TO 29
      END
```

```
EIGENVALUES    2.7321   2.0000  -0.7320
EIGENVECTORS   1.0000  -0.3660   1.0000
               0.7320  -0.7321  -2.7321
               1.0000  -1.0981   1.0000
```

EXERCISE

Use the deflation method to find the three eigenvalues and associated eigenvectors of

$$A = \begin{bmatrix} 3 & -4 & 3 \\ -4 & 6 & 3 \\ 3 & 3 & 1 \end{bmatrix}.$$

4.23 Solution of Systems of Nonlinear Equations

For the solution of one equation in one unknown by the Newton–Raphson method, the iteration is

$$x_{i+1} = x_i - f(x_i)/f'(x_i)$$

where $f(x)$, $f'(x)$, and also $f''(x)$ are assumed to be continuous and bounded in the neighborhood of the root. A similar notation can be used to solve a system of n nonlinear equations in n unknowns.

Consider the system of nonlinear equations:

$$\begin{aligned} f_1(x_1, x_2, \ldots, x_n) &= 0 \\ f_2(x_1, x_2, \ldots, x_n) &= 0 \\ \cdots\cdots\cdots\cdots & \\ f_n(x_1, x_2, \ldots, x_n) &= 0 \end{aligned} \tag{4.187}$$

where f_i and all their derivatives through the second order are assumed to be continuous and bounded. By expanding each f_i in a Taylor series, the following system of equations is developed:

$$\begin{aligned} f_1(x_1 + h_1, x_2 + h_2, \ldots, x_n + h_n) &= f_1 + \sum_{i=1}^{n} \frac{\partial f_1}{\partial x_i} h_i \cong 0 \\ f_2(x_1 + h_1, x_2 + h_2, \ldots, x_n + h_n) &= f_2 + \sum_{i=1}^{n} \frac{\partial f_2}{\partial x_i} h_i \cong 0 \\ f_n(x_1 + h_1, x_2 + h_2, \ldots, x_n + h_n) &= f_n + \sum_{i=1}^{n} \frac{\partial f_n}{\partial x_i} h_i \cong 0. \end{aligned} \tag{4.188}$$

If the set $\{x_1^0, x_2^0, \ldots, x_n^0\}$ is considered as the first approximation to the solution of the system of equations (4.187), then

$$\{x_1^0 + h_1, x_2^0 + h_2, \ldots, x_n^0 + h_n\}$$

is a second approximation. Equations 4.188 can be rewritten as

$$\begin{aligned} \frac{\partial f_1}{\partial x_1} h_1 + \frac{\partial f_1}{\partial x_2} h_2 + \cdots + \frac{\partial f_1}{\partial x_n} h_n &= -f_1 \\ \frac{\partial f_2}{\partial x_1} h_1 + \frac{\partial f_2}{\partial x_2} h_2 + \cdots + \frac{\partial f_2}{\partial x_n} h_n &= -f_2 \\ \cdots\cdots\cdots\cdots\cdots\cdots & \\ \frac{\partial f_n}{\partial x_1} h_1 + \frac{\partial f_n}{\partial x_2} h_2 + \cdots + \frac{\partial f_n}{\partial x_n} h_n &= -f_n, \end{aligned} \tag{4.189}$$

and this system may be written in matrix notation as

$$\begin{bmatrix} \frac{\partial f_1}{\partial x_1} & \frac{\partial f_1}{\partial x_2} & \cdots & \frac{\partial f_1}{\partial x_n} \\ \frac{\partial f_2}{\partial x_1} & \frac{\partial f_2}{\partial x_2} & \cdots & \frac{\partial f_2}{\partial x_n} \\ \cdot & \cdot & \cdot & \cdot \\ \frac{\partial f_n}{\partial x_1} & \frac{\partial f_n}{\partial x_2} & \cdots & \frac{\partial f_n}{\partial x_n} \end{bmatrix} \cdot \begin{bmatrix} h_1 \\ h_2 \\ \cdot \\ \cdot \\ \cdot \\ h_n \end{bmatrix} = \begin{bmatrix} -f_1 \\ -f_2 \\ \cdot \\ \cdot \\ \cdot \\ -f_n \end{bmatrix}. \tag{4.190}$$

The matrix

$$\begin{bmatrix} \frac{\partial f_1}{\partial x_1} & \frac{\partial f_1}{\partial x_2} & \cdots & \frac{\partial f_1}{\partial x_n} \\ \frac{\partial f_2}{\partial x_1} & \frac{\partial f_2}{\partial x_2} & \cdots & \frac{\partial f_2}{\partial x_n} \\ \cdot & \cdot & \cdot & \cdot \\ \frac{\partial f_n}{\partial x_1} & \frac{\partial f_n}{\partial x_2} & \cdots & \frac{\partial f_n}{\partial x_n} \end{bmatrix}$$

is called a Jacobian,

$$J = \left[\frac{\partial f_i}{\partial x_j}\right]_{(n)}.$$

If the inverse J^{-1} exists, then the set of solutions $\{h_1, h_2, \ldots, h_n\}$ (now considered as a vector H) can be found.

Let Eqs. 4.190 be written as $JH = F$, $F = -\{f_1, f_2, \ldots, f_n\}$; then

$$H = J^{-1}F, \qquad (\det J \neq 0). \tag{4.191}$$

Further, let

$$X = \begin{bmatrix} x_1^{(0)} \\ x_2^{(0)} \\ \cdot \\ \cdot \\ \cdot \\ x_n^{(0)} \end{bmatrix},$$

then the new approximation is

$$Z = X + H = X + J^{-1}F. \tag{4.192}$$

Example

Given:

$$f(x,y) = x^2 + y^2 - 16 = 0$$
$$g(x,y) = x^2 - y^2 - 9 = 0,$$

the four solutions are

$$x = \pm\frac{5}{\sqrt{2}}, \qquad y = \pm\frac{\sqrt{7}}{\sqrt{2}},$$

and the first derivatives are

$$\frac{\partial f}{\partial x} = 2x, \qquad \frac{\partial f}{\partial y} = 2y,$$

$$\frac{\partial g}{\partial x} = 2x, \qquad \frac{\partial g}{\partial y} = -2y.$$

Equations 4.188 become

$$\begin{aligned} x^2 + y^2 - 16 + 2xh_1 + 2yh_2 &= 0 \\ x^2 - y^2 - 9 + 2xh_1 - 2yh_2 &= 0. \end{aligned} \tag{4.193}$$

Let the initial values of x and y be 3 and 2. Then expressing Eq. 4.193 in the form of $JH = F$, and substituting in the initial values, the matrix equation is

$$\begin{bmatrix} 6 & 4 \\ 6 & -4 \end{bmatrix}\begin{bmatrix} h_1 \\ h_2 \end{bmatrix} = \begin{bmatrix} 3 \\ 4 \end{bmatrix} \tag{4.194}$$

and $H = J^{-1}F$ becomes

$$\begin{bmatrix} h_1 \\ h_2 \end{bmatrix} = \frac{\begin{bmatrix} -4 & -4 \\ -6 & 6 \end{bmatrix}}{-48}\begin{bmatrix} 3 \\ 4 \end{bmatrix} = \begin{bmatrix} 7/12 \\ -1/8 \end{bmatrix}. \tag{4.195}$$

Thus, $Z = X + J^{-1}F$ is

$$\begin{bmatrix} z_1 \\ z_2 \end{bmatrix} = \begin{bmatrix} 3 \\ 2 \end{bmatrix} + \begin{bmatrix} 7/12 \\ -1/8 \end{bmatrix}, \tag{4.196}$$

or

$$\begin{aligned} z_1 &= x + h_1 = 43/12 \\ z_2 &= y + h_2 = 15/8. \end{aligned} \tag{4.197}$$

If the iteration were repeated, the values of z_1 and z_2 would be substituted for x and y in Eqs. 4.193 and new values of z_1 and z_2 would be computed.

From the above example, it should be apparent that in a system of n equations in n unknowns, the amount of computation would be tremendous. For each iteration, n functions and n^2 partial derivative functions would have to be computed.

Indeed, a more rapidly convergent procedure can be obtained if for each iteration the matrices F and J are again computed. However, such a procedure would be quite costly in time. It is also true that, in general, convergence can be guaranteed, if not as rapidly, by keeping F fixed, if the starting values are sufficiently close to the solution $X = \{x_1, x_2, x_3, \ldots, x_n\}$. Otherwise, the Newton–Raphson method may not converge at all or may lead to another solution.

Other functional iteration methods of a single equation (Ch. 3), such as the false position method and the secant method, may be extended to systems of equations—however, even here, as in the extension of the Newton–Raphson method, convergence is not always guaranteed.[15]

4.23.1 Integrated Flow Chart

To solve a system of n nonlinear equations in n unknowns.

Definitions and Notations

$$
\begin{aligned}
X &= \{x_1, x_2, \ldots, x_n\} \\
B &= [b_i]_{(n,1)} = [f_i(x_1, x_2, \ldots, x_n)]_{(n,1)} \\
F &= [f_{ij}]_{(n,n)} = [\partial f_i / \partial x_j]_{(n,n)} \\
H &= [h_i]_{(n,1)} .
\end{aligned}
$$

Then Eqs. 4.190–4.192 are

$$
\begin{aligned}
FH &= -B \\
H &= -F^{-1}B \\
Z &= X + H.
\end{aligned}
\tag{4.198}
$$

EPS is an arbitrary small positive number to test convergence.
n is the number of equations and unknowns.
k is the maximum number of allowable iterations.
$JOB = 1, 2, \ldots$ is the count of iterations.

[15] See Ralston, *A First Course in Numerical Analysis*.

FLOW CHART 4.23.1 Integrated Flow Chart—n Nonlinear Equations in n Unknowns

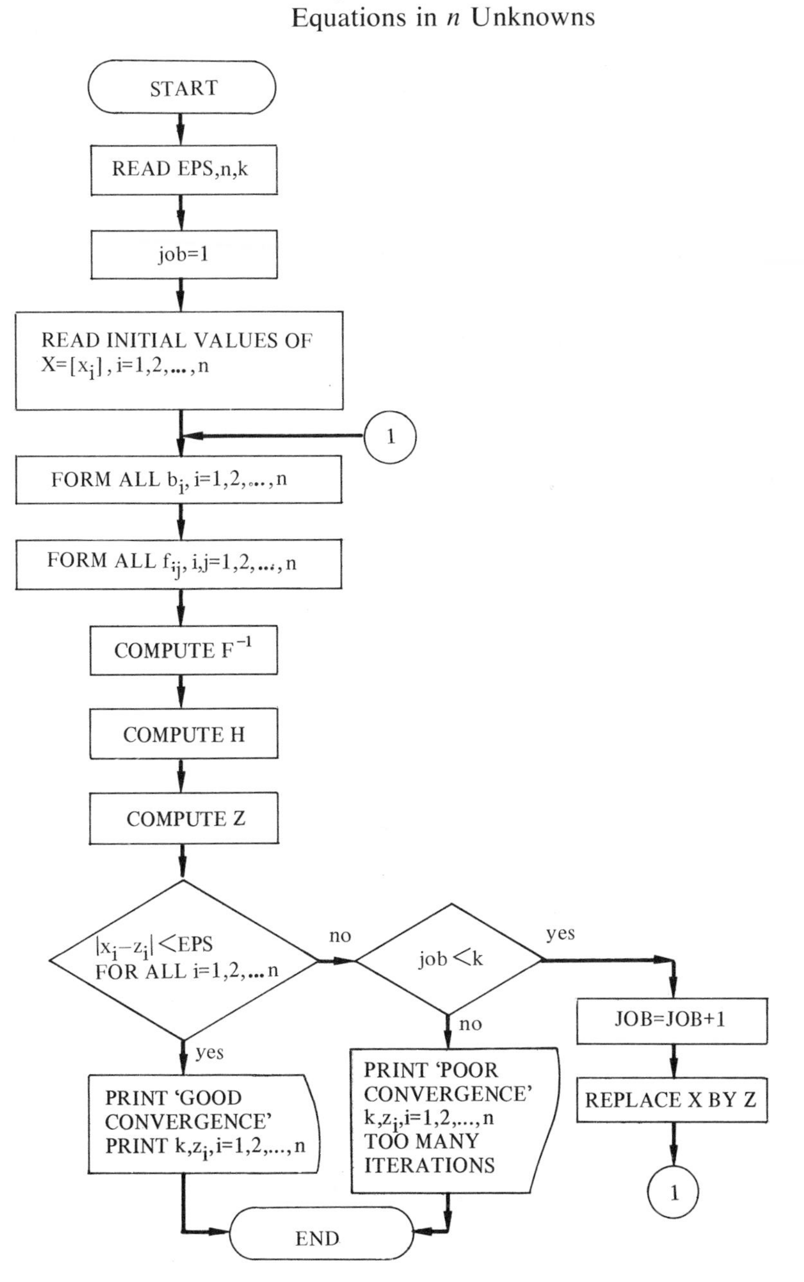

4.23.2 Flow Chart

To solve two nonlinear equations in two unknowns. Consider the system

$$f(x,y) = x^2 + y^2 - 16 = 0,$$
$$g(x,y) = x^2 - y^2 - 9 = 0. \tag{4.199}$$

Let $x^{(0)} = 3$, $y^{(0)} = 2$ be the initial values. Define:

$$f_x = \partial f / \partial x, \qquad f_y = \partial f / \partial y$$
$$g_x = \partial g / \partial x, \qquad g_y = \partial g / \partial y. \tag{4.200}$$

Then the iteration becomes

$$x_{i+1} = x_i - \left\{ \frac{f g_y - g f_y}{f_x g_y - f_y g_x} \right\}_i \tag{4.201}$$

$$y_{i+1} = y_i - \left\{ \frac{g f_x - f g_x}{f_x g_y - f_y g_x} \right\}_i . \tag{4.202}$$

The subscript i in Eqs. 4.201 and 4.202 indicates that these functions are evaluated for $x = x_i$ and $y = y_i$.

Definitions and Notation

x, y are starting values.
$fx(x,y)$ and $fy(x,y)$ are respectively the functions $\partial f/\partial x$ and $\partial f/\partial y$.
$gx(x,y)$ and $gy(x,y)$ are respectively the functions $\partial g/\partial x$ and $\partial g/\partial y$.
DENOM is the denominator in Eqs. 4.201 and 4.202.
TOPx and *TOPy* are the numerators in Eqs. 4.201 and 4.202, respectively.
XONE and *YONE* are used for current values of x and y, respectively.
k is the number of allowable iterations. *JOB* is the count of these iterations.
a and b are used so that the values of $f(x,y)$ and $g(x,y)$ can be printed for each evaluation.

FLOW CHART 4.23.2 Two Nonlinear Equations in Two Unknowns

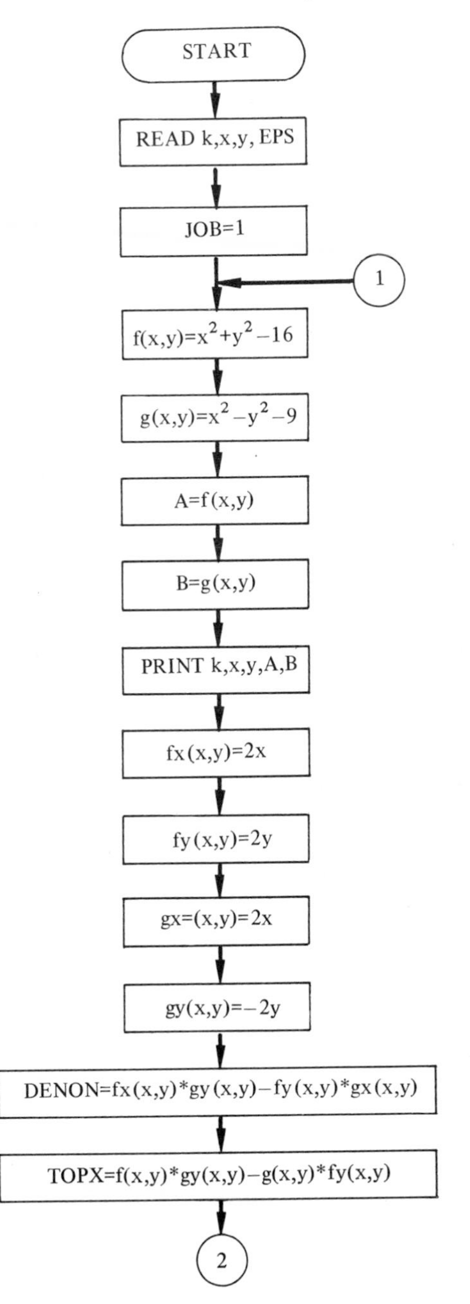

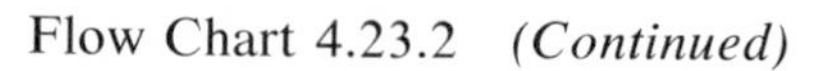

Flow Chart 4.23.2 *(Continued)*

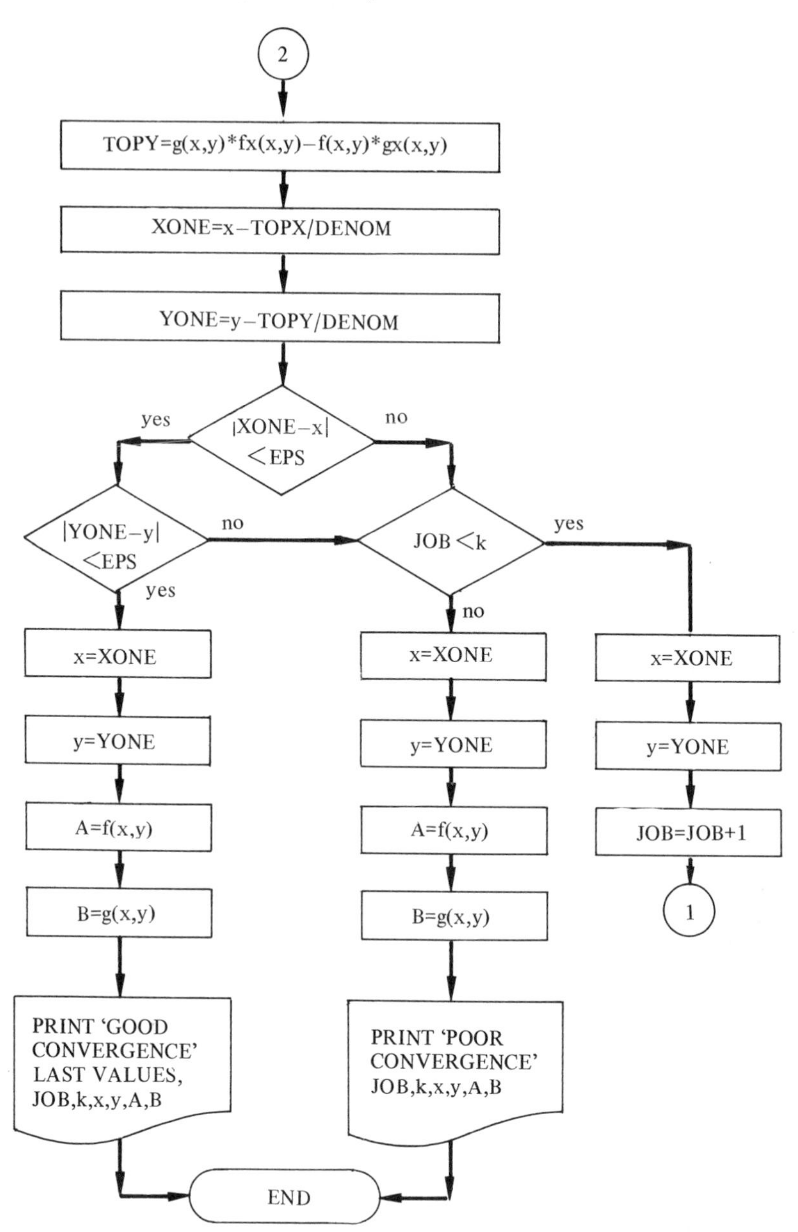

PROBLEMS

4-16. Write a program based on Flow Chart 4.23.2 to solve

$$f(x,y) = x^2 + y^2 - 16 = 0$$
$$g(x,y) = x^2 - y^2 - 9 = 0.$$

Let $x^{(0)} = 3$, $y^{(0)} = 2$. In addition to tests for convergence in the flow chart, add the following tests:

```
IF ABS(F(XONE,YONE))
```

and

```
IF ABS(G(XONE,YONE))
```

If both tests are satisfied, as well as other tests for convergence, transfer should be made to the print statement.

4-17. Consider the system of equations

$$f(x,y) = x^2 + y^2 - 16 = 0$$
$$g(x,y) = x^2 - y^2 - 9 = 0.$$

Taking the partial derivative of $f(x,y)$ with respect to x, and using the Newton–Raphson procedure, the following iteration is derived:

$$x_{i+1} = x_i - \left(\frac{f}{\partial f/\partial x}\right)_i.$$

Similarly, taking the partial derivative of $g(x,y)$ with respect to y,

$$y_{i+1} = y_i - \left(\frac{g}{\partial g/\partial y}\right)_i.$$

Replace x_i in the second equation by the computed x_{i+1} from the first equation. Thus,

$$x_{i+1} = x_i - \left[f(x_i,y_i) \Big/ \frac{\partial f(x_i,y_i)}{\partial x}\right]$$

$$y_{i+1} = y_{i+1} - \left[g(x_{i+1},y_i) \Big/ \frac{\partial g(x_{i+1},y_i)}{\partial y}\right].$$

Write a flow chart and program to solve the system of equations using the above two iterations. Which method converges more rapidly?

4-18. The secant method for solving $f(x) = 0$ can be modified so that the process can be used to solve a system of nonlinear equations. The iteration for the secant method for a single equation is

$$x_{i+1} = x_i + \frac{f(x_i)(x_i - x_{i-1})}{f(x_{i-1}) - f(x_i)}.$$

Applying this iteration to $f(x,y) = 0$, the iteration becomes

$$x_{i+1} = x_i + \frac{f(x_i,y_i)(x_i - x_{i-1})}{f(x_{i-1},y_{i-1}) - f(x_i,y_i)}.$$

Now applying the iteration to $g(x,y) = 0$ but using the new iterate x_{i+1} for x_i, and x_i for x_{i-1}, the iteration is

$$y_{i+1} = y_i + \frac{g(x_{i+1},y_i)(y_i - y_{i-1})}{g(x_i,y_{i-1}) - g(x_{i+1},y_i)}.$$

Using these iterations, write a flow chart and a program to solve

$$f(x,y) = x^2 + y^2 - 16 = 0$$
$$g(x,y) = x^2 - y^2 - 9 = 0.$$

Let $x_0^{(0)} = 3$, $x_1^{(0)} = 4$, and $y_0^{(0)} = 1$, $y_1^{(0)} = 2$.

Which of the three methods converges most rapidly?

5

Interpolation and Approximation

Interpolation is a method of approximating the value of a function at a given point. Suppose the true values (called tabular values) of a function $f(x)$ are known at a given set of points. Interpolation is used to estimate a value of $f(x)$ at a nontabulated point. The approximating function $g(x)$ may be a polynomial, a linear combination of polynomials, or it may be a linear combination of sine and cosine functions. Only polynomial interpolation will be considered here.

There are two types of polynomial interpolation. First, suppose that the exact values of $f(x)$ (except for round-off) are known and tabulated for a given set of points. Then a polynomial function $y(x)$, having the same values as the tabulated values of $f(x)$, may be constructed. The interpolating polynomial $y(x)$ is now used to find an approximate value of $f(x)$ at a nontabulated point. Since $y(x)$ and $f(x)$ have the same values at tabulated points, the truncation error is assumed to be of more importance than round-off error.

The second type of problem to be presented is based upon the fact that the tabulated values of $f(x)$ are known only empirically; that is, these values may not be the exact values of the function. Thus, round-off error is of major importance for this type of problem. For such a problem, the principle of least squares (Sec. 5.8) is used.

Polynomial interpolation of the first type has its most important use not in interpolation per se, but in the derivation of methods of numerical differentiation and integration. Values of functions such as

$\sin x$ and $\cos x$, e^x and $\ln x$ can be generated on the modern digital computer with a high degree of accuracy. For functions that do not have stored routines in a computer, linear or at most quadratic interpolation will yield accurate values, provided the values of $f(x)$ are tabulated at points very near each other (see Probs. 5-3 and 5-4).

In order to approach the subject of polynomial interpolation (type 1) with better understanding, a brief treatment of finite differences is first presented.

5.1 Finite Differences

Let $f(x)$ have known tabulated values at $x = x_0, x_0 + h, x_0 + 2h, \ldots, x_0 + nh$, where h is a constant. Finite differences are defined as follows:

1. Forward Differences: The first forward difference of $f(x)$ at x is

$$\Delta f(x) = f(x + h) - f(x). \tag{5.1}$$

Other differences are:

$$\begin{aligned}\Delta^2 f(x) &= \Delta f(x + h) - \Delta f(x) \\ &= f(x + 2h) - f(x + h) - f(x + h) + f(x) \\ &= f(x + 2h) - 2f(x + h) + f(x),\end{aligned} \tag{5.2}$$

$$\begin{aligned}\Delta^k f(x) &= \Delta^{k-1} f(x + h) - \Delta^{k-1} f(x) \\ &= f(x + kh) - kf(x + (k - 1)h) \\ &\quad + \frac{k(k-1)}{2} f(x + (k - 2)h) + \cdots + (-1)^k f(x), \\ &\qquad (k = 1, 2, \ldots),\end{aligned} \tag{5.3}$$

or[1]

$$\Delta^k f(x) = \sum_{i=0}^{k} (-1)^{k-i} \binom{k}{i} f(x + ih) \tag{5.4}$$

where the binomial coefficients $\binom{k}{i}$ are defined by the following equations:

$$\begin{aligned}&\binom{k}{0} = 1, \quad \binom{k}{1} = k, \quad \binom{k}{2} = \frac{k(k-1)}{2}, \quad \ldots, \\ &\binom{k}{i} = \frac{k(k-1)\cdots(k-i+1)}{i!}, \qquad (i \le k).\end{aligned} \tag{5.5}$$

[1] By defining $\Delta^0 f(x) \equiv f(x)$, k can take on values of 0, 1, 2, ...

2. Backward Differences:

$$\nabla f(x) = f(x) - f(x-h), \tag{5.6}$$

$$\begin{aligned}\nabla^2 f(x) &= \nabla f(x) - \nabla f(x-h) \\ &= f(x) - 2f(x-h) + f(x-2h),\end{aligned} \tag{5.7}$$

$$\nabla^k f(x) = \sum_{i=0}^{k} (-1)^{k-i} \binom{k}{i} f(x - ih). \tag{5.8}$$

3. Central Differences:

$$\delta f(x) = f(x + h/2) - f(x - h/2), \tag{5.9}$$

$$\begin{aligned}\delta^2 f(x) &= \delta f(x + h/2) - \delta f(x - h/2) \\ &= f(x+h) - 2f(x) + f(x-h),\end{aligned} \tag{5.10}$$

$$\delta^k f(x) = \sum_{i=0}^{k} (-1)^{i} \binom{k}{i} f(x + (k/2 - i)h). \tag{5.11}$$

On observation, it is seen that

$$\Delta^k f(x) \equiv \nabla^k f(x + kh) \equiv \delta^k f\left(x + \frac{k}{2}h\right). \tag{5.12}$$

In order to find a symbolic relation among the three types of differences, the operator E is defined by the equations:

$$Ef(x) = f(x+h) \tag{5.13}$$

$$E^{-1} f(x) = f(x-h) \tag{5.14}$$

$$E^k f(x) = f(x + kh). \tag{5.15}$$

Then Eq. 5.12 becomes

$$\Delta^k f(x) \equiv \nabla^k E^k f(x) \equiv \delta^k E^{k/2} f(x), \tag{5.16}$$

or the operators are related in the following manner:

$$\Delta^k \equiv \nabla^k E^k \equiv \delta^k E^{k/2}, \tag{5.17}$$

and, for $k = 1$,

$$\Delta = \nabla E = \delta E^{1/2}. \tag{5.18}$$

It can also be shown that any of the operators Δ, ∇, or δ is commutative with E,

$$E\Delta = \Delta E, \qquad E\nabla = \nabla E, \qquad E\delta = \delta E, \tag{5.19}$$

and that Δ, ∇, δ, and E are commutative with a scalar constant r; that is,

$$\Delta r = r\Delta, \qquad \nabla r = r\nabla, \qquad \text{etc.} \tag{5.20}$$

5.2 Difference Tables

Denoting $\Delta^k f(x + ih)$ by $\Delta^k f_i$, and $\nabla^k f(x + ih)$ by $\nabla^k f_i$ where $i = 0, 1, 2, \ldots$ and h is a constant, then differences (whether forward or backward) using this notation can be exhibited conveniently in a table.

For example, assume that $f(x)$ has tabulated values at the points $x = x_0 + ih$ where $i = -4, -3, -2, -1, 0, 1, 2, 3, 4$. Indicate these values of x by x_i, and $f(x_0 + ih)$ as f_i $(i = -4, -3, \ldots, 4)$. Tables 5.1 and 5.2 exhibit the differences in convenient form.

TABLE 5.1 Forward Differences

x_{-4}	f_{-4}						
		Δf_{-4}					
x_{-3}	f_{-3}		$\Delta^2 f_{-4}$				
		Δf_{-3}		$\Delta^3 f_{-4}$			
x_{-2}	f_{-2}		$\Delta^2 f_{-3}$		$\Delta^4 f_{-4}$		
		Δf_{-2}		$\Delta^3 f_{-3}$		$\Delta^5 f_{-4}$	·
x_{-1}	f_{-1}		$\Delta^2 f_{-2}$		$\Delta^4 f_{-3}$		·
		Δf_{-1}		$\Delta^3 f_{-2}$		$\Delta^5 f_{-3}$	·
x_0	f_0		$\Delta^2 f_{-1}$		$\Delta^4 f_{-2}$		·
		Δf_0		$\Delta^3 f_{-1}$		$\Delta^5 f_{-2}$	·
x_1	f_1		$\Delta^2 f_0$		$\Delta^4 f_{-1}$		·
		Δf_1		$\Delta^3 f_0$		$\Delta^5 f_{-1}$	·
x_2	f_2		$\Delta^2 f_1$		$\Delta^4 f_0$		
		Δf_2		$\Delta^3 f_1$			
x_3	f_3		$\Delta^2 f_2$				
		Δf_3					
x_4	f_4						

The same type of notation is used in constructing a table of central differences; that is, the kth central difference $\delta^k f(x_0 + ih)$ is denoted by $\delta^k f_i$. This notation needs a further word of explanation. The difference $f(x_0 + (i + 1)h) - f(x_0 + ih)$ expressed as a central difference is

$$\delta f(x_0 + (i + 1/2)h). \tag{5.21}$$

Hence, $\delta f_{i+1/2} = f_{i+1} - f_i$, and, in general,

$$\delta^k f_{i+1/2} = \delta^{k-1} f_{i+1} - \delta^{k-1} f_i. \tag{5.22}$$

TABLE 5.2 Backward Differences

x_{-4}	f_{-4}						
		∇f_{-3}					
x_{-3}	f_{-3}		$\nabla^2 f_{-2}$				
		∇f_{-2}		$\nabla^3 f_{-1}$			
x_{-2}	f_{-2}		$\nabla^2 f_{-1}$		$\nabla^4 f_0$		
		∇f_{-1}		$\nabla^3 f_0$		$\nabla^5 f_1$	·
x_{-1}	f_{-1}		$\nabla^2 f_0$		$\nabla^4 f_1$		·
		∇f_0		$\nabla^3 f_1$		$\nabla^5 f_2$	·
x_0	f_0		$\nabla^2 f_1$		$\nabla^4 f_2$		·
		∇f_1		$\nabla^3 f_2$		$\nabla^5 f_3$	·
x_1	f_1		$\nabla^2 f_2$		$\nabla^4 f_3$		·
		∇f_2		$\nabla^3 f_3$		$\nabla^5 f_4$	·
x_2	f_2		$\nabla^2 f_3$		$\nabla^4 f_4$		
		∇f_3		$\nabla^3 f_4$			
x_3	f_3		$\nabla^2 f_4$				
		∇f_4					
x_4	f_4						

For the assumed set of tabulated values, Table 5.3 represents the same differences, expressed in central differences, as Tables 5.1 and 5.2.

TABLE 5.3 Central Differences

x_{-4}	f_{-4}						
		$\delta f_{-7/2}$					
x_{-3}	f_{-3}		$\delta^2 f_{-3}$				
		$\delta f_{-5/2}$		$\delta^3 f_{-5/2}$			
x_{-2}	f_{-2}		$\delta^2 f_{-2}$		$\delta^4 f_{-2}$		
		$\delta f_{-3/2}$		$\delta^3 f_{-3/2}$		$\delta^5 f_{-3/2}$	·
x_{-1}	f_{-1}		$\delta^2 f_{-1}$		$\delta^4 f_{-1}$		·
		$\delta f_{-1/2}$		$\delta^3 f_{-1/2}$		$\delta^5 f_{-1/2}$	·
x_0	f_0		$\delta^2 f_0$		$\delta^4 f_0$		·
		$\delta f_{1/2}$		$\delta^3 f_{1/2}$		$\delta^5 f_{1/2}$	·
x_1	f_1		$\delta^2 f_1$		$\delta^4 f_1$		·
		$\delta f_{3/2}$		$\delta^3 f_{3/2}$		$\delta^5 f_{3/2}$	·
x_2	f_2		$\delta^2 f_2$		$\delta^4 f_2$		
		$\delta f_{5/2}$		$\delta^3 f_{5/2}$			
x_3	f_3		$\delta^2 f_3$				
		$\delta f_{7/2}$					
x_4	f_4						

5.2.1 A Numerical Example

Whether forward, backward, or central differences are applied to $f(x)$, the difference table will have the same values.

Let $f(x) = x^3$, $h = 2$. Let x have the values of 0, 2, 4, 6, 8, 10. Table 5.4 shows the differences.

TABLE 5.4 Differences for $f(x) = x^3$

x	$f(x)$	$\Delta f(x)$	$\Delta^2 f(x)$	$\Delta^3 f(x)$	$\Delta^4 f(x)$	$\Delta^5 f(x)$
0	0					
		8				
2	8		48			
		56		48		
4	64		96		0	
		152		48		0
6	216		144		0	
		296		48		
8	512		192			
		488				
10	1000					

If $f(x) = x^n$, then

$$\Delta f(x) = \Delta(x^n) = (x + h)^n - x^n$$

$$= \left\{x^n + \binom{n}{1} x^{n-1}h + \binom{n}{2} x^{n-2}h^2 + \cdots + h^n\right\} - x^n$$

$$= \binom{n}{1} x^{n-1}h + \binom{n}{2} x^{n-2}h^2 + \cdots + h^n.$$

Thus, $\Delta(x^n)$ is of degree $n - 1$. Continuing, it can be shown that $\Delta^n(x^n) = n!h$ and $\Delta^{n+1}(x^n) = 0$. Hence,

$$\Delta^n P_n(x) = a_0 n! h^n$$

where

$$P_n(x) = a_0 x^n + a_1 x^{n-1} + \cdots + a_n.$$

5.2.2 Flow Chart

In constructing a flow chart to form a difference table, it is more convenient to use a double subscripted variable for the values of $f(x)$ and all differences of $f(x)$. That is, let $y_{11} = f_1, y_{21} = f_2, \ldots, y_{n1} = f_n$ represent the tabulated values of $f(x)$ at $x = x_1, x_2, \ldots, x_n$.[2]

The first differences become

$$\begin{aligned} \Delta f_1 &= y_{22} = y_{21} - y_{11} \\ \Delta f_2 &= y_{32} = y_{31} - y_{21} \\ &\cdots\cdots\cdots \\ \Delta f_{n-1} &= y_{n2} = y_{n1} - y_{n-1,1}. \end{aligned} \tag{5.23}$$

Similarly, second differences are represented as

$$\begin{aligned} \Delta^2 f_1 &= y_{33} = y_{32} - y_{22} \\ \Delta^2 f_2 &= y_{43} = y_{42} - y_{32} \\ &\cdots\cdots\cdots \\ \Delta^2 f_{n-2} &= y_{n,3} = y_{n,2} - y_{n-1,2}, \end{aligned} \tag{5.24}$$

and the kth differences become

$$\begin{aligned} \Delta^k f_1 &= y_{k+1,k+1} = y_{k+1,k} - y_{k,k} \\ \Delta^k f_2 &= y_{k+2,k+1} = y_{k+2,k} - y_{k+1,k} \\ &\cdots\cdots\cdots \\ \Delta^k f_i &= y_{k+i,k+1} = y_{k+i,k} - y_{k+i-1,k}, \qquad (k + i \leq n). \end{aligned} \tag{5.25}$$

With this notation, a table of differences is shown by Table 5.5.

TABLE 5.5

x	$f(x)$	$\Delta f(x)$	$\Delta^2 f(x)$	$\cdots$	$\Delta^n f(x)$
x_1	y_{11}				
x_2	y_{21}	y_{22}			
x_3	y_{31}	y_{32}	y_{33}		
.	.	.	.		
.	.	.	.		
.	.	.	.		
x_n	y_{n1}	y_{n2}	y_{n3}	$\cdots$	y_{nn}

Write the last equation in (5.25) as

$$y_{ki,k1} = y_{ki,k} - y_{ki1,k}$$

where

$$\begin{aligned} ki &= k + i \\ k1 &= k + 1 \\ ki1 &= k + i - 1 \\ nk &= n - k. \end{aligned}$$

[2] The letter n is now equivalent to $n + 1$ in Sec. 5.1.

FLOW CHART 5.2.2 Forming a Difference Table

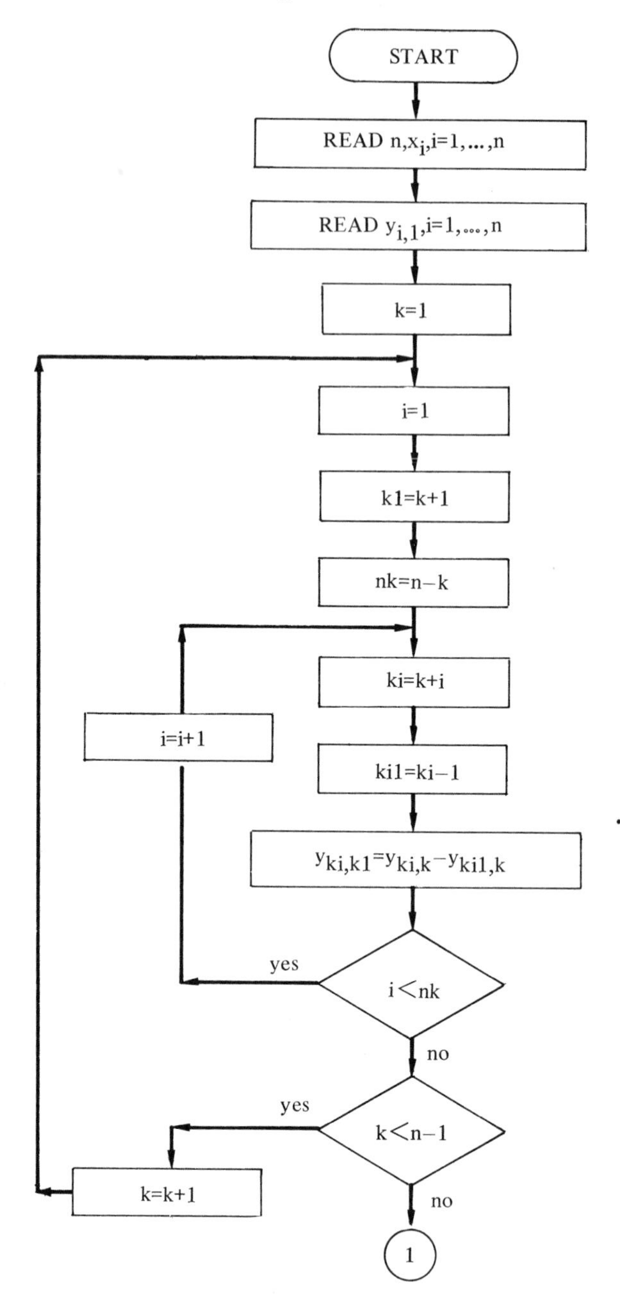

Flow Chart 5.2.2 *(Continued)*

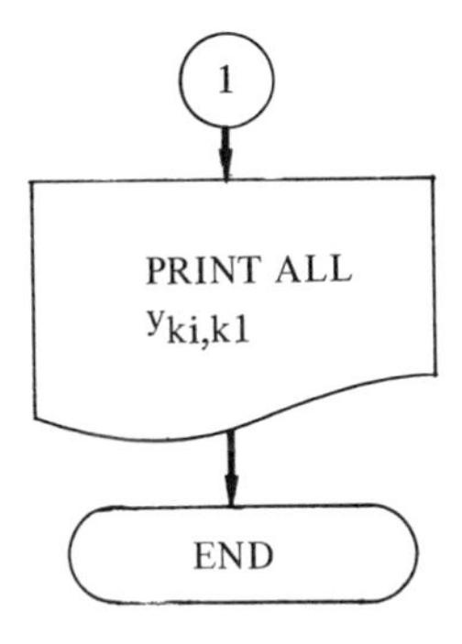

Flow Chart 5.2.2 would present a more understandable output if the lower triangular matrix were printed as shown in Table 5.5. Assume that $n = 3$. Then an output as shown in Table 5.6 would be desirable.

TABLE 5.6

X	Y	$DE11$	$DE12$
x_1	y_{11}		
x_2	y_{21}	y_{22}	
x_3	y_{31}	y_{32}	y_{33}

The following set of statements would yield the output given by Table 5.6:

```
10 FORMAT(3X,'X',8X,'Y',5X,'DE11',4X,'DE12',4X,'DE13')
   WRITE(6,10)
30 FORMAT(3F8.4)
   DO 20 I=1,3
20 WRITE(6,30)(X(I),Y(I,J),J=1,I)
```

EXERCISE

Write a program to form all differences of $f(x) = \ln x$ for the values of x given below, and to print a table of these differences in triangular form.

x	.3	.4	.5	.6	.7	.8
$\ln x$	−1.203973	−.916291	−.693147	−.510826	−.356675	−.223144

5.3 A Polynomial Expanded in Terms of Differences

A convenient change of variable is $u = (x - x_0)/h$ where x_0 may be chosen arbitrarily and $h = x_{i+1} - x_i$ is a constant. Note that if x is increased by h, u is accordingly increased by 1. With this substitution, the tabulated values of $x = x_{-m}, x_{-m+1}, \ldots, x_0, x_1, \ldots, x_m$ are replaced by $u = -m, -m + 1, \ldots, 0, 1, \ldots, m$.

Instead of using the variable x and differences of $f(x)$, the factorial polynomial u as defined below is introduced and a polynomial $P(u)$ is derived:

$$\begin{aligned} u^{[0]} &= 1 \\ u^{[1]} &= u \\ u^{[2]} &= u(u-1) \\ &\cdots\cdots\cdots \\ u^{[k]} &= u(u-1)\cdots(u-k+1). \end{aligned} \tag{5.26}$$

Thus, the first forward difference of $u^{[k]}$ becomes

$$\begin{aligned} \Delta u^{[k]} &= (u+1)^{[k]} - u^{[k]} \\ &= (u+1)u^{[k-1]} - (u-k+1)u^{[k-1]} \\ &= ku^{[k-1]}. \end{aligned} \tag{5.27}$$

In like manner,

$$\Delta^2 u^{[k]} = k(k-1)u^{[k-2]} \qquad \text{and} \qquad \Delta^k u^{[k]} = k! \tag{5.28}$$

To write a polynomial $P(u)$ in terms of factorial polynomials, synthetic division is helpful. For example by algebra it is seen that

$$\begin{aligned} u^1 &= u^{[1]} \\ u^2 &= u(u-1) + u = u^{[2]} + u^{[1]} \\ u^3 &= u(u-1)(u-2) + 3u(u-1) + u \\ &= u^{[3]} + 3u^{[2]} + u^{[1]}. \end{aligned}$$

But, the coefficients in factorial polynomials $u^{[3]}$ can be derived in the following manner:

1. Divide u^3 by u. The remainder coefficient is zero and the quotient is u^2.
2. Divide u^2 by $u - 1$. The remainder coefficient is 1 and the quotient is now $u + 1$.
3. Divide $u + 1$ by $u - 2$. The remainder coefficient is 3 and the quotient is 1.

Beginning with the last quotient and choosing the remainder coefficients in reverse of the order in which they were formed, then

$$u^3 = 1(u^{[3]}) + 3u^{[2]} + u^{[1]} + 0.$$

If u^3 is expressed as $u^3 + 0(u^2) + 0(u) + 0$, then synthetically the above division can be expressed as:

$$\begin{array}{ccccl}
1 & 0 & 0 & 0 & \lfloor 0 \\
 & 0 & 0 & 0 & \\
\hline
1 & 0 & 0 & 0 & \lfloor 1 \\
 & 1 & 1 & & \\
\hline
1 & 1 & 1 & & \lfloor 2 \\
 & 2 & & & \\
\hline
1 & 3 & & & \\
\hline
1 & & & &
\end{array}$$

By taking the last coefficient and the successive remainders in the upward direction as coefficients of $u^{[3]}$, $u^{[2]}$, $u^{[1]}$, $u^{[0]}$,

$$u^3 = u^{[3]} + 3u^{[2]} + u^{[1]}. \tag{5.29}$$

Now, let

$$u = \frac{x - x_0}{h} \qquad \text{or} \qquad x = x_0 + uh;$$

then

$$P_n(x) = P_n(x_0 + uh) = P_n(u). \tag{5.30}$$

Then, since u^k may be expressed in terms of $u^{[i]}$ $(i = k, k - 1, \ldots, 0)$, $P_n(x) = P_n(u)$ may be expressed as

$$P_n(x) = c_n u^{[n]} + c_{n-1} u^{[n-1]} + \cdots + c_1 u^{[1]} + c_0 u^{[0]}, \tag{5.31}$$

where $c_0, c_1, \ldots, c_n$ are to be determined.

The coefficients can be determined by evaluating $P_n(x)$ and its successive differences at $x = x_0$, that is, at $u = 0$. Thus,

$$P_n(x_0) = c_n(0)^{[n]} + c_{n-1}(0)^{[n-1]} + \cdots + c_1(0)^{[1]} + c_0$$

or

$$P_n(x_0) = c_0, \tag{5.32}$$

and

$$\Delta P_n(x) = nc_n u^{[n-1]} + (n - 1)c_{n-1} u^{[n-2]} + \cdots + c_1,$$

then

$$\Delta P_n(x_0) = c_1. \tag{5.33}$$

Therefore, the following set of equations may be derived:

$$
\begin{aligned}
P_n(x) &= c_n u^{[n]} + c_{n-1}u^{[n-1]} + \cdots + c_1 u^{[1]} + c_0 \\
\Delta P_n(x) &= nc_n u^{[n-1]} + (n-1)c_{n-1}u^{[n-2]} + \cdots + c_1 \\
\Delta^2 P_n(x) &= n(n-1)c_n u^{[n-2]} + (n-1)(n-2)u^{[n-3]} + \cdots + 2 \cdot 1 c_2 \\
\Delta^k P_n(x) &= n(n-1)\cdots(n-k+1)c_n u^{[n-k]} \cdots k!c_k \\
&\cdots\cdots\cdots\cdots\cdots \\
\Delta^n P_n(x) &= n!c_n .
\end{aligned}
\tag{5.34}
$$

Substituting $x = x_0$ and $u = 0$, the coefficients c_i are determined as follows:

$$
\begin{aligned}
P_n(x_0) &= c_0 \\
\Delta P_n(x_0) &= c_1 \\
\frac{\Delta^2 P_n(x_0)}{2} &= c_2 \\
\cdots\cdots & \\
\frac{\Delta^k P_n(x_0)}{k!} &= c_k \\
\cdots\cdots & \\
\frac{\Delta^n P_n(x_0)}{n!} &= c_n .
\end{aligned}
\tag{5.35}
$$

Thus, $P_n(x)$ is now expressed as

$$
P_n(x) = \frac{\Delta^n P_n(x_0)u^{[n]}}{n!} + \frac{\Delta^{n-1} P_n(x_0)u^{[n-1]}}{(n-1)!} + \cdots + \Delta P_n(x_0)u^{[1]} + P_n(x_0) \tag{5.36}
$$

or

$$
P_n(x) = \sum_{i=0}^{n} \frac{u^{[i]}\,\Delta^i P_n(x_0)}{i!}. \tag{5.37}
$$

As an example of the use of the factorial polynomial, Table 5.4 may be restated as Table 5.7.

Let $x_0 = 4$, $h = 2$, $u = (x-4)/2$. Then, using

$$
P_3(x) = \sum_{i=0}^{3} \frac{u^{[i]}\,\Delta^i P_3(x_0)}{i!},
$$

$f(x) = P_3(x) = x^3$ is stated as

$$
f(x) = 64 + 152u^{[1]} + 72u^{[2]} + 8u^{[3]}. \tag{5.38}
$$

TABLE 5.7 Differences for $f(x) = x^3$ where $u = (x - 4)/2$

x	u	$f(x)$	$\Delta f(x)$	$\Delta^2 f(x)$	$\Delta^3 f(x)$	$\Delta^4 f(x)$
$x_{-2} = 0$	-2	0				
			8		48	
$x_{-1} = 2$	-1	8		48		0
			56		48	
$x_0 = 4$	0	64		96		0
			152		48	
$x_1 = 6$	1	216		144		0
			296		48	
$x_2 = 8$	2	512		192		
			488			
$x_3 = 10$	3	1000				

If x_0 were chosen to be 2, then $u = (x - 2)/2$ and Table 5.8 would be used to express $f(x)$. Thus, $f(x)$ is now expressed as

$$f(x) = 8 + 56u^{[1]} + 48u^{[2]} + 8u^{[3]}. \tag{5.39}$$

TABLE 5.8 Differences for $f(x) = x^3$ where $u = (x - 2)/2$

x	u	$f(x)$	$\Delta f(x)$	$\Delta^2 f(x)$	$\Delta^3 f(x)$	$\Delta^4 f(x)$
$x_{-1} = 0$	-1	0				
			8			
$x_0 = 2$	0	8		48		
			56		48	
$x_1 = 4$	1	64		96		0
			152		48	
$x_2 = 6$	2	216		144		0
			296		48	
$x_3 = 8$	3	512		192		
			488			
$x_4 = 10$	4	1000				

5.4 Interpolation Formulas

The question now arises: Can $f(x)$ with tabulated values at x_i, $i = 0, 1, \ldots, n$ be safely represented by $P_n(x)$ where

$$P_n(x) = \sum_{i=0}^{n} \frac{u^{[i]} \Delta^i P_n(x_0)}{i!}?$$

Let $P_n(x_i) = f(x_i)$, $i = 0, 1, 2, \ldots, n$. Let $u = (x - x_0)/h$, h being a constant. Then

$$P_n(u) = \sum_{i=0}^{n} \frac{u^{[i]} \Delta^i P_n(x_0)}{i!} \tag{5.40}$$

is a polynomial of degree n and has the same tabulated values as $f(x)$ at $x = x_i$, $i = 0, 1, \ldots, n$.

Can Eq. 5.40 be used to find an approximate value of $f(x)$ at a non-tabulated point with a good degree of accuracy? This implies that the truncation error caused by replacing $f(x)$ with a polynomial $P_n(x)$ must be small. The truncation error, it can be shown, is

$$E = \frac{h^{n+1} u^{[n+1]} f^{n+1}(\xi)}{(n+1)!}, \qquad (x_0 < \xi < x_n). \tag{5.41}$$

If the following conditions are true, $|f^{n+1}(\xi)| < M$, M a positive number, and h is chosen sufficiently small, then $|E|$ can be made as small as required. Under these two conditions, the Gregory–Newton forward interpolation formula with the remainder term E is

$$y = \sum_{i=0}^{n} \frac{u^{[i]} \Delta^i y_0}{i!} + E, \qquad E = \frac{h^{n+1} u^{[n+1]} f^{n+1}(\xi)}{(n+1)!} \tag{5.42}$$

where

$$\Delta^i y_0 = \Delta^i P_n(x_0), \qquad (i = 0, 1, \ldots, n)$$

and

$$y_j = P_n(x_j) = f(x_j), \qquad (j = 0, 1, \ldots, n, x_0 < \xi < x_n). \tag{5.43}$$

The Gregory–Newton forward interpolation formula is most often used for a value of $f(x)$ where $x_0 < x < x_1$ and $x_0 < x_1 < x_2 < \cdots < x_n$, that is, at the top of the table. Table 5.9 shows the distribution of the tabulated values and the differences for $n = 3$.

TABLE 5.9 Forward Differences, $n = 3$

x	u	y	Δy	$\Delta^2 y$	$\Delta^3 y$
x_0	0	y_0			
			Δy_0		
x_1	1	y_1		$\Delta^2 y_0$	
			Δy_1		$\Delta^3 y_0$
x_2	2	y_2		$\Delta^2 y_1$	
			Δy_2		
x_3	3	y_3			

The forward interpolation formula could be used for interpolation near the end of the table, but it would be awkward. For this, it is preferable to derive another formula. Looking ahead to such a formula, Table 5.10 is constructed based upon backward differences for $n = 3$.

TABLE 5.10 Backward Differences, $n = 3$

x	u	y	∇y	$\nabla^2 y$	$\nabla^3 y$
x_{-3}	-3	y_{-3}			
			∇y_{-2}		
x_{-2}	-2	y_{-2}		$\nabla^2 y_{-1}$	
			∇y_{-1}		$\nabla^3 y_0$
x_{-1}	-1	y_{-1}		$\nabla^2 y_0$	
			∇y_0		
x_0	0	y_0			

The interpolating formula will be expressed in terms of factorial polynomials in u and $\nabla^k y_0$, $k = 0, 1, 2, 3$.

First, define factorial polynomials in u by the set of equations:

$$\begin{aligned} u &= \frac{x - x_0}{h}, \qquad (h \text{ a constant}) \\ u^{\{0\}} &= 1 \\ u^{\{1\}} &= u \\ u^{\{2\}} &= u(u+1) \\ &\cdots\cdots \\ u^{\{k\}} &= u(u+1)\ldots(u+k-1). \end{aligned} \tag{5.44}$$

The backward differences of $u^{\{k\}}$ are

$$\begin{aligned} \nabla u^{\{k\}} &= u^{\{k\}} - (u-1)^{\{k\}} \\ &= (u+k-1)u^{\{k-1\}} - (u-1)u^{\{k-1\}} \\ &= k u^{\{k-1\}}, \qquad (k = 1, 2, \ldots). \end{aligned} \tag{5.45}$$

Other backward differences are

$$\begin{aligned} \nabla^2 u^{\{k\}} &= k(k-1)u^{\{k-2\}}, \qquad (k = 2, 3, \ldots) \\ &\cdots\cdots\cdots \\ \nabla^k u^{\{k\}} &= k!, \qquad (k \text{ a positive integer}). \end{aligned} \tag{5.46}$$

It is now required to express u^k, $k = 1, 2, \ldots$, in terms of $u^{\{k\}}$, for example:

$$
\begin{aligned}
u^2 &= u(u+1) - u \\
&= u^{\{2\}} - u, \\
u^3 &= u(u+1)(u+2) - 3u(u+1) + u \\
&= u^{\{3\}} - 3u^{\{2\}} + u^{\{1\}}.
\end{aligned}
\tag{5.47}
$$

In general,

$$u^k = u^{\{k\}} + a_1 u^{\{k-1\}} + \cdots + a_{k-1} u^{\{1\}} + a_k . \tag{5.48}$$

By expressing u^k as

$$u^k + 0 \cdot u^{k-1} + 0 \cdot u^{k-2} + \cdots + 0 \cdot u + 0$$

and dividing by $u = 0, -1, -2, \ldots$ successively, the coefficients a_1, $a_2, \ldots, a_k$ are determined as the remainder terms in the division. For $k = 3$, by synthetic division,

$$
\begin{array}{cccc|l}
1 & 0 & 0 & 0 & \underline{0} \\
 & 0 & 0 & 0 & \\
\hline
1 & 0 & 0 & 0 & \underline{-1} \\
 & -1 & 1 & & \\
\hline
1 & -1 & 1 & & \underline{-2} \\
 & -2 & & & \\
\hline
1 & -3 & & & \\
\cline{1-2}
1 & & & &
\end{array}
$$

and by choosing remainder coefficients,

$$u^3 = u^{\{3\}} - 3u^{\{2\}} + u^{\{1\}}. \tag{5.49}$$

Since u^k is expressible in terms of $u^{\{k\}}, u^{\{k-1\}}, \ldots, u^{\{1\}}, 1, P_n(x) = P_n(u)$ can be stated as

$$P_n(x) = c_0 u^{\{n\}} + c_1 u^{\{k-1\}} + \cdots + c_{n-1} u^{\{1\}} + c_n . \tag{5.50}$$

Successive differences are

$$
\begin{aligned}
\nabla P_n(x) &= nc_0 u^{\{n-1\}} + (n-1)c_1 u^{\{n-2\}} + \cdots + c_{n-1} \\
\nabla^2 P_n(x) &= n(n-1)c_0 u^{\{n-2\}} + (n-1)(n-2)c_1 u^{\{n-3\}} + \cdots + 2c_{n-2} \\
&\cdots\cdots \\
\nabla^n P_n(x) &= n!c_0 .
\end{aligned}
\tag{5.51}
$$

Substituting $x = x_0$ and $u = 0$ in Eqs. 5.50 and 5.51,

$$\begin{aligned} P_n(x_0) &= c_n \\ \nabla P_n(x_0) &= c_{n-1} \\ \frac{\nabla^2 P_n(x_0)}{2!} &= c_{n-2} \\ \cdot \quad \cdot \quad \cdot & \quad \cdot \quad \cdot \quad \cdot \quad \cdot \\ \frac{\nabla^n P_n(x_0)}{n!} &= c_0 . \end{aligned} \tag{5.52}$$

Thus, Eq. 5.50 becomes

$$P_n(x) = \frac{u^{\{n\}}\, \nabla^n P_n(x_0)}{n!} + \frac{u^{\{n-1\}}\, \nabla^{n-1} P_n(x_0)}{(n-1)!} + \cdots + P_n(x_0) \tag{5.53}$$

or

$$P_n(x) = \sum_{i=0}^{n} \frac{u^{\{i\}}\, \nabla^i P_n(x_0)}{i!}. \tag{5.54}$$

The question now asked is: Can $f(x)$, whose tabulated values are $f(x_i) = y_i$ at $x = x_i$, $i = 0, 1, 2, \ldots, n$, be replaced by a polynomial in $u^{\{k\}}$ for interpolation purposes? The answer is yes, provided that h is chosen sufficiently small and that $|f^{n+1}(\xi)| < M$, M a positive number. That is,

$$y = \sum_{i=0}^{n} \frac{u^{\{i\}}\, \nabla^i y_0}{i!} + E, \qquad E = \frac{u^{\{n+1\}} h^{n+1} f^{n+1}(\xi)}{(n+1)!}, \tag{5.55}$$

where E is the truncation error.

Equation 5.55 is called the Gregory–Newton formula for backward interpolation with remainder term, and is usually used to interpolate for values of $f(x)$, where $x_{-1} < x < x_0$ in reference to Table 5.10.

Referring to Table 5.7, $x_0 = 4$, $h = (x - 4)/2$; then the Gregory–Newton backward interpolation formula is

$$y = y_0 + u^{\{1\}}\, \nabla y_0 + \frac{u^{\{2\}}\, \nabla^2 y_0}{2} + \frac{u^{\{3\}}\, \nabla^3 y_0}{3!} + E,$$

$$E = \frac{h^4 u^{\{4\}} f^4(\xi)}{4!}, \tag{5.56}$$

and substituting,

$$y = 64 + 56u^{\{1\}} + 24u^{\{2\}} + 8u^{\{3\}} + E,$$

$$E = \frac{2^4 u^{\{4\}} f^4(\xi)}{4!} = 0 \tag{5.57}$$

5.5 Gauss Interpolation Formulas

In addition to the two Gregory–Newton formulas, the Gauss forward and Gauss backward formulas both expressed in terms of central differences are convenient for interpolation of values of $f(x)$ where x is near the middle of the set of values $\{x_{-n}, x_{-n+1}, \ldots, x_{-1}, x_0, \ldots, x_n\}$.

Specifically for the Gauss forward interpolation formula, let $y = P(x)$ have the tabulated values $\{y_{-n}, y_{-n+1}, \ldots, y_{-1}, y_0, y_1, \ldots, y_n\}$, which are also the tabulated values of $f(x)$. It is desired to express y in terms of the differences:

$$y_0,\ \delta y_{1/2},\ \delta^2 y_0,\ \delta^3 y_{1/2},\ \ldots,\ \delta^{2k-1} y_{1/2},\ \delta^{2k} y_0.$$

In order to approach the development of the Gauss formulas, a table of central differences is presented in Table 5.11.

TABLE 5.11 Central Differences

x	u	y	δy	$\delta^2 y$	$\delta^3 y$	$\delta^4 y$	$\delta^5 y$		
x_{-5}	-5	y_{-5}							
			$\delta y_{-9/2}$						
x_{-4}	-4	y_{-4}		$\delta^2 y_{-4}$					
			$\delta y_{-7/2}$		$\delta^3 y_{-7/2}$				
x_{-3}	-3	y_{-3}		$\delta^2 y_{-3}$		$\delta^4 y_{-3}$			
			$\delta y_{-5/2}$		$\delta^3 y_{-5/2}$		$\delta^5 y_{-5/2}$		
x_{-2}	-2	y_{-2}		$\delta^2 y_{-2}$		$\delta^4 y_{-2}$		$\delta^6 y_{-2}$	
			$\delta y_{-3/2}$		$\delta^3 y_{-3/2}$		$\delta^5 y_{-3/2}$		.
x_{-1}	-1	y_{-1}		$\delta^2 y_{-1}$		$\delta^4 y_{-1}$		$\delta^6 y_{-1}$	
			$\delta y_{-1/2}$		$\delta^3 y_{-1/2}$		$\delta^5 y_{-1/2}$		.
x_0	0	y_0 ↘		↗ $\delta^2 y_0$ ↘		↗ $\delta^4 y_0$ ↘		↗ $\delta^6 y_0$	
			$\delta y_{1/2}$ ↗		$\delta^3 y_{1/2}$ ↗		$\delta^5 y_{1/2}$ ↗		.
x_1	1	y_1		$\delta^2 y_1$		$\delta^4 y_1$		$\delta^6 y_1$	
			$\delta y_{3/2}$		$\delta^3 y_{3/2}$		$\delta^5 y_{3/2}$		.
x_2	2	y_2		$\delta^2 y_2$		$\delta^4 y_2$		$\delta^6 y_2$	
			$\delta y_{5/2}$		$\delta^3 y_{5/2}$		$\delta^5 y_{5/2}$		
x_3	3	y_3		$\delta^2 y_3$		$\delta^4 y_3$			
			$\delta y_{7/2}$		$\delta^3 y_{7/2}$				
x_4	4	y_4		$\delta^2 y_4$					
			$\delta y_{9/2}$						
x_5	5	y_5							
.									
.									
.									

Taking a path as indicated by arrows and using the notation $(u - r)^{[k]}$ where r is a tabulated value of u, the Gauss forward interpolation formula is

$$y = y_0 + \left(u^{[1]}\,\delta y_{1/2} + \frac{u^{[2]}}{2!}\,\delta^2 y_0\right) + \left(\frac{(u+1)^{[3]}}{3!}\,\delta^3 y_{1/2} + (u+1)^{[4]}\,\delta^4 y_0\right)$$

$$+ \left(\frac{(u+2)^{[5]}}{5!}\,\delta^5 y_{1/2} + \frac{(u+2)^{[6]}}{6!}\,\delta^6 y_0\right) + \cdots$$

$$+ \left(\frac{(u+k-1)^{[2k-1]}}{(2k-1)!}\,\delta^{2k-1} y_{1/2} + \frac{(u+k-1)^{[2k]}}{(2k)!}\,\delta^{2k} y_0\right), \tag{5.58}$$

where the last two terms represent the general terms. This formula need not be memorized. It can be constructed by using the few suggestions listed below. For each tabulated value of u, such as 0, y must have the corresponding tabulated value, such as y_0. Hence for $u = 0$, $y = y_0$.

Considering now a partial table (Table 5.12), y must equal y_0 when $u = 0$, and y must equal y_1 when $u = 1$. Hence for $u = 0$, $y = y_0$,

$$y = y_0 + (u - 0)^{[1]}\,\delta y_{1/2} = y_0 + u^{[1]}\,\delta y_{1/2}; \tag{5.59}$$

for $u = 1$,

$$y = y_0 + \delta y_{1/2} = y_0 + (y_1 - y_0) = y_1. \tag{5.60}$$

Now consider Table 5.13, which is Table 5.12 extended to one more difference. As an example of the construction of a coefficient in $u^{[k]}$ of $\delta^k y_i$, consider the term $\delta^2 y_0$. The coefficient of $\delta^2 y_0$ can be found by

TABLE 5.12
Central Differences, $n = 1$

x	u	y	δy
x_0	0	y_0	
			$\delta y_{1/2}$
x_1	1	y_1	

TABLE 5.13
Central Differences, $n = 2$

x	u	y	δy	$\delta^2 y_0$
x_{-1}	-1	y_{-1}		
			$\delta y_{-1/2}$	
x_0	0	y_0		$\delta^2 y_0$
			$\delta y_{1/2}$	
x_1	1	y_1		

considering the triangle indicated in Table 5.13. The uppermost value of u in this triangle is zero. Then the corresponding term is

$$\frac{(u-0)^{[2]}}{2!}\,\delta^2 y_0 = \frac{u^{[2]}}{2!}\,\delta^2 y_0. \tag{5.61}$$

In general, any term can be formed in the same manner. Referring now to Table 5.11, the u coefficient of any central difference is found by mentally forming a triangle whose vertex is at the preceding term of the formula. The uppermost value of u in this triangle is the value of r in $(u - r)^{[k]}$. Thus for $\delta^3 y_{1/2}$, $(u - r)^{[k]}$ is

$$\frac{(u - (-1))^{[3]}}{3!} = \frac{(u + 1)^{[3]}}{3!}; \tag{5.62}$$

hence the term is

$$\frac{(u + 1)^{[3]}}{3!} \delta^3 y_{1/2}. \tag{5.63}$$

The Gauss backward interpolation formula is now easily obtained. The backward formula is expressed in terms of the differences:

$$y_0, \delta y_{-1/2}, \delta^2 y_0, \delta^3 y_{-1/2}, \delta^4 y_0, \ldots .$$

Following a path in Table 5.14 along these differences (indicated by arrows) and using the factorial in u explained above,

$$\begin{aligned} y = {} & (u^{[0]} y_0 + u^{[1]} \delta y_{-1/2}) + \left(\frac{(u + 1)^{[2]}}{2!} \delta^2 y_0 + \frac{(u + 1)^{[3]}}{3!} \delta^3 y_{-1/2}\right) \\ & + \left(\frac{(u + 2)^{[4]}}{4!} \delta^4 y_0 + \frac{(u + 2)^{[5]}}{5!} \delta^5 y_{-1/2}\right) + \cdots \\ & + \left(\frac{1}{(2k)!} (u + k)^{[2k]} \delta^{2k} y_0 + \frac{1}{(2k + 1)!} (u + k)^{[2k+1]} \delta^{2k+1} y_{-1/2}\right) + \cdots \end{aligned} \tag{5.64}$$

where the last two terms represent the general terms.

TABLE 5.14 Path of the Gauss Backward Interpolation Formula

x	u	y	δy	$\delta^2 y$	$\delta^3 y$	$\delta^4 y$	$\delta^5 y$	$\delta^6 y$
x_{-3}	-3	y_{-3}						
			$\delta y_{-5/2}$					
x_{-2}	-2	y_{-2}		$\delta^2 y_{-2}$				
			$\delta y_{-3/2}$		$\delta^3 y_{-3/2}$			
x_{-1}	-1	y_{-1}		$\delta^2 y_{-1}$		$\delta^4 y_{-1}$		
			$\delta y_{-1/2}$		$\delta^3 y_{-1/2}$		$\delta^5 y_{-1/2}$	
x_0	0	y_0		$\delta^2 y_0$		$\delta^4 y_0$		
			$\delta y_{1/2}$		$\delta^3 y_{1/2}$			
x_1	1	y_1		$\delta^2 y_1$				
			$\delta y_{3/2}$					
x_2	2	y_2						

The remainder term in either the Gauss forward or Gauss backward formula is found as follows: If the formula terminates on the nth central difference, consider the $(n + 1)$th term as if the series were extended to this term but replace the $(n + 1)$th difference by $h^{n+1}f^{n+1}(\xi)$. For example, suppose that a Gauss forward formula terminates on the term

$$\frac{(u + 2)^{[6]}\, \delta^6 y_0}{6!};$$

the next term of the extended series is

$$\frac{(u + 3)^{[7]}\, \delta^7 y_{1/2}}{7!},$$

and the remainder term would be

$$\frac{(u + 3)^{[7]}\, h^7 f^7(\xi)}{7!}.$$

In general, for the Gauss forward interpolation formula terminating on

$$\frac{(u + k - 1)^{[2k]}\, \delta^{2k} y_0}{(2k)!},$$

the remainder term is

$$\frac{(u + k)^{[2k+1]}\, h^{2k+1} f^{2k+1}(\xi)}{(2k + 1)!};$$

terminating on

$$\frac{(u + k - 1)^{[2k-1]}\, \delta^{2k-1} y_{1/2}}{(2k - 1)!},$$

the remainder term is

$$\frac{1}{(2k)!}\,(u + k - 1)^{[2k]}\, h^{2k} f^{2k}(\xi).$$

EXERCISE

Write the two remainder terms for the Gauss backward interpolation formula.

5.5.1 Observations on Difference Interpolation Formulas

First, it should be noted that the choice of x_0 is arbitrary; it may be the beginning value, the last value, or the middle value of the tabulated values of x. The Gregory–Newton formula for forward interpolation in general will be best suited for interpolation near the beginning of the table, while the Gregory–Newton backward formula usually is used for interpolation near the end of the table. The two Gauss formulas in general are more suited for interpolating for values of $f(x)$ near the middle of the table.

Since the truncation error in all formulas is a function of a high order derivative of $f(x)$, not much can be stated about the truncation error without a knowledge of the function $f(x)$.

5.5.2 Flow Chart

The Gregory–Newton forward interpolation formula (Eq. 5.42) may be written as

$$Y = \sum_{i=1}^{n} \frac{y_{ii}}{(i-1)!} \left\{ \prod_{j=0}^{i-2} (u-j) \right\} \tag{5.65}$$

where $\pi_{j=0}^{-1}(u-j)$ is defined as 1. This notation agrees with the notation used in Sec. 5.2.2 on the formation of a difference table. Flow Chart 5.5.2 is a continuation of Flow Chart 5.2.2.

FLOW CHART 5.5.2 Gregory–Newton Formula for Forward Interpolation

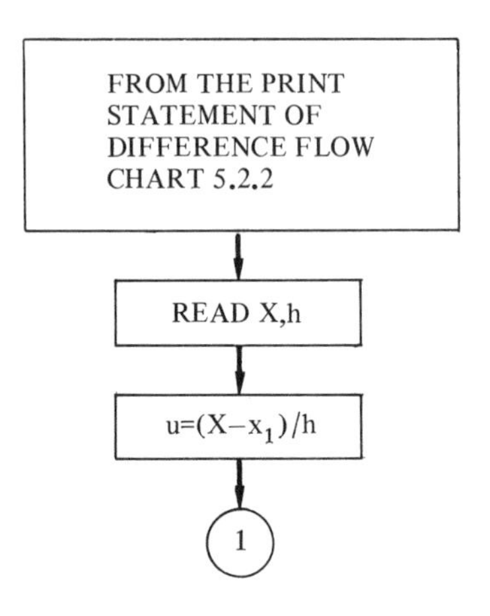

Flow Chart 5.5.2 *(Continued)*

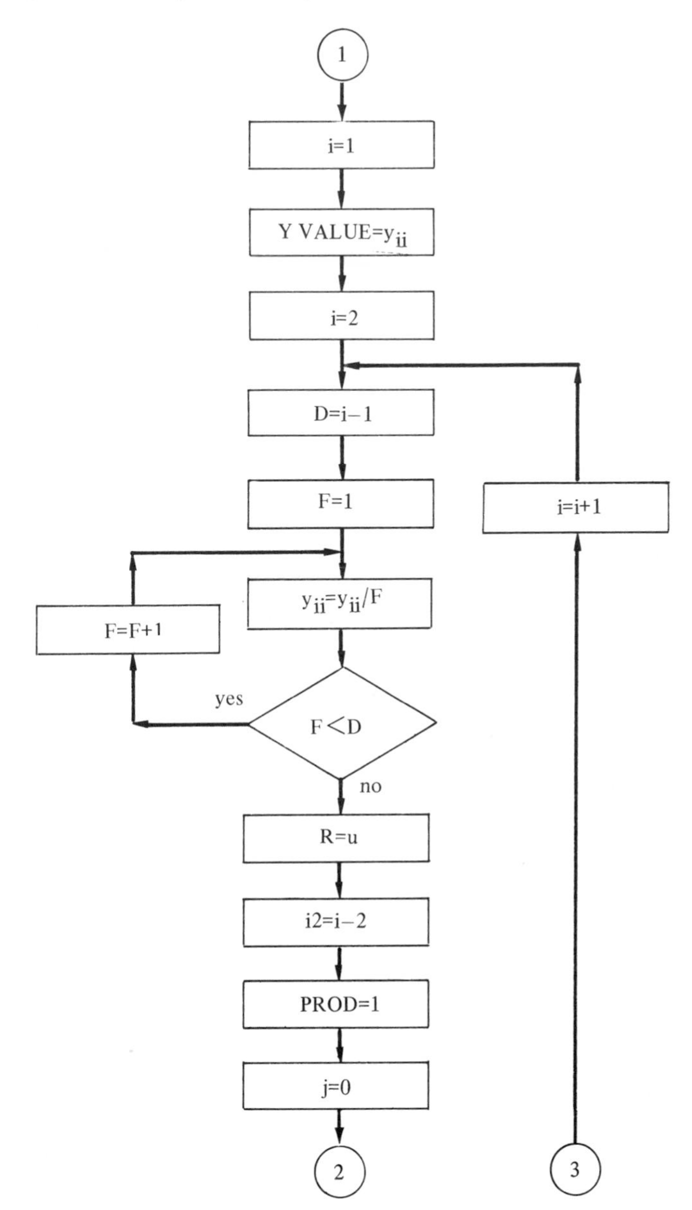

Flow Chart 5.5.2 *(Continued)*

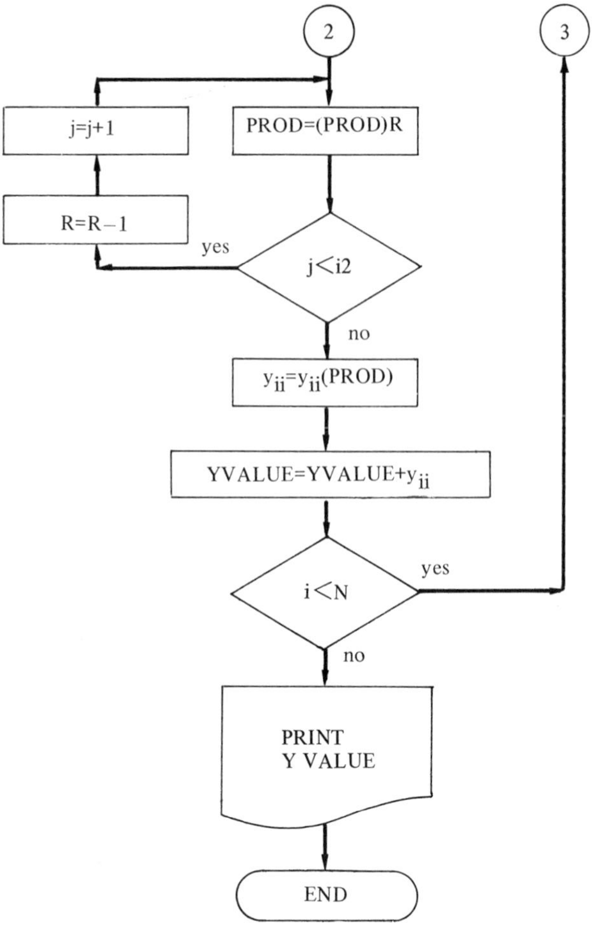

2

3

j=j+1

PROD=(PROD)R

R=R−1

yes

j<i2

no

$y_{ii}=y_{ii}$(PROD)

YVALUE=YVALUE+y_{ii}

yes

i<N

no

PRINT
Y VALUE

END

Definitions and Notation

Let *YVALUE* represent the interpolated value of $f(x)$, $x_1 < x < x_2$; $u = (X - x_1)/h$ is the value of u corresponding to X. F generates the factorial $(i - 1)!$. *PROD* (set initially equal to 1) and R generate the product

$$\prod_{j=0}^{i-2} (u - j) = u^{[i-2]}$$

where R takes on the values $u - j$, $j = 0, 1, \ldots, i - 2$.

PROBLEMS

Table 5.15 shows paths to be taken for the Gregory–Newton forward and backward and for the Gauss forward and backward interpolation formulas, using the notation below:

Gregory–Newton Forward ⟶
Gregory–Newton Backward ─┼→
Gauss Forward ─┼┼→
Gauss Backward ─┼┼┼→

TABLE 5.15 Paths of Gregory–Newton and Gauss Interpolation Formulas

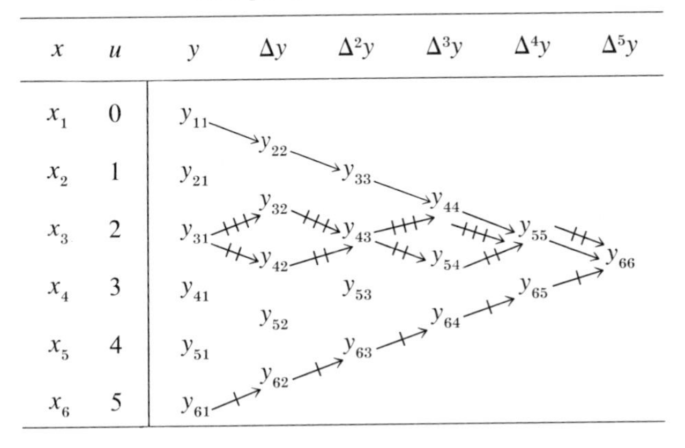

x	u	y	Δy	$\Delta^2 y$	$\Delta^3 y$	$\Delta^4 y$	$\Delta^5 y$
x_1	0	y_{11}					
			y_{22}				
x_2	1	y_{21}		y_{33}			
			y_{32}		y_{44}		
x_3	2	y_{31}		y_{43}		y_{55}	
			y_{42}		y_{54}		y_{66}
x_4	3	y_{41}		y_{53}		y_{65}	
			y_{52}		y_{64}		
x_5	4	y_{51}		y_{63}			
			y_{62}				
x_6	5	y_{61}					

The differences are denoted by y_{ij}. The zero differences, that is, the tabulated values of $f(x)$, are y_{i1}, $i = 1, 2, \ldots 6$. Based on this table, formulas for the four formulas can be derived for interpolation at the top, middle, or bottom of the table.

1. Gregory–Newton forward formula ($YNGF$):

$$YGNF = \sum_{i=1}^{2n} \frac{y_{ii}}{(i-1)!} \left\{ \prod_{j=0}^{i-2} (u-j) \right\} + E,$$

$$E = \frac{h^{2n}}{(2n)!} f^{2n}(\xi) \prod_{j=0}^{2n-1} (u-j). \tag{5.66}$$

2. Gregory–Newton backward formula ($YNGB$):

$$YGNB = \sum_{i=1}^{2n} \frac{y_{2n,i}}{(i-1)!} \prod_{j=0}^{i-2} [u+j-(2n-1)] + E,$$

$$E = \frac{h^{2n}}{(2n)!} f^{2n}(\xi) \prod_{j=0}^{2n-1} [u+j-(2n-1)]. \tag{5.67}$$

3. Gauss forward formula (YGF):

$$YGF = \sum_{i=0}^{n-1} \frac{y_{n+i,1+2i}}{(2i)!} \prod_{j=0}^{2i-1} [u + j - (n-1) - i]$$

$$+ \sum_{i=1}^{n} \frac{y_{n+i,2i}}{(2i-1)!} \prod_{j=1}^{2i-1} [u + j - (n-1) - i] + E,$$

$$E = \frac{h^{2n}}{(2n)!} f^{2n}(\xi) \prod_{j=1}^{2n} [u + j - 2n] \qquad (5.68)$$

where $2n$ is the number of tabulated values of x, and $\pi_{j=1}^{-1}(A)$, A a real number, is defined as 1.

5-1. Derive a formula with a remainder term similar to (5.68) for the Gauss backward interpolation (YGB).

5-2. Assume that the set of values

$$\{(x_1, y_{11}), (x_2, y_{21}), \ldots, (x_{2n}, y_{2n,1})\}$$

is the set of tabulated values of x and $f(x)$. Define the set of values of $u_i = (x_i - x_1)/h$ as $\{0, 1, 2, \ldots, 2n-1\}$. Let r, s, t, v be values of u for which interpolated values of $f(x)$ are to be determined by the interpolation formulas, where

$$0 < r < 1, \quad n-1 < s < n, \quad n-1 < t < n, \quad 2n-2 < v < 2n-1.$$

The corresponding values of x are

$$x_r = x_0 + rh, \quad x_s = x_0 + sh, \quad x_t = x_0 + th, \quad x_v = x_0 + vh.$$

Write a flow chart to

(a) Read (x_i, y_{i1}), $i = 1, 2, \ldots, 2n$.
(b) Form all differences.
(c) Interpolate for a value of $f(x_r)$ by the Gregory–Newton forward formula.
(d) Interpolate for a value of $f(x_s)$ by the Gauss backward formula.
(e) Interpolate for a value of $f(x_t)$ by the Gauss forward formula.
(f) Interpolate for $f(x_v)$ by the Gregory–Newton backward formula.
(g) Evaluate the remainder term in each formula.
(h) Print: $r, s, t, v, x_r, x_s, x_t, x_v$, the values of $f(x_r), f(x_s), f(x_t), f(x_v)$, and the remainder terms for each of these values.

5-3. Given the set of tabulated values of ln x:

x	.3	.4	.5	.6	.7	.8
ln x	−1.203973	−.916291	−.693147	−.510826	−.356675	−.223144

write a program based on the flow chart in Prob. 5-2 to find values of $f(x)$ and the remainder terms for $x = .375, .56, .78$. Find the value of ln .56 by the Gauss forward and Gauss backward formulas.

5-4. Use linear interpolation to find ln .375, ln .56, and ln .78. Compared with the answers in Prob. 5-3, how accurate are these values by linear interpolation?

5.6 Lagrange Interpolation

In the Gregory-Newton and Gauss interpolation formulas, spacing of tabular points was constant. But suppose that $f(x)$ is tabulated at nonconstant intervals—then the previously considered formulas cannot be applied.

For example, let $f(x)$ have tabulated values of $f(a_1)$ at $x = a_1$, $f(a_2)$ at $x = a_2$. (In this simple example, there is only one interval.) A polynomial function $y(x)$ is to be formed such that $y(x) = f(a_1)$ at $x = a_1$ and $y(x) = f(a_2)$ at $x = a_2$. By linear interpolation, the polynomial is

$$y = \frac{x - a_2}{a_1 - a_2} f(a_1) + \frac{x - a_1}{a_2 - a_1} f(a_2). \tag{5.69}$$

In a general application of Eq. 5.69, if $f(x)$ has tabulated values of $f(a_i)$ at $x = a_i$, $i = 1, 2, \ldots, n$, then each polynomial of degree $n - 1$ that multiplies $f(a_k)$ must equal 1 when $x = a_k$ and 0 when $x \neq a_k$. Thus,

$$\begin{aligned} y = {} & \frac{(x - a_2)(x - a_3) \cdots (x - a_n)}{(a_1 - a_2)(a_1 - a_3) \cdots (a_1 - a_n)} f(a_1) \\ & + \frac{(x - a_1)(x - a_3) \cdots (x - a_n)}{(a_2 - a_1)(a_2 - a_3) \cdots (a_2 - a_n)} f(a_2) \\ & + \frac{(x - a_1)(x - a_2)(x - a_4) \cdots (x - a_n)}{(a_3 - a_1)(a_3 - a_2)(a_3 - a_4) \cdots (a_3 - a_n)} f(a_3) \\ & \cdots\cdots\cdots\cdots\cdots\cdots \\ & + \frac{(x - a_1)(x - a_2)(x - a_3) \cdots (x - a_{n-1})}{(a_n - a_1)(a_n - a_2)(a_n - a_3) \cdots (a_n - a_{n-1})} f(a_n). \end{aligned} \tag{5.70}$$

This formula can be stated as

$$y(x) = \sum_{i=1}^{n} y_i \prod_{j=1, j \neq i}^{n} \left\{ \frac{x - a_j}{a_i - a_j} \right\} \tag{5.71}$$

where $y_i = f(a_i)$, $i = 1, 2, \ldots, n$.

It can be shown that the truncation error, due to the fact that $f(x)$ has been replaced by a polynomial, is

$$E = \frac{1}{n!} f^n(\xi) \left\{ \prod_{i=1}^{n} (x - a_i) \right\}, \qquad (a_1 < \xi < a_n). \tag{5.72}$$

By interchanging the role of x with that of y, the Lagrange interpolation formula can be used for inverse interpolation. *Direct* interpolation is the technique for finding a value of y for a given nontabulated value of x. *Inverse* interpolation may be defined as the technique for finding a value of x for a given nontabulated value of y.

Thus, for a set of tabulated values $(a_1, y_1)(a_2, y_2) \ldots (a_n, y_n)$, the inverse interpolation formula of Lagrange is

$$x = \sum_{i=1}^{n} a_i \prod_{j=1, j \neq i}^{n} \left\{ \frac{y - y_j}{y_i - y_j} \right\}. \tag{5.73}$$

The error in this formula depends upon the errors in the tabulated values of x, and also on the fact that the inverse function is approximated by a polynomial. For the latter error, the formula is

$$E = \prod_{i=1}^{n} \frac{y - y_i}{n!} F^n(Y) \tag{5.74}$$

where $y_1 < Y < y_n$ and $F(Y)$ is the inverse function of $f(x)$.

5.6.1 Flow Chart for Direct Interpolation

Definitions and Notation

The formula is

$$y = \sum_{i=1}^{n} y_i \left[\prod_{j=1, j \neq i}^{n} \frac{x - a_j}{a_i - a_j} \right] + E, \qquad E = \prod_{i=1}^{n} \frac{(x - a_i)R}{n!}.$$

The set $\{(a_1, y_1), (a_2, y_2), \ldots, (a_n, y_n)\}$ represents the set of tabulated values $\{a_i, f(a_i)\}$.
X is a given value of x.
R is an upper bound of $|f^n(\xi)|$.
E is the truncation error.

Initial and Current Values

SUM [representing the interpolated value of $y = f(X)$] initially set equal to zero.
E (representing truncation error) initially set equal to 1.
F (representing $n!$ in the error term) initially set equal to 1.
PROD [representing $\pi_{j=1, j \neq i}^{n}(X - a_j)/(a_i - a_j)$ for each value of i] initially set equal to 1.

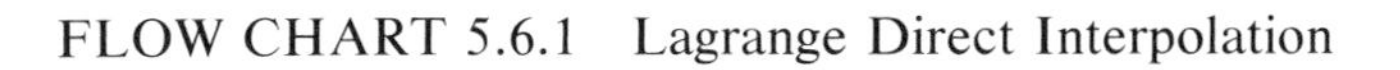

FLOW CHART 5.6.1 Lagrange Direct Interpolation

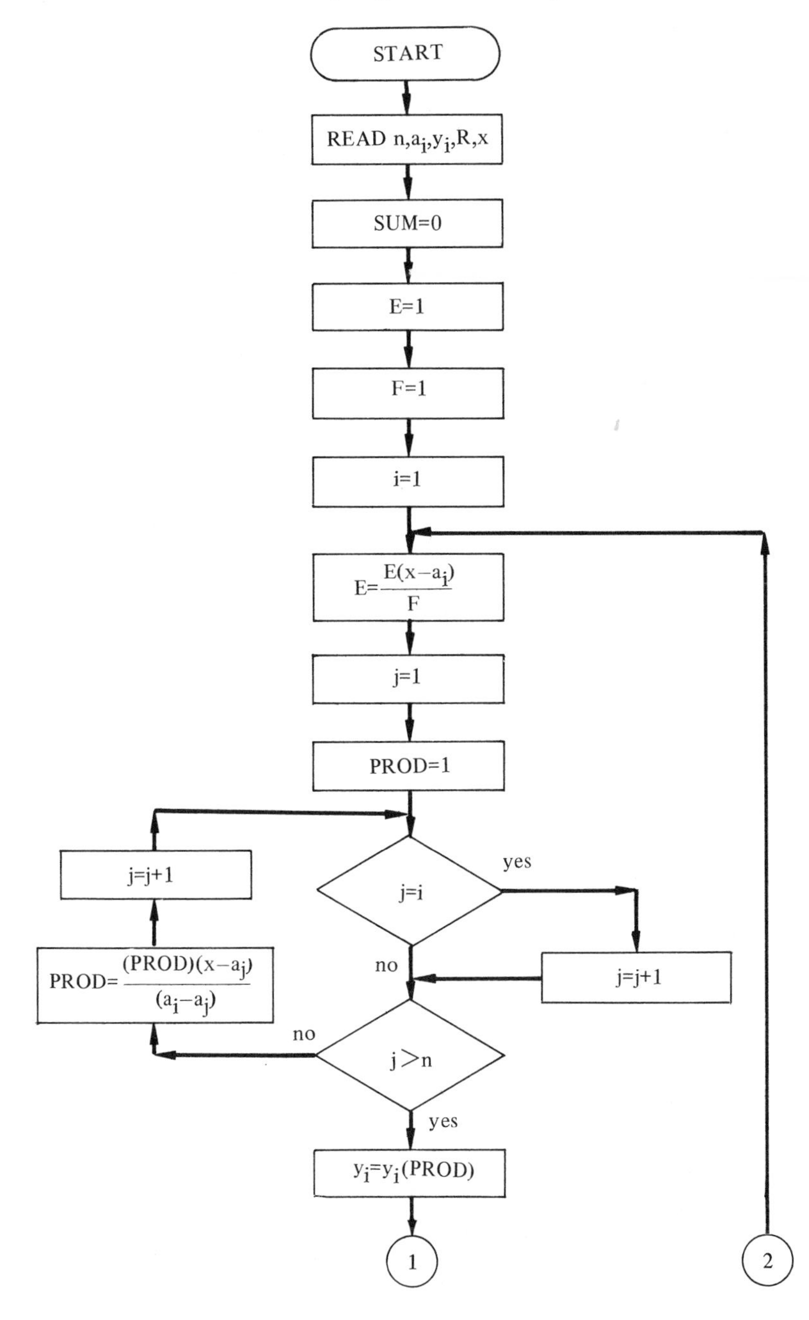

Flow Chart 5.6.1 *(Continued)*

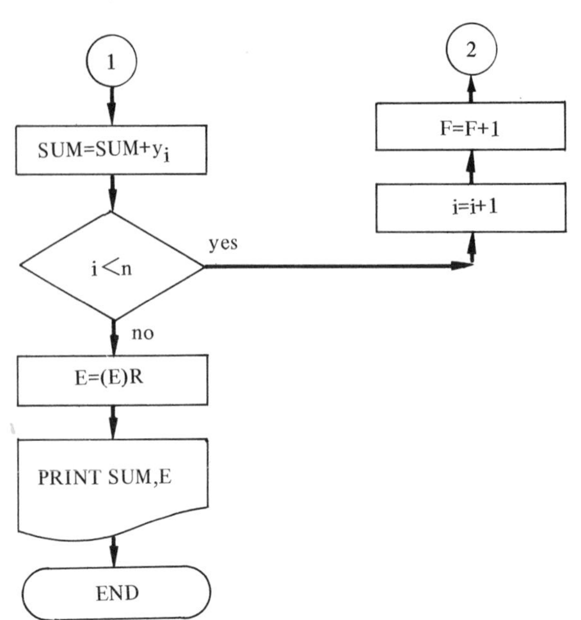

5.6.2 Further Remarks

The error due to round-off in the tabulated values in the direct formula has not been considered here. In the inverse interpolation formula, there is an inherent error dependent on the round-off error in the tabulated values of y_i. (For that matter, there may be errors in x_i.) In Flow Chart 5.6.1, the tabulated values y_i are continually being changed by the statement $y_i = y_i(PROD)$. This can be avoided by setting z_i equal to y_i, $i = 1, 2, \ldots, n$, and using z_i in all computations. Thus the y_i values can be saved for other purposes.

5.7 Iterated Interpolation

An apparently distinct disadvantage of the Lagrange interpolation method as compared with a finite difference method is that considerably more recalculation would be required in order to have a Lagrange formula extended so that it would include $n + 1$ points instead of n points. In formula 5.71, each coefficient of each y_i would have to be recalculated by multiplying by

$$\frac{x - a_{n+1}}{a_i - a_{n+1}}$$

and another term,

$$y_{n+1} \prod_{j=1}^{n} \frac{x - a_j}{a_{n+1} - a_j},$$

would have to be added. But a finite difference method can be extended by adding the next tabular point and computing a row of differences.

The iteration described below shows that the disadvantage is only apparent. For example, given a set of tabulated values (a_1, y_1), (a_2, y_2), the Lagrange interpolation formula is

$$\begin{aligned} y &= \frac{(a_2 - x)y_1}{a_2 - a_1} + \frac{(a_1 - x)y_2}{a_1 - a_2} \\ &= \frac{1}{a_2 - a_1}[(a_2 - x)y_1 - (a_1 - x)y_2] \end{aligned}$$

or

$$y = \frac{1}{a_2 - a_1}\begin{vmatrix} y_1 & a_1 - x \\ y_2 & a_2 - x \end{vmatrix}. \tag{5.75}$$

Denote y_1 as y_{11}, y_2 as y_{21}, and y as y_{22}. Then Eq. 5.75 becomes

$$y_{22} = \frac{1}{a_2 - a_1}\begin{vmatrix} y_{11} & a_1 - x \\ y_{21} & a_2 - x \end{vmatrix}. \tag{5.76}$$

Suppose now that (a_3, y_3), which may be denoted as (a_3, y_{31}), is added to the given set of data. Then

$$\begin{aligned} y_{32} &= \frac{1}{a_3 - a_1}\begin{vmatrix} y_{11} & a_1 - x \\ y_{31} & a_3 - x \end{vmatrix} \\ &= \frac{1}{a_3 - a_1}[(a_3 - x)y_{11} - (a_1 - x)y_{31}]. \end{aligned} \tag{5.77}$$

This is the Lagrange interpolation formula for the set of data (a_1, y_{11}) and (a_3, y_{31}).

Using notation similar to that in (5.76) and (5.77), the Lagrange interpolation formula for the set of data (a_1, y_{11}), (a_2, y_{21}), and (a_3, y_{31}) may be written as

$$y_{33} = \frac{1}{a_3 - a_2}\begin{vmatrix} y_{22} & a_2 - x \\ y_{32} & a_3 - x \end{vmatrix}; \tag{5.78}$$

that is,

$$y_{33} = \frac{(a_3 - x)y_{22}}{a_3 - a_2} - \frac{(a_2 - x)y_{32}}{a_3 - a_2}. \tag{5.79}$$

Substituting (5.76) for y_{22} and (5.77) for y_{32},

$$y_{33} = \frac{1}{a_3 - a_2}\left\{\frac{(a_3 - x)\,[(a_2 - x)y_{11} - (a_1 - x)y_{21}]}{a_2 - a_1} - (a_2 - x)\left[\frac{(a_3 - x)y_{11}}{(a_3 - a_1)} - \frac{(a_1 - x)y_{31}}{a_3 - a_1}\right]\right\}. \tag{5.80}$$

After simplification,

$$y_{33} = \frac{(a_3 - x)(a_2 - x)y_{11}}{(a_1 - a_3)(a_1 - a_2)} + \frac{(a_3 - x)(a_1 - x)y_{21}}{(a_2 - a_3)(a_2 - a_1)} + \frac{(a_2 - x)(a_1 - x)y_{31}}{(a_3 - a_1)(a_3 - a_2)}. \tag{5.81}$$

Equation 5.81 is the Lagrange interpolation formula for the set of data $\{(a_1, y_{11}), (a_2, y_{21}), (a_3, y_{31})\}$.

In general, the set of data may be denoted as $\{(a_1, y_{11}), (a_2, y_{21}), \ldots, (a_n, y_{n1})\}$. Thus the formula

$$y_{ij} = \frac{1}{a_i - a_{j-1}}\begin{vmatrix} y_{j-1,j-1} & a_{j-1} - x \\ y_{i,j-1} & a_i - x \end{vmatrix}, \qquad (i, j = 2, 3, \ldots, n) \tag{5.82}$$

is the Lagrange interpolation formula using the points a_i, and a_{j-1}, $a_{j-2}, \ldots, a_1$. Then y_{nn} yields the interpolated value of y for a given value of x. If $(a_{n+1}, y_{n+1,1})$ is added to the given set of values, formula 5.82 can be used by increasing the range of i and j to $n + 1$.

5.7.1 Program

For the given set of data $\{(1,1), (2,8), (6,216), (7,343)\}$, the following program computes

$$y_{i,j} = \frac{1}{a_i - a_{j-1}}\begin{vmatrix} y_{j-1,j-1} & a_{j-1} - x \\ y_{i,j-1} & a_i - x \end{vmatrix}, \qquad (i, j = 2, 3, 4);$$

$y_{44} = 125$ is the interpolated value of y for $x = 5$.

```
/JOB GO
/FTC LIST
BPS FORTRAN D COMPILER
    C PROGRAM FOR LAGRANGE ITERATED INTERPOLATION
```

```
C
      DIMENSION A(10),Y(10,10)
  600 FORMAT(I2,F5.0)
  601 FORMAT(5F10.0)
  602 FORMAT(6F10.2)
  603 FORMAT('1',//10X,'LAGRANGE INTERPOLATION',//,'Y=X**3',//,X=',
     1 F3.1)
  604 FORMAT(1H1)
      READ(5,600)N,X
      READ(5,601)(A(I),I=1,N)
      DO 10 I=1,N
   10 Y(I,1)=A(I)**3
      DO 20 J=2,N
      I=J
   50 Y(I,J)=(Y(J-1,J-1)*(A(I)-X)-Y(I,J-1)*(A(J-1)-X))/(A(I)-A(J-1))
      IF(I-N)30,20,20
   30 I=I+1
      GO TO 50
   20 CONTINUE
      WRITE(6,603)X
      DO 40 I=1,N
   40 WRITE(6,602)A(I),(Y(I,J),J=1,I)
      WRITE(6,604)
      STOP
      END
```

THE RESULTS ARE

x	y_{i1}	y_{i2}	y_{i3}	y_{i4}
1.00	1.00			
2.00	8.00	29.00		
6.00	216.00	173.00	137.00	
7.00	343.00	229.00	149.00	125.00

EXERCISE

For the set of tabulated values of $y = \ln x$ in Prob. 5-3, write a flow chart and program to interpolate for:

(a) ln (.375); find the error due to truncation.
(b) x, when $\ln x = -1.200000$; find the error due to truncation. By using formulas 5.71–5.74, only one program is needed for both (a) and (b).
(c) By the iterated interpolation method (Eq. 5.82), interpolate to find the value of ln (.375) if the set of tabulated values of $\ln x$ is extended to include (.9, −0.105367).

Compare answers in (a) with corresponding answers in Prob. 5-3, particularly with the result using the Gauss forward interpolation formula. (*Note:* It can be shown that the Lagrange interpolation polynomial for equal intervals is the same as the Gauss forward interpolation polynomial, provided they are both over the same set of values.)

5.8 Least Squares Approximation

In the first part of this chapter, Secs. 5.1 to 5.7.1, the function $f(x)$ was approximated by a polynomial $P(x)$. Whatever method was used to derive $P(x)$, it was required that the values of the approximating function $P(x_i)$ agree with the values of the function $f(x_i)$ at the points x_i, $i = 0, 1, 2, \ldots, n$.

Instead of approximating $f(x)$ by

$$P(x) = a_0 + a_1 x + \cdots + a_n x^n, \tag{5.83}$$

$f(x)$ could be approximated by a linear combination of polynomial functions, such as

$$Q(x) = a_0 q_0(x) + a_1 q_1(x) + \cdots + a_n q_n(x) \tag{5.84}$$

where $q_i(x)$ is of degree i, and a_i are determined such that $Q(x_i) = f(x_i)$, $i = 0, 1, 2, \ldots, n$.

A Taylor series expansion, truncated at its nth term, might be used as an approximating function. Also, the approximating function could consist of a linear combination of sine and cosine functions. But regardless of the class of functions used in approximating $f(x)$, the coefficients a_i are determined on the basis that the values of the approximating function agree with values of $f(x)$ at the points x_i, $i = 0, 1, 2, \ldots, n$.

If, however, the values of $f(x)$ are only known empirically, the above type of approximation might not be desirable, and perhaps might prove completely unsatisfactory. Thus, when the values of $f(x)$ are at most only good approximations of the exact values of $f(x)$, another criterion of choosing a_i is needed. This criterion is that the approximating function agree *as well as possible* with $f(x)$ over a given interval, or at $n + 1$ points according to some principle. The *least squares* principle is the basis of the criterion applied here, namely: The sum or the integral of the squared errors (which may be multiplied by a weight function) is minimized.

More precisely, let the exact values of $f(x)$ be denoted by $f(x_i)$ at the points x_i, $i = 1, 2, \ldots, n$.[3] Let the observed values of $f(x_i)$ be denoted by y_i (these values may be in error). Define the error as $E_i = f(x_i) - y_i$, $i = 1, 2, \ldots, n$. Then the observed value y_i is to be

[3] The letter n now represents the class number of $\{x_i\}$.

approximated by

$$y_i \cong a_0 + a_1 x_i + \cdots + a_m x_i^m = \sum_{j=0}^{m} a_j x_i^j. \qquad (5.85)$$

Define the residual R_i as

$$R_i = y_i - \sum_{j=0}^{m} a_j x_i^j. \qquad (5.86)$$

Then

$$\sum_{i=1}^{n} R_i^2 = \sum_{i=1}^{n} \left(y_i - \sum_{j=0}^{m} a_j x_i^j \right)^2 \qquad (5.87)$$

is required to be a minimum.[4] This requirement that $\sum_{i=1}^{n} R_i^2$ be a minimum imposes the conditions that

$$\frac{\partial}{\partial a_k}\left(\sum_{i=1}^{n} R_i^2 \right) = 0, \qquad (k = 0, 1, \ldots, m); \qquad (5.88)$$

that is,

$$\frac{\partial}{\partial a_k}\left\{ \sum_{i=1}^{n} \left(y_i - \sum_{j=0}^{m} a_j x_i^j \right)^2 \right\} = -2 \sum_{i=1}^{n} \left\{ \left(y_i - \sum_{j=0}^{m} a_j x_i^j \right) x_i^k \right\} = 0,$$

$$(k = 0, 1, \ldots, m). \qquad (5.89)$$

The set of Eqs. 5.89 simplified becomes

$$\sum_{i=1}^{n} y_i x_i^k = \sum_{j=0}^{m} a_j \left(\sum_{i=1}^{n} x_i^{j+k} \right), \qquad (k = 0, 1, \ldots, m), \qquad (5.90)$$

and may be expressed as:

$$\begin{aligned}
k = 0: &\quad n a_0 + a_1 \sum_{i=1}^{n} x_i + \cdots + a_m \sum_{i=1}^{n} x_i^m = \sum_{i=1}^{n} y_i, \\
k = 1: &\quad a_0 \sum_{i=1}^{n} x_i + a_1 \sum_{i=1}^{n} x_i^2 + \cdots + a_m \sum_{i=1}^{n} x_i^{m+1} = \sum_{i=1}^{n} x_i y_i, \qquad (5.91) \\
\cdots &\quad \cdots \\
k = m: &\quad a_0 \sum_{i=1}^{n} x_i^m + a_1 \sum_{i=1}^{n} x_i^{m+1} + \cdots + a_m \sum_{i=1}^{n} x_i^{2m} = \sum_{i=1}^{n} x_i^m y_i.
\end{aligned}$$

[4] A more general approach would be to approximate y_i by

$$y_i \cong \sum_{j=0}^{m} a_j q_j(x_i)$$

and define a weight function $w(x)$ such that $w(x_i) \geq 0$, $i = 1, \ldots, n$. Then,

$$\sum_{i=1}^{n} w(x_i) R_i^2 = \sum_{i=1}^{n} \left\{ w(x_i) \left[y_i - \sum_{j=0}^{m} a_j q_j(x_i) \right]^2 \right\}. \qquad (5.89f)$$

Thus a set of $(m + 1)$ equations in $(m + 1)$ unknowns $(a_0, a_1, \ldots, a_m)$ must be solved.

Writing the set of Eqs. 5.91 in matrix notation, it is seen that the coefficient matrix of $(a_0, a_1, \ldots, a_m)$ is symmetric; also, there is a certain relation among the coefficients convenient for formation of them in a program.

In matrix notation, Eqs. 5.91 become

$$\begin{bmatrix} n & \sum_{i=1}^{n} x_i & \sum_{i=1}^{n} x_i^2 & \sum_{i=1}^{n} x_i^3 & \cdot & \sum_{i=1}^{n} x_i^m \\ \sum_{i=1}^{n} x_i & \sum_{i=1}^{n} x_i^2 & \sum_{i=1}^{n} x_i^3 & \cdot & \cdot & \sum_{i=1}^{n} x_i^{m+1} \\ \sum_{i=1}^{n} x_i^2 & \sum_{i=1}^{n} x_i^3 & \cdot & \cdot & \cdot & \sum_{i=1}^{n} x_i^{m+2} \\ \cdot & \cdot & \cdot & \cdot & \cdot & \cdot \\ \sum_{i=1}^{n} x_i^{m-1} & \cdot & \cdot & \cdot & \cdot & \sum_{i=1}^{n} x_i^{2m-1} \\ \sum_{i=1}^{n} x_i^m & \sum_{i=1}^{n} x_i^{m+1} & \cdot & \cdot & \sum_{i=1}^{n} x_i^{2m-1} & \sum_{i=1}^{n} x_i^{2m} \end{bmatrix} \begin{bmatrix} a_0 \\ a_1 \\ \\ \cdot \\ a_{m-1} \\ a_m \end{bmatrix} = \begin{bmatrix} \sum_{i=1}^{n} y_i \\ \sum_{i=1}^{n} x_i y_i \\ \sum_{i=1}^{n} x_i^2 y_i \\ \cdot \\ \sum_{i=1}^{n} x_i^{m-1} y_i \\ \sum_{i=1}^{n} x_i^m y_i \end{bmatrix} \tag{5.92}$$

Following the arrows in the coefficient matrix, it is seen that only $2m$ coefficients need to be calculated, the first coefficient being n. For each coefficient in the first calculated row and last column, the coefficients along that diagonal are the same as the calculated one. Equations 5.92 may therefore be changed to

$$\begin{bmatrix} S_{11} & S_{12} & S_{13} & \cdots & S_{1,m+1} \\ S_{21} & S_{22} & S_{23} & \cdots & S_{2,m+1} \\ \cdot & \cdot & \cdot & \cdot & \cdot \\ \cdot & \cdot & \cdot & \cdot & \cdot \\ \cdot & \cdot & \cdot & \cdot & \cdot \\ S_{m+1,1} & S_{m+1,2} & S_{m+1,3} & \cdots & S_{m+1,m+1} \end{bmatrix} \begin{bmatrix} a_1 \\ a_2 \\ \cdot \\ \cdot \\ \cdot \\ a_{m+1} \end{bmatrix} = \begin{bmatrix} S_{1,m+2} \\ S_{2,m+2} \\ \cdot \\ \cdot \\ \cdot \\ S_{m+1,m+2} \end{bmatrix} \tag{5.93}$$

and Eqs. 5.93 may be expressed as $S \cdot A = S1$, where the first row and last column elements of S are

$$S_{1j} = \sum_{l=1}^{n} x_l^{j-1}, \qquad (j = 2, 3, \ldots, m + 1), \tag{5.94a}$$

$$S_{i,m+1} = \sum_{l=1}^{n} x_l^{m+i-1}, \qquad (i = 2, 3, \ldots, m + 1), \tag{5.94b}$$

and the elements of $S1$ are

$$S_{i,m+2} = \sum_{l=1}^{n} x_l^{i-1} y_l, \qquad (i = 1, 2, 3, \ldots, m + 1). \tag{5.94c}$$

Only the coefficients in the first row and the last column of the coefficient matrix have to be calculated. Then the following relation may be used to form the remaining coefficients:

$$\begin{aligned} &S_{12} = S_{21} \\ &S_{13} = S_{22} = S_{31} \\ &S_{14} = S_{23} = S_{32} = S_{41} \\ &\cdot\ \cdot\ \cdot\ \cdot\ \cdot\ \cdot\ \cdot\ \cdot\ \cdot\ \cdot \\ &S_{1j} = S_{2,j-1} = S_{3,j-2} = \cdots = S_{j1}, \qquad (j = 2, 3, \ldots, m + 1); \end{aligned} \tag{5.95}$$

and

$$\begin{aligned} &S_{2,m+1} = S_{3,m} = S_{4,m-1} = \cdots = S_{m+1,2} \\ &S_{3,m+1} = S_{4,m} = S_{5,m-1} = \cdots = S_{m+1,3} \\ &\cdot\ \cdot\ \cdot\ \cdot\ \cdot\ \cdot\ \cdot\ \cdot\ \cdot\ \cdot\ \cdot\ \cdot \\ &S_{i,m+1} = S_{i+1,m} = S_{i+2,m-1} = \cdots = S_{m+1,i}, \qquad (i = 2, 3, \ldots, m + 1). \end{aligned} \tag{5.96}$$

Example 1

A simple example illustrates the technique described. Given the set of values:

x	0	1	2	3	4
y	1.00	3.85	6.50	9.35	12.05

assume that $y = a_0 + a_1 x$ represents the best fit by the least squares technique. Then

$$R_i = y_i - (a_0 + a_1 x_i) \tag{5.97}$$

and

$$\sum_{i=1}^{5} R_i^2 = \sum_{i=1}^{5} [y_i - (a_0 + a_1 x_i)^2], \tag{5.98a}$$

$$\frac{\partial}{\partial a_0}\left(\sum_{i=1}^{5} R_i^2\right) = -2 \sum_{i=1}^{5} [y_i - (a_0 + a_1 x_1)], \tag{5.98b}$$

$$\frac{\partial}{\partial a_1}\left(\sum_{i=1}^{5} R_i^2\right) = -2 \sum_{i=1}^{5} [y_i - (a_0 + a_1 x_i) x_i]. \tag{5.98c}$$

Simplifying these equations, the set of equations to be solved becomes

$$5a_0 + a_1 \sum_{i=1}^{5} x_i = \sum_{i=1}^{5} y_i,$$
$$a_0 \sum_{i=1}^{5} x_i + a_1 \sum_{i=1}^{5} x_i^2 = \sum_{i=1}^{5} x_i y_i. \tag{5.99}$$

The coefficients are stated in Table 5.16; thus, the set of equations is

TABLE 5.16 Least Squares Coefficients for Example 1

n	x	y	x^2	xy
1	0	1.00	0	0
2	1	3.85	1	3.85
3	2	6.50	4	13.00
4	3	9.35	9	28.05
5	4	12.05	16	48.20
$\Sigma =$	10	32.75	30	93.10

$$5a_0 + 10a_1 = 32.75,$$
$$10a_0 + 30a_1 = 93.10. \tag{5.100}$$

Hence,

$$a_0 = 1.03, \qquad a_1 = 2.76, \qquad y = 1.03 + 2.76x. \tag{5.101}$$

In this example, it appears that the degree $m = 1$ is a good choice; however, the following questions might be posed: What would be the maximum degree polynomial that could be used for this set of values? And what degree would yield the minimum residual? That is, what $P_m(x)$ would be a best fit?

The answer to the first question is that m must be chosen equal to or less than $n - 1$. The second question requires more investigation, and will be answered after deriving a flow chart for the case where m is fixed.

5.8.1 Flow Chart

For the system of Eqs. 5.93, which symbolically represents the system 5.92, Flow Chart 5.8.1 forms all S_{ij}. The flow chart may be continued by applying the Gauss elimination method of Ch. 4 to solve the system of Eqs. 5.93 for all a_i, $i = 1, 2, \ldots, m + 1$.

Then, using the subscripted variable a_i, $i = 1, 2, \ldots, m + 1$,

$$y = a_1 + a_2x + a_3x^2 + \cdots + a_{m+1}x^m$$

will be the best-fitting curve for the set of data $\{(x_1, y_1), (x_2, y_2), \ldots, (x_n, y_n)\}$ by the least squares principle for a fixed m.

Definitions

n represents the number of ordered pairs of tabulated values of (x_i, y_i).
m represents the degree of the polynomial.
$m1 = m + 1$.
$m2 = m + 2$.

Steps

1. Read all data.
2. Form all $S_{1,j}$, $j = 1, 2, \ldots, m + 1$ (Eq. 5.94a).
3. As each term $S_{i,j}$ is formed, Eq. 5.95 is used to generate the same term along that diagonal.
4. Form all $S_{i,m+1}$ for $i = 2, 3, \ldots, m + 1$ (Eq. 5.94b).
5. As each term $S_{i,m+1}$ is formed, Eq. 5.96 is used to generate the same term along that diagonal.
6. Form all $S_{i,m+2}$ using formula 5.94c.
7. The flow chart can be completed employing the elimination method of Ch. 4.

Steps 2 and 4 are simplified in Flow Chart 5.8.1 by using the iteration

$$S_{ij} = \sum_{l=1}^{n} (x_l)^k$$

in both steps. For step 2,

$$i = 1 \quad \text{and} \quad S_{ij} = \sum_{l=1}^{n} (x_l)^k, \quad (k = j - 1).$$

For step 4,

$$j = m + 1 \quad \text{and} \quad S_{ij} = \sum_{l=1}^{n} (x_l)^k, \quad (i = 2, 3, \ldots, m1)$$

where

$$k = m1\ (i = 2),\ k = m1 + 1\ (i = 3), \ldots, k = 2m\ (i = m1).$$

Steps 3 and 5 are simplified into one statement, $S_{ii,jj} = S_{ij}$, where ii is initially set equal to $i + 1 = 2$ and jj to $j - 1$, $j = 2$. The subscript ii is incremented by 1 and the subscript jj is decremented by 1 to form a current $S_{ii,jj}$ as long as $ii \leq j$. Step 6 becomes

$$S_{ij} = \sum_{l=1}^{n} (x_l)^k y_l$$

FLOW CHART 5.8.1 Least Squares Method

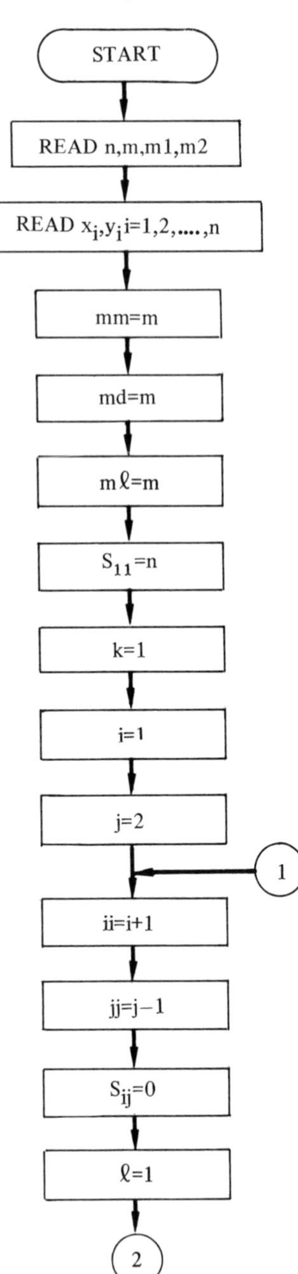

Flow Chart 5.8.1 *(Continued)*

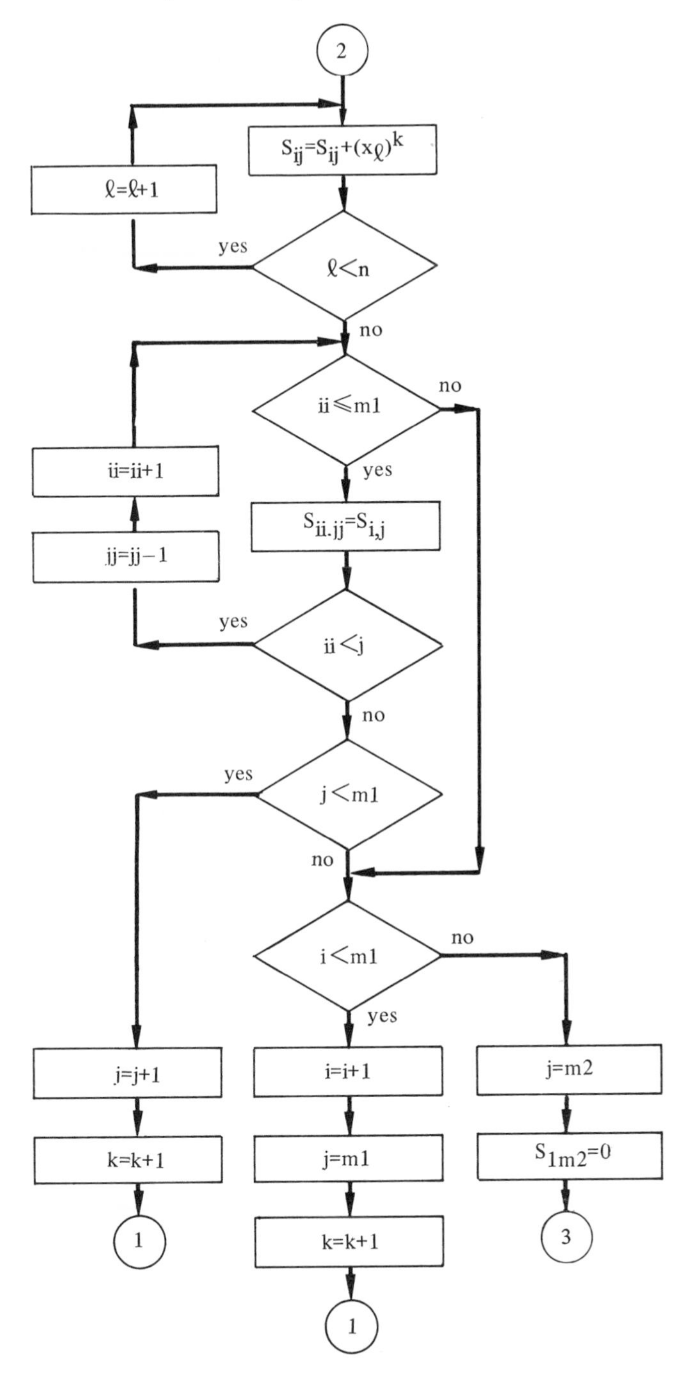

Flow Chart 5.8.1 *(Continued)*

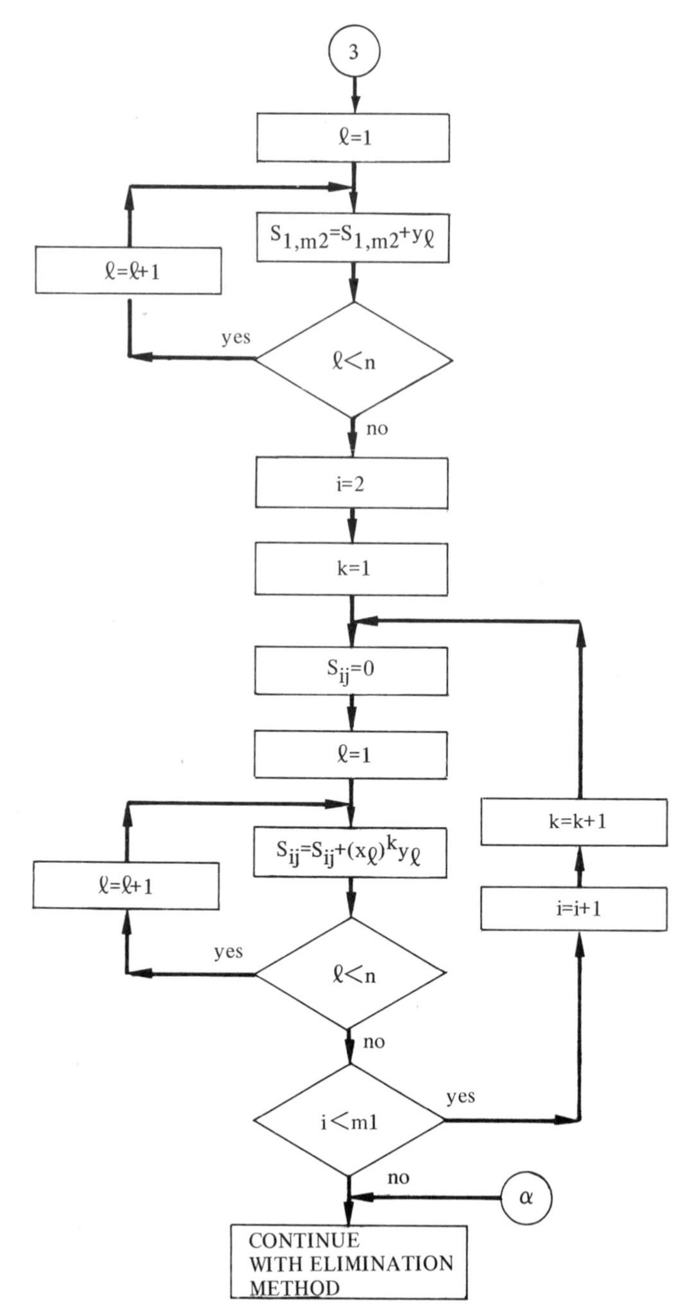

where $j = m + 2$, i takes on the values $1, 2, \ldots, m + 1$, and k takes on the values $0, 1, 2, \ldots, m$ for each summation on l.

The variables *mm, md,* and *ml* are not required for a fixed m, but in choosing a best m (Sec. 5.8.2), they are required. The reference α is also required for a best choice of m.

5.8.2 Choice of Degree

The question of Sec. 5.8 is raised again: What degree m of the approximating polynomial $P_m(x)$ would be a best choice for a given n (the number of tabulated values)? One method to determine a good choice of m would be to plot the values on graph paper and decide from the graph what degree for $P_m(x)$ appears to be good.

An analytical method, and an accurate one, is to evaluate

$$\tau_m^2 = \sum_{i=1}^{n} R_i^2/(n - m - 1), \qquad (m = 1, 2, \ldots). \qquad (5.102)$$

As long as τ_m^2 decreases significantly for each value of m, the best choice of m has not been found. Thus, as long as the ratio τ_m^2/τ_{m+1}^2 is much greater than one, the computation is continued. When

$$\tau_k^2/\tau_{k+1}^2 < 2, \qquad (5.103)$$

$m = k$ is the best choice of degree for the polynomial $P_m(x)$.[5]

If $m = M$ is the best choice of degree, then by extending the degree to $m + 1$, the coefficient of x^{m+1} will be statistically zero.

Example 2

To illustrate the test (5.103) as applied to the set of values in Example 1, assume $y = a_0 + a_1x + a_2x^2$ instead of $y = a_0 + a_1x$. Then the set of equations is

[5] Some computers have a library routine that will plot $f(x_i)$ versus x_i. This method may very well satisfy the requirements of the investigator based upon his knowledge of the problem.

The number 2 is chosen as an upper bound for τ_k^2/τ_{k+1}^2 because this ratio may be slightly greater than as well as slightly less than 1. A discussion of this test is beyond the scope here; the reader is referred to S. S. Wilks, *Mathematical Statistics,* 2d ed. (New York: John Wiley & Sons, Inc., 1962).

$$
\begin{aligned}
5a_0 + a_1 \sum_{i=1}^{5} x_i + a_2 \sum_{i=1}^{5} x_i^2 &= \sum_{i=1}^{5} y_i, \\
a_0 \sum_{i=1}^{5} x_i + a_1 \sum_{i=1}^{5} x_i^2 + a_2 \sum_{i=1}^{5} x_i^3 &= \sum_{i=1}^{5} x_i y_i, \\
a_0 \sum_{i=1}^{5} x_i^2 + a_1 \sum_{i=1}^{5} x_i^3 + a_2 \sum_{i=1}^{5} x_i^4 &= \sum_{i=1}^{5} x_i^2 y_i.
\end{aligned} \tag{5.104}
$$

Table 5.17 shows the results of the computation. Substituting in Eqs. 5.104, the set of equations becomes

$$
\begin{aligned}
5a_0 + 10a_1 + 30a_2 &= 32.75 \\
10a_0 + 30a_1 + 100a_2 &= 93.10 \\
30a_0 + 100a_1 + 354a_2 &= 306.80,
\end{aligned} \tag{5.105}
$$

and

$$
a_0 = 1.016, \qquad a_1 = 2.788, \qquad a_2 = -.007, \tag{5.106}
$$
$$
y = 1.016 + 2.788x - .007x^2.
$$

It should be noted that $a_2 = -.007$ is quite small. From Examples 1 and 2 respectively,

$$
\tau_1^2 = \sum_{i=1}^{5} (R_i^1)^2/(n - m - 1) = \sum_{i=1}^{5} (R_i^1)^2/3
$$

and (5.107)

$$
\tau_2^2 = \sum_{i=1}^{5} (R_i^2)^2/2
$$

are computed where the superscripts 1, 2 indicate the values of m. Denoting computed values of y by y_c^1 for $m = 1$, and by y_c^2 for $m = 2$, then

$$
(R_i^1)^2 = [y_i - y_c^1(x_i)]^2 \quad \text{and} \quad (R_i^2)^2 = [y_i - y_c^2(x_i)]^2. \tag{5.108}
$$

TABLE 5.17 Least Squares Coefficients for Example 2

n	x	y	x^2	x^3	x^4	xy	x^2y
1	0	1.00	0	0	0	0	0
2	1	3.85	1	1	1	3.85	3.85
3	2	6.50	4	8	16	13.00	26.00
4	3	9.35	9	27	81	28.05	84.15
5	4	12.05	16	64	256	48.20	192.80
Σ =	10	32.75	30	100	354	93.10	306.80

Table 5.18 shows these results. Hence,

$$\tau_1^2 = .0090/3 = .0030,$$
$$\tau_2^2 = (.008794)/2 = .004397, \tag{5.109}$$

and

$$\frac{\tau_1^2}{\tau_2^2} = \frac{.0030}{.004397} \cong .68 < 1. \tag{5.110}$$

TABLE 5.18 $\sum_{i=1}^{5} (R_i^1)^2$ and $\sum_{i=1}^{5} (R_i^2)^2$ for Example 2

x	y	y_c^1	y_c^2	$(R_i^1)^2$	$(R_i^2)^2$
0	1.00	1.03	1.016	.0009	.000256
1	3.85	3.79	3.997	.0036	.002809
2	6.50	6.55	6.568	.0025	.004604
3	9.35	9.31	9.317	.0016	.001089
4	12.05	12.07	12.056	.0004	.000036
Σ =				.0090	.008794

The best choice of m is 1 and $y = 1.03 + 2.76x$ is the best fit.

5.8.3 Partial Flow Chart

To derive a flow chart for the best choice of m, the least squares Flow Chart 5.8.1 must be extended to include the solution of the set of linear equations (5.93). Here it is assumed that this has been done and that Partial Flow Chart 5.8.3 for a best choice of m begins with the end of the flow chart for the solution.

The initial choice of m need not be 1. This initial choice of m should be based upon the knowledge of the investigator in regard to the problem at hand.

There are three general steps to be added to Flow Chart 5.8.1 and the flow chart to solve the set of equations.

1. Compute

$$\tau_m^2 = \sum_{i=1}^{n} R_i^2/(n - m - 1). \tag{5.111}$$

This computation is done twice before a test can be made.

FLOW CHART 5.8.3 Best Choice of m

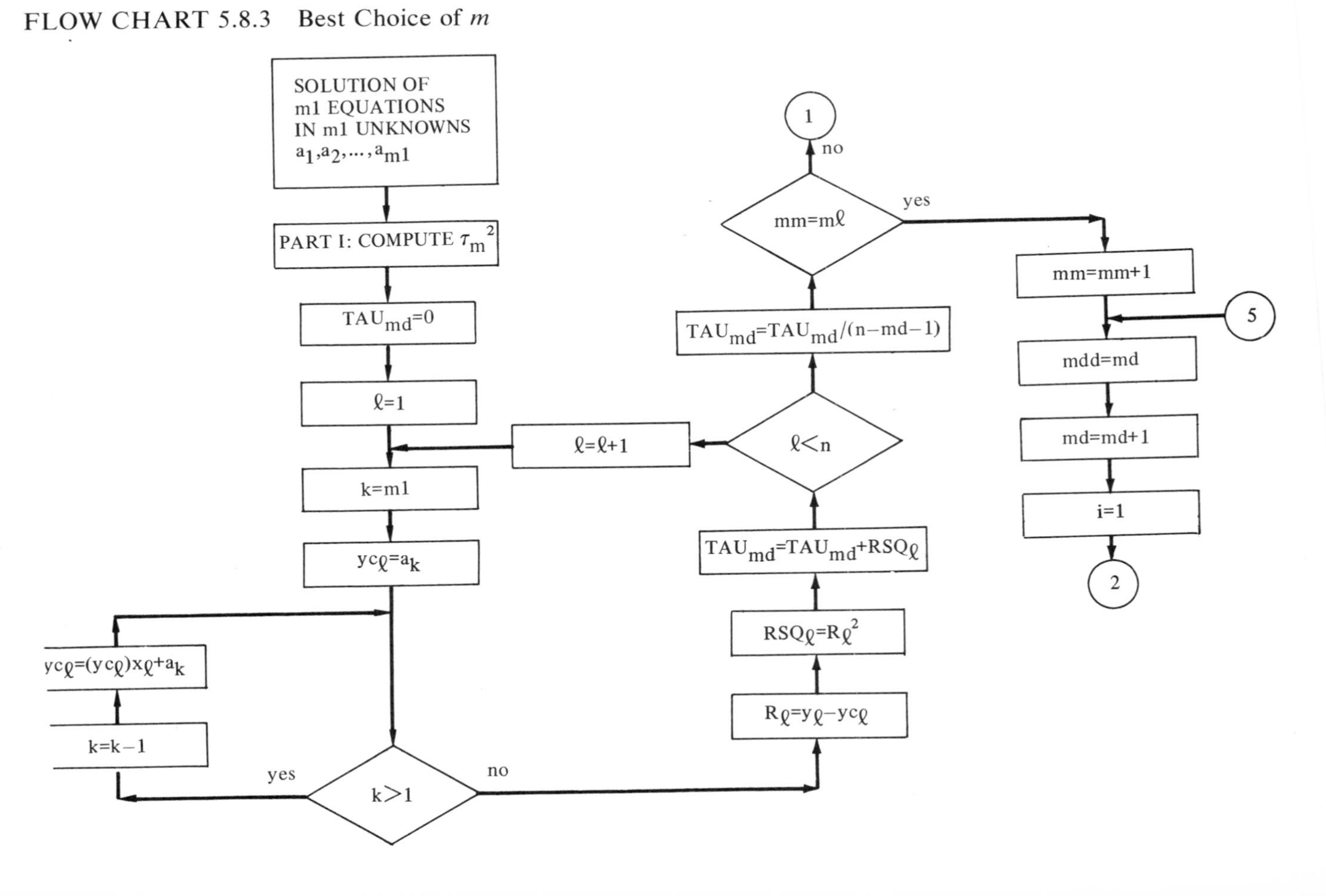

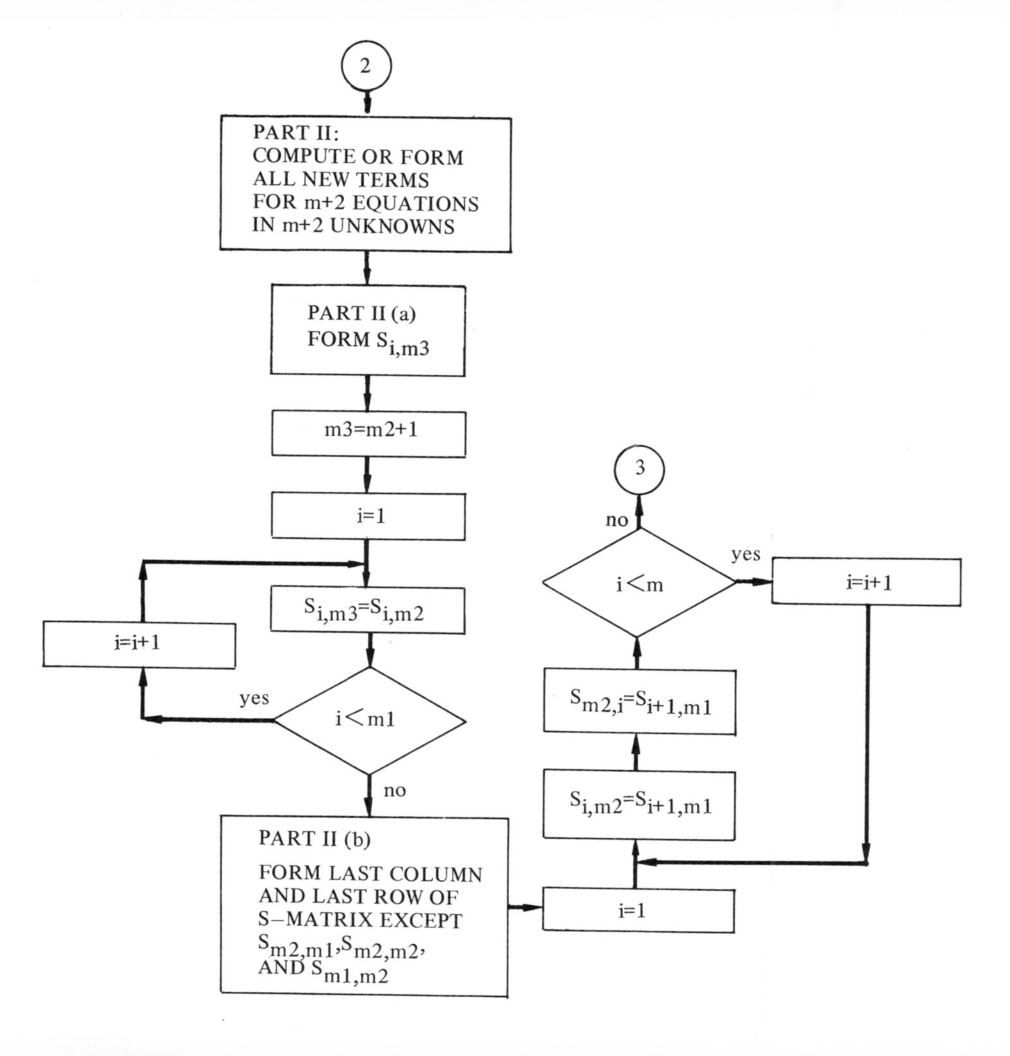

2
PART II:
COMPUTE OR FORM
ALL NEW TERMS
FOR m+2 EQUATIONS
IN m+2 UNKNOWNS
PART II (a)
FORM $S_{i,m3}$
m3=m2+1
i=1
$S_{i,m3}=S_{i,m2}$
i<m1
yes
i=i+1
no
PART II (b)
FORM LAST COLUMN
AND LAST ROW OF
S–MATRIX EXCEPT
$S_{m2,m1}$, $S_{m2,m2}$,
AND $S_{m1,m2}$
i=1
$S_{i,m2}=S_{i+1,m1}$
$S_{m2,i}=S_{i+1,m1}$
i<m
yes
i=i+1
no
3

Flow Chart 5.8.3 *(Continued)*

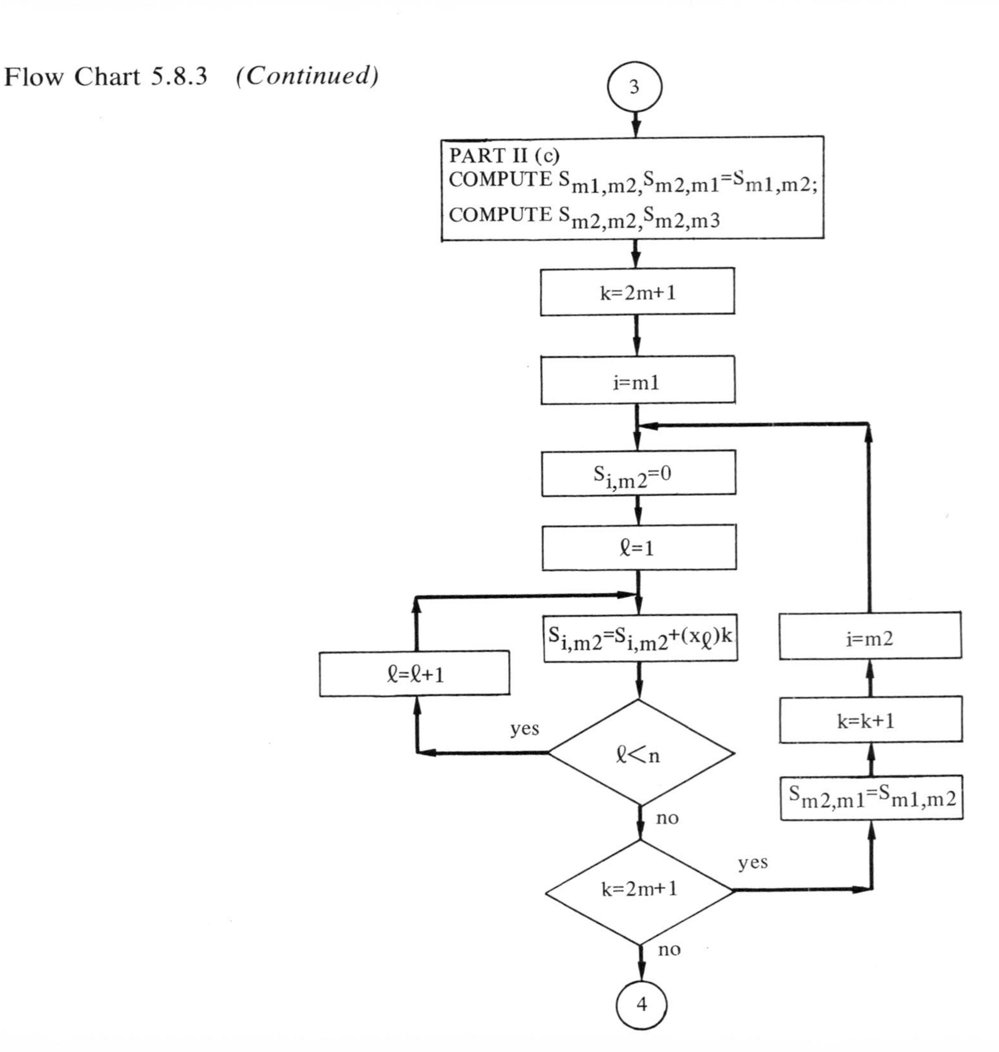

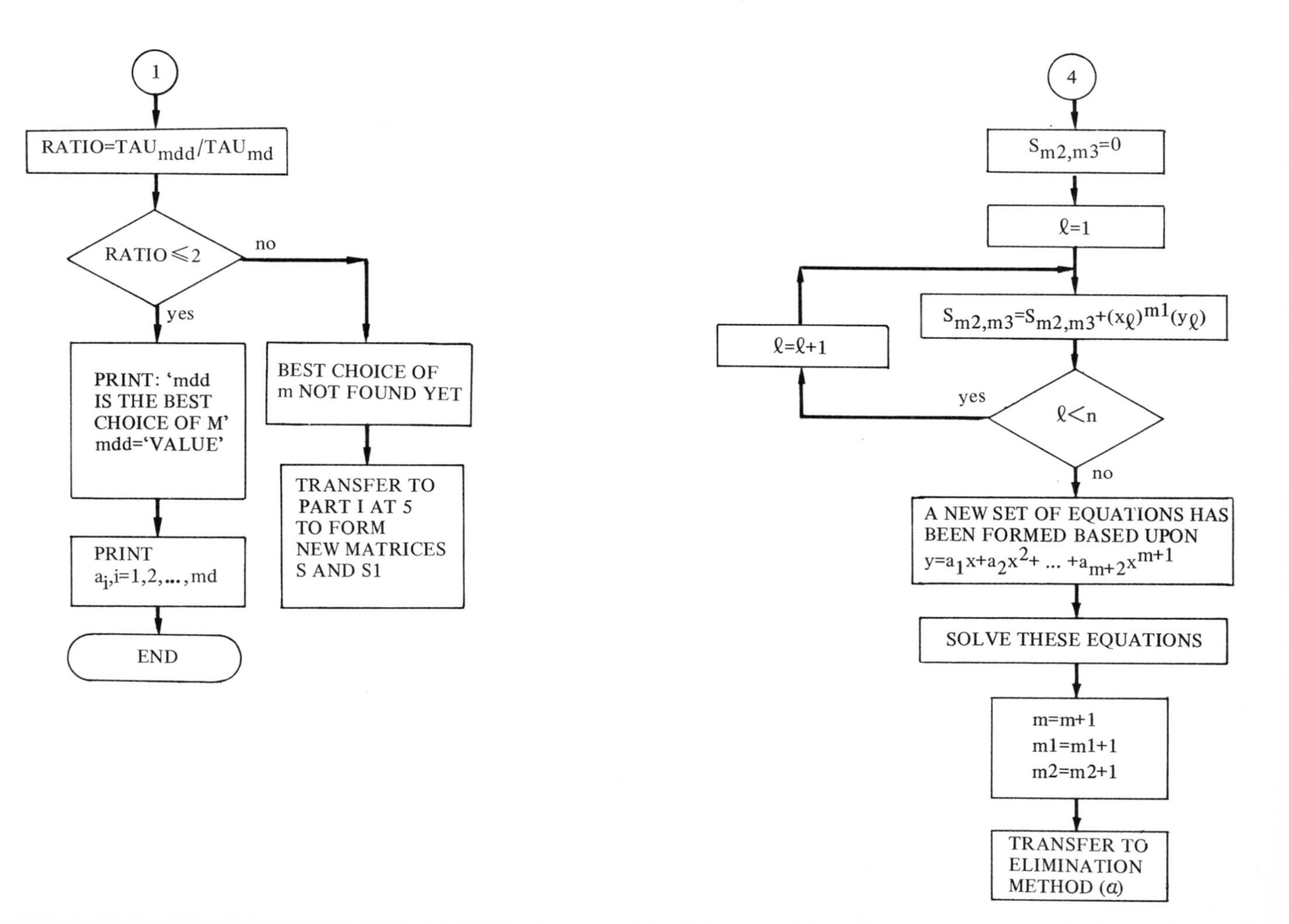
1
RATIO=TAUmdd/TAUmd
RATIO≤2
no
yes
PRINT: 'mdd IS THE BEST CHOICE OF M' mdd='VALUE'
PRINT ai,i=1,2,...,md
END
BEST CHOICE OF m NOT FOUND YET
TRANSFER TO PART I AT 5 TO FORM NEW MATRICES S AND S1
4
Sm2,m3=0
ℓ=1
Sm2,m3=Sm2,m3+(xℓ)m1(yℓ)
ℓ<n
yes
no
ℓ=ℓ+1
A NEW SET OF EQUATIONS HAS BEEN FORMED BASED UPON
y=a1x+a2x2+ ... +am+2xm+1
SOLVE THESE EQUATIONS
m=m+1
m1=m1+1
m2=m2+1
TRANSFER TO ELIMINATION METHOD (α)

(a) Find the ratio $R = \tau_m^2/\tau_{m+1}^2$.

(b) If $R \leq 2$, m is the best choice; otherwise, proceed to step 2.

2. Increase m by 1 and construct a new set of equations. The previous computation was based upon

$$y = a_1 + a_2 x + \cdots + a_{m+1} x^m. \tag{5.112}$$

Now it is necessary to consider

$$y = a_1 + a_2 x + \cdots + a_{m+1} x^m + a_{m+2} x^{m+1}. \tag{5.113}$$

The set of linear equations for Eq. 5.112 was

$$\begin{bmatrix} S_{11} & S_{12} & \cdots & S_{1,m1} \\ S_{21} & S_{22} & \cdots & S_{2,m1} \\ \cdot & \cdot & \cdot & \cdot \\ \cdot & \cdot & \cdot & \cdot \\ \cdot & \cdot & \cdot & \cdot \\ S_{m1,1} & S_{m1,2} & \cdots & S_{m1,m1} \end{bmatrix} \begin{bmatrix} a_1 \\ a_2 \\ \cdot \\ \cdot \\ \cdot \\ a_{m1} \end{bmatrix} = \begin{bmatrix} S_{1,m2} \\ S_{2,m2} \\ \cdot \\ \cdot \\ \cdot \\ S_{m1,m2} \end{bmatrix} \tag{5.114}$$

where $m1 = m + 1$ and $m2 = m + 2$.

The set of linear equations for Eq. 5.113 is

$$\begin{bmatrix} S_{11} & S_{12} & \cdots & S_{1,m1} & \boxed{S_{1,m2}} \\ S_{21} & S_{22} & \cdots & S_{2,m2} & \boxed{S_{2,m2}} \\ \cdot & \cdot & \cdot & \cdot & \cdot \\ \cdot & \cdot & \cdot & \cdot & \cdot \\ S_{m,1} & S_{m,2} & \cdot & \cdot & \boxed{S_{m,m2}} \\ S_{m1,1} & S_{m1,2} & \cdots & S_{m1,m1} & [S_{m1,m2}] \\ \boxed{S_{m2,1}} & \boxed{S_{m2,2}} & \cdots & [S_{m2,m1}] & [S_{m2,m2}] \end{bmatrix} \begin{bmatrix} a_1 \\ a_2 \\ \cdot \\ \cdot \\ \cdot \\ a_{m1} \\ a_{m2} \end{bmatrix} = \begin{bmatrix} \boxed{S_{1,m3}} \\ \boxed{S_{2,m3}} \\ \cdot \\ \cdot \\ \cdot \\ \boxed{S_{m1,m3}} \\ [S_{m2,m3}] \end{bmatrix} \tag{5.115}$$

where $m3 = m + 3$.

Referring to Eq. 5.115, the elements in the $m2$ column and the $m2$ row have to be determined. Also, the column matrix $\{S_{i,m3}\}$, $i = 1, 2, \ldots, m2$, must be determined. However, the only elements that have to be calculated are $S_{m1,m2}$, $S_{m2,m2}$, $S_{m2,m1}$, and $S_{m2,m3}$. The other elements can be found by using the relationship between elements along diagonals, and also by the fact that the elements $\{S_{i,m3}\}$, $i = 1, 2, \ldots, m1$, are equivalent to the elements of column $S_{i,m2}$, $i = 1, 2, \ldots, m1$, of Eq. 5.114.

Again referring to Eqs. 5.115, only the circled elements must be formed anew, and only those in brackets need to be computed. Thus, the set of equations to arrive at a new S matrix and also a new $S1$ matrix are

$$S_{i,m3} = S_{i,m2}, \qquad (i = 1, 2, \ldots, m1).$$

This transfers these elements of the column matrix of (5.114) to the corresponding elements of the column matrix of (5.115):

$$S_{i,m2} = S_{i+1,m1}, \qquad (i = 1, 2, \ldots, m),$$
$$S_{m2,i} = S_{i+1,m1}, \qquad (i = 1, 2, \ldots, m).$$

These are true because of equivalence of elements along a given diagonal.

3. Compute $S_{m1,m2}$. The procedure for this is the same as in Flow Chart 5.8.1. Then $S_{m2,m1}$ is equivalent to $S_{m1,m2}$. Finally, $S_{m2,m2}$ and $S_{m2,m3}$ are computed in like fashion. At this point, transfer is made in the flow chart to solve the set of $m + 2$ equations in $m + 2$ unknowns.

Definitions and Notation

$m3 = m2 + 1$.
mm is set equal to m in Flow Chart 5.8.1 and incremented by 1 only for the purpose of computing τ_m^2 twice.
ml initially set equal to m is used so that m can be used to indicate the current value of the degree.
md initially set equal to m and mdd provide for the test TAU_{mdd}/TAU_{md} where $md = mdd + 1$.
yc_l is the computed value of y.
y_l is the observed value of y.
$r_l = y_l - yc_l$; $rsq_l = r_l^2$.

5.8.4 Program

For the least squares method including the best choice of m, given the set of data:

x	0	1	2	3	4
y	1.00	3.85	6.50	9.35	12.05

and starting values: $m = 1$, $m1 = 2$, $m2 = 3$, then, for $m = 1$, values of a_0, a_1, and τ_1^2 are computed. Again, for $m = 2$, new values of a_0 and a_1 and values of a_2 and τ_2^2 are computed.

On the basis that the ratio τ_1^2/τ_2^2 is less than 1, m is chosen as 1. Thus, the best approximation for the set of data by the least squares method is $y = 1.03 + 2.76x$.

```
C     LEAST SQUARES METHOD
      DIMENSION S(20,20),A(20),YC(20),R(20),Y(20),RSQ(20),TAU(20)
      DIMENSION Z(20),USE(20,20)
      DIMENSION C(20,20)
      READ(5,100)N,M,N1,M2
  100 FORMAT(4I3)
      READ(5,101)(Z(I),I=1,N)
  101 FORMAT(16F5.2)
      READ(5,101)(Y(I),I=1,N)
C     PART I: FORM ALL S(I,J)
      MM=M
      MD=M
      ML=M
      S(1,1)=N
      K=1
      I=1
      J=2
      JL=1
    1 II=I+1
      JJ=J-1
      S(1,J)=0.
      DO 2 L=1,N
    2 S(I,J)=S(I,J)+Z(L)**K
      IF(II-M1)3,3,4
    3 S(II,JJ)=S(I,J)
      IF(II-J)5,6,6
    5 II=II+1
      JJ=JJ-1
      GO TO 3
    6 IF(J-M1)7,4,4
    7 J=J+1
      K=K+1
      GO TO 1
    4 IF(I-M1)8,9,9
    8 I=I+1
      J=M1
      K=K+1
      GO TO 1
    9 J=M2
      S(1,M2)=0
      DO 10 L=1,N
   10 S(1,M2)=S(1,M2)+Y(L)
      I=2
```

```
      K=1
  314 S(I,J)=0.
      DO 11 L=1,N
   11 S(I,J)=S(I,J)+(Z(L)**K)*Y(L)
      IF(I-M1)12,13,13
   12 I=I+1
      K=K+1
      GO TO 314
   13 DO 315 IR=1,M1
      DO 316 JR=1,M2
  316 USE(IR,JR)=S(IR,JR)
  315 CONTINUE
      DO 320 IR=1,M1
  320 WRITE(6,103)(S(IR,JR),JR=1,M2)
      DO 317 KR=1,M1
  317 A(KR)=0
      CALL ELIMIN(USE,M1,A,M2,M)
      WRITE(6,103)(A(KR),KR=1,M1)
      DO 500 KR=1,M1
  500 C(KR,JL)=A(KR)
      JL=JL+1
C     PART II COMPUTE TAU(M)**2
      TAU(MD)=0
      L=1
   14 K=M1
      YC(L)=A(K)
   15 IF(K-1)17,17,16
   16 K=K-1
      YC(L)=YC(L)*Z(L)+A(K)
      GO TO 15
   17 R(L)=ABS(Y(L))-ABS(YC(L))
      RSQ(L)=R(L)**2
      TAU(MD)=TAU(MD)+RSQ(L)
      IF(L-N)18,19,19
   18 L=L+1
      GO TO 14
   19 TAU(MD)=TAU(MD)/(N-MD-1)
      IF(MM-ML)29,20,29
   20 MM=MM+1
   21 MDD=MD
      MD=MD+1
      I=1
C     PART III COMPUTE OR FORM ALL NEW TERMS FOR M+2 EQUATIONS
      M3=M2+1
      DO 22 I=1,M1
   22 S(I,M3)=S(I,M2)
      DO 23 I=1,M
      S(I,M2)=S(I+1,M1)
   23 S(M2,I)=S(I+1,M1)
      K=2*M+1
```

```
      I=M1
   24 S(I,M2)=0
      DO 25 L=1,N
   25 S(I,M2)=S(I,M2)+Z(L)**K
      IF(K-2*M-1)27,26,27
   26 S(M2,M1)=S(M1,M2)
      K=K+1
      I=M2
      GO TO 24
   27 S(M2,M3)=0
      DO 28 L=1,N
   28 S(M2,M3)=S(M2,M3)+(Z(L)**M1)*Y(L)
C     A NEW SET OF EQUATIONS HAS BEEN FORMED
      M=M+1
      M1=M1+1
      M2=M2+1
      GO TO 13
   29 RATIO=TAU(MDD)/TAU(MD)
      IF(RATIO-1.0)30,20,20
   30 WRITE(6,102)MDD
  102 FORMAT(//,'MDD IS THE BEST CHOICE OF M',//,'MDD=',I4)
      WRITE(6,103)(C(KR,JL),KR=1,M1)
  103 FORMAT(10F10.4)
      WRITE(6,114)TAU(MDD),TAU(MD),RATIO
  114 FORMAT(//,'TAU(MDD) IS ',F8.4,/,'TAU(MD) IS ',F8.4,/,'RATIO IS ',F8.4)
      STOP
      END
      SUBROUTINE ELIMIN(E,N,X,M2,M)
      DIMENSION A(20,20),X(20),B(20),E(20,20)
      M1=N
      DO 20 IR=1,N
   20 B(IR)=E(IR,M2)
      DO 21 IR=1,N
      DO 22 JR=1,N
   22 A(IR,JR)=E(IR,JR)
   21 CONTINUE
      IR=1
  130 JR=1
  129 JN=JR+N
      IF(IR-JR)24,23,24
   23 A(IR,JN)=1.0
      GO TO 26
   24 A(IR,JN)=0.0
   26 IF(JR-N)27,28,28
   27 JR=JR+1
      GO TO 129
   28 IF(IR-N)29,30,30
   29 IR=IR+1
      GO TO 130
   30 N2=2*N
```

```
      MM9=M1+M1
      DO 999 K9=1,M1
  999 WRITE(6,1000)(A(K9,J7),J7=1,MM9)
      N2=2*N
      L=0
    1 L=L+1
      CLL=A(L,L)
      I=L
      DO 2 J=L,N2
    2 A(I,J)=A(I,J)/CLL
      I=1
   10 J=L
      IF(I-L)4,3,4
    3 I=I+1
    4 R=A(I,L)
      IF(I-N)5,5,6
    5 A(I,J)=A(I,J)-R*A(L,J)
      IF(J-N2)7,8,8
    7 J=J+1
      GO TO 5
    8 IF(I-N)9,1,1
    9 I=I+1
      GO TO 10
    6 I=1
   11 J=1
      X(I)=0
   12 JN=J+N
      X(I)=X(I)+A(I,JN)*B(J)
      IF(J-N)13,14,14
   13 J=J+1
      GO TO 12
   14 IF(I-N)15,16,16
   15 I=I+1
      GO TO 11
   16 WRITE(6,1000)(X(I),I=1,N)
 1000 FORMAT(////,10F10.4)
      RETURN
      END
```

For M=1
$a_0 = 1.0300$, $a_1 = 2.7600$
For M=2
$a_0 = 1.0157$, $a_1 = 2.7886$, $a_2 = -0.0072$
MDD IS THE BEST CHOICE OF M
MDD= 1
TAU(MDD) IS 0.0030
TAU(MD) IS 0.004143
RATIO IS 0.7241

5.8.5 Concluding Remarks

There is much more that can be said about the least squares method. Some points for future study should be noted.

In using $\sum_{j=0}^{m} a_j x_i^j$ as the approximation to $y(x)$, it is possible to arrive at what is known as an *ill-conditioned matrix,* described below.

Choose the largest element (in absolute value) of the matrix, and factor this element out of the matrix (this is called a *normalized* matrix). If the inverse of the normalized matrix has very large elements, the given matrix is said to be ill conditioned.

Since the inverse of an ill-conditioned matrix in its normalized form has very large elements, any round-off error in using such a matrix to solve the set of Eqs. 5.93 may result in extreme errors in the solution. It can also be shown that for m sufficiently large, the coefficient matrix of Eq. 5.93 is in general ill conditioned.

Any matrix such as

$$\begin{bmatrix} 1 & 1/2 & 1/3 & 1/4 \\ 1/2 & 1/3 & 1/4 & 1/5 \\ 1/3 & 1/4 & 1/5 & 1/6 \\ 1/4 & 1/5 & 1/6 & 1/7 \end{bmatrix}, \tag{5.116}$$

even though it is only of order 4, will have rather large elements in its inverse. Referring to Eqs. 5.105, the normalized coefficient matrix

$$\begin{bmatrix} 5/354 & 10/354 & 30/354 \\ 10/354 & 30/354 & 100/354 \\ 30/354 & 100/354 & 1 \end{bmatrix}, \tag{5.117}$$

which is not unlike (5.116) in pattern, will have some fairly large elements in its inverse.

Thus, for any approximation by the least squares method, if m is not too high (say, less than 6), it is safe from the standpoint of round-off error to use $P_m(x)$ as the approximating polynomial. But for any degree m that will most likely be rather high (i.e., greater than 6), it might very well be dangerous to use $P_m(x)$. Rather, it would be better to use Eq. 5.84 where each $q_i(x)$ is a polynomial of degree i. Further, instead of using Eq. 5.87 as the function to be minimized, it is wiser to introduce a weight function $w(x)$ and use Eq. 5.89f (footnote 4) as the function to be minimized.

The selection and determination of $w(x)$ and $q_i(x)$ are not within the scope of this book. With well-chosen $w(x)$ and $q_i(x)$, the danger of an ill-conditioned matrix is eliminated.

PROBLEMS

5-5. Write a complete integrated flow chart and program to find the best fit polynomial by the least squares technique for the set of empirical data in Example 1.

5-6. A best choice of degree M for the least squares method can be based upon the fact that a_{M+1} will be very small. Hence the ratio a_M/a_{M+1} will be large. Write a flow chart and program for the least squares method using this technique for the best choice of M for the data in Example 1. (M is assumed to be known.)

6

Numerical Differentiation and Integration

Numerical differentiation is defined as the study of how the numerical value of a derivative is found; numerical integration is the study of how the numerical value of an integral is found.

The interpolation formulas (Gregory, Newton, and Gauss) of Ch. 5 approximate a given function $f(x)$ by $y = P_m(x)$ or by its equivalent $y = P_m(u)$, where $x = x_0 + uh$. These formulas will be used as starting points instead of $f(x)$, and then $P_m(x)$ or $P_m(u)$ will be differentiated or integrated. These in turn will be evaluated at the given point.

6.1 Numerical Differentiation

Let $f(x)$ be approximated by the polynomial $y = P_n(u)$ where $u = (x - x_0)/h$. Let $x = \bar{x}$, $x_0 \leq \bar{x} < x$, or $0 \leq \bar{u} < 1$ be a point at which the derivative of $f(x)$ is desired.

Since $f(x) \cong P_n(u)$, then

$$\left.\frac{df(x)}{dx}\right|_{x=\bar{x}} \cong \frac{d}{du}(P_n(u)) \left.\frac{du}{dx}\right|_{x=\bar{x}}. \tag{6.1}$$

From $x = x_0 + uh$,

$$\frac{du}{dx} = \frac{1}{h}; \tag{6.2}$$

hence,

$$\left.\frac{df(x)}{dx}\right|_{x=\bar{x}} = \frac{1}{h}\left.\frac{dP_n(u)}{du}\right|_{u=\bar{u}}. \tag{6.3}$$

$P_n(u)$ can be any of the formulas—the two Gregory–Newton, the two Gauss formulas, or the LaGrange interpolation formula—of Ch. 5. The assumption is that $f(x)$ has the same values at the $n + 1$ tabulated points as $P_n(x)$, and therefore as $P_n(u)$.

A word of caution should be given at the very outset of this treatment: Unless there is some definite knowledge that $f(x)$ and its derivatives exist at the points in question, little or no value can be attached to numerical differentiation.

The two Gauss formulas, when differentiated, will in general yield better results than the two Gregory–Newton formulas. That the Gauss formulas are polynomials that pass through the same number of points (or almost the same number) above and below the point in question, whereas the two Gregory–Newton formulas are polynomials passing through a point x_i and either all points above or below this point, is the intuitive reason behind the above statement.

If the Lagrange interpolation formula is used, then the derivative is expressed directly in terms of the ordinates. Higher-ordered derivatives can be found by using Eq. 6.3 repeatedly. Thus,

$$\frac{d^k f(x)}{dx^k} \cong \frac{1}{h^k}\frac{d^k P_n(u)}{du}. \tag{6.4}$$

It is well to emphasize the importance of truncation error and round-off error in differentiation formulas, as compared with these errors in interpolation formulas. Consider the Gregory–Newton forward interpolation formula (5.42):

$$y = \sum_{i=0}^{n} \frac{u^{[i]}\,\Delta^i y_0}{i!} + E, \qquad \left(E = \frac{h^{n+1}u^{[n+1]}f^{n+1}(\xi)}{(n+1)!}\right). \tag{6.5}$$

In this formula, the round-off error in each term of the polynomial is independent of h, but the truncation error is proportional to a power of h.

In taking the kth derivative of (6.5), the result is

$$\frac{d^k y}{dx^k} = \frac{1}{h^k}\sum_{i=0}^{n}\frac{\Delta^i y_0}{i!}\frac{d^k}{du^k}\{u^{[i]}\} + \left(\frac{1}{h^k}\frac{d^k E}{du^k}\right)$$

where

$$\frac{1}{h^k}\frac{d^kE}{du^k} = \frac{h^{n+1-k}f^{n+1}(\xi)}{(n+1)!}\left(\frac{d^ku^{[n+1]}}{du^k}\right). \tag{6.6}$$

This formula indicates that the round-off error in each term is inversely proportional to h^k and the truncation error is directly proportional to h^{n+1-k}.

Thus the value h presents a dilemma. A small h causes a larger round-off error while minimizing the truncation error, but a large h causes a larger truncation error while minimizing the round-off error. In Sec. 6.2 this is discussed further.

6.2 Numerical Differentiation Formulas

It was shown in Ch. 5 that if

$$u = \frac{x - x_0}{h}, \tag{6.7}$$

then

$$P(x) = P(x_0 + uh). \tag{6.8}$$

Also, the operator E was introduced, such that

$$EP(x_0) = P(x_0 + h) \tag{6.9}$$

and

$$E^uP(x_0) = P(x_0 + uh). \tag{6.10}$$

Furthermore,

$$\Delta P(x_0) = P(x_0 + h) - P(x_0). \tag{6.11}$$

Symbolically,

$$\Delta \equiv E - 1 \qquad \text{or} \qquad E = \Delta + 1, \tag{6.12}$$

and it can be shown that

$$E^u = (1 + \Delta)^u. \tag{6.13}$$

Then

$$y = P(x) \qquad \text{or} \qquad y = P(x_0 + uh) = E^uP(x_0) \tag{6.14}$$

is the Gregory–Newton forward interpolation formula.

The derivative of y at $x = x_0$ is

$$\left.\frac{dy}{dx}\right|_{x=x_0} = \frac{1}{h}\left[\frac{dy}{du}\right]_{u=0}$$

$$= \frac{1}{h}(\ln E)E^u y_0\bigg|_{u=0} \tag{6.15}$$

$$= \frac{1}{h}(\ln E)y_0 = \frac{1}{h}(\ln(1+\Delta))y_0.$$

Since

$$\ln(1+\Delta) = \Delta - \frac{\Delta^2}{2} + \frac{\Delta^3}{3} - \cdots,$$

$$\left.\frac{dy}{dx}\right|_{x=x_0} = \frac{1}{h}\left\{\Delta - \frac{\Delta^2}{2} + \frac{\Delta^3}{3} - \cdots\right\} y_0. \tag{6.16}$$

Define the operator D by the equation

$$Dy_i = \left.\frac{dy}{dx}\right|_{x=x_i}. \tag{6.17}$$

Hence,

$$Dy_0 = \frac{1}{h}(\ln E)y_0. \tag{6.18}$$

Thus, the symbolic equation relating the operator D with the operator E is

$$D = \frac{1}{h}\ln E. \tag{6.19}$$

In Eq. 6.16, if it is assumed that $\Delta^n y_i$, $i = 0, 1, 2, \ldots$, is approximately constant, then the series may be terminated at the nth difference. In other words, it is assumed that the function behaves as a polynomial over the given set of tabulated points. Hence, Eq. 6.16 may be written as

$$\left.\frac{dy}{dx}\right|_{x=x_0} = \frac{1}{h}\sum_{i=1}^{n}\frac{(-1)^{i-1}\Delta^i y_0}{i}. \tag{6.20}$$

The remainder term (truncation error) can be found by extending the series to one more term but replacing $\Delta^{n+1}y_0$ by $h^{n+1}f^{n+1}(\xi)$ where ξ is within the range of $x_0, x_1, \ldots, x_n$. That is,

$$E = \frac{1}{h}\left\{\frac{(-1)^n h^{n+1} f^{n+1}(\xi)}{n+1}\right\}, \tag{6.21}$$

hence,

$$\left.\frac{dy}{dx}\right|_{x=x_0} = \frac{1}{h}\sum_{i=1}^{n}\frac{(-1)^{i-1}\,\Delta^i y_0}{i} + E,$$

$$\left(E = \frac{(-1)^n h^n f^{n+1}(\xi)}{n+1}\right). \tag{6.22}$$

If the round-off error in each term $\Delta^i y_0$ is called e_i, by choosing a positive number e such that

$$|e_i| \le e, \qquad (i = 1, \ldots, n), \tag{6.23}$$

the total round-off error in absolute value is

$$|R| = \frac{1}{h}\sum_{i=1}^{n}\frac{|e_i|}{i} \le \frac{1}{h}\sum_{i=1}^{n}\frac{e}{i} = \frac{e}{h}\sum_{i=1}^{n}\frac{1}{i}. \tag{6.24}$$

Also, let M be a positive number such that

$$|f^{n+1}(\xi)| \le M;$$

then

$$|E| = \frac{h^n|f^{n+1}(\xi)|}{n+1} \le \frac{h^n M}{n+1}. \tag{6.25}$$

A reasonable value of h can be found by assuming that the upper bound of the total round-off error is equal to the upper bound of the truncation error. That is, assume that

$$|R| = |E| \tag{6.26}$$

or

$$\frac{e}{h}\sum_{i=1}^{n}\frac{1}{i} = \frac{h^n M}{n+1}. \tag{6.27}$$

Thus,

$$h = \left[\frac{(n+1)e\displaystyle\sum_{i=1}^{n}\frac{1}{i}}{M}\right]^{\frac{1}{n+1}}. \tag{6.28}$$

The value of h as computed by Eq. 6.28 is not the best value to be found by this procedure. If h were computed for each value of $\bar{u}$, then a better value of h certainly could be found. However, this procedure would require a new formula and a new computation for each $\bar{u}$. The example below illustrates that the value of h obtained by Eq. 6.28 is reasonable.

Example

Assume that a table of natural logarithms accurate to the third decimal place has been given and that logarithms are stated at intervals of .01. It is desired to find the value of $(lnx)'$ at $x = 2.45$, using the best value of h according to Eq. 6.28.

1. Find h. Since the table is accurate to the third decimal place,

$$e = 5(10^{-4}). \tag{6.29}$$

For the range of values of x, $x = 2.40, \ldots$, M may be chosen as 1.
On the assumption that $\Delta^3 y_i$ are approximately constant, n is taken as 3; thus,

$$\sum_{i=1}^{3} \frac{1}{i} = \frac{11}{6}, \tag{6.30}$$

and then

$$h = \left[\frac{4[5(10^{-4})]\frac{11}{6}}{1}\right]^{1/4} \qquad \text{or} \qquad h \cong .245. \tag{6.31}$$

Thus a good choice of h is .2.

2. Construct a table of differences, as shown in Table 6.1. The values of ln x are tabulated at $x = 2.4, 2.6, 2.8, 3.0$.

TABLE 6.1 Differences of ln x, $x = 2.4, 2.6, 2.8, 3.0$

x	u	$\ln x$	$\Delta \ln x$	$\Delta^2 \ln x$	$\Delta^3 \ln x$
2.4	0	.875			
			.080		
2.6	1	.955		−.005	
			.075		−.001
2.8	2	1.030		−.006	
			.069		
3.0	3	1.099			

3. Use the Gregory–Newton forward interpolation formula to find dy/dx at $x = 2.45$:

$$y = y_0 + u\,\Delta y_0 + \left(\frac{u^2 - u}{2}\right)\Delta^2 y_0 + \left(\frac{u^3 - 3u^2 + 2u}{6}\right)\Delta^3 y_0 . \tag{6.32}$$

Hence

$$\frac{dy}{dx} = \frac{1}{h}\left\{\Delta y_0 + \frac{2u-1}{2}\Delta^2 y_0\right\} + \frac{(3u^2 - 6u + 2)}{6}\Delta^3 y_0 . \tag{6.33}$$

For $x = 2.45$, $u = (2.45 - 2.40)/.2 = 1/4$. Thus

$$\begin{aligned}\frac{dy}{dx} &= \frac{1}{.2}\left\{.080 - \frac{1}{4}(-.005) - (.12)(.001)\right\} \\ &= 5(.08113) = .40565,\end{aligned} \tag{6.34}$$

whereas by direct computation,

$$\frac{1}{2.45} \cong .40816. \tag{6.35}$$

4. Find $|R|$ and $|E|$:

$$|R| = \frac{5\cdot 10^{-4}\cdot 11}{(.2)6} \cong .004583 \tag{6.36}$$

and

$$|E| = \frac{h^3 M}{4} = \frac{(.2)^3}{4} = .002. \tag{6.37}$$

If h were chosen as .01, then $|R| \cong .09166$ and $|E| = .00000025$. Thus, for $h = .2$, the upper bound for the total error is

$$T = R + E = .006583, \tag{6.38}$$

but for $h = .01$, the upper bound is approximately $T = .09166$. Hence it is seen that total error T can be made much smaller by choosing h so that it will satisfy Eq. 6.28.

Turning to the question of finding higher-order derivatives, Eq. 6.14 may be differentiated k times to find an expression for the kth derivative; that is

$$\begin{aligned}\left.\frac{d^k y}{dx^k}\right|_{x=x_0} &= \frac{1}{h^k}\left\{\frac{d^k y}{du^k}\right\}_{u=0} \\ &= \frac{1}{h^k}\left[\frac{d^k E^u}{du^k}\right]_{u=0} y_0 \\ &= \left[\frac{1}{h}\ln E\right]^k y_0 .\end{aligned} \tag{6.39}$$

Thus,

$$\left.\frac{d^2y}{dx^2}\right|_{x=x_0} = \frac{1}{h^2}(\ln E)^2 y_0$$

$$= \frac{1}{h^2}\left(\Delta - \frac{\Delta^2}{2} + \frac{\Delta^3}{3} - \cdots\right)^2 y_0$$

$$= \frac{1}{h^2}\left(\Delta^2 - \Delta^3 + \frac{11}{2}\Delta^4 - \frac{5}{6}\Delta^5 + \cdots\right) y_0. \tag{6.40}$$

Another approach for finding numerical differentiation formulas regardless of the finite difference formula used is found in the construction of a table of differences for the derivative and the coefficients of these differences. That is, to find a formula for the derivative of $f(x)$ at $x = x_0$ by differentiating either of the two Gregory–Newton formulas or either of the Gauss formulas, a table of differences and coefficients can be constructed without deriving each formula. Only one formula is needed, for example, that based on the Gregory–Newton formula. Then, by the concept of differences, the whole table can be constructed.

From the Gregory–Newton forward interpolation formula:

$$y = y_0 + u\,\Delta y_0 + \frac{u^{[+2]}}{2}\Delta^2 y_0 + \cdots,$$

$$\left.\frac{dy}{dx}\right|_{x=x_0} = \frac{1}{h}\left\{\Delta y_0 - \frac{\Delta^2 y_0}{2} + \frac{\Delta^3 y_0}{3} - \cdots\right\}. \tag{6.41}$$

For a formula starting at $u = 1$,

$$y = y_1 + (u-1)^{[1]}\,\Delta y_1 + \frac{(u-1)^{[2]}}{2}\Delta^2 y_1 + \frac{(u-1)^{[3]}}{3!}\Delta^3 y_1 + \cdots, \tag{6.42}$$

then

$$\left.\frac{dy}{dx}\right|_{x=x_0} = \frac{1}{h}\left\{\Delta y_1 - \frac{3}{2}\Delta^2 y_1 + \frac{11}{6}\Delta^3 y_1 - \cdots\right\}. \tag{6.43}$$

Also for a formula starting at $u = -1$,

$$y = y_{-1} + (u+1)^{[1]}\,\Delta y_{-1} + \frac{(u+1)^{[2]}}{2!}\Delta^2 y_{-1} + \frac{(u+1)^{[3]}}{3!}\Delta^3 y_{-1} + \cdots, \tag{6.44}$$

$$\left.\frac{dy}{dx}\right|_{x=x_0} = \frac{1}{h}\left\{\Delta y_{-1} + \frac{1}{2}\Delta^2 y_{-1} - \frac{1}{6}\Delta^3 y_{-1} + \cdots\right\}. \tag{6.45}$$

Differences and coefficients for the first derivative at $x = x_0$ are given in Table 6.2. All formulas derived from the table are to be multiplied by $1/h$.

TABLE 6.2 Differences of dy/dx and Difference Coefficients

y	Δy	$\Delta^2 y$	$\Delta^3 y$	$\Delta^4 y$	$\Delta^5 y$	$\Delta^6 y$ *
0						
y_{-3}	1					
0	Δy_{-3}	5/2				
y_{-2}	1	$\Delta^2 y_{-3}$	11/6			
0	Δy_{-2}	3/2	$\Delta^3 y_{-3}$	1/4		
y_{-1}	1	$\Delta^2 y_{-2}$	1/3	$\Delta^4 y_{-3}$	−1/20	
0	Δy_{-1}	1/2	$\Delta^3 y_{-2}$	−1/12	$\Delta^5 y_{-3}$	1/60
y_0	1	$\Delta^2 y_{-1}$	−1/6	$\Delta^4 y_{-2}$	1/30	$\Delta^6 y_{-3}$
0	Δy_0	−1/2	$\Delta^3 y_{-1}$	1/12	$\Delta^5 y_{-2}$	−1/60
y_1	1	$\Delta^2 y_0$	1/3	$\Delta^4 y_{-1}$	−1/20	$\Delta^6 y_{-2}$
0	Δy_1	−3/2	$\Delta^3 y_0$	−1/4	$\Delta^5 y_{-1}$	1/30
y_2	1	$\Delta^2 y_1$		$\Delta^4 y_0$	1/5	$\Delta^6 y_{-1}$
0	Δy_2				$\Delta^5 y_0$	−1/6
y_3						$\Delta^6 y_0$

* This table is based upon the assumption that the last difference $\Delta^6 y_{-3}$ is a constant. The differences and coefficients below the broken line are given only to guide in the construction of coefficients within the broken lines.

In Table 6.2 the coefficients form a table of differences in an order inverse to the usual order of finding differences. The first difference Δy_0 is

$$\Delta y_0 = y_1 - y_0; \tag{6.46}$$

the second difference $\Delta^2 y_0$ is

$$\Delta^2 y_0 = \Delta y_1 - \Delta y_0. \tag{6.47}$$

However, the coefficients of $\Delta^2 y_0 = -1/2$ and of $\Delta^2 y_1 = -3/2$ yield in subtraction the coefficient of Δy_0, i.e., $-1/2 - (-3/2) = 1$, or, for the coefficients of $\Delta^3 y_0 = 1/3$ and of $\Delta^3 y_1 = 11/6$, the coefficient of $\Delta^2 y_1$ is $1/3 - 11/6 = -3/2$.

So, Table 6.2 consists of (a) a table of symbolic differences, and (b) a table of coefficients of these differences, which is rotated 180° so that the constant differences are in the second column from the left. Thus the table of differences of the coefficients can be constructed from only a knowledge of the values of coefficients in

$$\left.\frac{dy}{dx}\right|_{x=x_0} = \frac{1}{h}\left[\Delta y_0 - \frac{\Delta^2 y_0}{2} + \frac{\Delta^3 y_0}{3} - \cdots\right]. \tag{6.48}$$

The rules for finding these coefficients are: Add the coefficients of $\Delta^i y_0$ to the coefficient of $\Delta^{i+1} y_0$ to find the coefficient of $\Delta^{i+1} y_{-1}$. When the coefficients of all $\Delta^i y_{-1}$ have been found, the coefficients of $\Delta^i y_{-2}$ can be found in a similar manner.

In general, the coefficient of $\Delta^{i+1} y_{-j}$ is equal to the coefficient of $\Delta^{i+1} y_{-j+1}$ plus the coefficient of $\Delta^i y_{-j+1}$, $j = 1, 2, \ldots$. Similarly, the coefficient of $\Delta^{i+1} y_{j+1}$ is equal to the coefficient of $\Delta^{i+1} y_j$ minus the coefficient of $\Delta^i y_{j+1}$, $j = 1, 2, \ldots$. Denoting the coefficient of $\Delta^i y_j$ as c_j^i, $i = 1, 2, \ldots$, the rules can be precisely stated as:

$$c_j^1 = 1 \tag{6.49}$$

for all j,

$$c_j^{i+1} = c_{j+1}^i + c_{j+1}^{i+1} \tag{6.50}$$

for $j = -n, -n+1, \ldots, -1$, and

$$c_{j+1}^{i+1} = c_j^{i+1} - c_{j+1}^i \tag{6.51}$$

for $j = 0, 1, \ldots, n-2$, where there are $(2n+1)$ tabulated values of $f(x)$ and c_0^i are given values. In Table 6.2, the coefficients c_j^i were computed along lines of slope -1 and placed above the corresponding differences $\Delta^i y_i$. Thus, for any formula whose terms are found on a line of slope -1, the coefficients are found immediately above the terms. As an example, entering Table 6.2 at y_{-2} and following a slope of -1, the derivative of

$$y = y_{-2} + (u+2)\,\Delta y_{-2} + \frac{(u+2)^{[2]}}{2!}\,\Delta^2 y_{-2} + \frac{(u+2)^{[3]}}{3!}\,\Delta^3 y_{-2} \tag{6.52}$$

at $x = x_0$ is

$$\left.\frac{dy}{dx}\right|_{x=x_0} = \frac{1}{h}\left\{\Delta y_{-2} + \frac{3}{2}\,\Delta^2 y_{-2} + \frac{1}{3}\,\Delta^3 y_{-2}\right\}. \tag{6.53}$$

These coefficients are found immediately above the corresponding differences.

But the coefficient of a difference approached from a slope of +1 is found immediately below the difference. For example, the derivative of y expressed in the Gregory–Newton backward interpolation formula—that is, for

$$y = y_0 + u\,\Delta y_{-1} + \frac{(u+1)^{[2]}}{2!}\,\Delta^2 y_{-2} + \frac{(u+2)^{[3]}}{3!}\,\Delta^3 y_{-3}, \quad (6.54)$$

is

$$\left.\frac{dy}{dx}\right|_{x=x_0} = \frac{1}{h}\left\{\Delta y_{-1} + \frac{1}{2}\,\Delta^2 y_{-2} + \frac{1}{3}\,\Delta^3 y_{-3}\right\}. \quad (6.55)$$

Thus, coefficients of $\Delta^i y_j$ can be found as follows:

1. For a difference met at a slope of +1, the coefficient is found immediately below the difference.
2. For a difference met at a slope of −1, the coefficient is found immediately above the difference.[1]

Thus, to find the derivative of y at $x = x_0$ by using the Gauss forward interpolation formula, the coefficients will be found alternately above and below the differences. To illustrate,

$$y = y_0 + u\,\delta y_{1/2} + \frac{u^{[2]}}{2!}\,\delta^2 y_0 + \frac{(u+1)^{[3]}}{3!}\,\delta^3 y_{1/2}, \quad (6.56)$$

then

$$\left.\frac{dy}{dx}\right|_{x=x_0} = \delta y_{1/2} - \frac{1}{2}\,\delta^2 y_0 - \frac{1}{6}\,\delta^3 y_{1/2}; \quad (6.57)$$

or, from Table 6.2,

$$\left.\frac{dy}{dx}\right|_{x=x_0} = \frac{1}{h}\left\{\Delta y_0 - \frac{1}{2}\,\Delta^2 y_{-1} - \frac{1}{6}\,\Delta^3 y_{-1}\right\}. \quad (6.58)$$

6.2.1 Flow Chart

Let

$$y = \sum_{i=0}^{n} \frac{u^{[i]}\,\Delta^i y_0}{i!} + E, \qquad \left(E = \frac{h^{n+1} u^{[n+1]} f^{n+1}(\xi)}{(n+1)!}\right). \quad (6.59)$$

[1] For a coefficient met at slope 0, the coefficient is the average of the coefficients immediately above and below the difference.

Approximate $f(x)$ at $x = x_0$. Then

$$\left.\frac{dy}{dx}\right|_{x=x_0} = \frac{1}{h}\sum_{i=1}^{n}\frac{(-1)^{i-1}\,\Delta^i y_0}{i} + E,$$

$$\left(E = \frac{(-1)^n h^n f^{n+1}(\xi)}{n+1}\right) \tag{6.60}$$

approximates

$$\left.\frac{df(x)}{dx}\right|_{x=x_0}.$$

Let $|f^{n+1}(\xi)| \leq M$. Flow Chart 6.2.1 includes the computation of the truncation error E. Using the same notation as in Ch. 5,

$$\left.\frac{dy}{dx}\right|_{x=x_0} = \frac{1}{h}\left\{y_{22} - \frac{y_{33}}{2} + \frac{y_{44}}{3} - \cdots + \frac{(-1)^{n-1}y_{n+1,n+1}}{n}\right\},$$

$$E = \frac{(-1)^n h^n f^{n+1}(\xi)}{n+1}.$$

Notation

h is the interval.
n is the number of tabulated values.
y_{ij} are the tabulated values and successive differences.
$DyDx$ is dy/dx.

FLOW CHART 6.2.1 Finding a Derivative

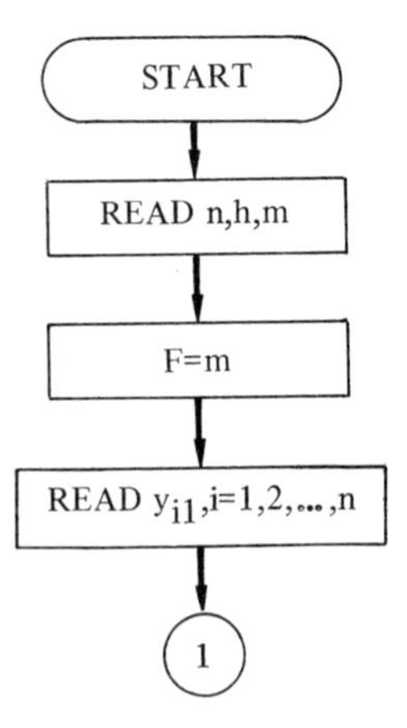

Flow Chart 6.2.1 *(Continued)*

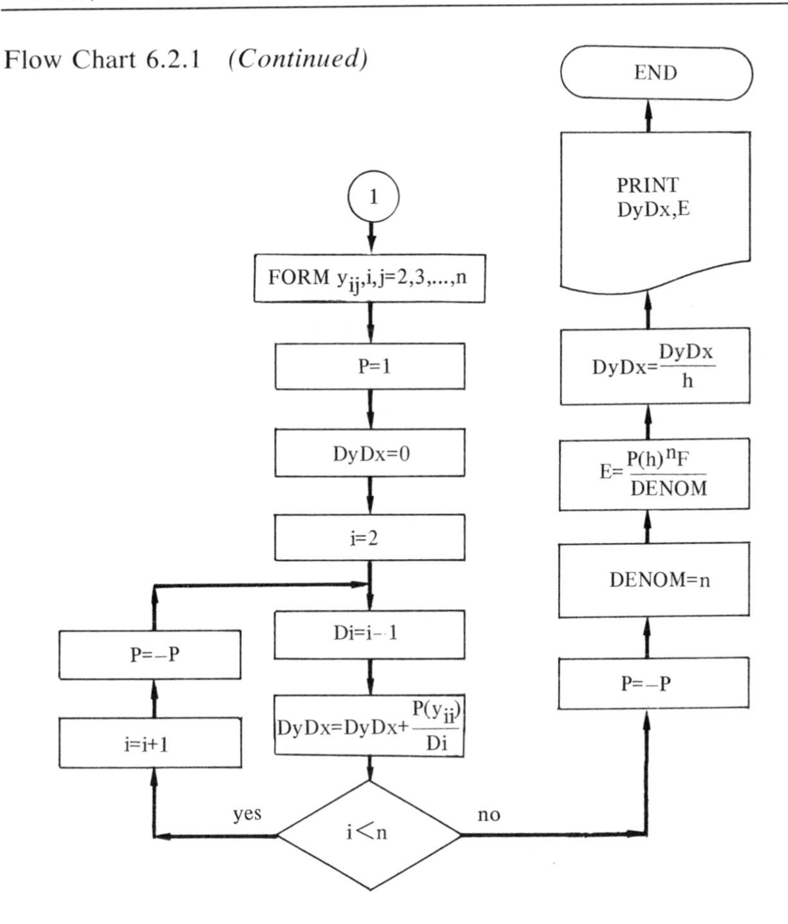

PROBLEMS

Refer to the set of tabulated values of ln x in Prob. 5-3.

6-1. Write a flow chart and program to compute

$$\left.\frac{d \ln x}{dx}\right|_{x=.8}$$

by differentiating the Gregory–Newton backward interpolation formula, and compute the truncation error E.

6-2. Write a flow chart and program to compute

$$\left.\frac{d \ln x}{dx}\right|_{x=.5}$$

by differentiating the Gauss forward interpolation formula, and compute the truncation error E.

6-3. Write a flow chart and program to compute

$$\left.\frac{d \ln x}{dx}\right|_{x=.375}$$

referring to the Example in Sec. 6.2. Assume that the values in Table 6.1 are accurate to 10^{-6}.

Determine M. Use Eq. 6.28 to determine the best choice of h. Values of M and h can be computed by slide rule or desk calculator; or a set of instructions can be included within the program to compute them.

Derive the formula for

$$\left.\frac{dy}{dx}\right|_{x=.375}$$

and compute the value of

$$\left.\frac{dy}{dx}\right|_{x=.375}.$$

Compute the upper bounds of $|R|$, $|E|$, and T on the basis of $h = .1$ as given in Table 6.1.

6.3 Extrapolated Derivative

In general, a better approximation to a derivative can be found by a technique known as extrapolation to the limit. Used here to find a linear combination of two previously computed derivatives, it is usually a more accurate approximation to the true derivative at a given point x_i. In Secs. 6.10 and 6.11, the same idea will also be used in numerical quadrature to find a more accurate value of $\int_a^b f(x)\,dx$.

By entering Table 6.2 at y_0 and following a path of zero slope, the derivative at x_0 can be approximated by summing each path term times the average of terms immediately above and below the path term.

Thus, from the table,

$$y_0' = \frac{1}{h}\frac{(\Delta y_{-1} + \Delta y_0)}{2} - \frac{1}{12}(\Delta^3 y_{-2} + \Delta^3 y_{-1}) + \frac{1}{60}(\Delta^5 y_{-3} + \Delta^5 y_{-2}) - \cdots. \tag{6.61}$$

Note: Formula 6.61 can be directly derived by differentiating the average of the Gauss forward and the Gauss backward interpolation formulas. This combination, known as Stirling's formula, is:

$$y = y_0 + \frac{u}{2}(\Delta y_{-1} + \Delta y_0) + \frac{1}{2}\left(\frac{(u+1)^{[2]}}{2} + \frac{u^{[2]}}{2}\right)\Delta^2 y_{-1}$$

$$+ \frac{1}{2}\left(\frac{(u+1)^{[3]}}{3!}(\Delta^3 y_{-2} + \Delta^3 y_{-1})\right) + \cdots, \qquad \left(u = \frac{x - x_0}{h}\right).$$

When Stirling's formula is differentiated at $u = 0$, the result is formula 6.61.

By using only linear terms as a measure of y_0' and replacing all other terms by error terms in h, the derivative at y_0 can be expressed as

$$y_0' = \frac{y_1 - y_{-1}}{2h} - \frac{h^2}{12}y'''(\xi_1) + \text{terms of } 0(h^4), \qquad (x_{-m} < \xi_1 < x_m). \tag{6.62}$$

Or, in a more general manner, if the function is differentiable $2m$ times,

$$y_0' = \frac{y_{+1} - y_{-1}}{2h} + \sum_{i=1}^{m-1} a_i h^{2i} \tag{6.63}$$

where the coefficients a_i depend upon derivatives of $f(x)$. In what follows, it is assumed that coefficients such as a_i are the same regardless of the size of h.

Now define

$$D_1 = \frac{y_1 - y_{-1}}{2h}. \tag{6.64}$$

Then,

$$y_0' = D_1 + a_1 h^2 + \sum_{i=2}^{m-1} a_i h^{2i}. \tag{6.65}$$

Let the step size h by replaced by H_1 equal to $h/2$. Defining

$$D_2 = \frac{y_1 - y_{-1}}{2H_1}, \tag{6.66}$$

then

$$y_0' = D_2 + a_1\frac{h^2}{4} + \sum_{i=2}^{m-1} a_i \left(\frac{h}{2}\right)^{2i}. \tag{6.67}$$

By multiplying this last equation by 4 and subtracting (6.65), a third approximation to y_0' is

$$y_0' = \frac{4D_2 - D_1}{3} + A_1 h^4 + \sum_{i=3}^{m-1} b_i h^{2i} \tag{6.68}$$

where A_1 and b_i are assumed computed by the algebra involved. Thus, a third approximation with an error term of order h^4 can be defined as

$$D_3 = \frac{4D_2 - D_1}{3}. \tag{6.69}$$

It can now be stated that

$$y_0' = D_3 + A_1h^4 + \sum_{i=3}^{m-1} b_ih^{2i}. \tag{6.70}$$

If the step size is again halved, by a procedure similar to the above,

$$y_0' = D_4 + \frac{A_1h^4}{16} + \sum_{i=3}^{m-1} c_ih^{2i} \tag{6.71}$$

with c_i assumed to be computed, and

$$D_4 = \frac{y_1 - y_{-1}}{2H_2}, \qquad (H_2 = h/4). \tag{6.72}$$

Then eliminating the term in h^4 from Eqs. 6.70 and 6.71,

$$y_0' = \frac{16D_4 - D_3}{15} + A_2h^6 + \sum_{i=4}^{m-1} d_ih^{2i} \tag{6.73}$$

where A_2 and d_i are assumed to have been computed. Thus,

$$D_5 = \frac{16D_4 - D_3}{15} \tag{6.74}$$

is a fifth approximation with an error of order h^6.

It should be tacitly understood that this method of extrapolation to the limit will lead to better approximations of $f'(x_0)$ only if the error in D_i, $i = 1, 2, \ldots$, is due largely to truncation rather than round-off error. In fact, if the errors in D_1 and D_2 were mostly due to round-off, D_3 might lead to poorer results.

This method of extrapolation to the limit may be summarized in convenient subscript notation. Define approximations $D_1, D_2, \ldots$ as

$$D_{i1} = \frac{y_1 - y_{-1}}{2H}, \qquad (H = h, h/2, \ldots; i = 1, 2, \ldots). \tag{6.75}$$

These D_{i1} are the elements of the first column of the array in Table 6.3.

Define approximations such as D_3 and D_5 as

$$D_{ij} = \frac{4^{j-1}D_{i,j-1} - D_{i-1,j-1}}{4^{j-1} - 1} \tag{6.76}$$

where $j = 2, 3, \ldots$, and for each fixed j, $i = j, j + 1, \ldots$. These D_{ij} are the elements in columns 2, 3, ... of Table 6.3.

TABLE 6.3 Extrapolated Derivatives

H	D_{i1}	D_{i2}	D_{i3}	D_{i4}
h	D_{11}			
$h/2$	D_{21}	D_{22}		
$h/4$	D_{31}	D_{32}	D_{33}	
$h/8$	D_{41}	D_{42}	D_{43}	D_{44}
. .	. .	. .	. .	. .

Based on the premise that error is due largely to truncation, the procedure to compute D_{ij} can be continued until two successive diagonal values agree within the prescribed degree of accuracy. Also, it is not necessary to start with a small h; a fairly large value of h can be used initially.

TABLE 6.4 Tabulated Values of $\log_{10} x$, $x = 1.01, 1.02, \ldots, 1.10$

x		$\log_{10} x$	
1.01	0043	2137	3782
1.02	0086	0017	1761
1.03	0128	3722	4705
1.04	0170	3333	9298
1.05	0211	8929	9069
1.06	0253	0586	5264
1.07	0293	8377	7685
1.08	0334	2375	5486
1.09	0374	2649	7940
1.10	0413	9268	5158

Example

To compute the value of

$$\frac{d}{dx} \log_{10} x \bigg|_{x=1.06}$$

by means of the extrapolated derivative, using formula 6.75 for $H = .04, .02, .01$, at $x = 1.06$, it is found that for $H = .04$,

$$D_{11} = \frac{.041392685158 - .008600171761}{.08}$$
$$= .4099064174;$$

for $H = .02$,

$$D_{21} = \frac{.033423755486 - .017033339298}{.04}$$
$$= .409760405;$$

and for $H = .01$,

$$D_{31} = \frac{.029383777685 - .021189299069}{.02}$$
$$= .409723931.$$

By means of formula 6.76,

$$D_{22} = \frac{4D_{21} - D_{11}}{3} = .409711734,$$

$$D_{32} = \frac{4D_{31} - D_{21}}{3} = .409711773,$$

$$D_{33} = \frac{16D_{32} - D_{22}}{15} = .409711760.$$

Table 6.5 shows these results.

TABLE 6.5 D_{ij} for $\log_{10} x$

H	D_{i1}	D_{i2}	D_{i3}
.04	.409906417		
.02	.409760405	.409711734	
.01	.409723931	.409711773	.409711760

Thus, $|D_{33} - D_{22}| < 3(10^{-8})$. By direct computation,

$$\frac{d}{dx} \log_{10} x \bigg|_{x=1.06} = .409711775.$$

Hence, the error:

$$\left| \frac{d}{dx} \log_{10} x \bigg|_{x=1.06} - D_{33} \right| < 2(10^{-8});$$

whereas, it should be noted that the error in using only D_{31} ($H = .01$) is

$$\left| \frac{d}{dx} \log_{10} x \Big|_{x=1.06} - D_{31} \right| < 10^{-5}.$$

In Secs. 6.9 (Richardson extrapolation) and 6.10–6.10.1 (Romberg integration), techniques for numerical integration similar in notation to the methods considered here are presented. Therefore, a problem (flow chart and program) for finding an extrapolated derivative is deferred to Prob. 6.6.

6.4 Numerical Integration

Consider the problem of evaluating $\int_a^b f(x)\,dx$. If the indefinite integral $F(x)$ is known, then

$$\int_a^b f(x)\,dx = F(a) - F(b). \tag{6.77}$$

This would appear to be the best way to evaluate (6.77). However, $F(x)$ may not be a simple function; it might consist of several transcendental functions that would have to be evaluated at $x = a$ and $x = b$. Even for such a simple integral as

$$\int \frac{dt}{\sqrt{1 + t^2}} = \ln |\sqrt{1 + t^2} + t| + c,$$

computations in the definite integral would require the evaluation of a logarithm at $t = a$ and $t = b$. Thus, an exact method of indefinite integration may lead to many computations—yet the end result may be only an approximation. And, for many indefinite integrals, the integration cannot be expressed as a finite linear combination of elementary functions (algebraic, logarithmic, and exponential terms). For example, $\int e^{-x^2}\,dx$ is such an integral. Furthermore, if only experimental data are available, the theoretical approach may not be applicable at all.

6.5 Quadrature Formulas

For the reasons stated in Sec. 6.4, formulas for the definite integral (quadrature formulas) are generally used to evaluate $\int_a^b f(x)\,dx$, especially if a digital computer is available.

The general procedure for finding a quadrature formula is first to approximate $f(x)$ by a polynomial over the range a to b. The interval

(a,b) is divided into n subintervals, and over each of these subintervals $f(x)$ is replaced by a polynomial. Any of the formulas of Ch. 5 (Gregory–Newton, Gauss, or Lagrange) may be used to obtain these polynomials. Second, these polynomials are integrated over the subintervals, and the sum of these integrations over the range is the approximation to $\int_a^b f(x)\,dx$.

The requirement for this procedure is that $f(x)$ be tabulated at points x_i in the range a to b. When the polynomial is integrated, a set of values called *weights* is obtained. These weights become the coefficients of the tabulated values $f(x_i)$.

6.5.1 Newton–Cotes Formulas, Closed and Composite

Let $f(x)$ have the tabulated values $f(x_0) = y_0$ and $f(x_1) = y_1$; then the Gregory–Newton forward interpolation formula for $f(x)$ is

$$y = y_0 + u\,\Delta y_0, \qquad E_0 = \frac{h^2 u^{[2]} f''(\xi_0)}{2!}, \tag{6.78}$$

$$h = x_1 - x_0, \qquad u = \frac{x - x_0}{h}, \qquad x_0 < \xi_0 < x_1.$$

Thus,

$$\int_{x_0}^{x_1} y\,dx = h \int_0^1 (y_0 + u\,\Delta y_0)\,du, \tag{6.79}$$

and R_0 is the remainder term given by

$$R_0 = \frac{h^3}{2} \int_0^1 (u^2 - u) f''(\xi_0)\,du, \tag{6.80}$$

where ξ_0 is a function of u.

It will be assumed in this text that a value of ξ_0' can be found such that R_0 can be expressed as

$$R_0 = \frac{h^3}{2} f''(\xi_0') \int_0^1 (u^2 - u)\,du$$

$$= -\frac{h^3 f''(\xi_0')}{12}, \qquad (x_0 < \xi_0' < x_1). \tag{6.81}$$

Then, in terms of $f(x_0)$, $f(x_1)$ and $f''(\xi_0')$,

$$\int_{x_0}^{x_1} f(x)\,dx = \frac{h}{2}(f(x_0) + f(x_1)) + R_0, \qquad R_0 = \frac{-h^3}{12} f''(\xi_0'). \tag{6.82}$$

Equation 6.82 is an example of a closed Newton–Cotes formula.[2] The general form of a closed Newton–Cotes formula is

$$\int_{x_0}^{x_m} f(x)\,dx = \sum_{i=0}^{m} W_i f(x_i) + R, \tag{6.83}$$

where W_i are the weights, $f(x_i)$ are the tabulated values of $f(x)$, and R is the remainder term.

Now, suppose that $f(x)$ has the tabulated values

$$f(a) = f(x_0), f(x_1), \ldots, f(x_{n-1}), \qquad f(b) = f(x_n),$$

that the interval (a,b) is divided into n subintervals, and $h = (b - a)/n$. Further, it is assumed that there is some value ξ of x in the interval (a,b) such that in each subinterval, R_i is proportional to $f''(\xi)$; that is, $R_i = (-h^3/12)f''(\xi)$. If formula 6.82 is used on each subinterval and the results are summed, then

$$\int_a^b f(x)\,dx \cong h\left\{\frac{f(a)}{2} + f(x_1) + f(x_2) + \cdots + \frac{f(b)}{2}\right\} \tag{6.84}$$

and

$$R = \sum_{i=0}^{n-1} R_i = \frac{-nh^3}{12} = \frac{-h^2(b-a)}{12} f''(\xi). \tag{6.85}$$

Formula 6.84 is of course the trapezoidal rule, and is an example of a composite Newton–Cotes formula. It should also be noted that the derivation of (6.84) suggests a general method of finding a composite quadrature formula, i.e.,

1. Divide the interval (a,b) into n subintervals.
2. Apply the quadrature formula on each subinterval and sum the results.

But why use a composite rule? What are the advantages over a quadrature formula of nth order applied to the interval (a,b) as a whole? One advantage is contained in the remainder terms. The remainder term of (6.84) is proportional to $f''(\xi)$, whereas in an nth-order formula, it would contain a derivative of order $n + 1$ or possibly $n + 2$. If $f(x)$ has derivatives that grow in magnitude, it would be difficult to find a reasonable bound on a high-order derivative or to estimate a value of it. Thus the error in such a case might be unnecessarily large. The fact that h would be of lower degree in the composite rule than in

[2] Since $u^{[2]}$ does not change sign from 0 to 1 and is continuous, and $f''(\xi)$ is assumed continuous, the mean value theorem can be applied; hence R_0 in Eq. 6.81 is true.

an nth-order quadrature formula is not of major importance, since h can always be made smaller.

Another advantage not immediately obvious in using a composite Newton–Cotes formula is that a lesser number of abscissas is needed, since abutting subintervals have the same end points.

From the above discussion and assumptions it is evident that the trapezoidal rule is accurate for polynomials of degree 1, and that the accuracy of composite Newton–Cotes formulas depends on the h size, the degree of the formula, and the points involved. Another composite Newton–Cotes formula, the well-known Simpson's $\frac{1}{3}$ rule, is derived below. Special emphasis is placed on the derivation of the remainder term.

Suppose now that $f(x_0) = y_0$, $f(x_1) = y_1$, and $f(x_2) = y_2$ are tabulated values of $f(x)$ at equally spaced intervals. Then the Gregory–Newton forward interpolation formula for $f(x)$ is

$$y = y_0 + u\,\Delta y_0 + \frac{u^{[2]}}{2!}\,\Delta^2 y_0, \qquad \left(E_0 = \frac{h^3 u^{[3]} f'''(\xi_0)}{3!}\right),$$

$$x_0 < \xi_0 < x_2, \qquad h = x_1 - x_0 = x_2 - x_1, \qquad u = \frac{x - x_0}{h}. \tag{6.86}$$

If it is assumed that the mean value theorem is applicable, then

$$\int_{x_0}^{x_2} f(x)\,dx \cong \int_{x_0}^{x_2} y\,dx = h\int_0^2 \left(y_0 + u\,\Delta y_0 + \frac{(u^2 - u)\,\Delta^2 y_0}{2}\right) du$$
$$= \frac{h}{3}(6y_0 + 6\,\Delta y_0 + \Delta^2 y_0) = \frac{h}{3}(y_0 + 4y_1 + y_2), \tag{6.87}$$

and

$$R_0 = h^4 f'''(\xi_0')\int_0^2 (u^3 - 3u^2 + 2u)\,du = 0,$$
$$(x_0 < \xi_0' < x_2). \tag{6.88}$$

Equation 6.87, expressed in the form of Eq. 6.83 for an interval of length $2h$ and $m = 2$, is

$$\int_{x_0}^{x_2} f(x)\,dx \cong \sum_{i=0}^{2} W_i f(x_i) = \frac{h}{3}[f(x_0) + 4f(x_1) + f(x_2)]. \tag{6.89}$$

That the integral $\int_0^2 u(u-1)(u-2)\,du$ is zero can be clearly seen by inspection. The area bounded by this curve, ($u = 0$ and $u = 2$), is equally positive and negative; hence it is zero. In general,

$$\int_0^{2k} u(u-1)\cdots(u-2k)\,du$$

is zero, since for each area above the u axis there is an area of equal magnitude below it.

To find a remainder term for this formula, the next term of the Gregory–Newton formula is chosen [$\Delta^4 y_0$ being replaced by $h^4 f^4(\xi_0)$], assuming that the mean value theorem can be applied:[3]

$$\begin{aligned} R_0 &= \frac{h^5 f^4(\xi_0')}{4!}\int_0^2 u^{[4]}\,du \\ &= \frac{-h^5 f^4(\xi_0')}{90}. \end{aligned} \tag{6.90}$$

Assuming that there exists a value ξ in the interval (a,b) such that in each subinterval of length $2h$, $R_i = [-h^5 f^{[4]}(\xi)]/90$, and that $f(x)$ has the tabulated values $f(a) = f(x_0), f(x_1), \ldots, f(x_{n-1}), f(b)$, where n is an even integer, then if the closed Newton–Cotes formula (6.89) is used on each subinterval of length $2h$ and the results are summed, the composite Newton–Cotes formula known as Simpson's $1/3$ rule is derived, namely,

$$\int_a^b f(x)\,dx = \frac{h}{3}\{f(a) + 4f(x_1) + 2f(x_2) + \cdots + 4f(x_{n-1}) + f(b)\}, \tag{6.91}$$

and by Eq. 6.85,

$$\begin{aligned} R = \sum_{i=0}^{(n/2)-i} R_1 &= \frac{-nh^5 f^4(\xi)}{90} \\ &= \frac{-nh^4 f^4(\xi)}{180}. \end{aligned} \tag{6.92}$$

Referring to Eqs. 6.81 and 6.90, these examples of remainder terms suggest that the closed Newton–Cotes formula 6.83 without the remainder term is accurate for polynomials of degree m or less if m is an odd integer, and for polynomials of degree $m + 1$ or less if m is an even integer.

Denoting a closed Newton–Cotes formula as

$$\int_{x_0}^{x_n} f(x)\,dx = h\sum_{i=0}^{m} w_i f(x_i) + \begin{cases} c\, h^{m+2} f^{m+1}(\xi), & m \text{ odd} \\ c\, h^{m+3} f^{m+2}(\xi), & m \text{ even} \end{cases} \tag{6.93}$$

[3] Since integration is over two panels, the theorem of the mean value cannot be applied directly.

where $x_0 < \xi < x_m$, then Table 6.6 lists the weights and the error term coefficients of closed Newton–Cotes formulas for $m = 1, 2, 3, 4$. Thus, for $m = 2$,

$$\int_{x_0}^{x_2} f(x)\,dx = h\left(\frac{1}{3}f_0 + \frac{4}{3}f_1 + \frac{1}{3}f_2\right), \qquad R = \frac{-h^5}{90}f^4(\xi). \tag{6.94}$$

It should be noted that the weights are symmetric, and that the sum of the weights is always the length of the range of integration. Why?

TABLE 6.6 Weights and Error Term Coefficients for Closed Newton–Cotes Formulas, $m = 1, 2, 3, 4$

m	w_0	w_1	w_2	w_3	w_4	c
1	1/2	1/2				−1/12
2	1/3	4/3	1/3			−1/90
3	3/8	9/8	9/8	3/8		−3/80
4	14/45	64/45	8/15	64/45	14/45	−8/945

6.5.2 Flow Chart

Consider the problem of evaluating π by using Simpson's ⅓ rule to compute

$$4\int_0^1 \frac{dx}{1+x^2} = \pi.$$

Let $h = (1-0)/n$ where n is an even number. Define $f(x) = 1/(1+x^2)$, $a = 0$, $b = 1$; x initially equals a. Then by Eqs. 6.91 and 6.92,

$$4\int_0^1 \frac{dx}{1+x^2} \cong \frac{4h}{3}\Big\{f(a) + 4f(a+h) + 2f(a+2h) + \cdots$$
$$+ 2f(a+(n-2)h) + 4f(a+(n-1)h) + f(b)\Big\},$$
$$R = -\frac{h^4 f^4(\xi)}{180}, \qquad (0 < \xi < 1). \tag{6.95}$$

Since $|f^4(\xi)| < 10$, $|R| < h^4/18$.

The program in Sec. 6.5.3 makes use of the computed GO TO statement. That is, by the statement

```
GO TO (10,20) I
```

for $I = 1$, control is transferred to statement 10, and for $I = 2$ control

FLOW CHART 6.5.2 Closed Newton–Cotes Formula

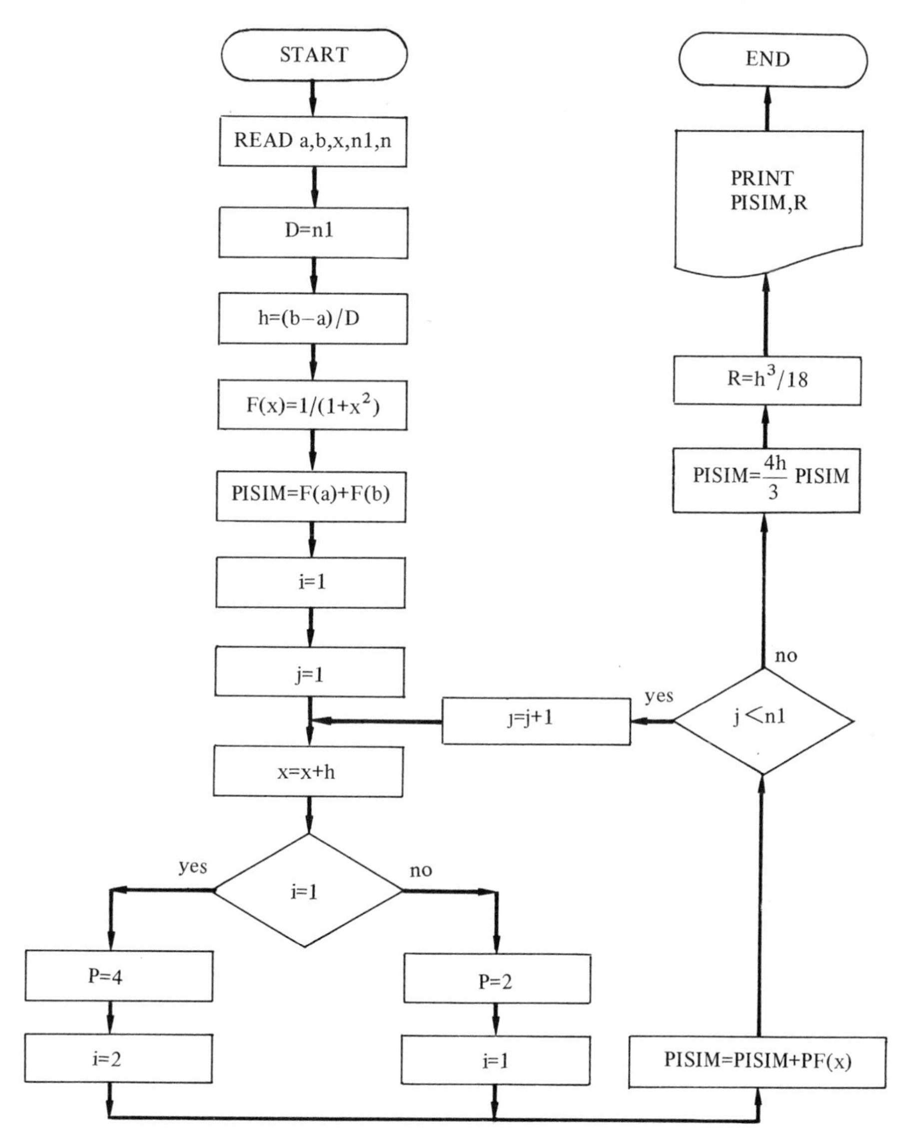

is transferred to statement 20. Equation 6.95 is restated (in the order of computer computation) as

$$Pisim = ((f(a) + f(b)) + 4f(a + h) + 2f(a + 2h)$$
$$+ \cdots + 2f(a + (n - 2)h) + 4f(a + (n - 1)h))\,\frac{4h}{3},$$
$$|R| = \frac{h^4}{18}, \qquad N1 = N - 1. \tag{6.96}$$

6.5.3 Program

To compute

$$4\int_0^1 \frac{dx}{1 + x^2} = \pi, \qquad N = 100, \qquad N1 = N - 1,$$

by Simpson's $1/3$ rule.

```
/ID
/JOB GO
/FTC LIST,REF
C     SIMPSON'S RULE TO EVALUATE π
    1 FORMAT(3F12.6,I2)
    2 FORMAT(1H1,//,5X,'PISIM='F12.6,//,5X,'R='F12.6)
      READ(5,1)A,B,X,N1
      H=.01
      F(X)=1.0/(1.0+X**2)
      PISIM=F(A)+F(B)
      I=1
      DO 30,J=1,N1
      X=X+H
      GO TO (10,20),I
   10 P=4.0
      I=2
      GO TO 30
   20 P=2.0
      I=1
   30 PISIM=PISIM+P*F(X)
      PISIM=(4.0*H*PISIM)/3.0
      R=H**3/18.0
      WRITE(6,2)PISIM,R
      STOP
      END

      RESULTS
      PISIM=3.14584
      R=0.00000
```

EXERCISE

Write a flow chart and program for the following problem. Given:

$$4\int_0^1 \frac{dx}{1+x^2} = \pi, \qquad (\pi = 3.14159265).$$

(a) Compute π by the trapezoidal rule. The formula is

$$\begin{aligned} Pitrap = (&f(a) + f(b) + 2(f(a+h) + f(a+2h) + \cdots \\ &+ f(a+(n-1)h))\frac{h}{2}. \end{aligned}$$

(b) Compute π by Simpson's ⅓ rule. The formula is

$$\begin{aligned} Pisim = (&f(a) + f(b) + 4f(a+h) + 2f(a+2h) + \cdots \\ &+ 2f(a+(n-2)h) + 4f(a+(n-1)h))\frac{4h}{3}. \end{aligned}$$

(c) Compute the differences:

$$\begin{aligned} Difsim &= Pisim - \text{pi} \\ Diftrp &= Pitrap - \text{pi}. \end{aligned}$$

Suggestion: A computed GO TO statement can be used to good advantage to compute alternately $4f(a + (2k - 1)h)$ and $2f(a + (2k)h)$, $k = 1, 2, 3, \ldots, n/2$ in *Pisim*. For each of these terms computed and added to the current *Pisim*, a term in *Pitrap* must be computed and added to the current *Pitrap*.

6.6 Repeated Subdivision of the Interval—Trapezoidal Rule

Consider the computation and evaluation of $\int_a^b f(x)\,dx$ by repeated application of the trapezoidal rule. For a fixed $h = (b - a)/n$, the formula becomes

$$\int_a^b f(x)\,dx \cong \left(\frac{f(a)}{2} + \frac{f(b)}{2} + f(x_1) + \cdots + f(x_{n-1})\right) h,$$

$$R = -\frac{(b-a)}{12} h^2 f''(\xi), \qquad (a < \xi < b), \tag{6.97}$$

where $f(a), f(x_i), \ldots, f(b)$ are the tabulated values of $f(x)$.

Now consider h having successive values of $(b - a)$, $(b - a)/2$, $\ldots$, $(b - a)/2^{k-1}$, and for each value of h compute $\int_a^b f(x)\,dx$. Call these successive computations $TS_1, TS_2, \ldots, TS_k$. When $|TS_j - TS_{j-1}| < \epsilon$, where ϵ is a small positive number arbitrarily chosen for the desired accuracy, TS_j will be the approximated value of the definite integral, and $h = (b - a)/2^{j-1}$ will be the subinterval.

6.6.1 Flow Chart

The following notation will be used in Flow Chart 6.6.1 and the program of Sec. 6.6.2. Let h represent the width of a subinterval;

$$SUM1 = \frac{f(a)}{2} + \frac{f(b)}{2} + \sum_{j=1}^{m} f(x_j), \qquad \left(m = 2^k - 1 \text{ for } h_1 = \frac{b-a}{2^k}\right).$$

$SUM2$ will be the sum of all values of $f(x)$ at the newly selected points, due to the fact that now $h_2 = (b - a)/2^{k+1}$. Then let

$$SUM12 = SUM1 + SUM2 = \frac{f(a)}{2} + \frac{f(b)}{2} + \sum_{j=1}^{nn} f(x_j), \qquad (nn = 2^{k+1} - 1).$$

Also, let $TSUM_1 = (SUM1)h_1$ and $TSUM12 = (SUM12)h_2$. When $|TSUM12 - TSUM1| < \epsilon$, $TSUM12 \cong \int_a^b f(x)\,dx$, within the desired accuracy.

Using only coefficient weights in Table 6.7, at the respective points, the general idea is brought out that the values of $f(x)$ at the newly selected points are added to the previously computed values.

TABLE 6.7 Coefficient Weights for Repeated Use of the Trapezoidal Rule

Coefficients

In:	a	$a + h_2$	$a + h_1$	$a + 3h_2$	$a + 2h_1$	$a + 5h_2$	$a + 3h_1$	$a + 7h_2$	b
$SUM1$	1/2		1		1		1		1/2
$SUM2$		1		1		1		1	
$SUM12$	1/2	1	1	1	1	1	1	1	1/2

Thus, $TSUM1 = (SUM1)h_1$; $TSUM12 = (SUM12)h_2$. In Flow Chart 6.6.1 only the terms $SUM1$, $SUM2$, $TSUM1$, and $TSUM2$ are necessary.

FLOW CHART 6.6.1 Trapezoidal Rule by Repeated Subdivision of the Interval

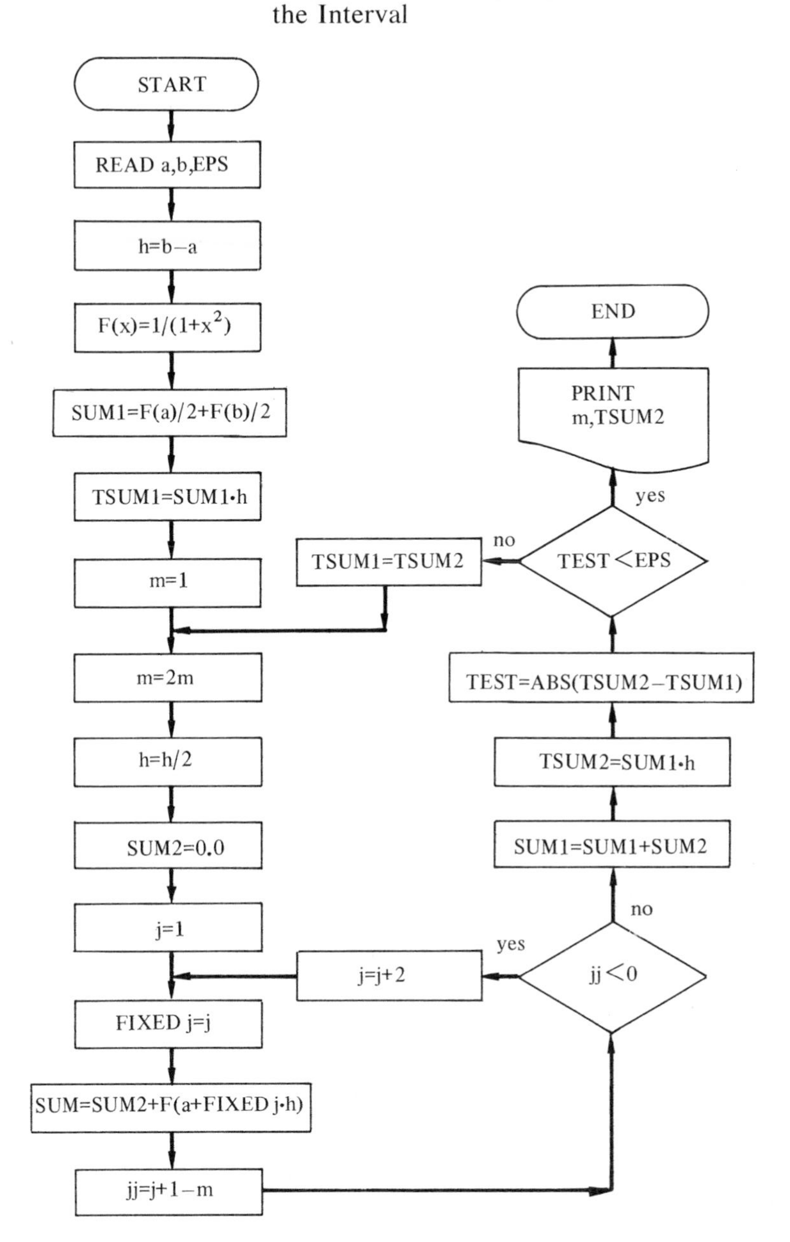

6.6.2 Program

To evaluate

$$4 \int_0^1 \frac{dx}{1 + x^2}$$

by repeated subdivision of the interval using the trapezoidal rule.

```
C
C       TRAPEZOIDAL RULE BY REPEATED SUBDIVISION OF THE INTERVAL
C
        F(X)=1./(1+X**2)
        READ(5,101)A,B,EPS
    101 FORMAT(3F10.5)
        M=1
        H=B-A
        SUM1=(F(A)+F(B))/2.
        TSUM1=4*H*SUM1
      1 J=1
        M=M*2
        H=H/2
        SUM2=0
      4 SUM2=SUM2+F(A+J*H)
        JJ=J+1-M
        IF(JJ)2,3,3
      2 J=J+2
        GO TO 4
      3 SUM1=SUM1+SUM2
        TSUM2=4*H*SUM1
        TEST=ABS(TSUM2-TSUM1)
        IF(TEST-EPS)6,5,5
      5 TSUM1=TSUM2
        GO TO 1
      6 WRITE(6,102)TSUM2,M
    100 FORMAT('THE RESULT IS ',F12.6,5X,I5)
        STOP
        END

        /DATA
        THE RESULT IS    3.141565
        STOP     00000
        END OF JOB
```

6.7 Repeated Subdivision of the Interval—Simpson's 1/3 Rule

Repeated use of Simpson's 1/3 rule may be stated as

$$\int_a^b f(x)\,dx = [f(a) + f(b) + SUM1 + 2SUM2]\,\frac{h_2}{3}$$

where

$$SUM1 = 2[f(a + h_1) + f(a + 2h_1) + \cdots + f(a + (m - 1)h_1)].$$
$$SUM2 = 2[f(a + h_2) + f(a + 3h_2) + \cdots + f(a + (2m - 1)h_2)].$$

Hence,

$$SUM1 + 2SUM2 = 4f(a + h_2) + 2f(a + 2h_2) + 4f(a + 3h_2) + \cdots + 4f(a + (2m - 1)h_2)$$

where

$$h_1 = (b - a)/2^k, \quad h_2 = (b - a)/2^{k+1}, \quad m = 2^k, \quad k = 1, 2, \ldots.$$

Guidelines for the construction of Flow Chart 6.7, the application of Simpson's 1/3 rule based on repeated subdivision of the interval, are:

1. Set $h = b - a$.
2. Set $SUM1 = f(a) + f(b)$.
3. Set $TSUM1 = (SUM1)h/3$.
4. Set $m = 1$.
5. Replace h by $h/2$.
6. Set $m = 2m$.
7. Compute

$$SUM2 = 2(f(a + h) + f(a + 3h) + \cdots + f(a + (m - 1)h)).$$

8. Set $SUM21 = SUM1 + 2(SUM2)$.
9. Set $SUM1 = SUM1 + SUM2$.
10. Set $TSUM21 = (SUM21)h/3$.
11. Form $ABS(TSUM21 - TSUM1) = TEST$.
12. If $TEST < \epsilon$ replace $TSUM1$ by $TSUM\ 2$ and repeat steps 5 through 11; otherwise continue with step 13.
13. Print m, h, $TSUM21$.

FLOW CHART 6.7 Simpson's ⅓ Rule by Repeated Subdivision of the Interval

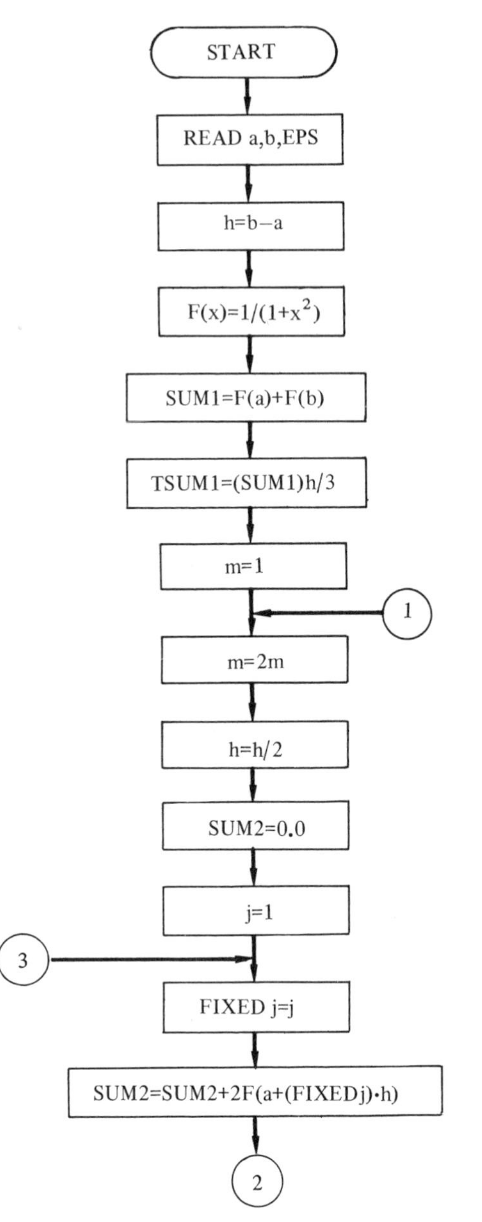

Flow Chart 6.7 *(Continued)*

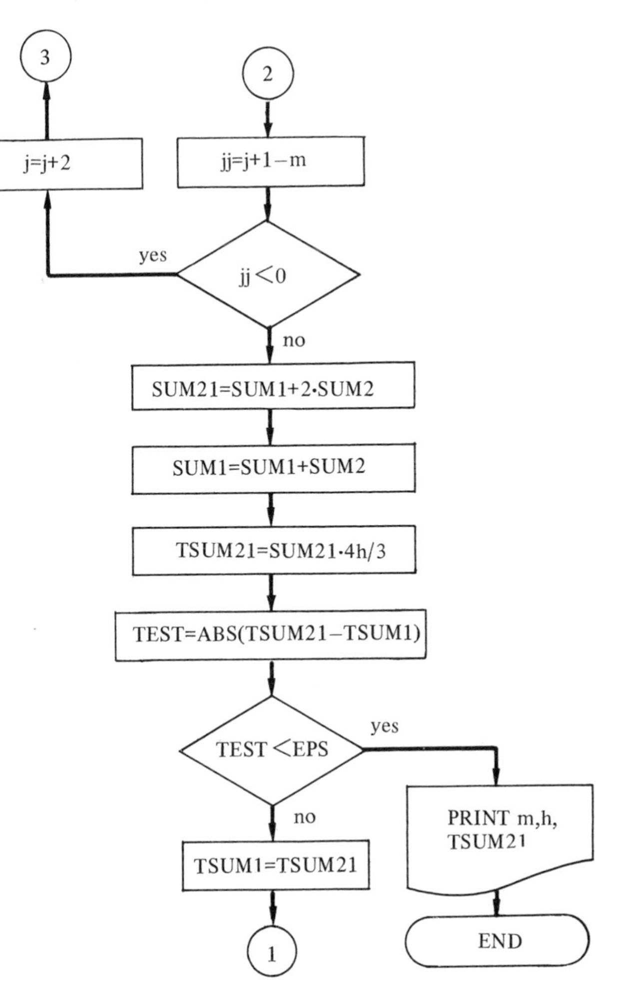

6.7.1 Program

To evaluate

$$4 \int_0^1 \frac{dx}{1 + x^2}$$

by repeated subdivision of the interval using Simpson's ⅓ rule.

```
C
C     SIMPSONS RULE BY REPEATED SUBDIVISION OF THE INTERVAL
C
      F(X)=1./(1+X**2)
      READ(5,101)A,B,EPS
  101 FORMAT(3F10.5)
      H=B-A
      SUM1=F(A)+F(B)
      TSUM1=4*H*SUM1/3
      M=1
    1 H=H/2
      M=M*2
      SUM2=0.
      J=1
    4 SUM2=SUM2+2.*F(A+J*H)
      IF(J+1-M)2,3,3
    2 J=J+2
      GO TO 4
    3 SUM21=SUM1+SUM2*2.
      SUM1=SUM1+SUM2
      TSUM21=SUM21*4*H/3
      IF(ABS(TSUM21-TSUM1)-EPS)5,6,6
    6 TSUM1=TSUM21
      GO TO 1
    5 WRITE(6,102)H,M,TSUM21
  102 FORMAT(F10.4,5X,I4,'THE RESULT IS ',F12.6)
      STOP
      END

      THE RESULT IS    3.141591
```

6.7.2 Remarks

It is well to note how accurate each of the methods presented in the previous section is:
Accurate to eight decimal places, $\pi = 3.14159265$.
Pisim (π by Simpson's $1/3$ rule) = 3.141584.
Pitrapr (π using repeated subdivision of the interval and the trapezoidal rule) = 3.141565.
Pisimr (π using repeated subdivision of the interval and Simpson's $1/3$ rule) = 3.141591.
Pisimr is accurate to the fifth decimal place, whereas *Pisim* and *Pitrapr* are accurate only to the fourth decimal place.

It should also be noted that *Pitrap* (π by the trapezoidal rule but not with subdivision of the interval) was computed on a computer with $H = .001$ and $N = 1000$ using the method of double precision.

The value of π by this method is 3.14159234902. This result is accurate to six decimal places.

EXERCISE

Write one program to compute *PITRAP* and *PISIM* based upon the repeated subdivision of the interval.

6.8 Open Newton–Cotes Formula

A closed Newton–Cotes formula, Eq. 6.83, may be derived from:

$$\int_{x_0}^{x_m} f(x)\,dx = h\int_0^m \left(y_0 + u\,\Delta y_0 + \cdots + \frac{u^{[m]}\,\Delta^m y_0}{m!}\right) du + R \tag{6.98}$$

where $f(x_i) = y_i$, $i = 0, 1, \ldots, m$, $u = (x - x_0)/h$, and h is constant.

Open Newton–Cotes formulas have the form

$$\int_{x_0}^{x_m} f(x)\,dx = \sum_{i=1}^{m-1} W_i f(x_i) + R, \tag{6.99}$$

and may be derived from:

$$\int_{x_0}^{x_m} f(x)\,dx = h\int_0^m \left(y_1 + (u-1)\,\Delta y_1 + \cdots + \frac{(u-1)^{[m-2]}}{(m-2)!}\right) du + R, \tag{6.100}$$

where for m odd,

$$R = h\int_0^m \frac{(u-1)^{[m-1]} f^{m-1}(\xi) h^{m-1}}{(m-1)!}\,du, \tag{6.101}$$

and for m even,

$$R = h\int_0^m \frac{(u-1)^{[m]} f^{m}(\xi) h^{m}}{m!}\,du. \tag{6.102}$$

If the mean value theorem applies, it is seen from the remainder terms (Eqs. 6.101–6.102) that for m odd, an open Newton–Cotes formula is exact for polynomials of degree $m - 2$ or less, but for m even it is exact for polynomials of degree $m - 1$ or less.

For example, the open Newton–Cotes formula for $m = 3$ is based upon Table 6.8. Since y_0 and y_3 are not considered, the formula becomes

$$\int_{x_0}^{x_3} f(x)\,dx = h\int_0^3 \{y_1 + (u-1)\,\Delta y_1\}\,du = h\left\{3y_1 + \frac{3}{2}\,\Delta y_1\right\} \tag{6.103}$$

or

$$\int_{x_0}^{x_3} f(x)\,dx = \frac{3}{2}\,h(y_2 + y_1).$$

Also,

$$R = h\int_0^3 \frac{(u-1)^{[2]} f''(\xi)h^2}{2!}\,du$$

$$= \frac{3h^3}{4} f''(\xi), \qquad (x_0 < \xi' < x_3), \tag{6.104}$$

where it is assumed that the mean value theorem can be applied. Thus Eq. 6.103 is exact for a linear polynomial or a constant.

TABLE 6.8 Open Newton–Cotes Differences, $m = 3$

x	u	y	Δy	$\Delta^2 y$	$\Delta^3 y$
x_0	0	~~y_0~~			
			~~Δy_0~~		
x_1	1	y_1		~~$\Delta^2 y_0$~~	
			Δy_1		~~$\Delta^3 y_0$~~
x_2	2	y_2		~~$\Delta^2 y_1$~~	
			~~Δy_2~~		
x_3	3	~~y_3~~			

As an example of an open formula for m even, consider

$$\int_{x_0}^{x_4} f(x)\,dx = h\int_0^4 \left[y_1 + (u-1)\,\Delta y_1 + \frac{(u-1)^{[2]}}{2}\,\Delta^2 y_1\right] du + R$$

$$= \frac{4}{3}\,h(2y_1 - y_2 + 2y_3) + R. \tag{6.105}$$

R should be found by extending the polynomial to the next term with appropriate changes; that is

$$R = h\int_0^4 \frac{h^3(u-1)^{[3]}}{3!} f'''(\xi)\,du$$

$$= \frac{h^4 f'''(\xi')}{6}\int_0^4 (u-1)^{[3]}\,du.$$

However, this integral vanishes because of the symmetry over the range. Thus for $m = 4$,

$$R = \frac{h^5 f^4(\xi')}{4!} \int_0^4 (u-1)^{[4]}\, du$$

$$= \frac{14 h^5 f^4(\xi')}{45}. \tag{6.106}$$

Equation 6.106 shows that Eq. 6.105 without the remainder term is exact for polynomials of degree three or less.

Denoting an open Newton–Cotes formula as

$$\int_{x_0}^{x_m} f(x)\, dx = h \sum_{i=1}^{m-1} w_i f(x_i) + \begin{cases} c\, h^m f^{m-1}(\xi), & \text{for } m \text{ odd} \\ c\, h^{m+1} f^m(\xi), & \text{for } m \text{ even} \end{cases}$$

where $x_0 < \xi < x_m$, then Table 6.9 lists the weights and error term coefficients of the Newton–Cotes open formulas for $m = 2, 3, 4$. Open Newton–Cotes formulas for the same number of points do not present any advantage over the closed formulas in most cases. In the numerical solution of ordinary differential equations, these open formulas are used (see Ch. 7).

TABLE 6.9 Weights and Error Term Coefficients for Open Newton–Cotes Formulas

m	w_1	w_2	w_3	c
2	2			1/3
3	3/2	3/2		3/4
4	8/3	−4/3	8/3	14/45

6.9 Richardson Extrapolation

Consider the composite Newton–Cotes formula

$$\int_a^b f(x)\, dx \cong h\left(\frac{f(a)}{2} + f(x_1) + \cdots + f(x_{n-1}) + \frac{f(b)}{2}\right),$$

$$R = -\frac{(b-a)}{12} h_1^2 f''(\xi_1), \tag{6.107}$$

for n subintervals, where

$$h_1 = \frac{b-a}{n}, \quad a < \xi_1 < b, \quad f(x_i) = f(a + ih_1), \quad i = 1, 2, \ldots, n-1.$$

Consider also

$$\int_a^b f(x)\,dx \cong h\left[\frac{f(a)}{2} + f(x_1) + \cdots + f(x_{m-1}) + \frac{f(b)}{2}\right],$$

$$R = -\frac{(b-a)}{12}\,h_2^2 f''(\xi_2), \qquad (6.108)$$

for $m \neq n$ subintervals, where

$$h_2 = \frac{b-a}{m}, \quad a < \xi_2 < b, \quad f(x_j) = f(a + jh_2), \quad j = 1, 2, \ldots, m-1.$$

Let $I = \int_a^b f(x)\,dx$ be the exact value of the integral. Let I_1 and I_2 represent the approximations for n and m intervals respectively. Since $h_1 = (b-a)/n$ and $h_2 = (b-a)/m$, the error terms now become

$$R_1 = -\frac{(b-a)^3}{12n^2} f''(\xi_1), \qquad R_2 = -\frac{(b-a)^3}{12m^2} f''(\xi_2). \qquad (6.109)$$

Now, assume that $f''(\xi_1) = f''(\xi_2) = f''(\xi)$; then

$$I = I_1 - \frac{(b-a)^3}{12n^2} f''(\xi) = I_2 - \frac{(b-a)^3}{12m^2} f''(\xi). \qquad (6.110)$$

Thus,

$$\frac{I - I_1}{I - I_2} = \frac{m^2}{n^2},$$

and simplifying,

$$I = I_2 + \frac{n^2(I_2 - I_1)}{m^2 - n^2}. \qquad (6.111)$$

Formula 6.111 depends upon the assumption that $f''(\xi_1)$ is approximately equal to $f''(\xi_2)$. Any such procedure derived from two approximations to find a third approximation is called a Richardson extrapolation method, and in general leads to a more accurate approximation than either I_1 or I_2.

A flow chart and a program for a combination of a composite Newton–Cotes formula and the Richardson extrapolation procedure can be obtained by making the changes listed below in the flow chart and program of Secs. 6.6.1 and 6.6.2 for the trapezoidal rule.

The trapezoidal rule is

$$\int_a^b f(x)\,dx = \left(\frac{f(a)}{2} + \frac{f(b)}{2} + f(a+h) + f(a+2h) + \cdots \right.$$
$$\left. + f(a + (m-1)h\right) + R \qquad (6.112)$$

where $h = (b - a)/2^k$, and k takes on the values 0, 1, 2, ... The number of subintervals will be successively $m = 1, 2, 4, 8, \ldots$. The current value of m (equal to 2^k) and the preceding value of m (equal to 2^{k-1}) will be stored in $m2$ and $m1$, respectively, in order to compute

$$I_3 = I_2 + \frac{m1^2(I_2 - I_1)}{m2^2 - m1^2}$$

when the desired accuracy is obtained.

In Flow Chart 6.6.1, the following statements must be inserted:

$DM1 = M$ immediately after the statement $M = 1$.
$DM2 = M$ immediately after the statement $M = 2M$.
$DM1 = DM2$ immediately after the statement $TSUM1 = TSUM2$.
$TSUM3 = TSUM2 + (DM1)^2(TSUM2 - TSUM1)/((DM2)^2 - (DM1)^2)$ immediately before the *PRINT* statement.
In the print box, add $TSUM3$.

EXERCISE

Write a flow chart and program to compute

$$4\int_0^1 \frac{dx}{1 + x^2}$$

using the method based on repeated subdivision of the interval for the trapezoidal rule and the Richardson extrapolation technique.

6.10 Romberg Integration

The trapezoidal rule may be written as

$$\int_a^b f(x)\,dx \cong h\left(\frac{f(a)}{2} + f(a + h) + f(a + 2h) + \cdots + f(a + (n - 1)h) + \frac{f(b)}{2}\right) \tag{6.113}$$

where R may be expressed as

$$R = a_1h^2 + a_2h^4 + \cdots = \sum_{i=1}^{\infty} a_ih^{2i}. \tag{6.114}$$

The constants a_i depend upon a, b, and $f(x)$; $h = (b - a)/n$, $n = 2^k$,

k a positive integer. That R can be expressed as a series (Eq. 6.114) is shown in the derivation of the Euler–Maclaurin sum formula.[4]

Now apply the trapezoidal rule twice, for $n = 2^k$ and $m = 2^{k+1}$. If $I = \int_a^b f(x)\,dx$ and I_1, I_2 represent the trapezoidal rule for n and m subintervals, then

$$I = I_1 + \sum_{i=1}^{\infty} a_i h_1^{2i} = I_1 + a_1 h_1^2 + a_2 h_1^4 + \cdots, \tag{6.115}$$

$$I = I_2 + \sum_{i=1}^{\infty} a_i h_2^{2i} = I_2 + a_1 h_2^2 + a_2 h_2^4 + \cdots. \tag{6.116}$$

Multiplying (6.115) by h_2^2 and (6.116) by h_1^2, then

$$(h_1^2 - h_2^2)I = h_1^2 I_2 - h_2^2 I_1 + a_1(h_1^2 h_2^2 - h_1^2 h_2^2) + a_2(h_1^2 h_2^4 - h_2^2 h_1^4) + \cdots.$$

Since $h_1 = 2h_2$,

$$I = \frac{4I_2 - I_1}{3} - 4a_2 h_2^4 + (0)h_2^6 \tag{6.117}$$

where $(0)h_2^6$ means that all terms following are of order h_2^6 or higher. Thus, the lowest degree of h in (6.117) is 4, rather than 2 as in the case of the trapezoidal rule.

Equation 6.117 is in fact Simpson's ⅓ rule applied to 2^k subintervals. It should also be noted that Eq. 6.111 is the same as (6.117) if $m = 2n$ in (6.111). Let

$$A_{k1} = \left(\frac{b-a}{2^k}\right)\left(\frac{f(a)}{2} + f(a+h) + \cdots + \frac{f(b)}{2}\right) \tag{6.118}$$

be the trapezoidal rule for 2^k subintervals. Then Eq. 6.117 without the error term is

$$A_{k2} = \frac{1}{3}(4A_{k,1} - A_{k-1,1}), \qquad (k = 2, 3, \ldots). \tag{6.119}$$

Thus, A_{k2} is a linear combination of the trapezoidal rule for 2^k intervals and the trapezoidal rule for 2^{k-1} intervals, wherein the leading term in the error is a constant times h^4.

These approximations A_{k1} and A_{k2} can be regarded as terms in the first and second columns of a matrix—that is, they can be listed as:

[4] See Anthony Ralston, *A First Course in Numerical Analysis* (New York: McGraw-Hill Book Company, Inc., 1965), Ch. 4.

$$\begin{bmatrix} A_{11} & & & \\ A_{21} & A_{22} & & \\ A_{31} & A_{32} & & \\ \cdot & \cdot & \cdot & \cdot \\ A_{k1} & A_{k2} & & \\ \cdot & \cdot & \cdot & \cdot \\ A_{m1} & A_{m2} & & \end{bmatrix} \tag{6.120}$$

To form other terms in a lower triangular matrix, the following definition is given:

$$A_{ij} = \frac{1}{4^{j-1} - 1}(4^{j-1}A_{i,j-1} - A_{i-1,j-1}),$$

$$(j > 2,\ i = j, j + 1, \ldots). \tag{6.121}$$

It can be shown that the leading term in the error of A_{ij}, as an approximation to I, is h^{2j} where $h = (b - a)/2^i$. Each A_{ij} is a linear combination of the trapezoidal rules for 2^i, 2^{i-1}, . . . , $2^{i-(j-1)}$ subintervals. It should be noted here that choosing $k = 1$ first means that the interval has two subintervals. The interval (a,b) is not the first choice. Formula 6.121 can be derived in a manner similar to that used for the derivation of the formula (6.76) for the extrapolated derivative.

Thus, the A_{ij} form a lower triangular matrix:

$$\begin{bmatrix} A_{11} & & & \\ A_{21} & A_{22} & & \\ A_{31} & A_{32} & A_{33} & \\ \cdot & \cdot & \cdot & \cdot \\ A_{m1} & A_{m2} & \cdots & A_{mm} \end{bmatrix} \tag{6.122}$$

The terms in the first column $(A_{11}, A_{21}, \ldots, A_{m1})$ are the evaluations of $\int_a^b f(x)\,dx$ by repeated subdivision of the interval using the trapezoidal rule. If $f''(x)$ is bounded in $[a,b]$ then A_{m1} converges to I.[5] The terms in the second column $(A_{22}, A_{32}, \ldots, A_{m2})$ each are linear combinations of the approximations in the first column; that is,

$$A_{k2} = \frac{1}{4 - 1}(4A_{k,1} - A_{k-1,1}), \qquad (k = 2, 3, \ldots), \tag{6.123}$$

and the terms in the third column are linear combinations of terms in the second column:

$$A_{k3} = \frac{1}{4^2 - 1}(4^2A_{k,2} - A_{k-1,2}), \qquad (k = 3, 4, \ldots). \tag{6.124}$$

[5] It should be noted that the trapezoidal rule for $f(x)$ continuous is a Reimann sum and converges to $\int_a^b f(x)\,dx$ as $h \to 0$.

The leading term in the error of any approximation by the trapezoidal rule (column 1) is $[(b - a)/2^k]^2$ for A_{k1}, but the leading term in the error for $A_{k,2}$ is $[(b - a)/2^k]^4$; for A_{k3} is $[(b - a)/2^k]^6$; and for A_{mm} the leading term in the error is $[(b - a)/2^m]^{2m}$. Thus, if A_{mI} approaches I as $M \rightarrow \infty$, then A_{mm} converges much more rapidly than A_{m1}.[6]

The procedure described above for the trapezoidal rule is attributed to W. Romberg. It should be noted that Romberg integration as a technique is analogous to the technique for the extrapolated derivative (Sec. 6.3).

6.10.1 Flow Chart

In the triangular matrix A_{ij} (6.122), no provision was made for the subinterval being equal to the interval. Thus, for $h = b - a$ initially, there was no computation. However, in Flow Chart 6.10.1, A_{11} is the evaluation based upon $h = b - a$; A_{21} is the evaluation for $h = (b - a)/2^1$, and in general A_{k1} is the evaluation for $h = (b - a)/2^{k-1}$.

The general procedure is to use the subscripted variable A_{i1} to store the computations by the trapezoidal rule until $|A_{m1} - A_{m-1,1}|$ is less than a prescribed epsilon. Once the desired accuracy has been obtained in column 1, then A_{22} will be determined. Next, A_{32} and A_{33} will be computed, and this procedure will be continued until A_{mm} is computed. A_{mm} will be the value of $\int_a^b f(x)\, dx$ by the Romberg method.

[6] The proof that A_{mm} converges is given in Ralston's *A First Course in Numerical Analysis*.

FLOW CHART 6.10.1 Evaluation of $\int_0^1 \frac{dx}{1+x^2}$ by the Romberg Method

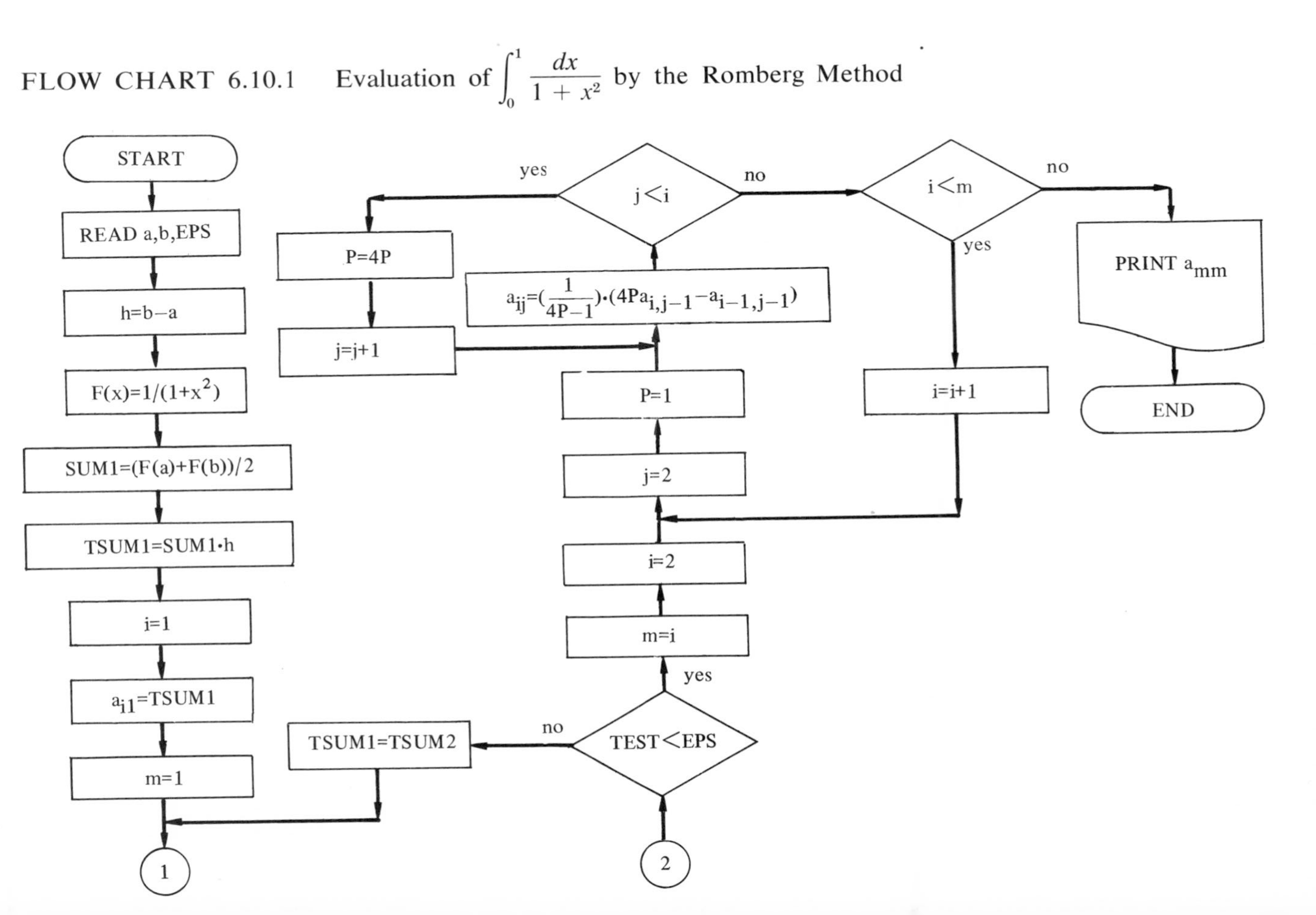

Flow Chart 6.10.1 *(Continued)*

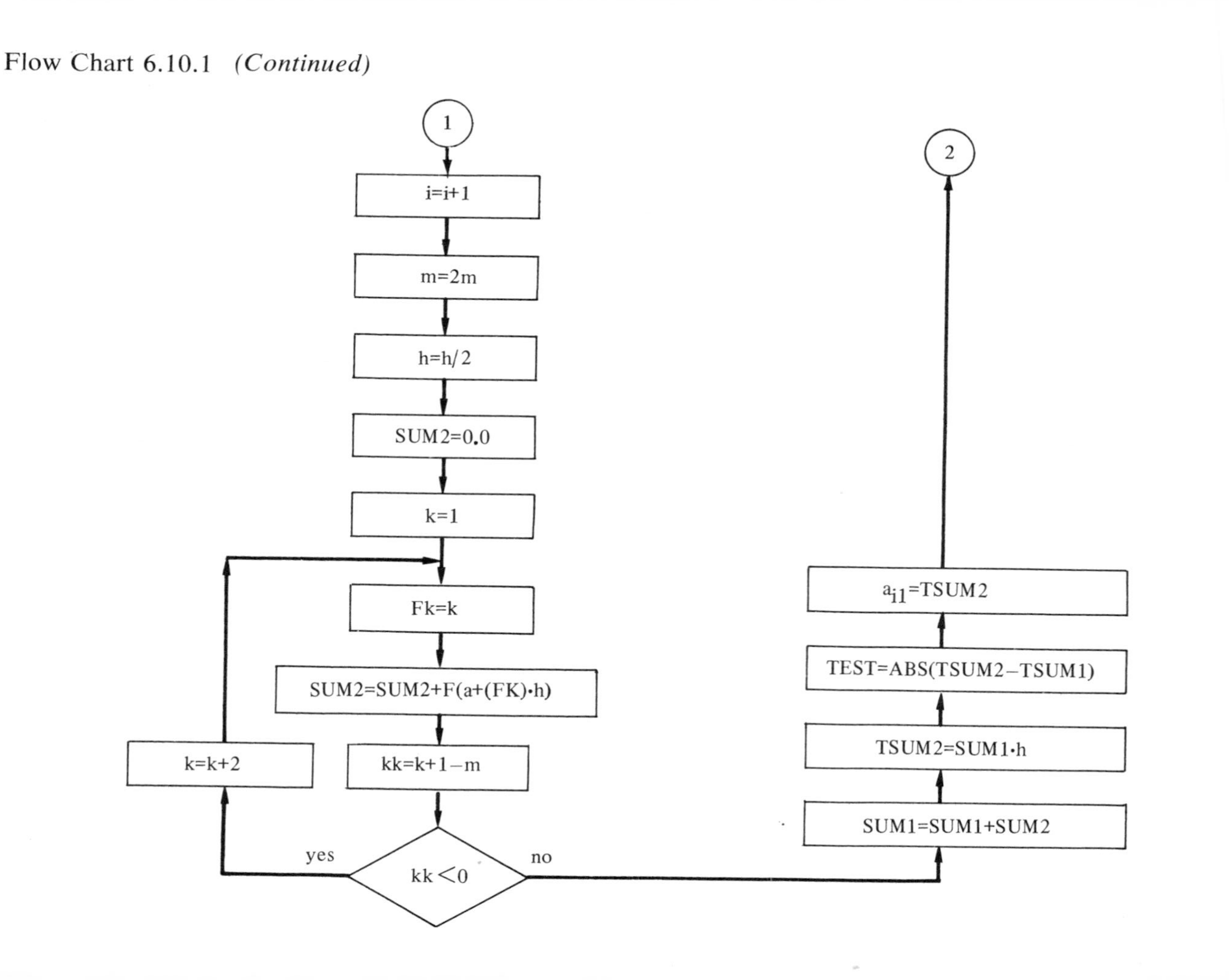

6.11 Gaussian Quadrature

In any of the Newton–Cotes formulas, the points at which values of $f(x)$ were taken were equally spaced. If no constraints are placed on the points and on the coefficients (weights), formulas of greater accuracy can be obtained, in general, for a lesser number of points. If in the formula

$$\int_a^b f(x)\,dx = w_0 f(x_0) + w_1 f(x_1) + \cdots + w_n f(x_n), \qquad (6.125)$$

w_i and x_i ($i = 0, \ldots, n$) are to be determined, it is seen that there are $(n + 1)$ weights (w_i) and $(n + 1)$ abscissas (x_i). The best possible accuracy of a formula means that the formula will be exact for polynomials of the highest possible degree. Since there are $2n + 2$ arbitrary parameters (w_i and x_i), it is possible to obtain a formula that will be exact for polynomials of degree $2n + 1$ or less.

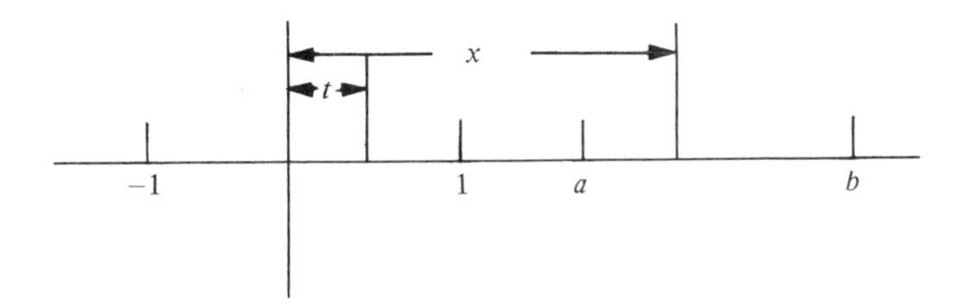

FIGURE 6.1 Change of Interval

It is convenient to transform the interval $[a,b]$ into $[-1,1]$. Consider Fig. 6.1. Then

$$\frac{t - (-1)}{1 - (-1)} = \frac{x - a}{b - a} \qquad \text{or} \qquad t = \frac{2x - (a + b)}{b - a}, \qquad (6.126)$$

and

$$x = \tfrac{1}{2}(b - a)t + \tfrac{1}{2}(a + b). \qquad (6.127)$$

Thus, Eq. (6.125) becomes

$$\begin{aligned}\int_a^b f(x)\,dx &= \frac{b-a}{2}\int_{-1}^{1} F(t)\,dt \\ &= \frac{b-a}{2}\{w_0 F(t_0) + w_1 F(t_1) + \cdots + w_n F(t_n)\}, \qquad (6.128)\end{aligned}$$

where t_i and w_i are to be determined. The following procedure can be used to compute w_i and t_i.

Since the formula is exact for a polynomial of degree $2n + 1$ and integration is a linear operator, $F(t)$ can be chosen as t^k. Thus

$$\int_{-1}^{1} t^k \, dt = w_0 t_0^k + w_1 t_1^k + \cdots + w_n t_n^k,$$

$$(k = 0, 1, 2, \ldots, 2n + 1). \qquad (6.129)$$

The system of Eqs. 6.129 consists of $2n + 2$ unknowns [$(n + 1)$ weights and $(n + 1)$ abscissas] in $2n + 2$ equations. The system is linear in w_i but nonlinear in t_i. Hence for $n > 1$, the solution would be complicated. Since

$$\int_{-1}^{1} t^k \, dt = \begin{cases} 0, & \text{for } k \text{ odd} \\ \dfrac{2}{k + 1}, & \text{for } k \text{ even,} \end{cases} \qquad (6.130)$$

the system (6.129) becomes

$$\begin{aligned} &W_0 + W_1 + \cdots + W_n = 2 \\ &W_0 t_0 + W_1 t_1 + \cdots + W_n t_n = 0 \\ &W_0 t_0^2 + W_1 t_1^2 + \cdots + W_n t_n^2 = 2/3 \\ &\cdot \quad \cdot \quad \cdot \quad \cdot \quad \cdot \quad \cdot \quad \cdot \quad \cdot \quad \cdot \quad \cdot \quad \cdot \\ &W_0 t_0^{2n+1} + W_1 t_1^{2n+1} + \cdots + W_n t_n^{2n+1} = 0. \end{aligned} \qquad (6.131)$$

It is evident that the system (6.131) for $n > 1$ is too formidable to attempt solution. But for $n = 1$, the system can be solved with ease. For $n = 1$, k takes on the values 0, 1, 2, 3 and the following four equations are to be solved:

$$\begin{aligned} k &= 0, \qquad W_0 + W_1 = 2 \\ k &= 1, \qquad W_0 t_0 + W_1 t_1 = 0 \\ k &= 2, \qquad W_0 t_0^2 + W_1 t_1^2 = 2/3 \\ k &= 3, \qquad W_0 t_0^3 + W_1 t_1^3 = 0. \end{aligned} \qquad (6.132)$$

From (6.132) choose:

$$\begin{aligned} W_0 t_0 + W_1 t_1 &= 0 \\ W_0 t_0^3 + W_1 t_1^3 &= 0. \end{aligned} \qquad (6.133)$$

W_0 and W_1 can be eliminated by multiplying the first of these equations by t_0^2 and subtracting the result from the second equation; that is,

$$t_1^3 - t_1 t_0^2 = 0 \qquad \text{or} \qquad t_1(t_1 - t_0)(t_1 + t_0) = 0. \tag{6.134}$$

Thus, $t_1 = t_0, -t_0$, and $t_1 = 0$. For $t_1 = t_0$ or 0, the other two equations of (6.132) are not compatible with Eqs. 6.133. Hence for $t_1 = -t_0$, the system (6.132) becomes

$$\begin{aligned} W_0 + W_1 &= 2 \\ W_0 t_0 - W_1 t_0 &= 0 \\ W_0 t_0^2 + W_1 t_0^2 &= 2/3 \\ W_0 t_0^3 - W_1 t_0^3 &= 0. \end{aligned} \tag{6.135}$$

Thus, $W_0 = W_1 = 1$ and $t_0^2 = 1/3$. Choosing $t_0 = -1/\sqrt{3}$, then $t_1 = 1/\sqrt{3}$. For $n = 1$,

$$\begin{aligned} \int_{-1}^{1} F(t)\,dt &= W_0 F(x_0) + W_1 F(x_1) \\ &= F(-1/\sqrt{3}) + F(1/\sqrt{3}). \end{aligned} \tag{6.136}$$

Formula 6.136 is exact for a polynomial of degree 3 or less. For example,

$$\int_{2}^{3} x^3\,dx = \frac{65}{4}, \tag{6.137}$$

and by Eq. 6.128, Eq. 6.137 is transformed into

$$\begin{aligned} \frac{1}{16}\int_{-1}^{1} (t+5)^3\,dt &= \left(\frac{-1}{\sqrt{3}} + 5\right)^3 + \left(\frac{1}{\sqrt{3}} + 5\right)^3 \\ &= \frac{65}{4}. \end{aligned} \tag{6.138}$$

For $n > 1$, the solution of (6.131) would become too tedious and too complicated, but it can be shown that the system has a unique solution.[7] Assuming that there is a unique solution, it is necessary at this time to introduce orthogonal functions known as Legendre polynomials, for it can also be shown that t_i are zeros of these polynomials. The Legendre polynomials $P_n(x)$ are defined by the recursion formula:

$$\begin{aligned} P_0(x) &= 1 \\ P_1(x) &= x \\ P_{n+1}(x) &= \frac{1}{n+1}\,[(2n+1)xP_n(x) - nP_{n-1}(x)], \qquad (n = 1, 2, 3, \ldots). \end{aligned} \tag{6.139}$$

[7] See Ralston, *A First Course in Numerical Analysis.*

Thus, for

$$\begin{aligned} n = 1, \quad & P_2(x) = \tfrac{1}{2}(3x^2 - 1) \\ n = 2, \quad & P_3(x) = \tfrac{1}{2}(5x^3 - 3x) \\ n = 3, \quad & P_4(x) = \tfrac{1}{8}(35x^4 - 30x^2 + 3). \end{aligned} \tag{6.140}$$

In each of these equations, $P_k(x)$ ($k = 0, 1, 2, 3, 4$) is of degree k, and in general $P_n(x)$ is of degree n, which follows directly from the recursion formula 6.139.

The zeros of $P_n(x)$ are real, distinct, and lie on the interval $[-1,1]$. Further, these zeros are symmetrically placed with respect to the origin. Table 6.10 lists $P_n(x)$, $n = 0, 1, 2, 3$, and its zeros.

TABLE 6.10 $P_n(x)$ and zeros, $n = 0, 1, 2, 3$

n	$P_n(x)$	zeros
0	$P_1(x) = x$	$x_0 = 0$
1	$P_2(x) = \tfrac{1}{2}(3x^2 - 1)$	$x_0 = -1/\sqrt{3}, \quad x_1 = 1/\sqrt{3}$
2	$P_3(x) = \tfrac{1}{2}(5x^3 - 3x)$	$x_0 = -\sqrt{3/5}, \quad x_1 = 0, \quad x_2 = \sqrt{3/5}$
3	$P_4(x) = \tfrac{1}{8}(35x^4 - 30x^2 + 3)$	$x_0 = -(3/7 + 2/7 \cdot \sqrt{6/5})^{1/2}$
		$x_1 = -(3/7 - 2/7 \cdot \sqrt{6/5})^{1/2}$
		$x_2 = (3/7 - 2/7 \cdot \sqrt{6/5})^{1/2}$
		$x_3 = (3/7 + 2/7\sqrt{6/5})^{1/2}$

The zeros of $P_{n+1}(x)$ are the abscissas of the Gaussian formula

$$\int_{-1}^{1} F(t)\, dt = \sum_{i=0}^{n} w_i F(t_i).$$

For example, from Table 6.10, for $n = 1$, the zeros are $x_0 = -1/\sqrt{3}$, $x_1 = 1/\sqrt{3}$. Thus,

$$\begin{aligned} \int_{-1}^{1} F(t)\, dt &= \sum_{i=0}^{1} w_i F(t_i) \\ &= w_0 F(-1/3) + w_1 F(1/3). \end{aligned}$$

It now becomes a chore to solve the system of Eq. 6.131 for w_i, $i = 0, 1, 2, \ldots, n$. Obviously, a solution even for $n = 2$ in (6.131) would become quite a complicated task.

A less complicated procedure derives from the Lagrange interpolation formula, Eq. 5.71. It can be shown that after the abscissas t_i for a given n are assumed determined, the weights w_i can be determined by the following procedure:

$$w_i = \int_{-1}^{1} \prod_{j \neq i}^{n} (t - t_j)\, dt \Big/ \prod_{j \neq i}^{n} (t_i - t_j). \tag{6.141}$$

It should be noted that w_i are found by integrating the corresponding coefficients in the Lagrange interpolation formula, namely

$$\begin{aligned} f(x) = {} & \frac{(x - x_1)(x - x_2) \cdots (x - x_n)}{(x_0 - x_1) \cdots (x_0 - x_n)} f(x_0) \\ & + \frac{(x - x_0)(x - x_2) \cdots (x - x_n)}{(x_1 - x_0)(x_1 - x_2) \cdots (x_1 - x_n)} f(x_1) + \cdots \\ & + \frac{(x - x_0)(x - x_1) \cdots (x - x_{n-1})}{(x_n - x_0)(x_n - x_1) \cdots (x_n - x_{n-1})} f(x_n). \end{aligned} \tag{6.142}$$

Example

Compute the ln 2 by using the Gaussian formula for $n = 2$:

$$\int_1^2 \frac{dx}{x} = \ln 2.$$

Use the transformation

$$x = t/2(b - a) + 1/2(b + a),$$
$$x = t/2 + 3/2;$$

then,

$$\int_1^2 \frac{dx}{x} = \int_{-1}^{1} \frac{dt}{(t + 3)}$$

for $n = 2$, $t_0 = -\sqrt{3/5}$, $t_1 = 0$, $t_2 = \sqrt{3/5}$. Then

$$w_0 = \int_{-1}^{1} \frac{(t)(t - \sqrt{3/5})\, dt}{-\sqrt{3/5}(-\sqrt{3/5} - \sqrt{3/5})} = \frac{5}{9}$$

$$w_1 = \int_{-1}^{1} \frac{(t + \sqrt{3/5})(t - \sqrt{3/5})\, dt}{(\sqrt{3/5})(-\sqrt{3/5})} = \frac{8}{9}$$

$$w_2 = \int_{-1}^{1} \frac{(t + \sqrt{3/5})(t)\, dt}{(\sqrt{3/5} + \sqrt{3/5})(\sqrt{3/5})} = \frac{5}{9},$$

and

$$\int_1^2 \frac{dx}{x} = \int_{-1}^1 \frac{dt}{(t+3)} \cong w_0 F(t_0) + w_1 F(t_1) + w_2 F(t_2)$$

or

$$\ln 2 \cong \frac{5}{9}\left(\frac{1}{3 - \sqrt{3/5}}\right) + \frac{8}{9}\left(\frac{1}{3}\right) + \frac{5}{9}\left(\frac{1}{3 + \sqrt{3/5}}\right).$$

Carrying computations to the fifth decimal place, $\ln 2 \cong .69299$, the error of which is less than .0002. If n were taken as 3, then $\ln 2 \cong .69312169$, which is in error by three units in the fifth decimal place.

The disadvantage in a Gaussian formula of having, in general, irrational numbers for coefficients, and for the arguments of $F(t)$, is outweighed by the fact that greater accuracy is gained with less computation in the Gaussian formula, as compared to application of a composite Newton–Cotes formula. Another advantage in using Gaussian numerical quadrature is that the program is simpler than one for a Newton–Cotes formula.

6.11.1 Flow Chart

Evaluate

$$4\int_0^1 \frac{dx}{1+x^2} = \pi$$

by a Gaussian four-point formula ($n = 3$). Let $x = (t+1)/2$, then

$$4\int_0^1 \frac{dx}{1+x^2} = 2\int_{-1}^1 \frac{dt}{1 + [(t+1)^2/2^2]}$$
$$= 2\{w_0[F(t_0) + F(t_3)] + w_1[F(t_1) + F(t_2)]\}.$$

Flow Chart 6.11.1 uses the values from Table 6.10; the values of t_i and w_i are listed in Table 6.11.

FLOW CHART 6.11.1 Gaussian Quadrature

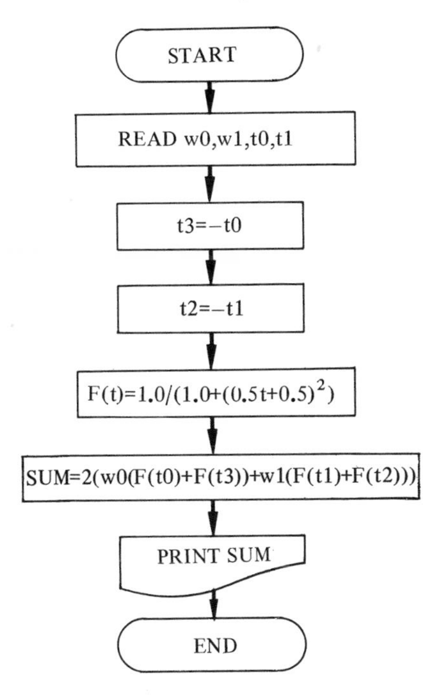

TABLE 6.11 Gaussian Quadrature Abscissas t_i and Weights w_i, $i = 0, 1, 2, 3$

n	t_k	w_k
0	$t_0 = 0.00000000$	$w_0 = 2.00000000$
1	$t_0 = -0.57735027$ $t_1 = 0.57735027$	$w_0 = 1.00000000$ $w_1 = 1.00000000$
2	$t_0 = -0.77459667$ $t_1 = 0.00000000$ $t_2 = 0.77459667$	$w_0 = 0.55555556$ $w_1 = 0.88888889$ $w_2 = 0.55555556$
3	$t_0 = -0.86113631$ $t_1 = -0.33998104$ $t_2 = -t_1$ $t_3 = -t_0$	$w_0 = 0.34785485$ $w_1 = 0.65214515$ $w_2 = w_1$ $w_3 = w_0$

PROBLEMS

6-4. Write a flow chart and program to find the derivative of

$$\log_{10} x \big|_{x=1.06}$$

by the extrapolated derivative method of Sec. 6.3. Use the values of $\log_{10} x$ in Table 6.4. Choose .04, .02, and .01 as values of H. Use formulas 6.75 and 6.76.

6-5. Write a program to evaluate π by the use of

$$4\int_0^1 \frac{dx}{1+x^2} = \pi$$

using Romberg integration and Flow Chart 6.10.1. The true value of π accurate to the eighth decimal place is 3.14159265.

6-6. Compute t_k and w_k for $n = 4$ in Gaussian quadrature.

(a) Use Eq. 6.139 to find $P_5(x)$. Solve $P_5(x) = 0$ to find t_k.
(b) Use Eq. 6.141 to compute w_k, $k = 0, 1, 2, 3, 4$.
(c) Show that the Gaussian formula

$$\int_{-1}^{1} F(t)\,dt = w_0F(t_0) + w_1F(t_1) + w_2F(t_2) + w_3F(t_3) + w_4F(t_4)$$

is exact for $n = 9$ (except for round-off error) by applying the formula to $\int_1^2 x^9\,dx$.

A program should include all computations of irrational quantities and the evaluation of the integral. Double precision arithmetic should also be used. In the output, values of t_k and w_k should be listed.

6-7. Write a program to compute

$$4\int_0^1 \frac{dx}{1+x^2} = \pi$$

by the five-point Gaussian formula derived in Prob. 6-6.

6.12 Numerical Evaluation of Multiple Integrals

Given the double integral

$$\int_a^b \int_c^d f(x,y)\,dy\,dx \tag{6.143}$$

where a, b, c, d are constants, first consider

$$\int_c^d f(x,y)\,dy = F(x). \tag{6.144}$$

Any of the quadrature formulas already developed in this chapter may be used to evaluate (6.144). Thus,

$$F(x) = \int_c^d f(x,y)\,dy = \sum_{j=1}^{n} w_j f(x,y_j) + E[f(x,y)], \qquad (6.145)$$

where $E[f(x,y)]$ is expressed in terms of partial derivatives of $f(x,y)$ with respect to y.

Now the same quadrature formula or another one may be used to evaluate $\int_a^b F(x)\,dx$:

$$\int_a^b F(x)\,dx = \sum_{i=1}^{m} \overline{w}_i F(x_i) + \overline{E}[F(x)]. \qquad (6.146)$$

Hence, combining (6.145) and (6.146),

$$\int_a^b \int_c^d f(x,y)\,dy\,dx = \sum_{i=1}^{m} \sum_{j=1}^{n} \overline{w}_i w_j f(x_i,y_j) + E. \qquad (6.147)$$

E is defined in Sec. 6.13. Equation 6.147 can be extended for higher order integrals.

6.13 Numerical Double Integration by Simpson's 1/3 Rule

The double integral

$$V = \int_c^d \int_a^b f(x,y)\,dy\,dx \qquad (6.148)$$

can be evaluated numerically by two successive applications of Simpson's 1/3 rule, once in the x direction, followed by an application in the y direction.

Divide the rectangle bounded by $x = a$, $x = b$, $y = c$, $y = d$ into a number $m \cdot n$ of small rectangles whose sides are $h = (b - a)/n$ and $k = (d - c)/m$. Denote the values of $f(x,y)$ as $f_{ij} = f(a + ih, c + jk)$ at the tabulated points

$$x_i = a + ih, \qquad y_j = c + jh$$

where $i = 0, 1, 2, \ldots, n$; $j = 0, 1, 2, \ldots, m$ (Fig. 6.2); and m, n are even integers.

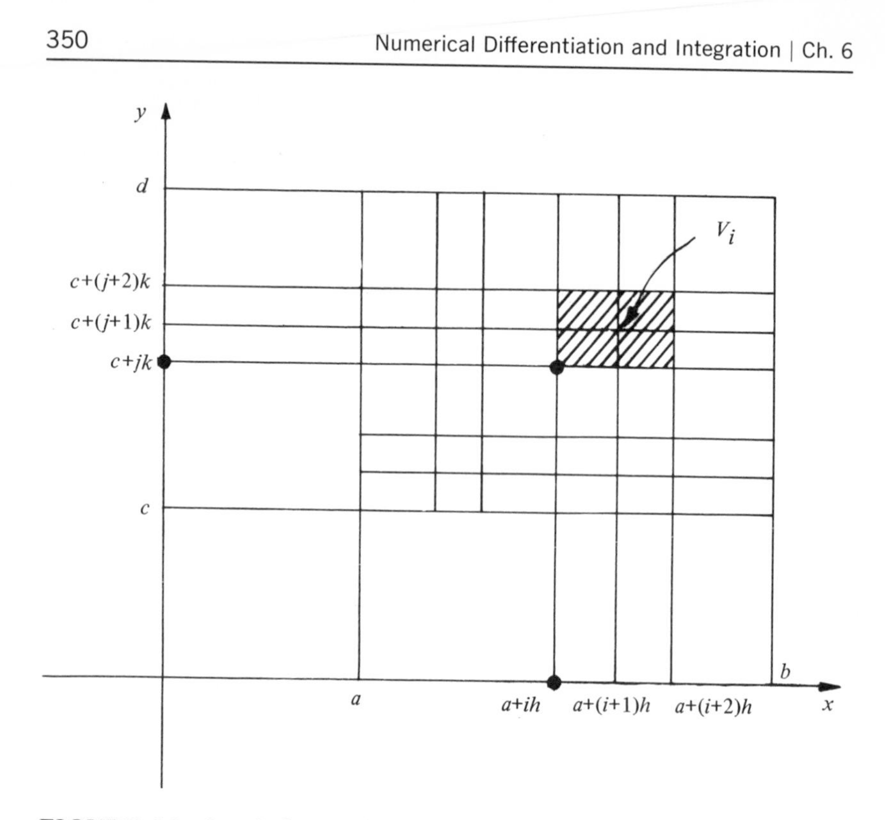

FIGURE 6.2 Panels for Double Integration

Consider value V_i in Fig. 6.3 of the integral extended over four small rectangles of sides h, k, with the lower left corner at $x = a + ih$, $y = c + jk$.

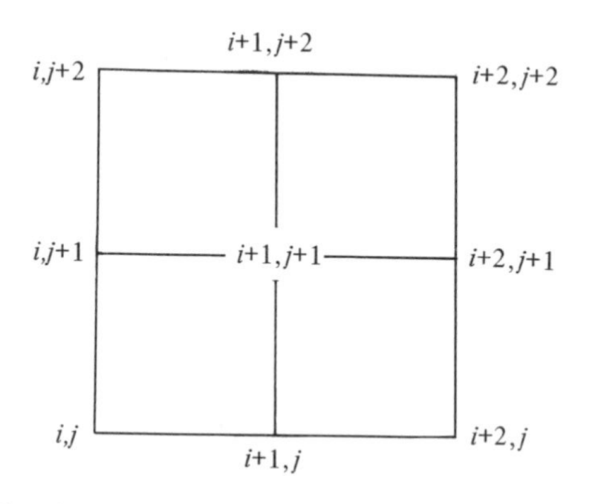

FIGURE 6.3 Panels for Evaluating V_i

By application of the rule in the x direction,

$$V_i = \int_{y_j}^{y_{j+2}} dy \int_{x_i}^{x_{i+2}} f(x,y)\, dx \tag{6.149}$$

becomes

$$V_i \cong \int_{y_j}^{y_{j+2}} dy \frac{h}{3} [f(x_i,y) + 4f(x_{i+1},y) + f(x_{i+2},y)] \tag{6.150}$$

or

$$V_i \cong \frac{h}{3}\left[\int_{y_j}^{y_{j+2}} f(x_i,y)\, dy + 4\int_{y_j}^{y_{j+2}} f(x_{i+1},y)\, dy + \int_{y_j}^{y_{j+2}} f(x_{i+2},y)\, dy\right]. \tag{6.151}$$

Applying the rule in the y direction to each of these integrals,

$$\begin{aligned} V_i = \left(\frac{h}{3}\right)\left(\frac{k}{3}\right)\{&[f(x_i,y_j) + 4f(x_i,y_{j+1}) + f(x_i,y_{j+2})] \\ &+ 4[f(x_{i+1},y_j) + 4f(x_{i+1},y_{j+1}) + f(x_{i+1},y_{j+2})] \\ &+ [f(x_{i+2},y_j) + 4f(x_{i+2},y_{j+1}) + f(x_{i+2},y_{j+2})]\}. \end{aligned}$$

Rearranging terms and using f_{ij} to denote values $f(x_i,y_j)$,

$$\begin{aligned} V_i = \frac{hk}{9}(f_{ij} &+ 4f_{i+1,j} + f_{i+2,j} + 4f_{i,j+1} + 16f_{i+1,j+1} + 4f_{i+2,j+1} \\ &+ f_{i,j+2} + 4f_{i+1,j+2} + f_{i+2,j+2}). \end{aligned} \tag{6.152}$$

Extending formula 6.152 over the large rectangle (Fig. 6.2), it can be easily verified that the weight coefficients in (6.147) form a "molecule" system, as shown in Fig. 6.4.

Weight coefficients for Simpson's rule, $n = m = 4$, are shown in Fig. 6.4. For the purpose of writing a program, these coefficients can be indicated for any horizontal line as

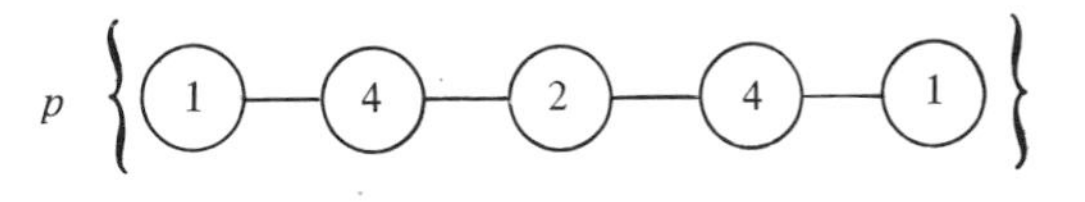

where $p = 1, 4, 2, 4, 1$, respectively, from the bottom line to the top in Fig. 6.4.

The error in a single application of Simpson's ⅓ rule is $-h^5 f^4(\xi)/90$ (Eq. 6.90). If the double integral is considered as a volume, found by

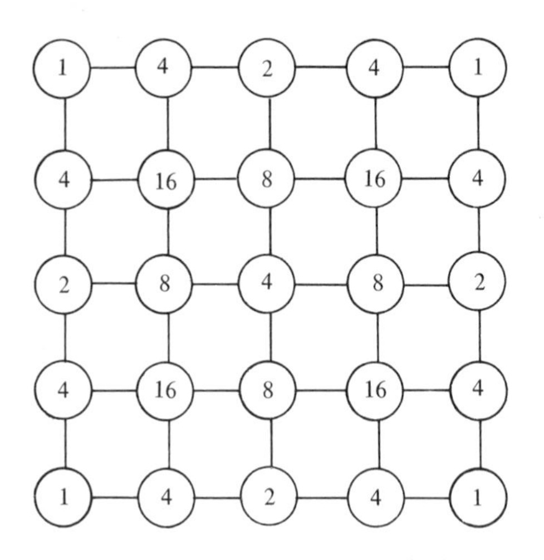

FIGURE 6.4 Molecule System (Double Integration)

summing the areas of sections obtained by means of planes parallel to the $x - z$ plane, each area has an error of order h^4:

$$A(y_j) = \int_a^b f(x,y_j)\,dx$$
$$= A_j + K_j h^4 \tag{6.153}$$

where A_j is the area and K_j is assumed to be a constant in the region of interest (see Fig. 6.5).

Applying Simpson's ⅓ rule to Eq. 6.153 in the y direction, the double integral V becomes

$$V = \frac{k}{3}(A_0 + 4A_1 + 2A_2 + \cdots + 4A_{m-1} + A_m)$$
$$+ \frac{k}{3}(K_0 + 4K_1 + 2K_2 + \cdots + 4K_{m-1} + K_m)h^4 + K^1k^4, \tag{6.154}$$

where K^1k^4 is error due to integration in the y direction and K^1 is assumed to be a constant. Letting

$$\overline{K} = \frac{d-c}{3m}(K_0 + 4K_1 + \cdots + K_m) \tag{6.155}$$

where $(d - c)/m = k$, then the error is of the form

$$E = \overline{K}h^4 + K^1k^4. \tag{6.156}$$

Let $\alpha = k/h$, then

$$E = (\overline{K} + \alpha^4 K^1)h^4. \tag{6.157}$$

This error may be reduced by applying Richardson's extrapolation.

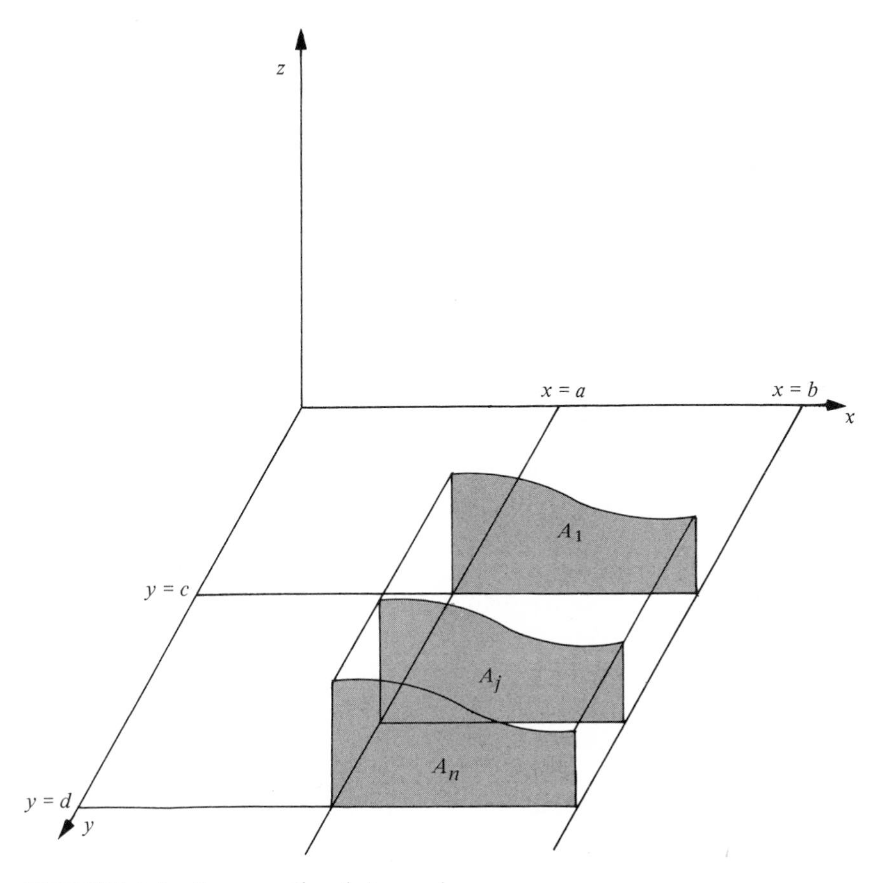

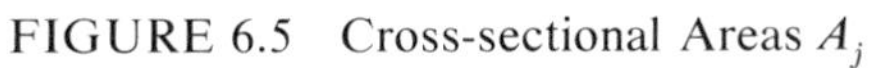
FIGURE 6.5 Cross-sectional Areas A_j

6.13.1 Flow Chart

Consider:

$$SUM = \int_0^1 \int_0^1 (x^3 + y^3)\, dx\, dy = \frac{1}{2},$$

which is of the form $\int_c^d \int_a^b f(x,y)\, dx\, dy$. Since $f(x,y)$ is of degree 3, the

evaluation of SUM by this rule is exact except for round-off error.
Let $h = k = 1/n$; $n = 4$. Then

$$\int_c^d \int_a^b f(x,y)\,dx\,dy \cong \frac{h^2}{9}\left\{\sum_{j=0}^{n} \sum_{i=0,2}^{n} P[f(a + ih, c + jk) + 4f(a + (i + 1)h, c + jk) + f(a + (i + 2)h, c + jk)]\right\} \tag{6.158}$$

where P takes on the values of 1, 4, 2, . . . , 4, 1 for $j = 0, 1, 2, \ldots, n$. The notation

$$\sum_{i=0,2}^{n}$$

means that $i = 0, 2, 4, \ldots, n$. Values of limits are:

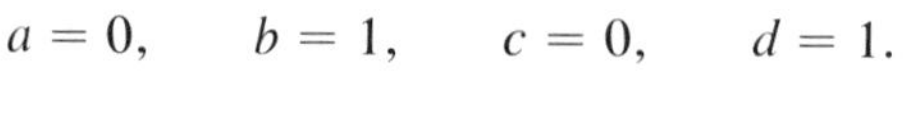

$$a = 0, \qquad b = 1, \qquad c = 0, \qquad d = 1.$$

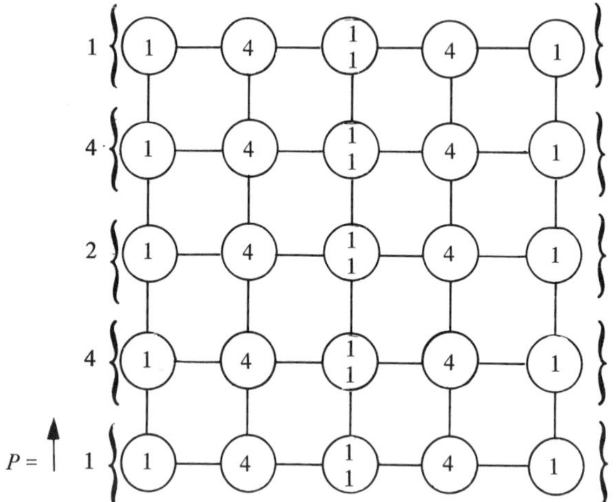

FIGURE 6.6 Molecule System (Double Integration)

From Fig. 6.6, it is indicated that values will be computed first on the bottom line, then the next line, continuing to the top line. For each successive value of y, numerical integration in the x direction is over two panels, then x is increased by $2h$ and the rule is repeated.

FLOW CHART 6.13.1 Double Integration by Simpson's 1/3 Rule

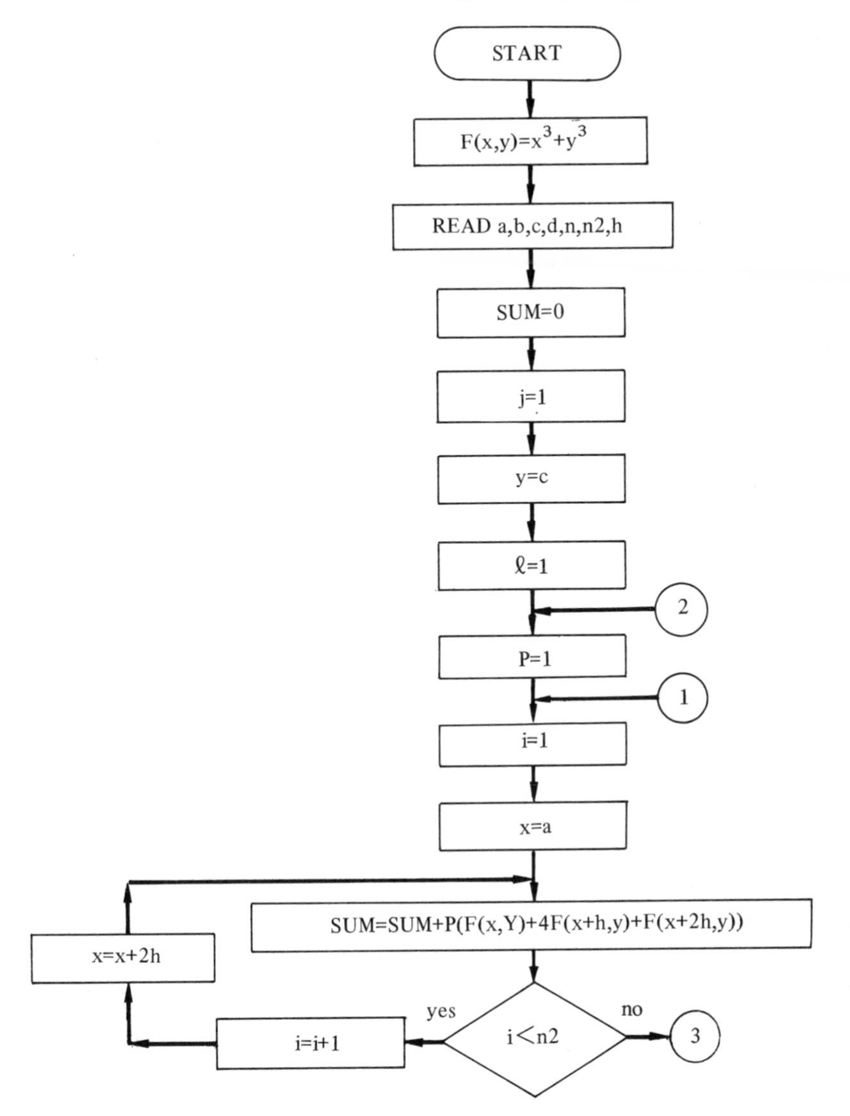

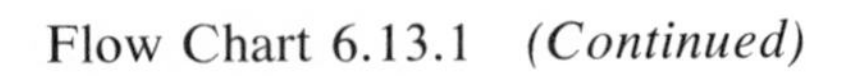

Flow Chart 6.13.1 *(Continued)*

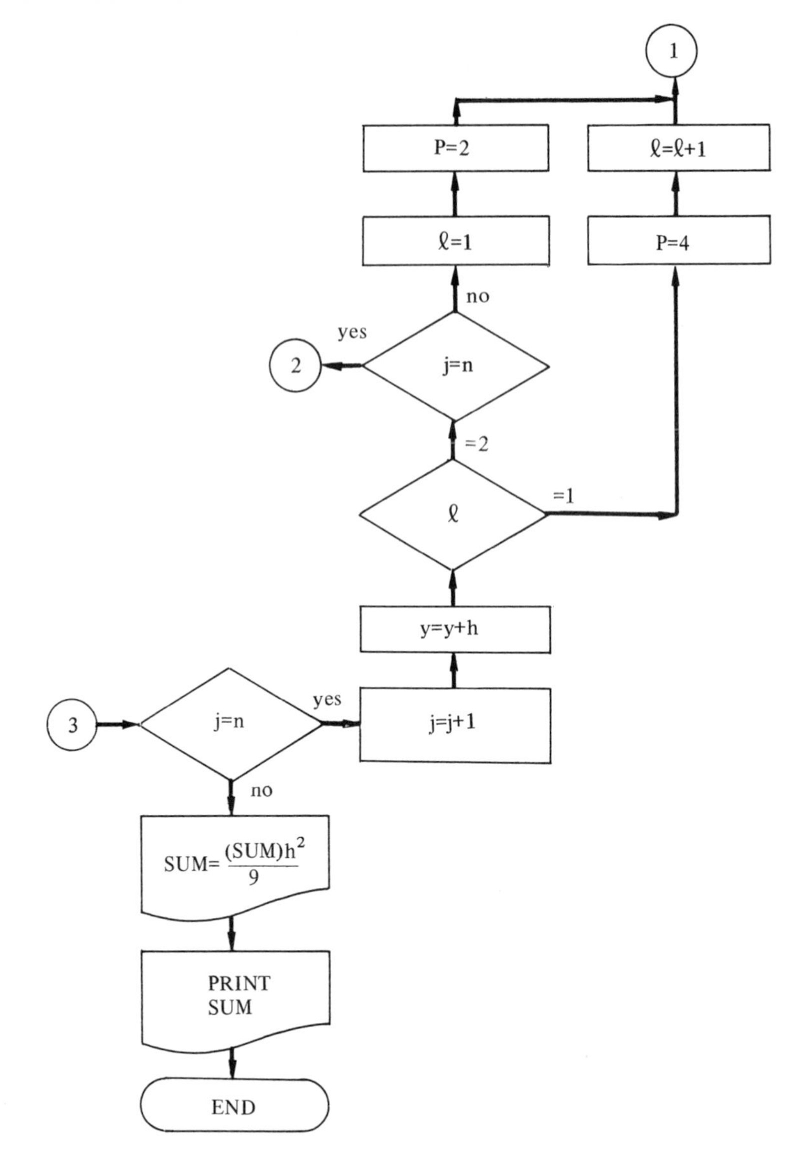

6.13.2 Program

For Simpson's $1/3$ Rule Applied Twice to a Double Integral

```
      F(X,Y)=X**3+Y**3
 10   FORMAT(4F12.6,2I3)
110   FORMAT(1H1,///,'THE VALUE OF SUM IS ',F12.6)
      READ(5,10)A,B,C,D,N,N2
      SUM=0.0
      J=1
      Y=C
      L=1
 90   P=1.0
 60   X=A
      DO 20,I=1,N2
      SUM=SUM+P*(F(X,Y)+4.0*F(X+H,Y)+F(X+2.0*H,Y))
 20   X=X+2.0*H
      IF(J-N)30,120,100
 30   J=J+1
      Y=Y+H
      GO TO(40,50),L
 40   P=4.0
      L=L+1
      GO TO 60
120   J=J+1
      Y=Y+H
      GO TO 90
 50   L=1
      P=2.0
      GO TO 60
100   SUM=SUM*H**2/9.0
      WRITE(6,110)SUM
      STOP
      END

      THE VALUE OF SUM IS 0.500000
```

6.14 Numerical Triple Integration by Simpson's $1/3$ Rule

To evaluate

$$\int_{a3}^{b3}\int_{a2}^{b2}\int_{a1}^{b1} f(x,y,z)\,dx\,dy\,dz,$$

Simpson's $1/3$ rule can be applied three times—first in the x direction, next in the y direction, and last in the z direction. Following a procedure similar to that of Sec. 6.13, the three-dimensional rectangular block is divided into $m \cdot n \cdot l$ smaller blocks.

Let

$$h1 = \frac{b1 - a1}{n}, \qquad h2 = \frac{b2 - a2}{m}, \qquad h3 = \frac{b3 - a3}{l}. \tag{6.159}$$

Denote values of $f(x,y,z)$ as

$$f_{ijk} = f(a1 + ih1, a2 + jh2, a3 + kh3), \tag{6.160}$$

at the tabulated points:

$$x_i = a1 + ih1, \qquad y_j = a2 + jh2, \qquad z_k = a3 + kh3$$
$$i = 0, 1, 2, \ldots, n; \qquad j = 0, 1, 2, \ldots, m; \qquad k = 0, 1, 2, \ldots, l.$$

Select the rectangular block bounded by:

$$\begin{aligned} x_i &= a1 + ih1 \quad \text{to} \quad x_{i+2} = a1 + (i+2)h1 \\ y_j &= a2 + jh2 \quad \text{to} \quad y_{j+2} = a2 + (j+2)h2 \\ z_k &= a3 + kh3 \quad \text{to} \quad z_{k+2} = a3 + (k+2)h3, \end{aligned} \tag{6.161}$$

(see Fig. 6.7), then

$$\begin{aligned} S_i &= \int_{z_k}^{z_{k+2}} \int_{y_j}^{y_{j+2}} \int_{x_i}^{x_{i+2}} [f(x,y,z)\, dx\, dy\, dz] \\ &= \int_{z_k}^{z_{k+2}} \int_{y_j}^{y_{j+2}} \frac{h1}{3} [f_i(y,z) + 4f_{i+1}(y,z) + f_{i+2}(y,z)\, dy\, dz] \\ &= \int_{z_k}^{z_{k+2}} \left(\frac{h1}{3}\right)\left(\frac{h2}{3}\right) \{[f_{ij}(z) + 4f_{i,j+1}(z) + f_{i,j+2}(z)] \\ &\quad + 4[f_{i+1,j}(z) + 4f_{i+1,j+1}(z) + f_{i+1,j+2}(z)] \\ &\quad + [f_{i+2,j}(z) + 4f_{i+2,j+1}(z) + f_{i+2,j+2}(z)]\}\, dz \\ &= \left(\frac{h1}{3}\right)\left(\frac{h2}{3}\right)\left(\frac{h3}{3}\right)[(f_{ijk} + 4f_{ij,k+1} + f_{ij,k+2}) \\ &\quad + 4(f_{i,j+1,k} + 4f_{i,j+1,k+1} + f_{i,j+1,k+2}) \\ &\quad + (f_{i,j+2,k} + 4f_{i,j+2,k+1} + f_{i,j+2,k+2}) \\ &\quad + 4(f_{i+1,j,k} + 4f_{i+1,j,k+1} + f_{i+1,j,k+2}) \\ &\quad + 16(f_{i+1,j+1,k} + 4f_{i+1,j+1,k+1} + f_{i+1,j+1,k+2}) \\ &\quad + 4(f_{i+1,j+2,k} + 4f_{i+1,j+2,k+1} + f_{i+1,j+2,k+2}) \\ &\quad + (f_{i+2,j,k} + 4f_{i+2,j,k+1} + f_{i+2,j,k+2}) \\ &\quad + 4(f_{i+2,j+1,k} + 4f_{i+2,j+1,k+1} + f_{i+2,j+1,k+2}) \\ &\quad + (f_{i+2,j+2,k} + 4f_{i+2,j+2,k+1} + f_{i+2,j+2,k+2})]. \end{aligned} \tag{6.162}$$

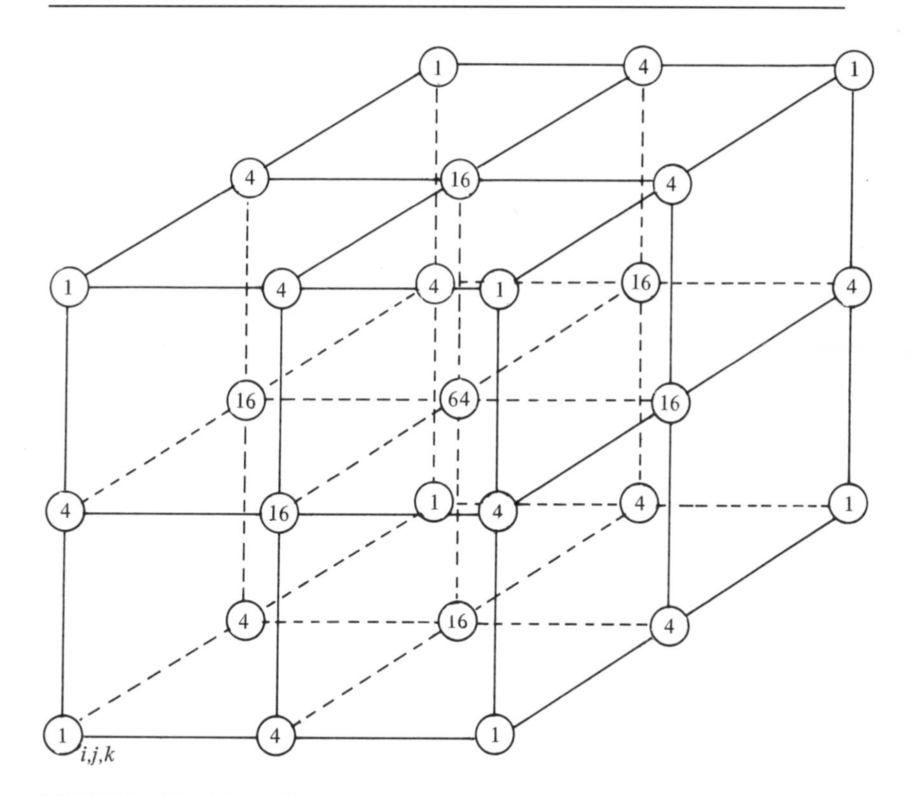

FIGURE 6.7 Molecule System (Triple Integration)

Figure 6.7 shows also the weight coefficients for one double rectangular block. For any block located wholly within all limits of integration, the weight coefficients along the edges, sides, and at the corners will be repeated by adjacent integrations.

The technique employed here is to integrate over two panels in the x direction for fixed values of $y = a2$ and $z = a3$; then the x value is incremented by $2h1$ and the process is repeated over the next two panels in the x direction. When the process is applied to the last two panels in the x direction, y is incremented by $h2$ and the integration is repeated again, starting of course with $x = a1$, $z = a3$. When y reaches its upper limit $b2$, z is incremented by $h3$, and x is reset equal to $a1$ and y to $a2$. Then the technique is repeated. Thus, integration is by levels, first on level $z = a3$, then on level $z = a3 + h3$, and continuing until $z = b3$.

Hence, Eq. 6.162 can be stated as

$$\int_{a3}^{b3}\int_{a2}^{b2}\int_{a1}^{b1} f(x,y,z)\,dx\,dy\,dz$$

$$\cong \left(\frac{h1}{3}\right)\left(\frac{h2}{3}\right)\left(\frac{h3}{3}\right)\sum_{k=0}^{l}\sum_{j=0}^{m} Q \sum_{i=0,2}^{n} Pf[a1 + i(h1), a2 + j(h2), a3 + k(h3)]$$
$$+ 4f[a1 + (i+1)(h1), a2 + j(h2), a3 + k(h3)]$$
$$+ f[a1 + (i+2)(h1), a2 + j(h2), a3 + k(h3)]. \tag{6.163}$$

where

$$\begin{aligned} P &= 1 \quad \text{for} \quad j = 0 \text{ and } j = m \\ P &= 4 \quad \text{for} \quad j = 1, 3, 5, \ldots, m-1 \\ P &= 2 \quad \text{for} \quad j = 2, 4, 6, \ldots, m-2, \end{aligned}$$

and

$$\begin{aligned} Q &= 1 \quad \text{for} \quad k = 0, l \\ Q &= 4 \quad \text{for} \quad k = 1, 3, 5, \ldots, l-1 \\ Q &= 2 \quad \text{for} \quad k = 2, 4, 6, \ldots, l-2. \end{aligned}$$

6.14.1 Flow Chart

Consider

$$\int_0^1\int_0^1\int_0^1 (x^3 + y^3 + z^3)\,dx\,dy\,dz = \frac{3}{4}.$$

Evaluation by repeated use of Simpson's ⅓ rule will be exact (except for round-off error), since $f(x,y,z)$ is of degree 3.

Definitions and Notation

$a1 = a2 = a3 = 0$; $b1 = b2 = b3 = 1$.
$h1 = h2 = h3 = 1/4$; $N = M = L = 4$.
$N2 = N/2$.
The control KK, which has a value of 1 or 2, is used to decide whether Q should equal 4 or 2, and that at the beginning and end of the program the value of Q should equal 1.
The control K with a value of 1 or 2 is used to decide whether P should equal 4 or 2, and that at the beginning and end the value of P should equal 1.

The value of the integral is denoted by

$$SUM = \frac{h^3}{27} \sum_{k=0}^{n} Q \sum_{j=0}^{n} P \sum_{i=0,2}^{n2} \{f[a1 + ih, a2 + jh, a3 + kh]$$
$$+ 4f[a1 + (i + 1)h, a2 + jh, a3 + kh]$$
$$+ f[a1 + (i + 2)h, a2 + jh, a3 + kh]\}.$$

Note that the letter l is used as the subscript on z, since the letter k is used as a control on the value of P.

FLOW CHART 6.14.1 Triple Integration by Simpson's ⅓ Rule

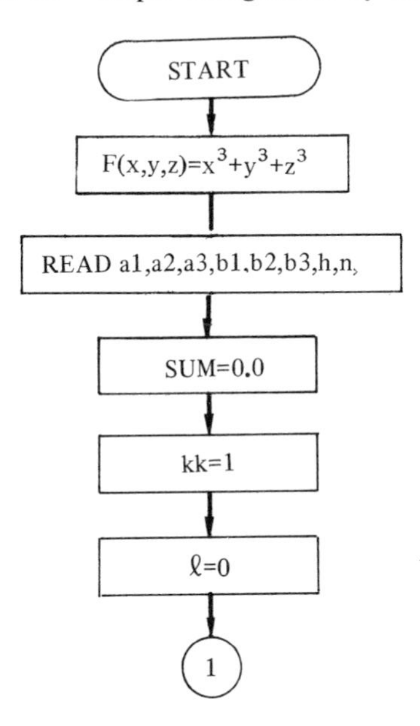

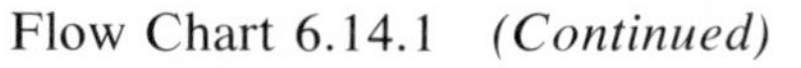

Flow Chart 6.14.1 *(Continued)*

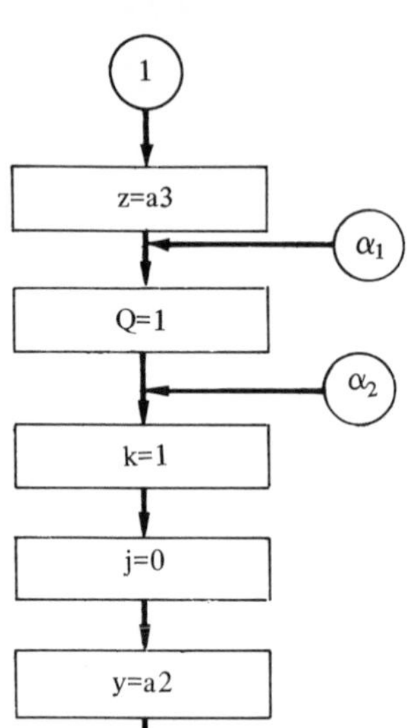

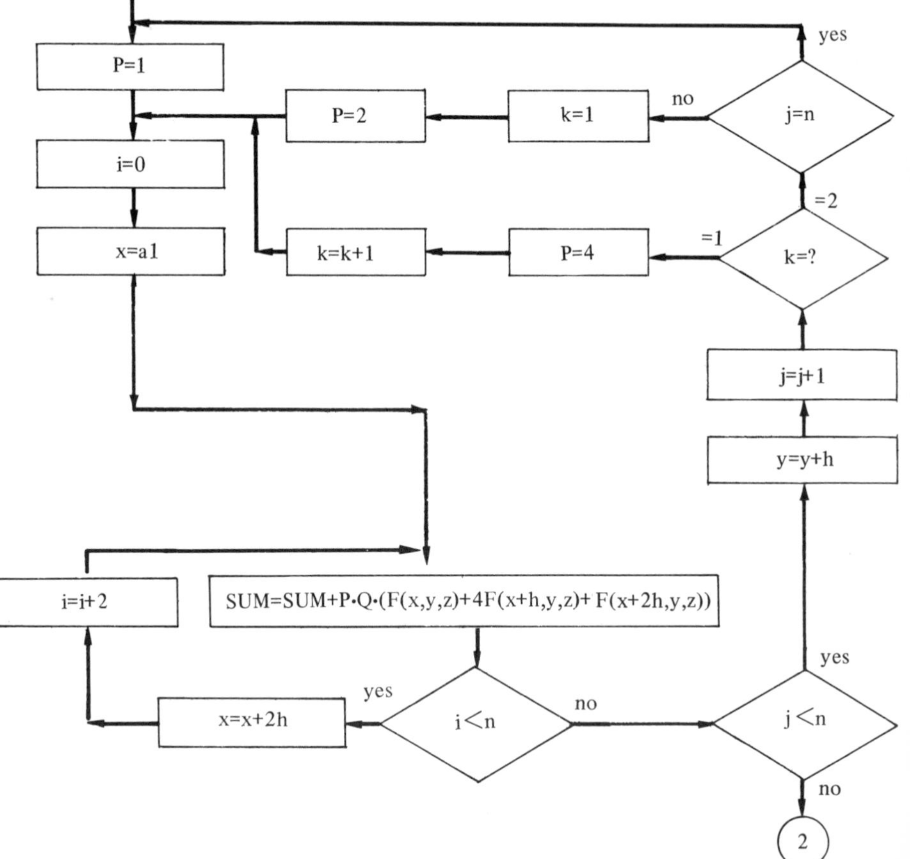

Flow Chart 6.14.1 *(Continued)*

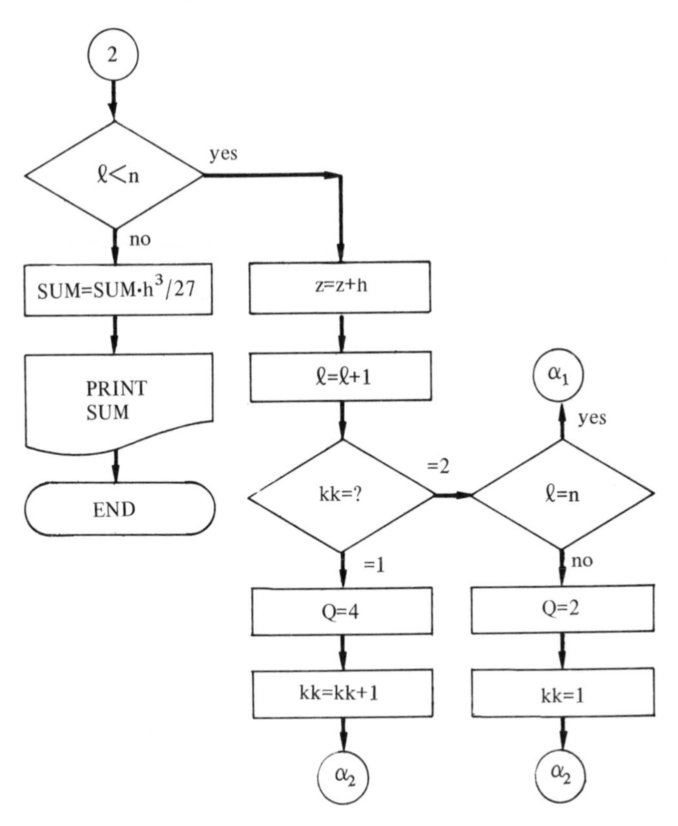

PROBLEMS

6-8. Write a flow chart and program to evaluate

$$\int_c^d \int_a^b f(x,y)\, dx\, dy$$

by the trapezoidal rule.

6-9. Evaluate the following integrals for $n = 2$ and $n = 4$ subintervals in the x and y directions, by applying the program of Prob. 6-8:

(a) $\int_2^4 \int_4^6 \ln xy^2 \, dx \, dy.$

(b) $\int_1^5 \int_1^5 \frac{dx \, dy}{(x^2 + y^2)^{1/2}}.$

Answers: (a) 15.02
(b) 3.997

6-10. Evaluate the integrals in Prob. 6-9 by applying the program for double integration by Simpson's $\frac{1}{3}$ rule (Sec. 6.13.2).

6-11. Apply Richardson's extrapolation formula (6.111) to the answers of Prob. 6-9 to find more accurate results.

Answers: (a) 15.04
(b) 3.952

6-12. Write a program, using Simpson's $\frac{1}{3}$ rule, to evaluate

$$\int_0^1 \int_0^1 \int_0^1 (x^3 + y^3 + z^3) \, dx \, dy \, dz,$$

using $n = 4$ subintervals in all three directions.

6-13. (a) Derive a formula to evaluate

$$\int_{a4}^{b4} \int_{a3}^{b3} \int_{a2}^{b2} \int_{a1}^{b1} f(x,y,z,t) \, dx \, dy \, dz \, dt$$

by applying Simpson's $\frac{1}{3}$ rule.

(b) Write a flow chart and program based upon the formula in (a) above to evaluate

$$\int_0^1 \int_0^1 \int_0^1 \int_0^1 (x^3 + y^3 + z^3 + t^3) \, dx \, dy \, dz \, dt.$$

7

Numerical Solution of Ordinary Differential Equations

Consider a single first-order differential equation of the form

$$\frac{dy}{dx} = f(x,y), \qquad (y(x_0) = y_0). \tag{7.1}$$

It is assumed here that certain conditions are satisfied such that there exists a differentiable function $y(x)$ that is the unique solution of (7.1).[1]

The problem is to find the solution of Eq. 7.1. Whatever method is used for this may also be used, in general, to solve a set of n simultaneous equations of the first order, such as

$$\frac{dy_i}{dx} = f_i(x,y_1,y_2, \ldots, y_n), \qquad (i = 1, 2, \ldots, n), \tag{7.2}$$

with initial conditions $y_i = a_i$ at $x = x_0$.

Moreover, any method of solving (7.1) can be extended to a higher-order equation, or to a system of higher-order equations provided that it can be expressed as a set of first-order equations. For example,

[1] These conditions are:
(a) $f(x,y)$ is defined and continuous in $x_0 \leq x \leq a$, $-\infty < y < \infty$, where x_0 and a are finite;
(b) there is a constant L that depends on $f(x,y)$ such that $|f(x,y) - f(x,Y)| \leq L|y - Y|$ in the interval $[x_0,a]$, and y,Y are any two numbers. This is called the Lipschitz condition.

$$\frac{dx}{dt} = x + y - t$$
$$\frac{d^2y}{dt^2} = x + t, \tag{7.3}$$

with initial conditions $x = 1$, $y = 0$, $dy/dt = -1$ at $t = 0$, becomes

$$\frac{dx}{dt} = x + y - t$$
$$\frac{dy}{dt} = u \tag{7.4}$$
$$\frac{du}{dt} = x + t,$$

with initial conditions $x = 1$, $y = 0$, $u = -1$ at $t = 0$ Most numerical integration methods require that values of y be known at more than one point in order to compute another value of y at some other point. But since in Eq. 7.1 only one condition is given at $x = x_0$, it is necessary to start the solution by a method dependent upon only one condition; after it has been started, the solution can be continued by another method requiring more than one value of y. However, some methods for starting a solution may also be used for continuing it.

There are two types of methods for starting a solution. In the first type to be discussed, the solution y of Eq. 7.1 is approximated by a truncated series whose terms are functions of the independent variable x. For a given range of x (in some cases small), the series represents y within the required degree of accuracy. In this type, $f(x,y)$ is evaluated only at the points (x_i, y_i) where y_i is the computed value of y at $x = x_i$. Taylor's method, the method of undetermined coefficients, and Picard's method (also known as the method of successive approximation) are of this type. Although useful in the proof of existence theorems, Picard's method will not be discussed here, since it is not as well suited to numerical work as the other two.[2]

The second type of method includes the methods of Euler and those of Runge and Kutta. In these the solution y of Eq. 7.1 is not found as an expression in terms of x, but rather for each increment in x, a change in y is computed. Also, $f(x,y)$ is evaluated at points other than (x_i, y_i) in the Runge–Kutta methods. In both types, however, y is approximated at a sequence of values x_i. Graphical methods, another means of starting a solution of (7.1), are not considered in this text.[3]

[2] See Martinus Esser, *Differential Equations* (Philadelphia: W. B. Saunders Company, 1968), Ch. 4.

[3] See Esser, *Differential Equations*, Ch. 6.

METHODS OF THE FIRST TYPE FOR STARTING THE SOLUTION

7.1 Taylor's Method

Consider Eq. 7.1, namely,

$$\frac{dy}{dx} = f(x,y), \qquad (y(x_0) = y_0).$$

Let $y = \phi(x)$ be the required solution of (7.1). If $x = x_0$ is not a singular point, then $y = \phi(x)$ can be expanded in a Taylor's series about this point.[4] Using the notation

$$y_T = y_0 + (x - x_0)y_0^{(1)} + \frac{(x - x_0)^2 y_0^{(2)}}{2!} + \frac{1}{3!}(x - x_0)^3 y_0^{(3)} + \cdots, \tag{7.5}$$

the coefficients $y_0^{(i)}$ can be determined by repeatedly differentiating (7.1) using the initial condition.

Example

Given:

$$y^{(1)} = -\frac{.9}{1 + 2x}y, \qquad (y(0) = y_0 = 1), \tag{7.6}$$

thus

$$y_0^{(1)} = -.9.$$

By repeatedly differentiating (7.6) and using initial conditions,

$$\begin{aligned} y_0^{(2)} &= -.9[(1 + 2x)^{-1}y^{(1)} - 2(1 + 2x)^{-2}y]_0, \\ &= -.9[y_0^{(1)} - 2y_0] = 2.610, \\ y_0^{(3)} &= -.9[(1 + 2x)^{-1}y^{(2)} - 4(1 + 2x)^{-2}y^{(1)} + 8(1 + 2x)^{-3}y]_0, \\ &= -.9[y_0^{(2)} - 4y_0^{(1)} + 8y_0] = -12.79, \\ y_0^{(4)} &= -.9[(1 + 2x)^{-1}y^{(3)} - 6(1 + 2x)^{-2}y^{(2)} + 24(1 + 2x)^{-3}y^{(1)} \\ &\quad -48(1 + 2x)^{-4}y]_0, \\ &= -.9[y_0^{(3)} - 6y_0^{(2)} + 24y_0^{(1)} - 48y_0] = 88.24. \end{aligned} \tag{7.7}$$

Then the first five terms of the Taylor expansion y_T of $y(x)$ about $x = 0$ become

[4] For a treatment of singular points, see William E. Boyce and R. C. Di Prima, *Elementary Differential Equations and Boundary Value Problems*, 2d ed. (New York: John Wiley & Sons, Inc., 1969).

$$y_T = y_0 + \frac{y_0^{(1)}}{1!}x + \frac{y_0^{(2)}}{2!}x^2 + \frac{y_0^{(3)}}{3!}x^3 + \frac{y_0^{(4)}}{4!}x^4$$

$$= 1 - .9x + 1.305x^2 - 2.132x^3 + 3.677x^4 + \cdots. \qquad (7.8)$$

Assuming that the truncation is approximated by the last term in the above series, then if the series is to be an approximation of the values of y to the third decimal place, it is required that

$$3.677x^4 \leq .0005$$

or (7.9)

$$x \leq .104.$$

Thus, the solution y is approximated by

$$y_T = 1 - .9x + 1.305x^2 - 2.132x^3, \qquad (0 \leq x \leq .104). \qquad (7.10)$$

Then y_T will yield values of $y(x)$ accurate to approximately three decimal places for all values of x_i in the interval.

Starting values for the solution of the differential equation (7.6) can now be found for values $0 \leq x \leq .1$. These values at intervals of .02

TABLE 7.1 Taylor Series Starting Values for Solution of Equation 7.6

x	y_T
0	1.000
.02	.982
.04	.966
.06	.950
.08	.935
.1	.921

are listed in Table 7.1. Using these starting values of y_T, another method of the second type can then be applied for continuing the solution. However, a distinct disadvantage of this method is that $f(x,y)$ may be too cumbersome to differentiate. In order to eliminate unnecessary tedious hand computation, a program should include the evaluation of all coefficients as well as evaluation of y_T for each x_i.

7.1.1 Flow Chart

Given:

$$y^{(1)} = \frac{dy}{dx} = \frac{-.9y}{1 + 2x}, \qquad (y = 1 \text{ at } x = 0) \qquad (7.11)$$

and the following set of derivatives of $y^{(1)}$ with respect to x:

$$y^{(2)} = -.9[(1+2x)^{-1}y^{(1)} - 2(1+2x)^{-2}y]$$
$$y^{(3)} = -.9[(1+2x)^{-1}y^{(2)} - 4(1+2x)^{-2}y^{(1)} + 8(1+2x)^{-3}y]$$
$$y^{(4)} = -.9[(1+2x)^{-1}y^{(3)} - 6(1+2x)^{-2}y^{(2)} + 24(1+2x)^{-3}y^{(1)} -48(1+2x)^{-4}y]. \qquad (7.12)$$

Notation

$YTAY(j)$ denotes the value of $y_T(x)$, $x = 0, 0.02, \ldots$.
$Y(k)$ denotes the value of $y_0^{(j-1)}$, $j = 1, 2, 3, 4$, where $y_0^{(0)}$ is the initial value of y.
Then

$$YTAY(j) = Y(1) + Y(2)(X) + \frac{Y(3)}{2!}(X)^2 + \frac{Y(4)}{3!}(X)^3, \qquad (j = 1, 2, \ldots)$$

will be the formula to compute values of y at $x = x_i$, $i = 1, 2, \ldots$. The last term of the truncated series $y(5)x^4/24$ is used to calculate the upper bound of the range of x—that is, the upper bound

$$UB = \left[\frac{24E}{y(5)}\right]^{1/4} = .104, \qquad (E = .0005).$$

The program provides a method to truncate $UB = .104$ to $UB = .1$. X is initially set equal to zero and is incremented by .02 until $x = .1$.

FLOW CHART 7.1.1 Taylor's Method

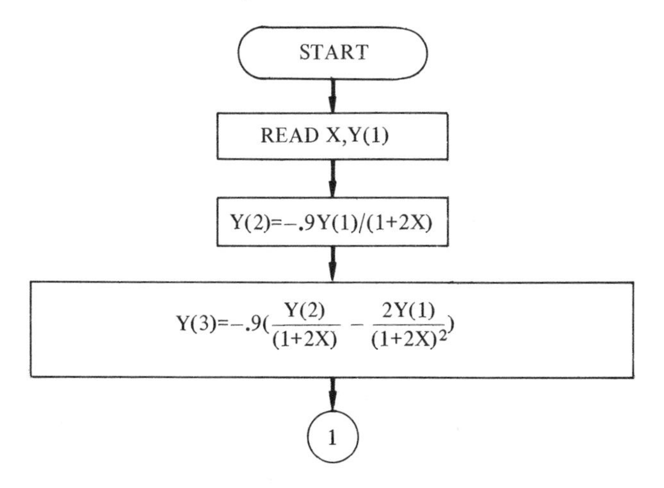

Flow Chart 7.1.1 *(Continued)*

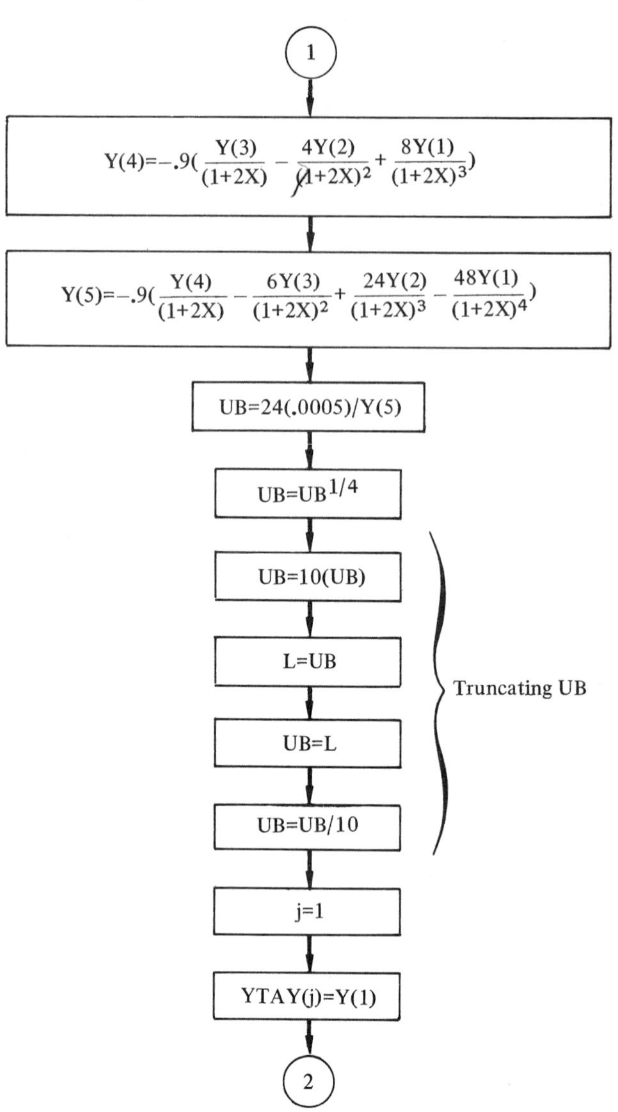

Flow Chart 7.1.1 *(Continued)*

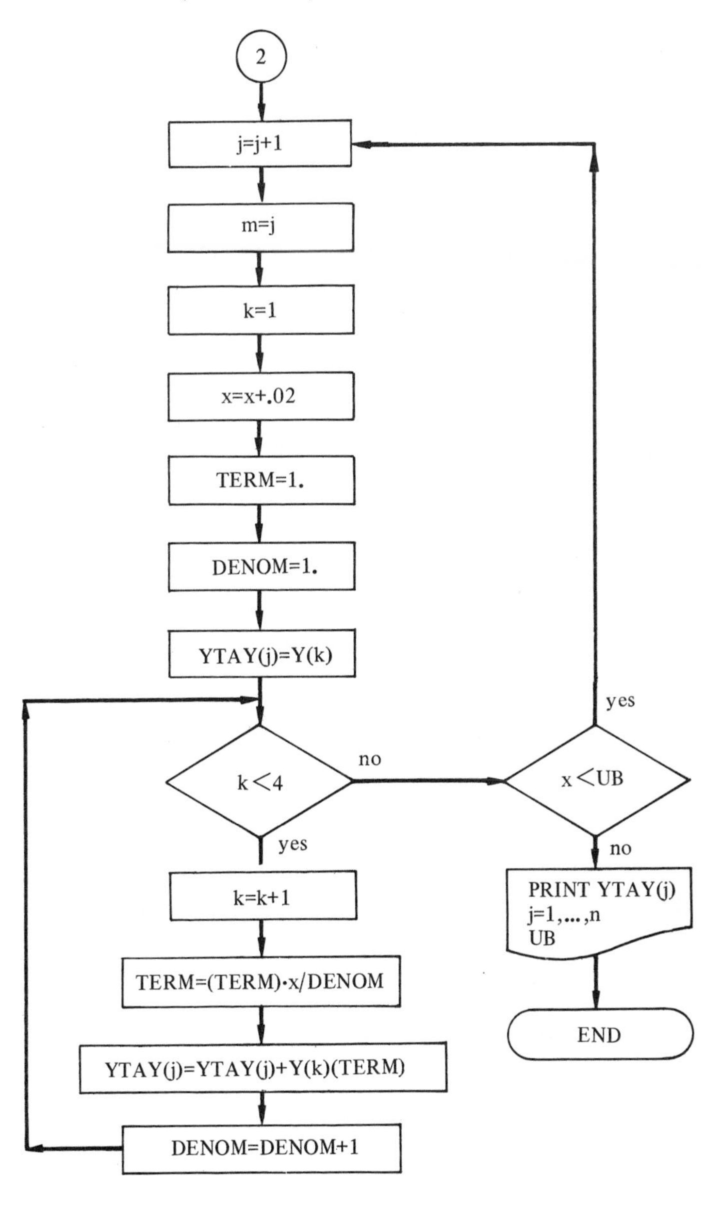

7.1.2 Program

To find the iterates $yTAY(j)$, $j = 1, 2, 3, 4, 5, 6$, for Eq. 7.11.

```
C          TAYLOR'S METHOD
      DIMENSION Y(5),YTAY(10)
      READ(5,100)X,Y(1)
  100 FORMAT(2F10.4)
      Y(2)=-.9*Y(1)/(1+2*X)
      Y(3)=-.9(Y(2)/(1+2*X)-2*Y(1)/(1+2*X)**2)
      TERM1=Y(3)/(1+2*X)
      TERM2=4*Y(2)/(1+2*X)**2
      TERM3=8*Y(1)/(1+2*X)**3
      Y(4)=-.9*(TERM1-TERM2+TERM3)
      TERM4=Y(4)/(1+2*X)
      TERM5=6*Y(3)/(1+2*X)**2
      TERM6=24*Y(2)/(1+2*X)**3
      TERM7=48*Y(1)/(1+2*X)**4
      Y(5)=-.9*(TERM4-TERM5+TERM6-TERM7)
      UB=24*.0005/Y(5)
      UB=UB**.25
      UB=10*UB
      L=UB
      UB=L
      UB=UB/10
      J=1
      YTAY(J)=Y(1)
    1 J=J+1
      M=J
      K=1
      X=X+.02
      TERM=1.
      DENOM=1.
      YTAY(J)=Y(K)
    2 IF(K-4)3,4,4
    3 K=K+1
      TERM=TERM*X/DENOM
      YTAY(J)=YTAY(J)+Y(K)*TERM
      DENOM=DENOM+1
      GO TO 2
    4 IF(X-UB)1,5,5
    5 WRITE(6,101)(YTAY(J),J=1,M)
  101 FORMAT(//,'YTAY(J)',/,F10.4)
      WRITE(6,102)UB
  102 FORMAT(//,'UB=',F4.2)
      STOP
      END

      THE RESULTS ARE:
      YTAY(J)
```

```
    1.0000  0.9829  0.9664  0.9504  0.9355  0.9208
UB=0.10
```

7.2 Method of Undetermined Coefficients

A series solution can also be found by the following process known as the method of undetermined coefficients.

1. Assume that the solution is a series of the form

$$y = a_0 + a_1(x - x_0) + a_2(x - x_0)^2 + \cdots + a_n(x - x_0)^n + \cdots$$

or (7.13)

$$y = \sum_{i=0}^{\infty} a_i(x - x_0)^i.$$

2. Substitute (7.13) in the differential equation

$$\frac{dy}{dx} - f(x,y) = 0, \qquad (y = y_0 \text{ at } x = x_0). \tag{7.14}$$

This will yield a series of the form

$$h_0 + h_1(x - x_0) + h_2(x - x_0)^2 + \cdots + h_n(x - x_0)^n + \cdots = 0$$

or (7.15)

$$\sum_{i=0}^{\infty} h_i(x - x_0)^i = 0.$$

3. Determine the coefficients a_i by the fact that all h_i must vanish.

Example

Consider Eq. 7.6 in the form

$$y^{(1)} + \frac{.9}{1 + 2x}y = 0, \qquad (y(0) = 1). \tag{7.16}$$

Let the assumed solution be

$$y = a_0 + a_1x + a_2x^2 + \cdots + a_nx^n + \cdots . \tag{7.17}$$

With the initial condition $y(0) = 1$, Eq. 7.17 becomes

$$y = 1 + a_1x + a_2x^2 + \cdots + a_nx^n + \cdots . \tag{7.18}$$

Then

$$y^1 = a_1 + 2a_2x + 3a_3x^2 + 4a_4x^3 + \cdots + na_nx^{n-1} + \cdots . \qquad (7.19)$$

Substituting Eqs. 7.18 and 7.19 in the differential equation (7.16), Eq. 7.16 becomes

$$(a_1 + 2a_2x + 3a_3x^2 + 4a_4x^3 + 5a_5x^4 + \cdots)$$
$$+ \frac{.9}{1 + 2x}(1 + a_1x + a_2x^2 + a_3x^3 + a_4x^4 + \cdots) = 0. \qquad (7.20)$$

Express $.9/(1 + 2x)$ as an infinite series, i.e.,

$$\frac{.9}{1 + 2x} = .9(1 - 2x + 4x^2 - 8x^3 + 16x^4 - \cdots).$$

Then

$$\frac{.9}{1 + 2x}(1 + a_1x + a_2x^2 + a_3x^3 + a_4x^4 + \cdots)$$

becomes

$$(.9 - 1.8x + 3.6x^2 - 7.2x^3 + 14.4x^4 - \cdots)$$
$$(1 + a_1x + a_2x^2 + a_3x^3 + a_4x^4 + \cdots)$$
$$= .9 + (.9a_1 - 1.8)x + (.9a_2 - 1.8a_1 + 3.6)x^2$$
$$+ (.9a_3 - 1.8a_2 + 3.6a_1 - 7.2)x^3$$
$$+ (.9a_4 - 1.8a_3 + 3.6a_2 - 7.2a_1 + 14.4)x^4 + \cdots . \qquad (7.21)$$

Equation 7.20 becomes

$$(a_1 + .9) + (2a_2 + .9a_1 - 1.8)x + (3a_3 + .9a_2 - 1.8a_1 + 3.6)x^2$$
$$+ (4a_4 + .9a_3 - 1.8a_2 + 3.6a_1 - 7.2)x^3 + \cdots = 0, \qquad (7.22)$$

which is of the form

$$h_0 + h_1(x - x_0) + h_2(x - x_0)^2 + \cdots = 0.$$

Each h_i is set equal to zero; hence

$$\begin{aligned} a_1 + .9 = 0 \quad &\text{yields} \quad a_1 = -.9 \\ 2a_2 + .9a_1 - 1.8 = 0 \quad &\text{yields} \quad a_2 = 1.305 \\ 3a_3 + .9a_2 - 1.8a_1 + 3.6 = 0 \quad &\text{yields} \quad a_3 = 12.132 \\ 4a_4 + .9a_3 - 1.8a_2 + 3.6a_1 - 7.2 = 0 \quad &\text{yields} \quad a_4 = 3.677. \qquad (7.23) \end{aligned}$$

Substituting a_1, a_2, a_3, a_4 into the equation

$$y = 1 + a_1x + a_2x^2 + a_3x^3 + a_4x^4 + \cdots ,$$

the approximate general solution of Eq. 7.16 is

$$y = 1 - .9x + 1.305x^2 - 2.132x^3 + 3.677x^4. \quad (7.24)$$

Equation 7.24 is of course the same as Eq. 7.8. The last term can be used to approximate the truncation as was done in (7.8). From this point on, the method of undetermined coefficients is the same as the Taylor method.

This method has the advantage in general of being faster than Taylor's method of successive differentiations.

PROBLEMS

7-1. Write a program to find a series solution for

$$\frac{dy}{dx} = \frac{-.9y}{1 + 2x}, \qquad (y(0) = 1)$$

at the points $x = x_i$ $(0 \leq x \leq 1)$ and $x_{i+1} - x_i = .02$ by the method of determined coefficients.

7-2. Consider the differential equation $y'' + \sin y = 0$, with initial values $y(0) = 0$, $y'(0) = 1$.

(a) Use Taylor's method to find a truncated series of degree 5. Use the last term $(y_0^5 x^5)/5!$ to find the truncation error.

(b) Write a flow chart and program to compute and print values of y at points $x_i = 0, .02, \ldots$.

7-3. (a) Use the method of undetermined coefficients to find a solution of $y' - 2y = 3e^x$, $y(0) = 0$. Note that

$$e^x = 1 + x + \frac{x^2}{2!} + \frac{x^3}{3!} + \cdots .$$

Truncate the series with the x^5 term, and use the last calculated term to determine the truncation error.

(b) Write a flow chart and program to compute and print values of y at points $x_i = 0, .02, \ldots$.

METHODS OF THE SECOND TYPE FOR STARTING THE SOLUTION

7.3 Euler's Method

Consider the first-order ordinary differential equation

$$\frac{dy}{dx} = f(x,y), \qquad (y(x_0) = y_0). \quad (7.25)$$

Using finite differences (Ch. 5), an approximation for dy/dx at $x = x_0$ is

$$\left.\frac{dy}{dx}\right|_{x=x_0} = \frac{1}{h}\Delta y_0 = \frac{y_1 - y_0}{h}. \tag{7.26}$$

Using (7.26) in Eq. 7.25, an approximation to $y(x_1)$ is $y_1 = y_0 + hf(x_0, y_0)$. With this approximation of $y(x_1)$, (7.26) can again be used to approximate dy/dx at $x = x_1$, and in turn by inserting this approximation in (7.25), $y(x_2)$ is approximated as $y_2 = y_1 + hf(x_1, y_1)$.

In general, the approximation of $y(x_{i+1})$ is given by

$$y_{i+1} = y_i + hf(x_i, y_i). \tag{7.27}$$

This technique, known as the Euler method, although not too important from a practical point of view is nevertheless an introduction to methods of the second type in which a change in y is calculated for a corresponding change in x.

It can be shown that the truncation error e_i at the ith iteration has an upper bound

$$|e_i| \le \frac{hK}{2R}(e^{(x_i - x_0)R} - 1) \tag{7.28}$$

where e_i is defined as $e_i = y_i - y(x_i)$; y_i is the approximate solution and $y(x_i)$ is the true solution of Eq. 7.25. (The irrational number e should not be confused with e_i, the error.) Also, for a fixed h and $x_i = x_0 + ih$, the constants K and R are defined by the inequalities[5]

$$|y''(x)| \le K, \qquad \left|\frac{\partial f(x,y)}{\partial y}\right| \le R.$$

Equation 7.28 shows that the error e_i approaches zero as h approaches zero provided that $y''(x)$ and $\partial f(x,y)/\partial y$ are bounded within the stated range and x_i is fixed. What actually is being asked and answered by Eq. 7.28 is, "Does Euler's method converge?" However, (7.28) considered as an a priori error estimate is not realistic.

Example

Determine an upper bound of the truncation error in the solution of

$$\frac{dy}{dx} = \frac{-.9y}{1 + 2x}, \qquad (y(0) = 1)$$

[5] For a proof of Eq. 7.28, see Kaiser L. Kunz, *Numerical Analysis* (New York: McGraw-Hill Book Company, Inc., 1957), Ch. 8.

from $x = 0$ to $x = .1$. The true solution is

$$\int_1^y \frac{dy}{y} = -.9 \int_0^x \frac{dx}{1 + 2x} \qquad \text{or} \qquad y(x) = (1 + 2x)^{-0.45}.$$

Since $y''(0) = 2.61$, K may be chosen as 2.61. Also, an upper bound of $\partial f(x,y)/\partial y$ is

$$R = |-.9| = .9, \qquad x_i - x_0 = .1.$$

Hence, an upper bound of the truncation error (7.28) is

$$|e(.1)| \leq \frac{h(2.61)}{2(.9)}(e^{.09} - 1) = h(1.45)(1.094 - 1)$$

or

$$|e(.1)| \leq .136h. \tag{7.29}$$

For a fixed $h = .02$, Eq. 7.29 shows that error $e(.1)$ at $x = .1$ is

$$|e(.1)| \leq (.02)(.136) = .0027. \tag{7.30}$$

The true value of the solution $y(.1)$ is .9212, and the approximate value of $y(.1)$ using Euler's method with $h = .02$ is .9220. Hence, the true error (excluding roundoff error) is

$$e = .9220 - .9212 = .0008. \tag{7.31}$$

Comparing $e(.1)$ with e, it is seen that upper bound on the error by Eq. 7.28 is not very realistic. For this reason, Eq. 7.28 should be considered as a test for convergence rather than a good error estimate.

7.3.1 Flow Chart

Given

$$\frac{dy}{dx} = \frac{y - x}{y + x}, \qquad (y = 1 \text{ at } x = 0), \tag{7.32}$$

the Euler formula is

$$y_{i+1} = y_i + f(x_i, y_i)h.$$

Choose $h = .02$, $n = 6$, $x = 0$, $y = 1$ initially. The problem is to compute and print values of x and y at $x = 0, .02, .04, .06, .08$, and $.1$.

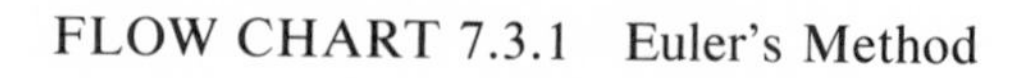

FLOW CHART 7.3.1 Euler's Method

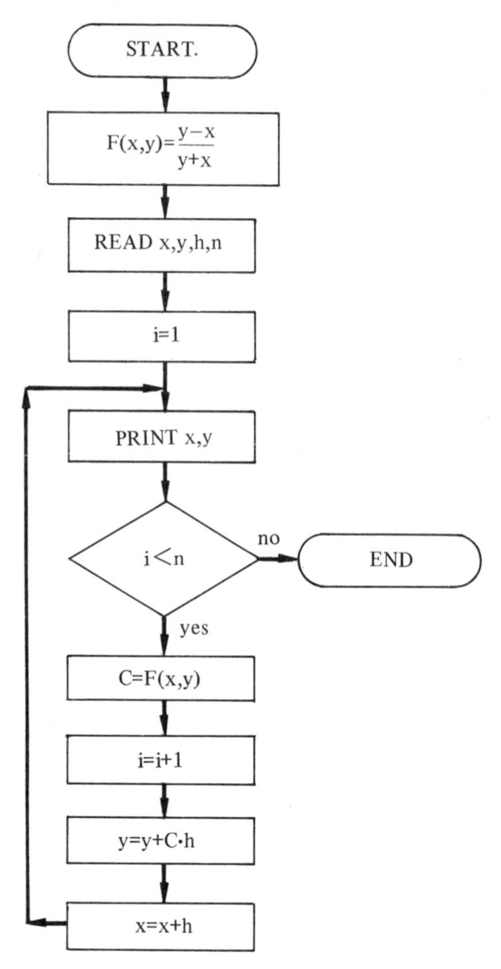

7.3.2 Program

Consider Eq. 7.32. The following program computes and prints the values of x, y, and $f(x,y)$ for each iteration.

```
  F(X,Y)=(Y−X)/(Y+X)
2 FORMAT(10X,'THE VALUES ARE X=',F10.4/25X,'Y=',F10.4/25X,'F(X,Y)=',F10.4)
4 FORMAT(I6)
5 FORMAT(3F10.4)
```

```
3 FORMAT(10X,'THE NUMBER OF ITERATIONS IS',I6,//)
  READ(5,4)N
  READ(5,5)X,Y,H
  DO 8 I=1,N
  C=F(X,Y)
  WRITE(6,3)I
  WRITE(6,2)X,Y,C
  DELY=C*H
  Y=Y+DELY
  X=X+H
8 CONTINUE
  END
  THE NUMBER OF ITERATIONS IS   1
  THE VALUES ARE X=  0.0
                 Y=  1.0000
                 F(X,Y)=  1.0000
  THE NUMBER OF ITERATIONS IS   2
  THE VALUES ARE X=  0.0200
                 Y=  1.0200
                 F(X,Y)=  0.9615
  THE NUMBER OF ITERATIONS IS   3
  THE VALUES ARE X=  0.0400
                 Y=  1.0392
                 F(X,Y)=  0.9259
  THE NUMBER OF ITERATIONS IS   4
  THE VALUES ARE X=  0.0600
                 Y=  1.0577
                 F(X,Y)=  0.8926
  THE NUMBER OF ITERATIONS IS   5
  THE VALUES ARE X=  0.0800
                 Y=  1.0756
                 F(X,Y)=  0.8615
  THE NUMBER OF ITERATIONS IS   6
  THE VALUES ARE X=  0.1000
                 Y=  1.0928
                 F(X,Y)=  0.8323
```

7.4 Modified Method of Euler

For

$$\frac{dy}{dx} = f(x,y), \qquad (y = y_0 \text{ at } x_0), \tag{7.33}$$

the ith Euler iteration is

$$y_{i+1} = y_i + f(x_i, y_i)h \tag{7.34}$$

where h is a constant. However, using the Newton–Cotes trapezoidal formula, namely

$$\int_{x_i}^{x_{i+1}} f(x)\,dx = \frac{h}{2}\{f(x_{i+1}) + f(x_i)\}, \tag{7.35}$$

and applying this formula to $dy/dx = y'$, the result is

$$y_{i+1} - y_i = \frac{h}{2}\{y'_{i+1} + y'_i\}$$

or (7.36)

$$y_{i+1} = y_i + \frac{h}{2}\{y'_{i+1} + y'_i\}.$$

Since

$$\left.\frac{dy}{dx}\right|_{x=x_i} = \left. f(x,y)\right|_{\substack{x=x_i\\ y=y_i}}, \tag{7.37}$$

Eq. 7.36 becomes

$$y_{i+1} = y_i + \frac{h}{2}\{f(x_{i+1},y_{i+1}) + f(x_i,y_i)\}. \tag{7.38}$$

In Eq. 7.38, y_{i+1} appears on both sides of the equation, and in general may be solved for y_{i+1} in terms of x_i and y_i.

The two formulas 7.34 and 7.38 constitute Euler's modified method. The general procedure is to find a first approximation y_1 by using the initial values x_0 and y_0 and substituting these values in (7.34). Then, this computed value of y_1 is used to find a better approximation $Y_1^{(1)}$ by substituting x_0, y_0, x_1, and y_1 in Eq. 7.38. This second step can be repeated by substituting x_0, y_0, x_1, and $Y_1^{(1)}$ in (7.38) to find the approximation $Y_1^{(2)}$ for y_1. When $|Y_1^{(j)} - Y_1^{(j-1)}| < \epsilon$, ϵ an arbitrarily small number, the first step is repeated with $x = x_1$ and $y_1 = Y_1^{(j)}$. Thus the whole process is continued for $x = x_0, x_1, \ldots, x_n$.

If, as is assumed in footnote 1, for the differential equation (7.1) the Lipschitz condition

$$|f(x,Y) - f(x,y)| < K|Y - y| \tag{7.39}$$

is satisfied in the given interval, then the iterations in the modified Euler method will converge provided that h is chosen small enough.

Let $Y_{i+1}^{(j)}$ be the jth approximation to Y_{i+1}, Y_{i+1} being the value to which the modified method converges. Iteration in the modified Euler formula (Eq. 7.38) can then be written as

$$Y_{i+1}^{(j)} = y_i + \frac{h}{2}[f(x_i,y_i) + f(x_{i+1},Y_{i+1}^{(j-1)})], \qquad (j \geq 2). \tag{7.40}$$

It should be noted that $Y_{i+1}^{(1)}$ is computed by means of Eq. 7.34. Equation 7.38, with Y_{i+1} replacing $Y_{i+1}^{(j)}$, now becomes

$$Y_{i+1} = y_i + \frac{h}{2}[f(x_i,y_i) + f(x_{i+1},Y_{i+1})]. \tag{7.41}$$

Subtracting (7.41) from (7.40),

$$Y_{i+1}^{(j)} - Y_{i+1} = \frac{h}{2}[f(x_{i+1},Y_{i+1}^{(j-1)}) - f(x_{i+1},Y_{i+1})]. \tag{7.42}$$

If $f(x,y)$ satisfies the Lipschitz condition (Eq. 7.39), then for any two values $Y_{i+1}^{(j-1)}$ and Y_{i+1}, terms in parentheses on the right side of Eq. 7.42 will satisfy the inequality

$$|f(x_{i+1},Y_{i+1}^{(j-1)}) - f(x_{i+1},Y_{i+1})| < K_i|Y_{i+1}^{(j-1)} - Y_{i+1}| \tag{7.43}$$

where K_i is a constant (for the ith iteration). Thus, the left side of Eq. 7.42 in absolute value satisfies

$$|Y_{i+1}^{(j)} - Y_{i+1}| < \frac{hK_i}{2}|Y_{i+1}^{(j-1)} - Y_{i+1}|. \tag{7.44}$$

From (7.44), it is seen that

$$|Y_{i+1}^{(j-1)} - Y_{i+1}| < \frac{hK_i}{2}|Y_{i+1}^{(j-2)} - Y_{i+1}|, \tag{7.45}$$

so that

$$|Y_{i+1}^{(j)} - Y_{i+1}| < \left(\frac{hK_i}{2}\right)^2 |Y_{i+1}^{(j-2)} - Y_{i+1}|. \tag{7.46}$$

Continuing in this manner to the first iterate on the right side, the inequality (7.44) becomes

$$|Y_{i+1}^{(j)} - Y_{i+1}| < \left(\frac{hK_i}{2}\right)^{j-1} |Y_{i+1}^{(1)} - Y_{i+1}|. \tag{7.47}$$

Thus, in addition to the Lipschitz condition, it is necessary to choose h so that $hK_i/2$ is less than unity in order that the modified method of Euler converge. That is, as $j \to \infty$, $Y_{i+1}^{(j)} \to Y_{i+1}$. Hence, if the truncation error e_i satisfies (7.28) and if in the modified method h is chosen so that (7.47) is satisfied, then $Y_{i+1}^{(j)}$ converges to Y_{i+1} where Y_{i+1} is the value to which the modified method converges. (It should be noted that Y_{i+1} is not necessarily the true value $y(x_{i+1})$.) However, if the truncation error e_i in Euler's method satisfies the upper-bound requirement (7.28), then Y_{i+1} would be a very close approximation of $y(x_{i+1})$.

Example

Given:

$$\frac{dy}{dx} = \frac{-.9y}{1 + 2x}, \qquad (y = 1 \text{ at } x = 0),$$

let $h = .02$. Using $y_{i+1} = y_i + f(x_i, y_i)h$,

$$y_1 = 1 - \frac{.9}{1}(.02) = .982.$$

Then, by application of the modified Euler method, for $j = 1$,

$$Y_1^{(1)} = y_0 + \frac{h}{2}\left\{\frac{-.9(.982)}{1 + 2(.02)} - \frac{.9(1)}{1}\right\}$$

or

$$y_1^{(1)} = .1 + .01\{-1.75\} = .9825 \cong .982.$$

By a second application, where $j = 2$,

$$y_1^{(2)} = 1 + .01\left\{\frac{-.9(.982)}{1 + 2(.02)} - \frac{.9(1)}{1}\right\}$$

or

$$Y_1^{(2)} = .982.$$

Thus, to three decimal places the value y_1 is .982.

7.4.1 Flow Chart

Given:

$$\frac{dy}{dx} = \frac{-.9y}{1 + 2x}, \qquad (y = 1 \text{ at } x = 0). \tag{7.48}$$

Compute and print all values of y at $x = 0, .02, .04, .06, .08, .1$, $h = .02$. The Euler formula is

$$y_{i+1} = y_i + hf(x_i, y_i),$$

and the modified Euler formula is

$$y_{i+1} = y_i + \frac{h}{2}\{f(x_{i+1}, y_{i+1}) + f(x_i, y_i)\}.$$

In Flow Chart 7.4.1, these formulas will be stated respectively as

$$y1 = y0 + h \cdot F(x0,y0)$$

and

$$z1 = y0 + \frac{h}{2}\{F(x0 + h,y1) + F(x0,y0)\}$$

with starting values of $x0 = 0$ and $y0 = 1$. If $|z1 - y1| < \epsilon$, Euler's formula is applied to find the first approximation $y1$ at $x = x0 + h$. If the test is not satisfied, $y1$ is replaced by $z1$ and another value $z1$ is computed.

$EPS = 10^{-4}$, $L = 5$ is the maximum number of allowed iterations in the modified formula and $n = 6$ is the number of y values required to be printed.

FLOW CHART 7.4.1 Modified Method of Euler

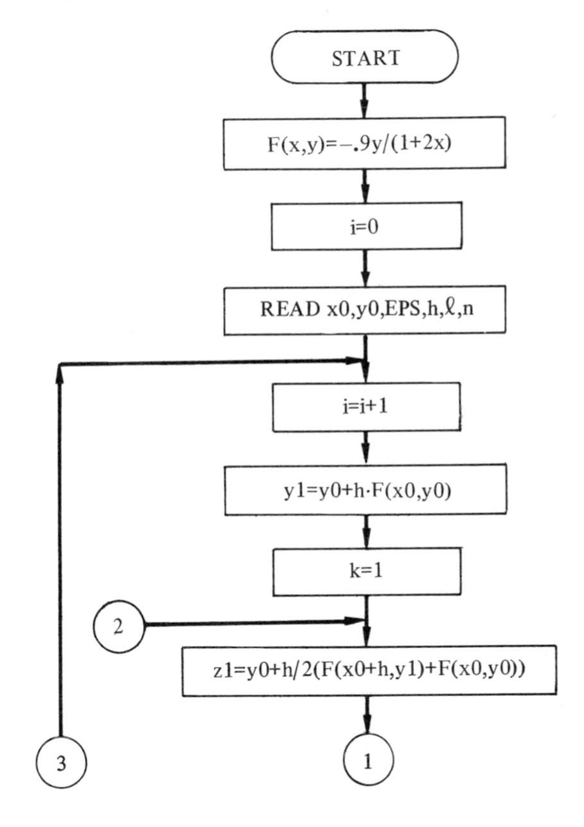

Flow Chart 7.4.1 *(Continued)*

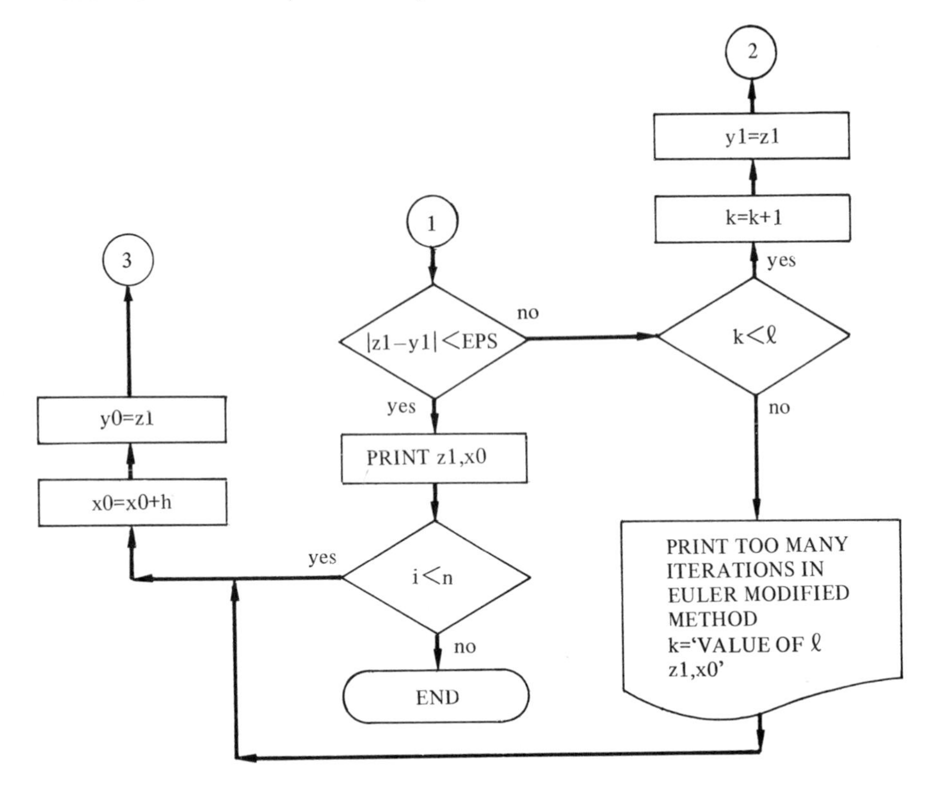

7.5 Euler's Method for a Second-order Differential Equation

Euler's method can be extended to solve an equation of the form

$$\frac{d^2y}{dx^2} + A\frac{dy}{dx} + By = f(x,y), \tag{7.49}$$

where $y = y_0$, $dy/dx = (dy/dx)_0$ at $x = x_0$, and $A = A(x,y)$, $B = B(x,y)$.

For the discussion below, A and B are assumed to be constants and $f(x,y) = 0$. Euler's equation is

$$y_{i+1} = y_i + hy'_i\,. \tag{7.50}$$

In (7.49), replacing y_{i+1} with y'_{i+1}, y_i with y'_i, and y'_i with y''_i, the Euler formula for dy/dx is

$$y'_{i+1} = y'_i + hy''_i. \tag{7.51}$$

Substituting the computed values y_{i+1} and y'_{i+1} in the differential equation (7.49),

$$y''_{i+1} = f(x_{i+1}, y_{i+1}) - Ay'_{i+1} - By_{i+1}. \tag{7.52}$$

Equations 7.50, 7.51, and 7.52 will yield values of y, dy/dx, and d^2y/dx^2, respectively at points $x_i = x_0 + ih$, h a constant.

7.5.1 Flow Chart

Given:

$$\frac{d^2y}{dx^2} + 2\frac{dy}{dx} + 3xy = 0,$$

$$\left(y = 1, \frac{dy}{dx} = 1 \text{ at } x = 0\right).$$

Notation

Initial values:

$$x = 0, y = 1, DYDX = \frac{dy}{dx} = 1,$$

$$D2YDX = \frac{d^2y}{dx^2}, A = 2, B = 3, h = .05,$$

$$n = 20 \text{ (number of iterations)}.$$

The value of x and values of y, $DYDX$, and $D2YDX$ are printed for each iteration.

FLOW CHART 7.5.1 Euler's Method Applied to a Second-order Differential Equation

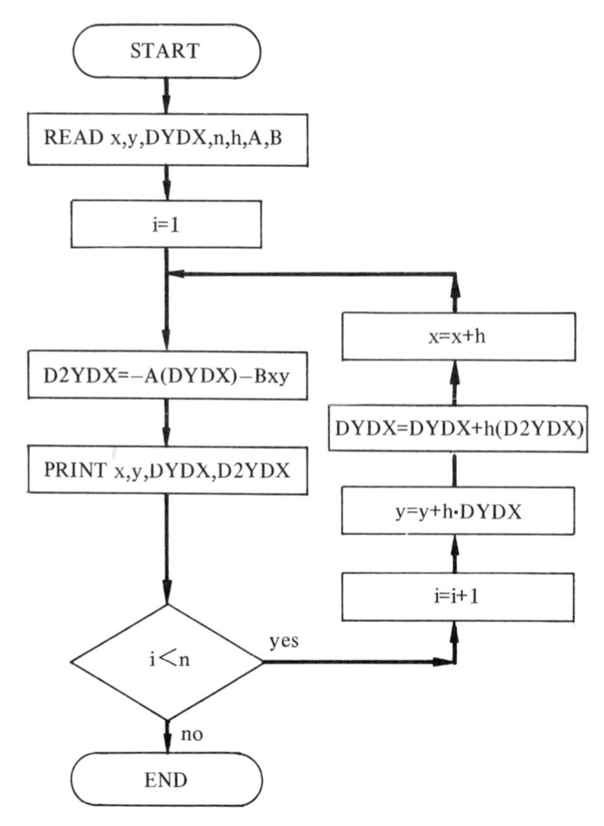

Problems

7-4. Write a program from Flow Chart 7.4.1 to solve the differential equation (7.48) with the given initial conditions for $x = 0, .02, .04, .06, .08,$ and $.1$. Compare your values with values listed in Table 7.1.

7-5. Consider the differential equations:

$$\frac{dy}{dx} = y^{2/3}, \qquad (y = 0 \text{ at } x = 0), \tag{a}$$

$$\frac{dy}{dx} = x^2 + y^2, \qquad (y = 0 \text{ at } x = 0). \tag{b}$$

For equation (a), a value of K must be chosen so that

$$|y^{2/3} - Y^{2/3}| \leq K|y - Y|.$$

Let $y = px^3$ and $Y = qx^3$, p and q both constants. Then K must be found such that

$$x^2|p^{2/3} - q^{2/3}| \leq K|x^3||p - q|,$$

or, for $x \neq 0$,

$$|p^{2/3} - q^{2/3}| \leq K|x||p - q|.$$

Therefore, since a K cannot be found for any region including the origin to satisfy the Lipschitz condition, it cannot be said that there is a unique solution in this region.

For equation (b) show that the Lipschitz condition is satisfied in any region that includes the origin. Would $K = 1$ be a satisfactory choice if the interval of interest is $(-1,1)$? Use the modified Euler method and write a program to compute and print values of y at $x = 0, .02, \ldots, .1$.

7-6. Given the system of differential equations:

$$\frac{d^2y}{dt^2} + C\frac{dx}{dt} + xy = A$$

$$\frac{dx}{dt} + \frac{dy}{dt} + C = B$$

where $A = 2$, $B = 3$, $C = t + \sin t$; the initial conditions are $y = 1$, $x = 0$, $dy/dt = 0$ at $t = 0$. Such a system is called nonlinear because of C. These equations can be solved for x and y by the Euler method, but C must be computed for each value of t.

Using Euler's method for first-order and second-order equations, and the above system of equations, the following set of equations is derived:

(a) $y_{i+1} = y_i + h\left(\frac{dy}{dt}\right)_i,$

(b) $C_i = t_i + \sin t_i,$

(c) $\left(\frac{dx}{dt}\right)_i = B - C_i - \left(\frac{dy}{dt}\right)_i,$

(d) $x_{i+1} = x_i + h\left(\frac{dx}{dt}\right)_i.$

(e) $\left(\frac{d^2y}{dt^2}\right)_i = A - x_iy_i - C_i\left(\frac{dx}{dt}\right)_i,$

(f) $\left(\frac{dy}{dt}\right)_{i+1} = \left(\frac{dy}{dt}\right)_i + h\left(\frac{d^2y}{dt^2}\right)_i.$

Write a flow chart and program to compute and print values of y, C, dx/dt, x, d^2y/dt^2, dy/dt at $t = 0, .01, .02, \ldots, .1$.

7-7. Suppose that $C = t + \sin ct$ in Prob. 7-6. What method would be suitable to find each C for the current value of t? What is a good choice for the initial value of C for each value t_i if $t_i = 0, .01, \ldots, .1$? Write a flow chart and program to compute and print all values in Prob. 7-6 with $C = t + \sin ct$.

7.6 Runge–Kutta Methods

Since the truncation error in Euler's method is of order h^2, its practical disadvantage is that the step size, h, must be quite small for reasonable accuracy. Taylor's method requires that high-order derivatives be found. The method of undetermined coefficients can be quite complicated due to series expansions, multiplication and division of series, and substitutions of series into series.

The Runge–Kutta methods yield greater accuracy and do not require analytically finding higher-order derivatives. These methods can be used not only for starting the solution but may also be used for the total solution. However, as methods for completing solution, there are the disadvantages of estimating error and speed in comparison to predictor–director methods (Sec. 7.9).

To find an approximation to the solution of

$$\frac{dy}{dx} = f(x,y), \qquad (y = y_0, x = x_0) \text{ at } x = x_{i+1}, \tag{7.53}$$

the Euler method consists of evaluating

$$y_{i+1} = y_i + f(x_i, y_i)h = y_i + \Delta y. \tag{7.54}$$

A technique known as the Runge–Kutta method of order 2 is obtained in the following manner.

Express the difference between the values of y at x_{i+1} and at x_i as

$$y_{i+1} - y_i = ah[f(x_i, y_i)] + bh[f(x_i + \alpha h, y_i + \beta h f(x_i, y_i))] \tag{7.55}$$

or

$$y_{i+1} = y_i + a\,\Delta y + bh\,f(x_i + \alpha h, y_i + \beta\,\Delta y) \tag{7.56}$$

where $h = x_{i+1} - x_i$ and a, b, and β are constants to be determined. To determine the values of these constants:

1. Expand y_{i+1} in Taylor series about the point x_i.
2. Expand $f(x_i + \alpha h, y_i + \beta\,\Delta y)$ in a Taylor series for a function of two variables.
3. Equate coefficients of like terms in h from these Taylor series in steps 1 and 2.

For step one, the Taylor series for the left side of (7.56) is

$$y_{i+1} = y_i + hy_i' + \frac{h^2}{2}y_i'' + \frac{h^3}{3!}y_i''' + \cdots. \tag{7.57}$$

From the differential equation[6]

$$y_i' = f(x_i,y_i), \tag{7.58}$$

$$y_i'' = \left[\frac{\partial f}{\partial x} + \frac{\partial f}{\partial y}f\right]_i \tag{7.59}$$

and

$$y_i''' = \left[\frac{\partial^2 f}{\partial x^2} + 2f\frac{\partial^2 f}{\partial x\,\partial y} + \frac{\partial^2 f}{\partial y^2}f^2 + \frac{\partial f}{\partial x}\frac{\partial f}{\partial y} + \left[\frac{\partial f}{\partial y}\right]^2 f\right]_i. \tag{7.60}$$

For step 2, the Taylor series expansion for $f(x_i + \alpha h,\ y_i + \beta\,\Delta y)$ is

$$f(x_i + \alpha h,\ y_i + \beta\,\Delta y) = \Bigg[f + \frac{\alpha h\,\partial f}{dx} + \beta\,\Delta y\,\frac{\partial f}{\partial y} + \frac{1}{2}\left\{\frac{\alpha^2 h^2\,\partial^2 f}{\partial x^2} + 2\alpha h\beta\,\Delta y\,\frac{\partial^2 f}{\partial x\,\partial y} + \beta^2(\Delta y)^2\frac{\partial^2 f}{\partial y^2}\right\}\Bigg]_i + 0(h)^3. \tag{7.61}$$

By substituting the right sides of Eqs. 7.58, 7.59, and 7.60 for y_i', y_i'', and y_i''', respectively in Eq. 7.57,

$$y_{i+1} = y_i + hf_i + \frac{h^2}{2}\left[\frac{\partial f}{\partial x} + \frac{\partial f}{\partial y}f\right]_i + \frac{h^3}{3!}\left\{\frac{\partial^2 f}{\partial x^2} + 2f\,\frac{\partial^2 f}{\partial x\,\partial y} + \frac{\partial^2 f}{\partial y^2}f^2 + \frac{\partial f}{\partial x}\frac{\partial f}{\partial y} + \left[\frac{\partial f}{\partial y}\right]^2 f\right\}_i + 0(h^4), \tag{7.62}$$

where the subscript i designates that functions are to be evaluated at the point (x_i, y_i). Further, by substituting the Taylor series expansion (Eq. 7.61) for the right side of Eq. 7.56, noting that $y_i' = hf(x_i, y_i)$ and after rearrangement of terms,

$$y_{i+1} = y_i + \Bigg\{h(a + b)f + h^2\left[\alpha b\,\frac{\partial f}{\partial x} + b\beta f\,\frac{\partial f}{\partial y}\right] + h^3\left[\frac{b\alpha^2}{2}\cdot\frac{\partial^2 f}{\partial x^2} + b\alpha\beta f\,\frac{\partial^2 f}{\partial x\,\partial y} + \frac{b\beta^2}{2}f^2\frac{\partial^2 f}{\partial y^2}\right]\Bigg\}_i + 0(h^4). \tag{7.63}$$

Equating coefficients of h and h^2 in Eqs. 7.62 and 7.63,

$$a + b = 1 \qquad \text{and} \qquad b\alpha = b\beta = 1/2. \tag{7.64}$$

[6] No distinction in notation is being made between the true solution and the approximate solution.

One solution of Eqs. 7.64 is

$$a = b = 1/2 \qquad \text{and } \alpha = \beta = 1. \tag{7.65}$$

Thus, by substituting values of a, b, α, and β in Eq. 7.55, the Runge–Kutta method of order 2 becomes

$$y_{i+1} - y_i = \frac{h}{2}\{f(x_i,y_i) + f(x_i + h, y_i + hf(x_i,y_i))\}$$

or

$$y_{i+1} = y_i + \frac{h}{2}\{f(x_i,y_i) + f(x_i + h, y_i + hf(x_i,y_i))\}. \tag{7.66}$$

For $dy/dx = f(x,y)$, $y = y_0$ and $x = x_0$, the approximations y_i to $y(x_0 + ih)$ are generated by (7.66) for h fixed and $i = 1, 2, \ldots$. If $f(x,y)$ is a function of x only, then Eq. 7.66 may be written as

$$y_{i+1} - y_i = \frac{h}{2}\{f(x_i) + f(x_i + h)\}. \tag{7.67}$$

The right side of (7.67) is the trapezoidal rule.

The truncation error is found by substituting values of a, b, α, β in the h^3 term in (7.63) and subtracting from this the h^3 term of Eq. 7.62. Truncation error is

$$E = \frac{h^3}{12}\left\{\frac{\partial^2 f}{\partial x^2} + 2f\frac{\partial^2 f}{\partial x\,\partial y} + f^2\frac{\partial^2 f}{\partial y^2} - 2\frac{\partial f}{\partial x}\frac{\partial f}{\partial y} + 2f^2\left[\frac{f}{y}\right]^2\right\}_i + 0(h^4). \tag{7.68}$$

This equation reflects the statement made previously, that an estimate of the error of a Runge–Kutta method is quite formidable. However, the error is of order h^3, whereas the error in the Euler method is of order h^2. Hence, a larger h in a Runge–Kutta method may be used.

Other choices of a, b, α, β as solutions of Eq. 7.64 are: $a = 0$, $b = 1$, $\alpha = \beta = 1/2$. By substituting these values in Eq. 7.55, a second-order method becomes

$$y_{i+1} = y_i + hf\left[x_i + \frac{h}{2}, y_i + \frac{h}{2}f(x_i, y_i)\right]. \tag{7.69}$$

For $f(x,y)$ a function of x only, Eq. 7.69 becomes

$$y_{i+1} = y_i + hf\left(x_i + \frac{h}{2}\right), \tag{7.70}$$

which is an open Newton–Cotes formula for one point.

7.6.1 Third and Fourth-order Runge–Kutta Methods

Higher-order Runge–Kutta formulas can be derived by a method similar to the one for a second-order method. For example, a third-order formula can be found in the following outlined manner:

1. Let y_{i+1} be expressed as

$$y_{i+1} = y_i + a_1k_1 + a_2k_2 + a_3k_3 \tag{7.71}$$

where

$$k_1 = hf(x_i, y_i), \tag{7.72}$$

$$k_2 = hf(x_i + \alpha_2 h, y_i + \beta_{21}k_1), \tag{7.73}$$

$$k_3 = hf(x_i + \alpha_3 h, y_i + \beta_{31}k_1 + \beta_{32}k_2), \tag{7.74}$$

and h is a fixed constant equal to $x_{i+1} - x_i$, $i = 0, 1, 2, \ldots$.

2. Expand (7.73) and (7.74) in Taylor series about the point x_i, y_i.
3. Expand y_{i+1} in a Taylor series about the point x_i.
4. Determine a set of equations in a_i, α_i, β_{ij} by equating coefficients of like terms in h^r for $r = 1, 2, 3$.
5. From this set of equations, reasonable values of a_i, α_i, β_{ij} can be chosen.
6. Substitute these values in Eq. 7.71, where k_i are given by Eqs. 7.72–74.

Thus, one third-order method has the set of formulas

$$y_{i+1} = y_i + \frac{1}{4}(k_2 + 3k_3), \tag{7.75}$$

where

$$\begin{aligned} k_1 &= hf(x_i, y_i), \\ k_2 &= hf\left(x_i + \frac{1}{3}h, y_i + \frac{1}{3}k_1\right), \\ k_3 &= hf\left(x_i + \frac{2}{3}h, y_i + \frac{2}{3}k_2\right). \end{aligned} \tag{7.76}$$

Another choice of a_i, α_i, β_{ij} leads to the following set of formulas:

$$y_{i+1} = y_i + \frac{1}{4}(3k_2 + k_3) \tag{7.77}$$

where

$$
\begin{aligned}
k_1 &= hf(x_i, y_i),\\
k_2 &= hf\left(x_i + \frac{2}{3}h, y_i + \frac{2}{3}k_1\right),\\
k_3 &= hf(x_i, y_i + k_2 - k_1).
\end{aligned} \tag{7.78}
$$

These third-order formulas are correct for h^r, $r = 1, 2, 3$. Hence the error is of order h^4.

To derive a fourth-order Runge–Kutta formula, let

$$y_{i+1} = y_i + a_1k_1 + a_2k_2 + a_3k_3 + a_4k_4 \tag{7.79}$$

where

$$
\begin{aligned}
k_1 &= hf(x_i, y_i),\\
k_2 &= hf(x_i + \alpha_2 h, y_i + \beta_{21}k_1),\\
k_3 &= hf(x_i + \alpha_3 h, y_i + \beta_{31}k_1 + \beta_{32}k_2),\\
k_4 &= hf(x_i + \alpha_4 h, y_i + \beta_{41}k_1 + \beta_{42}k_2 + \beta_{43}k_3),
\end{aligned} \tag{7.80}
$$

$h = x_{i+1} - x_i$, $i = 0, 1, 2, \ldots$. Using these equations (7.79 and 7.80) and following a procedure similar to that outlined for the third-order method, a choice of values of a_i, α_i, β_{ij} as solutions to the resulting equations leads to the formula

$$y_{i+1} = y_i + \frac{1}{6}(k_1 + 2k_2 + 2k_3 + k_4) \tag{7.81}$$

where

$$
\begin{aligned}
k_1 &= hf(x_i, y_i),\\
k_2 &= hf\left(x_i + \frac{h}{2}, y_i + \frac{k_1}{2}\right),\\
k_3 &= hf\left(x_i + \frac{h}{2}, y_i + \frac{k_2}{2}\right),\\
k_4 &= hf(x_i + h, y_i + k_3).
\end{aligned} \tag{7.82}
$$

If $f(x,y)$ is a function only of x, then Eq. 7.81 with Eqs. 7.82 reduces to

$$y_{i+1} = y_i + \frac{h}{6}\left\{f(x_i) + 4f\left(x_i + \frac{h}{2}\right) + f(x_i + h)\right\}. \tag{7.83}$$

It should be noted that the terms within brackets of (7.83) constitute Simpson's ⅓ rule, where the usual step size h is replaced by $h/2$. The fourth-order formulas are correct for h^r, $r = 0, 1, 2, 3, 4$; hence, the error is of order h^5.

7.6.2 Flow Chart

For the fourth-order Runge–Kutta method, given

$$\frac{dy}{dx} = \frac{1}{x^2} - \frac{1}{x}y, \qquad (y(1) = 1). \tag{7.84}$$

To find the starting values y_i at $x_i = 1.01, 1.02, 1.03$, and to print values of x_i, y_i including initial values. The method is based upon the recursion formula

$$y_{i+1} = y_i + \frac{h}{6}(k_1 + 2k_2 + 2k_3 + k_4) \tag{7.85}$$

where

$$\begin{aligned} k_1 &= f(x_i, y_i), \\ k_2 &= f\left(x_i + \frac{h}{2}, y_i + \frac{k_1}{2}\right), \\ k_3 &= f\left(x_i + \frac{h}{2}, y_i + \frac{k_2}{2}\right), \\ k_4 &= f(x_i + h, y_i + k_3). \end{aligned} \tag{7.86}$$

Equation 7.85 is more conveniently expressed in the form

$$Y_{i+1} = Y_i + \frac{h}{6}\sum_{j=1}^{4} a_j K_j,$$

$h = .01$, $a_1 = 1$, $a_2 = 2$, $a_3 = 2$, $a_4 = 1$, and Eqs. 7.86 are given as

$$K_j = f(x_i + b_j h, y_i + b_j k_{j-1}),$$

where

$$j = 1, 2, 3, 4$$

$$b_1 = 0,\ b_2 = 1/2,\ b_3 = 1/2,\ b_4 = 1$$

$$x_0 = 1,\ y_0 = 1,\ x_i = x_0 + ih,\ i = 1, 2, 3.$$

FLOW CHART 7.6.2 Fourth-order Runge-Kutta Method

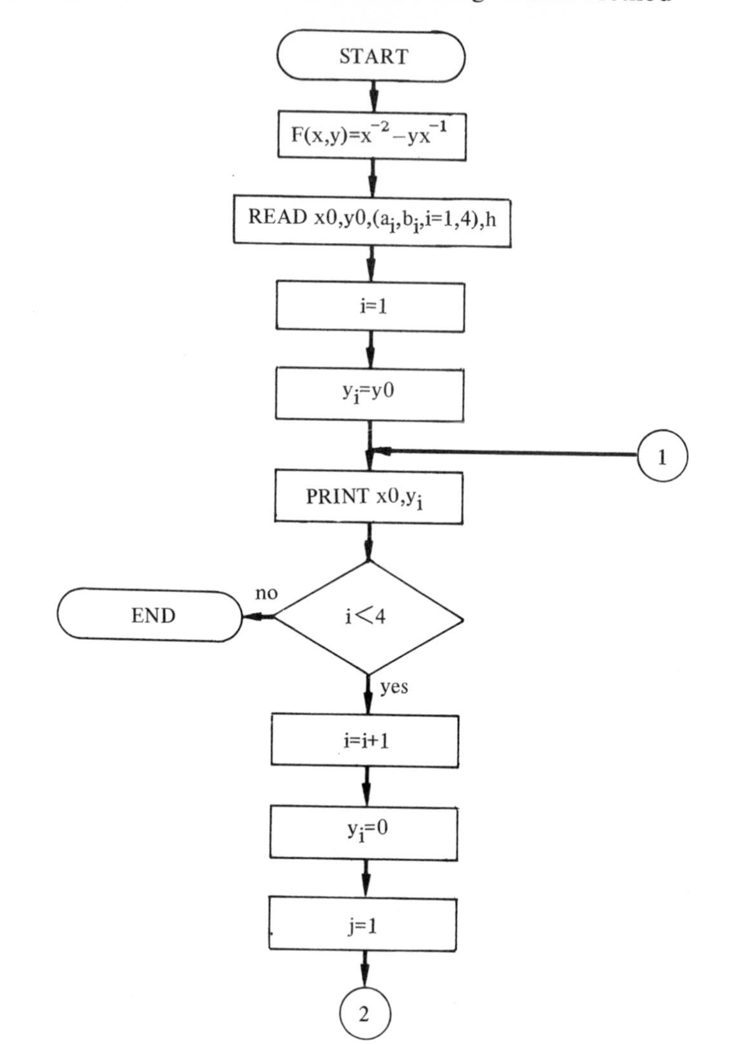

Flow Chart 7.6.2 (*Continued*)

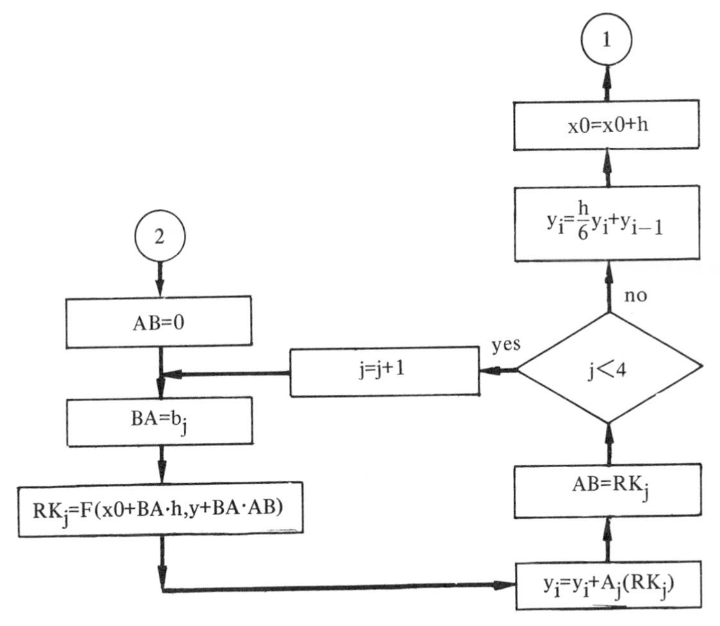

7.6.3 Program

```
      DIMENSION  A(10),B(10),Y(50),RK(50)
      DOUBLE PRECISION XO,YO,Y,A,B,AB,BA,RK
      F(X,Y)=(1/X**2)-Y/X
      READ(5,100)XO,YO,(A(I),I=1,4),(B(I),I=1,4)
  100 FORMAT(10F5.0)
      H=0.01
      I=1
      Y(I)=YO
    1 WRITE(6,101)XO,Y(I)
  101 FORMAT('XO=',F10.4,'  Y(I)=',F14.10,/)
      IF(I-4)2,6,6
    2 I=I+1
      Y(I)=0
      J=1
      AB=0
    3 BA=B(J)
      RK(J)=F(XO+BA*H,YO+BA*AB)
      Y(I)=Y(I)+A(J)*RK(J)
      AB=RK(J)
      IF(J-4)4,5,5
    4 J=J+1
       GO TO 3
```

```
5 Y(I)=(H/6)*Y(I)+Y(I-1)
  XO=XO+H
  GO TO 1
6 STOP
  END
```

THE RESULTS ARE:

```
XO = 1.0000    Y(1) = 1.0000
XO = 1.0100    Y(2) = 1.0000
XO = 1.0200    Y(3) =  .9999
XO = 1.0300    Y(4) =  .9997
```

THE TRUE ANSWERS ACCURATE TO THE FIFTH DECIMAL PLACE ARE:

X	Y
1.00	1.0000
1.01	.99994
1.02	.99982
1.03	.99956

7.7 A General Runge–Kutta Method of Order N

A Runge–Kutta method of order n is defined by

$$y_{l+1} = y_l + h \sum_{i=1}^{n} a_i k_i \tag{7.87}$$

where

$$k_i = f(x_l + \alpha_i(h), y_l + \sum_{j=1}^{i-1} \beta_{ij} k_j), \tag{7.88}$$

$l = 1, 2, \ldots, m$, n is the order of the method, and all coefficients a_i, α_i ($\alpha_1 = 0$), and β_{ij} have been determined by a method similar to that of Sec. 7.6. Some of these coefficients may vanish as they do in the third- and fourth-order methods of Sec. 7.6.1. However, such coefficients can easily be read in as zero, and consequently only one general program need be written, which in turn can be used for any order method.

7.7.1 Flow Chart

For the approximate solutions y_k, $k = 1, 2, \ldots, m$, of

$$\frac{dy}{dx} = f(x,y) \qquad (y = y_1 \text{ at } x = x_1)$$

by a Runge–Kutta method of any order n, a program based on Flow Chart 7.7.1 computes and prints all y_k, $k = 1, 2, \ldots, m$.

Definitions and Notation

The subscripted variables a_i, alpha$_i$ (alpha$_1$ = 0), and beta$_{ij}$ represent a_i, α_i, β_{ij}.
The variables XT and YT represent respectively $X_l + \alpha_i h$ and $Y_l + \sum_{j=1}^{i-1} \beta_{ij} k_j$ for each value of l.
Then $k_i = F(XT,YT)$.

FLOW CHART 7.7.1 General Runge–Kutta Method

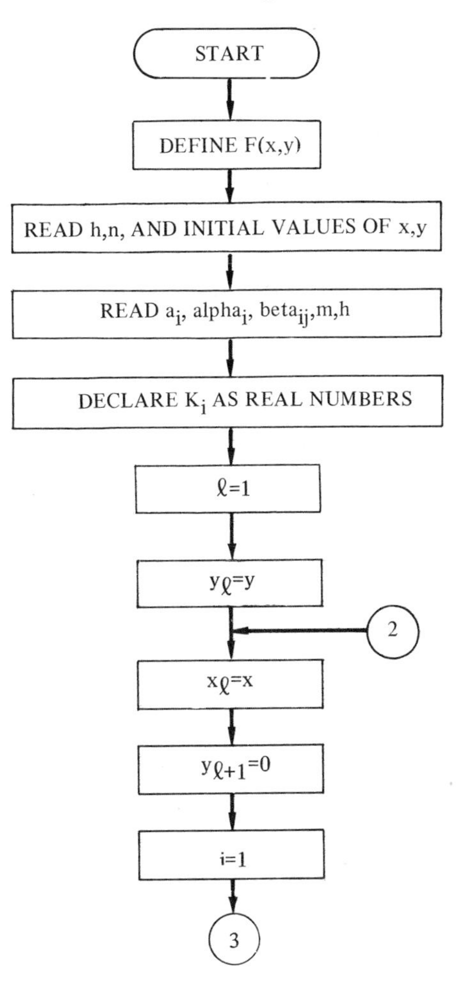

Flow Chart 7.7.1 (*Continued*)

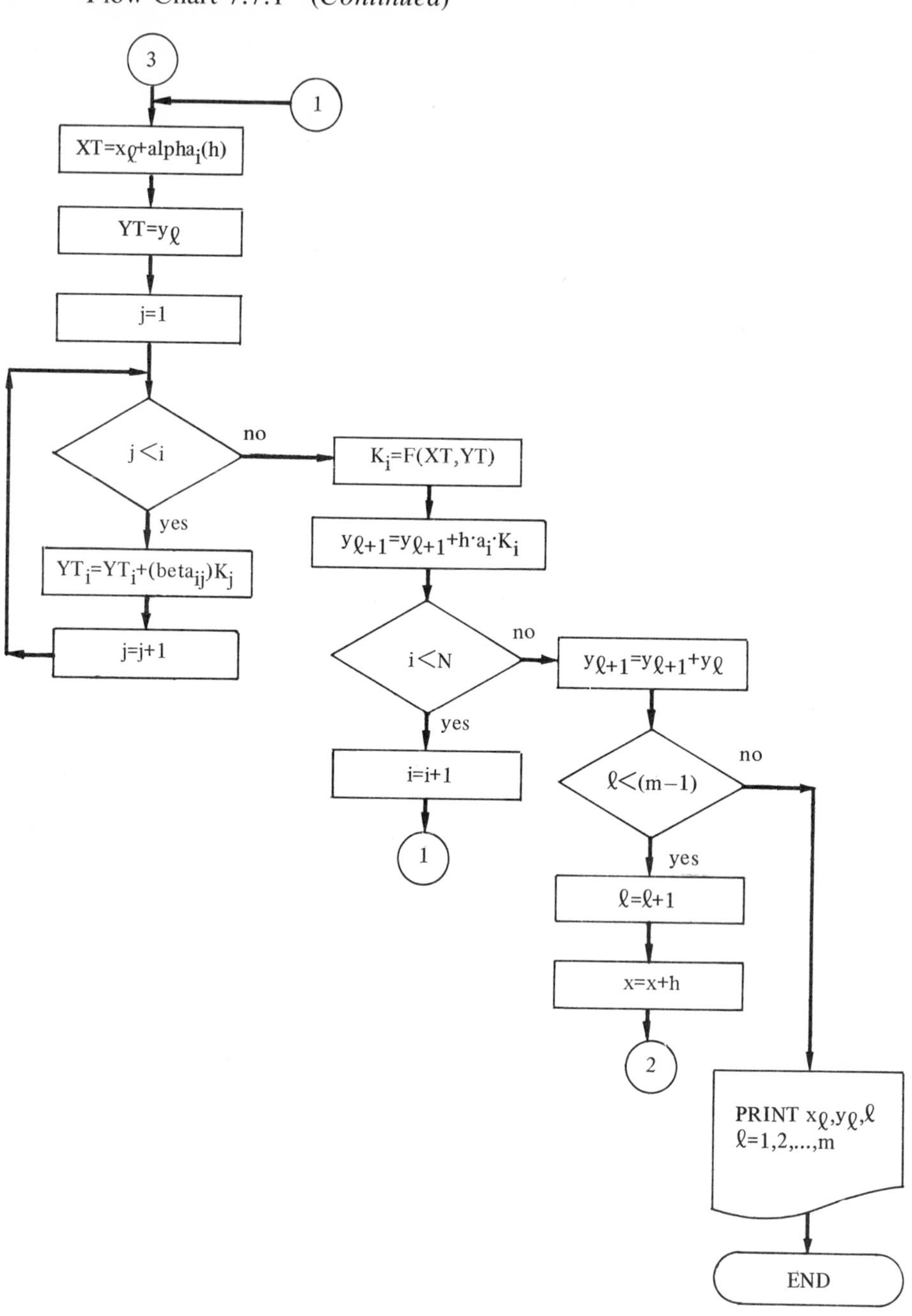

PROBLEM

7-8. Write a program to compute and print the approximations y_i to the solutions of the differential equation

$$\frac{dy}{dx} = \frac{1}{x^2} - \frac{1}{x}y,$$

$y(x_0) = 1$ at $x_0 = 1$, $x = 1.0, 1.1, 1.2, \ldots, 1.6$.

(a) By the Runge–Kutta method of order 2 (Eq. 7.66).

(b) By the Runge–Kutta method of order 4 (Eqs. 7.79–82) following Flow Chart 7.7.1.

7.8 Systems of Differential Equations

Runge–Kutta methods can be extended to solve a system of n first-order differential equations. To illustrate the method, consider two differential equations:

$$\begin{aligned} \frac{dy}{dx} &= f(x,y,z) \\ \frac{dz}{dx} &= g(x,y,z), \qquad (y = y_0, z = z_0 \text{ at } x = x_0). \end{aligned} \tag{7.89}$$

The general formulas (7.87, 7.88) for a single equation become, for Eqs. 7.89,

$$\begin{aligned} y_{l+1} &= y_l + h \sum_{i=1}^{n} a_i k_i \\ z_{l+1} &= z_l + h \sum_{i=1}^{n} a_i kk_i, \end{aligned} \tag{7.90}$$

where

$$\begin{aligned} k_i &= f(x_l + \alpha_i h, y_l + \sum_{j=1}^{i-1} \beta_{ij} k_j, z_l + \sum_{j=1}^{i-1} \beta_{ij} kk_j), \\ kk_i &= g(x_l + \alpha_i h, y_l + \sum_{j=1}^{i-1} \beta_{ij} k_j, z_l + \sum_{j=1}^{i-1} \beta_{ij} kk_j). \end{aligned} \tag{7.91}$$

For the Runge–Kutta method of order 4 (7.85 and 7.86) Eqs. 7.90 and 7.91 become

$$y_{l+1} = y_l + \frac{h}{6}(k_1 + 2k_2 + 2k_3 + k_4)$$

and (7.92)

$$z_{l+1} = z_l + \frac{h}{6}(kk_1 + 2kk_2 + 2kk_3 + kk_6)$$

where

$$\begin{aligned}
k_1 &= f(x_l, y_l, z_l), \\
kk_1 &= g(x_l, y_l, z_l), \\
k_2 &= f(x_l + h/2,\ y_l + k_1/2,\ z_l + kk_1/2), \\
kk_2 &= g(x_l + h/2,\ y_l + k_1/2,\ z_l + kk_1/2), \\
k_3 &= f(x_l + h/2,\ y_l + k_2/2,\ z_l + kk_2/2), \\
kk_3 &= g(x_l + h/2,\ y_l + k_2/2,\ z_l + kk_2/2), \\
k_4 &= f(x_l + h,\ y_l + k_3,\ z_l + kk_3), \\
kk_4 &= g(x_l + h,\ y_l + k_3,\ z_l + kk_3).
\end{aligned} \tag{7.93}$$

7.8.1 Flow Chart

The only additional features to Flow Chart 7.7.1 for a general Runge–Kutta method to solve a single equation are that z_{l+1} must be computed and the values k_i and kk_i must be alternately computed.

FLOW CHART 7.8.1 General Runge–Kutta Method for Two Differential Equations

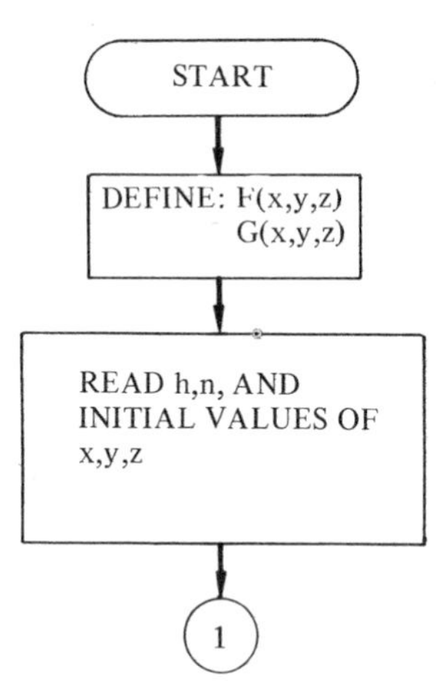

Flow Chart 7.8.1 (*Continued*)

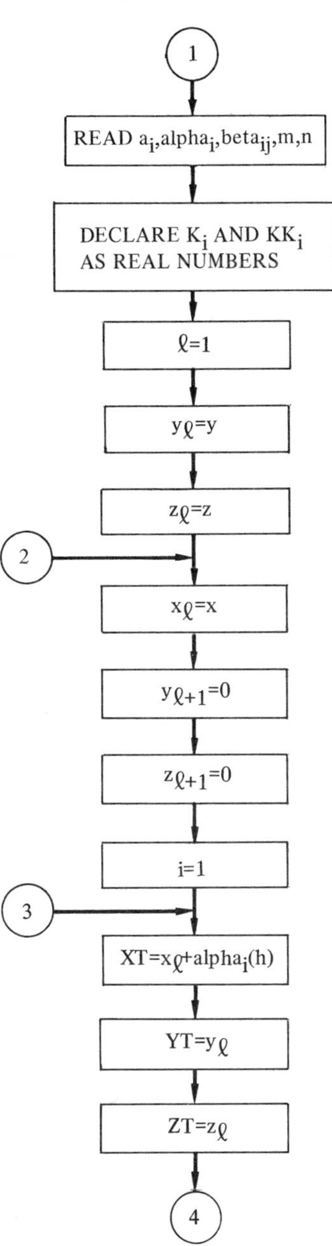

Flow Chart 7.8.1 (*Continued*)

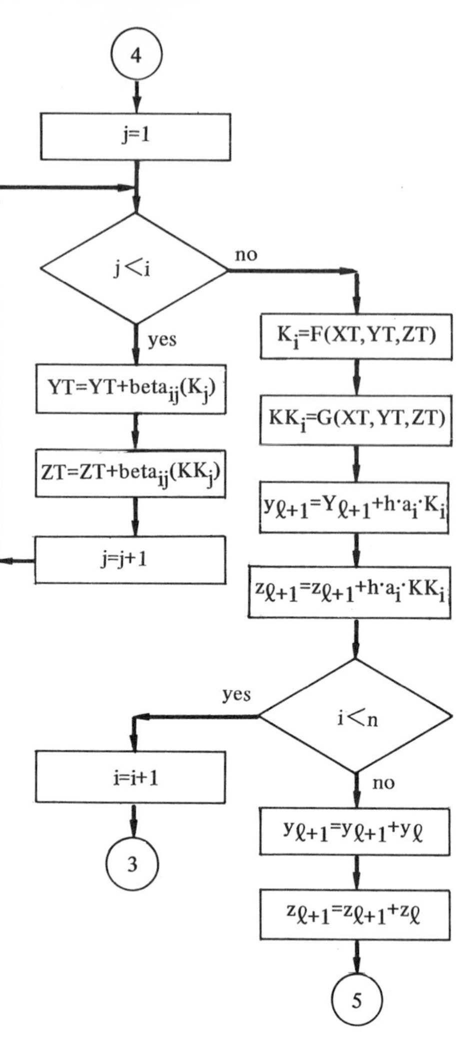

Flow Chart 7.8.1 (*Continued*)

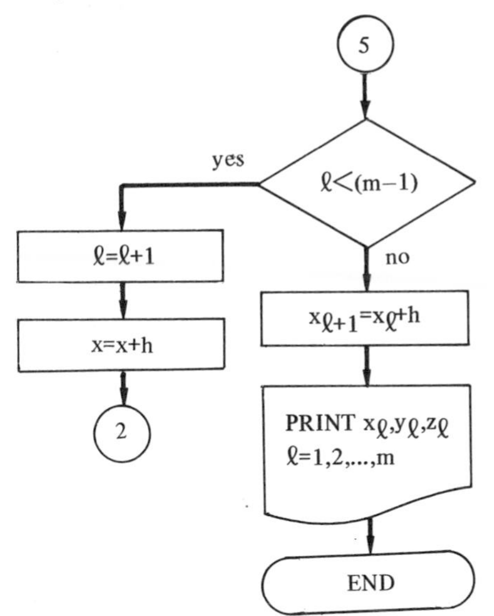

7.8.2 Program

For a general Runge–Kutta method for three differential equations, given the system of equations

$$\frac{du}{dx} = x + u + z, \qquad (u(0) = 0)$$

$$\frac{dz}{dx} = -x + u, \qquad (z(0) = 1)$$

$$\frac{dw}{dx} = u + w, \qquad (w(0) = 1)$$

the following program computes values of u, z, and w for $x = 0$, .02, .04, . . . , 1. The program is simple in structure, using equations similar to (7.92) and (7.93), except that there are three equations of the form of (7.92) and twelve of the form of (7.93). The results are accurate to 10^{-5}.

```
C     KUTTA METHOD, FOURTH ORDER
      DOUBLE PRECISION F1,F2,F3,X,U,Z,W,H,DEL1U,DEL2U,DEL3U,DEL4U,
     1DEL1Z,DEL2Z,DEL3Z,DEL4Z,DEL1W,DEL2W,DEL3W,DEL4W
   11 FORMAT(6F8.3,2I2)
```

```
12 FORMAT(1H1,T11,'H=',F12.3//T15,'X',T45,'U',T75,'Z',T105,'W')
13 FORMAT(5X,F25.10,5X,F25.10,5X,F25.10,5X,F25.10)
   F1(X,U,Z,W)=X+U+Z+O*W
   F2(X,U,Z,W)=-X+U+O*Z+O*W
   F3(X,U,Z,W)=O*X+U+O*Z+W
   READ(5,11)X,U,Z,W,H,B,N1
   WRITE(6,12)H
21 WRITE(6,13)X,U,Z,W
   DEL1U=H*F1(X,U,Z,W)
   DEL1Z=H*F2(X,U,Z,W)
   DEL1W=H*F3(X,U,Z,W)
   DEL2U=H*F1(X+H/2,U+DEL1U/2,Z+DEL1Z/2,W+DEL1W/2)
   DEL2Z=F2(X+H/2,U+DEL1U/2,Z+DEL1Z/2,W+DEL1W/2)*H
   DEL2W=F3(X+H/2,U+DEL1U/2,Z+DEL1Z/2,W+DEL1W/2)*H
   DEL3U=H*F1(X+H/2,U+DEL2U/2,Z+DEL2Z/2,W+DEL2W/2)
   DEL3Z=H*F2(X+H/2,U+DEL2U/2,Z+DEL2Z/2,W+DEL2W/2)
   DEL3W=H*F3(X+H/2,U+DEL2U/2,Z+DEL2Z/2,W+DEL2W/2)
   DEL4U=H*F1(X+H,U+DEL3U,Z+DEL3Z,W+DEL3W)
   DEL4Z=H*F2(X+H,U+DEL3U,Z+DEL3Z,W+DEL3W)
   DEL4W=H*F3(X+H,U+DEL3U,Z+DEL3Z,W+DEL3W)
   DELU=(DEL1U+2*DEL2U+2*DEL3U+DEL4U)/6
   DELZ=(DEL1Z+2*DEL2Z+2*DEL3Z+DEL4Z)/6
   DELW=(DEL1W+DEL2W*2+2*DEL3Z+DEL4Z)/6
   U=U+DELU
   Z=Z+DELZ
   W=W+DELW
   IF(X-B)18,19,19
18 X=X+H
   GO TO 21
19 X=X+H
   WRITE(6,13)X,U,Z,W,
   STOP
   END
```

THE RESULTS ARE:

H=0.020

X	U	Z	W
0.0	0.0	1.0000000000	1.0000000000
0.0200000000	0.0204026923	1.0000026800	1.0204053707
0.0400000000	0.0416217633	1.0000215499	1.0416433103
0.0600000000	0.0636741966	1.0000731059	1.0637472980
0.0800000000	0.0865776576	1.0001741909	1.0867518410
0.1000000000	0.1103505082	1.0003420077	1.1106925085
0.1200000000	0.1350118369	1.0005941340	1.1356059648
0.1400000000	0.1605814770	1.0009485362	1.1615300067
0.1600000000	0.1870800294	1.0014235852	1.1885036081
0.1800000000	0.2145288810	1.0020380721	1.2165669464
0.2000000000	0.2429502420	1.0028112233	1.2457614578
0.2200000000	0.2723671608	1.0037627181	1.2761298716

X	U	Z	W
0.2400000000	0.3028035536	1.0049127054	1.3077162504
0.2600000000	0.3342842311	1.0062818213	1.3405660428
0.2800000000	0.3668349274	1.0078912073	1.3747261241
0.3000000000	0.4004823305	1.0097625291	1.4102448486
0.3200000000	0.4352541082	1.0119179955	1.4471720941
0.3400000000	0.4711789452	1.0143803796	1.4855593145
0.3600000000	0.5082865655	1.0171730379	1.5254595913
0.3800000000	0.5466077775	1.0203199322	1.5669276975
0.4000000000	0.5861744992	1.0238456517	1.6100201383
0.4200000000	0.6270197965	1.0277754343	1.6547952183
0.4400000000	0.6691779234	1.0321351937	1.7013131045
0.4600000000	0.7126843520	1.0369515359	1.7496358752
0.4800000000	0.7575758137	1.0422517969	1.7998276018
0.5000000000	0.8038903512	1.0480640507	1.8519543968
0.5200000000	0.8516673408	1.0544171534	1.9060844928
0.5400000000	0.9009475522	1.0613407619	1.9622883126
0.5600000000	0.9517731778	1.0688653565	2.0206385367
0.5800000000	1.0041878968	1.0770222782	2.0812101811
0.6000000000	1.0582369044	1.0858437619	2.1440806240
0.6200000000	1.1139669754	1.0953629553	2.2093298882
0.6400000000	1.1714265049	1.1056139632	2.2770404071
0.6600000000	1.2306655645	1.1166318744	2.3472973555
0.6800000000	1.2917359583	1.1284527905	2.4201886505
0.7000000000	1.3546912186	1.1411138750	2.4958050102
0.7200000000	1.4195868485	1.1546533718	2.5742401332
0.7400000000	1.4864801876	1.1691106609	2.6555907577
0.7600000000	1.5554305427	1.1845262884	2.7399567217
0.7800000000	1.6264991872	1.2009419999	2.8274410814
0.8000000000	1.6997496001	1.2184007064	2.9181502908
0.8200000000	1.7752473466	1.2369469642	3.0121942014
0.8400000000	1.8530602567	1.2566261231	3.1096863002
0.8600000000	1.9332584850	1.2774852752	3.2107436508
0.8800000000	2.0159145109	1.2995728455	3.3154872507
0.9000000000	2.1011033170	1.3229387379	3.4240419716
0.9200000000	2.1889023893	1.3476343765	3.5365366787
0.9400000000	2.2793918960	1.3737127646	3.6531045288
0.9600000000	2.3726546280	1.4012285336	3.7738830298
0.9800000000	2.4687761776	1.4302380025	3.8990140408
1.0000000000	2.5678451173	1.4607992261	4.0286441892

PROBLEMS

7-9. Solve the system of equations

$$\frac{dx}{dz} = 3x - 4y + e^z, \qquad (x(0) = 1)$$

$$\frac{dy}{dz} = x - y - e^z, \qquad (y(0) = -1)$$

by the Runge–Kutta method of order 4 with $h = .05$. Find values from $z = 0$ to $z = 1$ and print these values. The analytic solutions are

$$x = e^z + 7ze^z + 3z^2e^z,$$
$$y = -e^z + 2ze^z + 3z^2e^z/2.$$

For the approximations of x and y computed and printed by the Runge–Kutta method, insert a set of statements in the program to compute and print corresponding values using the solutions above.

7-10. Given the system of equations:

$$\frac{dx}{dt} = x + y + z, \qquad (x(0) = 1)$$

$$\frac{dy}{dt} = 2x + y - z, \qquad (y(0) = 1)$$

$$\frac{dz}{dt} = -y + z, \qquad (z(0) = -1)$$

(a) Develop the necessary equations for a general Runge–Kutta method to approximate the solutions of these equations at t_i, $i = 1, 2, \ldots$ similar to Eqs. 7.90 and 7.91.

(b) Write a flow chart and program for (a) using the Runge–Kutta methods of order 2 and order 4 to approximate values of x, y, z for $t = 0, .05, .1, \ldots$. The program should also include part (c) below.

(c) The analytic solutions are

$$x = \frac{1}{3}e^{-t} + \frac{2}{3}e^{2t},$$

$$y = -\frac{4}{9}e^{-t} + \frac{13}{9}e^{t} + \frac{2}{3}te^{t},$$

$$z = -\frac{2}{9}e^{-t} - \frac{13}{9}e^{t} - \frac{2}{3}te^{t} + \frac{2}{3}e^{2t}.$$

Insert a set of statements to compute and print approximations of x, y, and z by using the above analytic solutions.

METHODS FOR CONTINUING THE SOLUTION

In the first part of this chapter, various methods for starting a numerical solution of a differential equation were discussed. Some of those methods can also be used for continuing a solution, but in most, the amount of labor is quite costly in computer time. For example, fourth-order Runge–Kutta methods require four evaluations of $f(x,y)$ per step, while fourth-order predictor–corrector methods (to be considered here) require, in general, only two evaluations of $f(x,y)$.

Methods for continuing a solution of an initial value problem will be considered here, and later in the chapter the boundary value problem will be discussed.[7]

7.9 Predictor–Corrector Methods

In Sec. 7.4, the modified Euler Method was presented. A review of that section shows that the first approximation y_{i+1} to the solution $y(x_{i+1})$ of the differential equation (7.33) is found using the formula

$$y_{i+1} = y_i + hf(x_i, y_i) \tag{7.94}$$

where h is constant and $i = 1, 2, \ldots$.

With this approximation, which is stated as $y_{i+1}^{(1)}$, Eq. 7.38 is used repeatedly, until

$$|y_{i+1}^{(j)} - y_{i+1}^{(j-1)}| < \epsilon, \tag{7.95}$$

where ϵ is a small positive number, and $j = 2, 3, \ldots$ indicates the iteration. Summarizing the method of solving Eq. 7.33, the approximation y_{i+1} at $x = x_{i+1}$ is predicted by (7.94). Then the iteration

$$y_{i+1}^{(j)} = y_i + \frac{h}{2}[f(x_i, y_i) + f(x_{i+1}, y_{i+1}^{(j-1)})] \tag{7.96}$$

is used until (7.95) is satisfied.

The steps of this method are:

1. Compute $y_{i+1}^{(1)}$ using (7.94).
2. Improve the solution $y_{i+1}^{(1)}$ by computing $y_{i+1}^{(j)}$ using (7.96) until (7.95) is satisfied.

Thus, the final value y_{i+1} is first predicted by an open type formula (7.94) and then corrected by an iterative closed type formula (7.96). This combination of formulas is termed a *predictor–corrector method*.

To help clarify the relation between the open type Newton–Cotes formula (predictor) and the closed type Newton–Cotes formula (corrector), assume that the values y_i and y_i', $i = 0, 1, 2, 3, 4$, are already known and tabulated. Then consider the following method for the numerical solution of $dy/dx = f(x,y)$, $y = y_0$ at $x = x_0$.

From Table 7.2, the open type polynomial to be used for an open numerical integration formula excludes the end points x_0 and x_4 and

[7] In an initial value problem, all conditions are specified at one point; in a boundary value problem, conditions are specified at more than one point.

TABLE 7.2

x	u	y'	$\Delta y'$	$\Delta^2 y'$	$\Delta^3 y'$	$\Delta^4 y'$
x_0	0	y_0'				
			$\Delta y_0'$			
x_1	1	y_1'		$\Delta^2 y_0'$		
			$\Delta y_1'$		$\Delta^3 y_0'$	
x_2	2	y_2'		$\Delta^2 y_1'$		$\Delta^4 y_0'$
			$\Delta y_2'$		$\Delta^3 y_1'$	
x_3	3	y_3'		$\Delta^2 y_2'$		
			$\Delta y_3'$			
x_4	4	y_4'				

also all differences based upon the values y_0' and y_4'. Hence, the open type polynomial is

$$y' = y_1' + (u - 1)\,\Delta y_1' + \frac{(u-1)^{[2]}}{2}\,\Delta^2 y_1' + R,$$

$$R' = \frac{u^{[4]} h^4 y^5(\xi)}{4!} \tag{7.97}$$

where $u = (x - x_0)/h$, $x_0 < \xi < x_4$. It should be noted that although the formula is an open type, the remainder is based upon the range from x_0 to x_4.

Integrating,

$$\int_{x_0}^{x_4} dy = y_4 - y_0 = \int_{x_0}^{x_4} y'\,dx$$

$$= h\left[\int_0^4 \left(y_1' + (u-1)\,\Delta y_1' + \frac{(u-1)^{[2]}}{2}\,\Delta^2 y_1'\right) du\right] + R,$$

$$R = \frac{h^5 y^5(\xi_1) \int_0^4 u^{[4]}\,du}{4!}.$$

Thus,

$$y_4 = y_0 + \frac{4h}{3}(2y_1' - y_2' + 2y_3') + R,$$

$$R = \frac{14 h^5 y^5(\xi_1)}{45} \tag{7.98}$$

where $x_0 < \xi_1 < x_4$.

In general, Eq. 7.98 may be written in the form

$$y_{i+1} = y_{i-3} + \frac{4h}{3}(2y'_{i-2} - y'_{i-1} + 2y'_i) + R,$$

$$R = \frac{14}{45}h^5y^5(\xi_1) \qquad (7.99)$$

where $x_{i-3} < \xi_1 < x_{i+1}$. Now, the polynomial

$$y' = y'_2 + (u-2)\,\Delta y'_2 + \frac{(u-2)^{[2]}}{2}\,\Delta^2 y'_2 + R'$$

is integrated over the range x_2 to x_4:

$$\int_{x_2}^{x_4} dy = \int_{x_2}^{x_4} y'\,dx = h\int_2^4 \left(y'_2 + (u-2)\,\Delta y'_2 + \frac{(u-2)^{[2]}}{2}\,\Delta^2 y'_2\right) du + h\int_2^4 R'\,du$$

or (7.100)

$$y_4 = y_2 + \frac{h}{3}(y'_2 + 4y'_3 + y'_4) - \frac{h^5y^5(\xi_2)}{90}$$

where $x_2 < \xi_2 < x_4$. In general,

$$y_{i+1} = y_{i-1} + \frac{h}{3}(y'_{i-1} + 4y'_i + y'_{i+1}) - \frac{h^5y^5(\xi_2)}{90}, \qquad (x_{i-1} < \xi_2 < x_{i+1}). \qquad (7.101)$$

Thus, Eq. 7.99 predicts a value y_{i+1}, and Eq. 7.101 corrects the value of y_{i+1}. The method of using Eq. 7.99 to predict a value of y_{i+1} and then applying Eq. 7.101 to correct the value is called the Milne method.[8] See Sec. 7.9.1 for a program using (7.99) and (7.101).

Although the points listed below refer specifically to the modified Euler method (Eqs. 7.94–96), they apply in general to any predictor–corrector method with certain modifications.

1. The corrector formula is usually the more accurate of the two, even when both formulas have a truncation error of the same order, because the coefficient of the error term in the correction formula is, in most cases, smaller.

[8] See William E. Milne, *Numerical Calculus* (Princeton, N.J.: Princeton University Press, 1949).

2. The predictor and the iterative corrector may, in general, be expressed as:
   (a) *Predictor:*

$$y_{i+1}^{(1)} = y_{i-r1} + h \sum_{k=0}^{r} a_k y'_{i-k}, \tag{7.102}$$

   where $r1$ depends on range of integration and a_k are weights.
   (b) *Corrector:*

$$y_{i+1}^{(j+1)} = y_{i-p1} + \left(h \sum_{k=0}^{p} b_k y'_{i-k}\right) + hC[y_{i+1}^{(j)\prime}], \tag{7.103}$$

   where $p1$ depends on range of integration and b_k, C are weights. In these formulas, r and p depend upon the integration formula. Some a_k and b_k may be zero, but it is assumed that a_r and b_p are not zero. An open type Newton–Cotes formula is used as a predictor and a closed type is used as a corrector. Exceptions to these general rules are mentioned in (5) below.
3. The iteration on j in the corrector formula leads to convergence if conditions similar to those in Sec. 7.4 (Eqs. 7.39 and 7.47) are satisfied.

   By Eq. 7.47 in the modified Euler method, it was shown that $y_{i+1}^{(j)}$ converges to y_{i+1} (the convergent value) provided that $\dfrac{hK_i}{2}$ is less than unity. For a general predictor–corrector method, a similar line of reasoning will show that if h is chosen small enough so that $|hCK| < 1$ where C is a weight (Eq. 7.103) and K satisfies the Lipschitz condition, then $y_{i+1}^{(j+1)}$ approaches y (the value to which the corrector would converge, iterating on j). In practice, however, with a good initial choice of h, only one or two applications of the corrector are needed. To insure that h is sufficiently small for each iterate y_{i+1}, a safe estimate of K can be found using Eq. 7.43 in the following manner.

   If it is assumed that the corrected values of the iterates of y and y' have been found up to the ith iterates, then a value of K of more than enough tolerance can be found by the approximation

$$K \cong \left|\frac{(y_i)' - (y_{i-1})'}{y_i - y_{i-1}}\right|. \tag{7.104}$$

   The approximation of K by (7.104) is, in general, a conservative estimate, since usually $|\partial f/\partial y| < K$ within the region of concern, and also

$$\left|\frac{\partial f}{\partial y}\right| \cong \left|\frac{(y_i)' - (y_{i-1})'}{y_i - y_{i-1}}\right|. \tag{7.105}$$

Then by the fact that $|hCK| < 1$, h can be determined. However, for rapid convergence of the corrector, it is best to choose an h so that $|hCK|$ is much smaller than 1.

4. Both predictor and corrector should have the same order—i.e., both should have error terms with the same degree of h. A basic reason for this is that if a predictor has an error of order h^3, a corrector with an error of higher order (say h^6) would not be a logical choice.
5. Newton's backward interpolation formula may be integrated to find both predictor and corrector. The Adams–Bashforth method (Sec. 7.12) is an example of this procedure. Also, looking back, the modified Euler method employs this technique.
6. In any predictor–corrector method, it is necessary to develop a means for finding some starting values and adjusting values of h in using the corrector (whether the interval has to be halved or doubled). These troublesome features can be avoided by first using a Runge–Kutta method that has self-starting values and then use the predictor–corrector method. A Runge–Kutta method can be used to find the initial values of the iterates, and to halve the interval or to double it (in case there is too much accuracy). Then the predictor–corrector method can be used with a fixed step size.

It should also be noted that Runge–Kutta methods may be used exclusively of predictor–corrector methods. In addition to the fact that they are self-starting, the advantages to this procedure are that Runge–Kutta methods are quite accurate, stable, and as a program they do not require much core storage in a computer.

However, even though they are fairly accurate, there is no built-in technique to estimate the accuracy. The only way that this could be accomplished would be to try a few different values of h and compare results. Also mentioned previously, a Runge–Kutta method is costly in machine time, since (in a fourth-order method) four evaluations of the derivative are required for each integration, whereas in a fourth-order predictor–corrector method, only two evaluations of the derivative are necessary.

7.9.1 Program

For the Milne predictor--corrector method, given

$$\frac{dy}{dx} = \frac{y - x}{y + x}, \qquad (y = 1 \text{ at } x = 0),$$

the formulas

$$y_{i+1} = y_i + hy'_i \qquad \text{for the first 10 iterates, } x = .01, \ldots, 0.1,$$

$$y_{i+1} = y_{i-3} + \frac{4h}{3}(2y'_{i-2} - y'_{i-1} + 2y'_i) \qquad \text{as a predictor,}$$

and

$$y_{i+1} = y_{i-1} + \frac{h}{3}(y'_{i-1} + 4y'_i + y'_{i+1}) \qquad \text{as a corrector,}$$

are used for $x = .2, .225, .250, \ldots, 1.025$.

In the program, when the convergence factor $|z_{i+1} - y|$ is greater than or equal to $10^{-5} = EPS$ (y is the predictor value of z_{i+1}), $H1$ becomes $H1/2$ and the predictor is used again. The results show that $H1$ became equal to .025 and remained so for the rest of the program.

```
C     MILNE'S PREDICTOR-CORRECTOR METHOD WITH CONVERGENCE
      FACTOR
      DOUBLE PRECISION X,Y,H,H1,DELY,D,F,Z(110),PF(110)
    1 FORMAT(6F10.3,I4)
    2 FORMAT(1H1,3X,4H X=,F10.3,3X,4H Y=,F10.3,3X,4H H=,F10.3,3X,EPS,
     15H H1 =,F10.3,3X,4H A =,F10.3,3X,4H B =,F10.3,3X,4H I =,I6,//T15,
     2'X',T40,'Y',T60,'Y PRIME')
    3 FORMAT(5X,3F20.10)
    4 FORMAT(10X,5F15.8)
    5 FORMAT(1HO,T17,'X',T35,'Y',T50,'D',T65,'F(X,Y)')
      F(X,Y)=(Y-X)/(Y+X)
      READ(5,1)X,Y,H,H1,A,B,N
      WRITE(6,2)X,Y,H,H1,A,B,N
   10 I=I+1
      Z(I)=Y
      PF(I)=F(X,Y)
      WRITE(6,3)X,Y,PF(I)
      DELY=F(X,Y)*H
      Y=Y+DELY
      IF(X-A)11,30,30
   11 X=X+H
      GO TO 10
   30 WRITE(6,5)
   13 IF(X-B)14,18,18
   14 X=X+H1
   15 Z(I+1)=Z(I-3)+H1*4.0*(PF(I-2)*2.0-PF(I-1)+PF(I)*2.0)/3.0
      Y=Z(I+1)
      PF(I+1)=F(X,Y)
      Z(I+1)=Z(I-1)+H1*(PF(I-1)+PF(I)*4.0+PF(I+1))/3.0
      D=DABS(Z(I+1)-Y)
      IF(D-EPS)16,17,17
```

```
16 WRITE(6,4)X,Y,PF(I)
   I=I+1
   GO TO 13
17 H1=H1/2.0
   GO TO 15
18 STOP
   END
```

X=0.0 Y=1.000 H=0.010 H1=0.100 A=0.100 B=1.000 I=4

X	Y	Y PRIME
0.0	1.0000000000	1.0000000000
0.0100000000	1.0100000000	0.9803921569
0.0200000000	1.0198039216	0.9615312087
0.0300000000	1.0294192337	0.9433651966
0.0400000000	1.0388528856	0.9258471650
0.0500000000	1.0481113573	0.9089345545
0.0600000000	1.0572007028	0.8925886820
0.0700000000	1.0661265896	0.8767742950
0.0800000000	1.0758943326	0.8614591868
0.0900000000	1.0835089245	0.8466138636
0.1000000000	1.0928750631	0.8322112549

X	Y	F(X,Y)
0.20000000	1.15081749	0.83221125
0.22500000	1.15052042	0.70388302
0.25000000	1.16038365	0.67285109
0.27500000	1.15950466	0.64548653
0.30000000	1.18861679	0.61659239
0.32500000	1.19025546	0.59694126
0.35000000	1.21711997	0.57102943
0.37500000	1.21789142	0.55332073
0.40000000	1.24365168	0.52915811
0.42500000	1.24350452	0.51327887
0.45000000	1.26824173	0.49056176
0.47500000	1.26726252	0.47620874
0.50000000	1.29104259	0.45473200
0.52500000	1.28928962	0.44166599
0.55000000	1.31217176	0.42126109
0.57500000	1.30969526	0.40929187
0.60000000	1.33173024	0.38982178
0.62500000	1.32857400	0.37879525
0.65000000	1.34980588	0.36014709
0.67500000	1.34600824	0.34993690
0.70000000	1.36647560	0.33201658
0.72500000	1.36207036	0.32251801
0.75000000	1.38180717	0.30524623
0.77500000	1.37682428	0.29637163
0.80000000	1.39586069	0.27968096
0.82500000	1.39032680	0.27135633
0.85000000	1.40868966	0.25518890
0.87500000	1.40262862	0.24735123

X	Y	F(X,Y)
0.90000000	1.42034200	0.23165700
0.92500000	1.41377521	0.22425229
0.95000000	1.43086074	0.20898768
0.97500000	1.42380748	0.20196929
1.00000000	1.44028471	0.18709608
1.02500000	1.43276240	0.18042350

STABILITY

It might very well be expected that the smaller the truncation error in each integration step, the more accurate the formula should be. For example, the corrector formula in the Milne method has a truncation error of order h^5 and the Euler formula has an error of order h^2. One would assume that use of the Milne method would lead to the true solution more rapidly than the Euler method. However, in some cases the Milne method may not converge at all, while the Euler method for h sufficiently small always converges to the true solution.[9]

Another phenomenon is that accuracy is not always improved as the step size h is made smaller. The errors for a fixed value of x are not always reduced by making h smaller. There is, theoretically, an optimum h to achieve best results.

When a numerical method exhibits such characteristics as those mentioned above, the method is said to be *numerically unstable*. Thus, a numerical procedure is said to be stable if each error, once made, is damped as calculations proceed. It will be seen that in some methods an error once made will tend to grow (exponentially) as calculations proceed and will lead to completely erroneous results.

Before continuing with the subject of stability, it is necessary first to consider briefly difference equations upon which the theory of numerical stability depends.

7.10 Difference Equations

Any equation between the independent variable x, the dependent variable y, and finite differences of y is called a difference equation. The order of a difference equation is the maximum difference of the difference intervals. For example,

$$\Delta y(x) = y(x + h) - y(x) = 0$$

[9] The corrector may not be stable. See Sec. 7.11.

is a first-order difference equation, and

$$\Delta^2 y(x) = y(x + 2h) - 2y(x + h) + y(x) = 0$$

is a second-order difference equation.

Let $h = 1$ and the above equations become

$$y(x + 1) - y(x) = 0,$$
$$y(x + 2) - 2y(x + 1) + y(x) = 0.$$

For convenience, the notation is changed as follows:

$$y(x + 1) = y_{x+1}, \qquad y(x + 2) = y_{x+2},$$

and the two equations above become

$$y_{x+1} = y_x, \qquad y_{x+2} - 2y_{x+1} + y_x = 0.$$

Thus, with this notation, the general form of a linear homogeneous difference equation of order n with constant coefficients can be written as

$$y_{x+n} + a_1 y_{x+n-1} + a_2 y_{x+n-2} + \cdots + a_n y_x = 0. \qquad (7.106)$$

Such an equation may be solved by letting $y_x = \beta^x$ (β a constant). This is analogous to $y = e^{mx}$ for a linear homogeneous differential equation with constant coefficients. Then $y_{x+\alpha} = \beta^{x+\alpha}$ where $\alpha = n, n - 1, \ldots, 0$. Upon substitution, Eq. 7.106 becomes

$$\beta^{x+n} + a_1\beta^{x+n-1} + a_2\beta^{x+n-2} + \cdots + a_n\beta^x = 0$$

or

$$\beta^n + a_1\beta^{n-1} + a_2\beta^{n-2} + \cdots + a_n = 0. \qquad (7.107)$$

Equation 7.107 is called the auxiliary or characteristic equation of the difference equation 7.106. Let the roots of this equation be $\beta_1, \beta_2, \ldots, \beta_n$. Then $y_x = \beta_i^x$, $i = 1, 2, \ldots, n$, and the general solution of Eq. 7.106 is given by

$$y_x = c_1\beta_1^x + c_2\beta_2^x + \cdots + c_n\beta_n^x,$$

c_i arbitrary constants, provided that β_i are distinct.[10]

Example 1

Given: $y_{x+2} - 7y_{x+1} + 12y_x = 0$, let $y_x = \beta^x$. Then

$$\beta^{x+2} - 7\beta^{x+1} + 12\beta^x = 0$$

[10] For a proof that β_i are solutions of the difference equation, see Samuel Goldberg, *Introduction to Difference Equations* (New York: John Wiley & Sons, Inc., 1958).

or

$$\beta^2 - 7\beta + 12 = 0 \qquad \text{and} \qquad \beta_1 = 3, \beta_2 = 4;$$

thus $y_x = c_1 3^x + c_2 4^x$.

Check:

$$\begin{aligned} y_{x+2} &= c_1 3^{x+2} + c_2 4^{x+2}, \\ -7y_{x+1} &= -7c_1 3^{x+1} - 7c_2 4^{x+1}, \\ 12y_x &= 12c_1 3^x + 12c_2 4^x, \\ y_{x+2} - 7y_{x+1} + 12y_x &= c_1[3^{x+2} - 7(3^{x+1}) + 12(3^x)] \\ &\quad + c_2[4^{x+2} - 7(4^{x+1}) + 12(4^x)] \equiv 0. \end{aligned}$$

As in the analogous case for differential equations, when β is a root of multiplicity r, then in part the solution is

$$y_x = (c_1 + c_2 x + c_3 x^2 + \cdots + c_r x^{r-1})\beta^x.$$

Example 2

For $y_{x+2} - 6y_{x+1} + 9y_x = 0$, the auxiliary equation is $\beta^2 - 6\beta + 9 = 0$; $\beta = 3, 3$. Thus $y_x = (c_1 + c_2 x)3^x$.

When two roots are conjugate complex numbers, they are usually expressed in polar form, i.e.,

$$\begin{aligned} \beta_1 &= a + ib = \rho(\cos\theta + i \sin\theta), \\ \beta_2 &= a - ib = \rho(\cos\theta - i \sin\theta). \end{aligned}$$

Thus $y_x = d_1\beta_1^x + d_2\beta_2^x$, and by DeMoivre's theorem

$$\begin{aligned} \beta_1^x &= \rho^x(\cos\theta + i\sin\theta)^x = \rho^x(\cos x\theta + i \sin x\theta) \\ \beta_2^x &= \rho^x(\cos\theta - i\sin\theta)^x = \rho^x(\cos x\theta - i \sin x\theta) \end{aligned}$$

where

$$\rho = \sqrt{a^2 + b^2}, \qquad \theta = \tan^{-1}\frac{b}{a}, \qquad i = \sqrt{-1}.$$

Now since y_x is real, let $d_1 = m + in$, $d_2 = m - in$. Thus

$$d_1 + d_2 = 2m \qquad \text{and} \qquad id_1 - id_2 = -2n,$$

and

$$y_x = \rho^x[(d_1 \cos x\theta + id_1 \sin x\theta) + (d_2 \cos x\theta - id_2 \sin x\theta)]$$

or

$$y_x = \rho^x[2m \cos x\theta - 2n \sin x\theta].$$

Thus y_x is of the form

$$y_x = \rho^x(c_1 \cos x\theta + c_2 \cos x\theta)$$

where c_1, c_2 are real.

Example 3

Given: $y_{x+2} - y_{x+1} + y_x = 0$, the auxiliary equation is $\beta^2 - \beta + 1 = 0$. Thus,

$$\beta_1 = \frac{1}{2} + \frac{\sqrt{3}i}{2}, \qquad \beta_2 = \frac{1}{2} - \frac{\sqrt{3}i}{2}, \qquad \left(\rho = 1,\ \theta = \tan^{-1}\sqrt{3} = \frac{\pi}{3}\right)$$

and hence

$$y_x = \left[c_1 \cos\left(\frac{\pi}{3}x\right) + c_2 \sin\left(\frac{\pi}{3}x\right)\right].$$

Particular solutions of nonhomogeneous linear equations can be found by the method of undetermined coefficients. As in differential equations, the general solution is then expressed as

general solution = (homogeneous solution) + (particular solution).

Consider the first-order linear nonhomogeneous difference equation

$$y_{x+1} = Ay_x + B$$

where A, B are constants, $A \neq 1$. To find the homogeneous solution, let $y_x = \beta^x$; then, substituting in $y_{x+1} = Ay_x$, $\beta = A$ and the homogeneous solution is $y_x = c_1A^x$.

For the particular solution, let y_0 be the initial value; then

$$y_1 = Ay_0 + B \quad \text{for } x = 0,$$
$$y_2 = Ay_1 + B = A^2y_0 + AB + B \quad \text{for } x = 1,$$
$$y_3 = Ay_2 + B = A^3y_0 + A^2B + AB + B \quad \text{for } x = 2,$$
$$\cdots\cdots\cdots\cdots\cdots\cdots$$
$$y_n = A^nY_0 + (A^{n-1} + A^{n-2} + \cdots A + 1)B$$

or

$$y_n = A^ny_0 + B\sum_{i=0}^{n-1} A^i \quad \text{for } x = n.$$

Hence

$$y_x = A^xy_0 + B\sum_{i=0}^{x-1} A^i,$$

and since

$$\sum_{i=0}^{x-1} A^i = \frac{1 - A^x}{1 - A},$$

$$y_x = A^x y_0 + B\left(\frac{1 - A^x}{1 - A}\right), \qquad (A \neq 1),$$

or in general,

$$y_x = c_1 A^x + B\left(\frac{1 - A^x}{1 - A}\right), \qquad (A \neq 1). \tag{7.108}$$

EXERCISE

It is left to the student to show that (7.108) is the solution. However, for $A = 1$, the solution is

$$y_x = C + Bx. \tag{7.109}$$

Can you derive (7.109)?

Example 4

Given:

$$y_{x+1} = 4y_x + 4, \qquad x = 0, 1, 2, \ldots$$
$$y_0 = 2, A = 4, B = 4,$$

then using Eq. 7.108,

$$y_x = c_1 4^x + 4\left(\frac{1 - 4^x}{1 - 4}\right).$$

Since $y_0 = 2$ when $x = 0$, $2 = c_1$. Thus,

$$y_x = 2(4^x) - \frac{4}{3}(1 - 4^x) \qquad \text{or} \qquad y_x = \frac{(10(4^x) - 4)}{3}.$$

Example 5

Given: $y_{x+1} = y_x + 2$, $(y_0 = 2, x = 0)$. Since $A = 1$ and $B = 2$ from (7.109),

$$y_x = C + 2x,$$
$$2 = C,$$
$$y_x = 2 + 2x.$$

For a second-order linear nonhomogeneous difference equation,

$$y_{x+2} + a_1 y_{x+1} + a_2 y_x = f_x, \tag{7.110}$$

if f_x is of the form A^x or is a polynomial in x, the following methods of finding the particular solution may be applied.

Example 6

If $f_x = A^x$, let $y_x = CA^x$ and use the method of undetermined coefficients. Given $y_{x+2} - 5y_{x+1} + 6y_x = 4^x$, first the homogeneous equation is solved:

$$y_{x+2} - 5y_{x+1} + 6y_x = 0.$$

Let $(y_x)_h = \beta^x$, then β_1, β_2 are found to be 2, 3. Hence, $(y_x)_h = c_1(2^x) + c_2(3^x)$.

Second, let the particular solution be $(y_x)_p = c(4^x)$; then

$$c(4^{x+2}) - 5c(4^{x+1}) + 6c(4^x) = 4^x$$

or

$$(16c - 20c + 6c)4^x = 4^x, \qquad (2c = 1,\ c = 1/2).$$

Thus, $(y_x)_p = 1/2(4^x)$, and the general solution is

$$y_x = (y_x)_h + (y_x)_p = c_1(2^x) + c_2(3^x) + 1/2(4^x).$$

Example 7

If $f_x = x^n$, let $(y_x)_p = A_0 + A_1 x + \cdots + A_n x^n$. For $y_{x+2} - 7y_{x+1} + 12y_x = x$, the homogeneous solution is $(y_x)_h = c_1(3^x) + c_2(4^x)$. For the particular solution, let $(y_x)_p = A_0 + A_1 x$; then, by substitution in the equation,

$$A_0 + A_1(x + 2) - 7(A_0 + A_1(x + 1)) + 12(A_0 + A_1 x) = x.$$

Equating coefficients of like terms,

$$\begin{aligned} 6A_0 - 5A_1 &= 0 \quad \text{(constant term)},\\ 6A_1 &= 1 \quad \text{(coefficient of } x). \end{aligned}$$

Thus, $A_1 = 1/6$, $A_0 = 5/36$, and $(y_x)_p = 5/36 + 1/6(x)$; therefore, the general solution is

$$y_x = c_1(3^x) + c_2(4^x) + \frac{5}{36} + \frac{1}{6}x.$$

If in either case (Example 6 or 7) the particular trial solution has terms similar to some terms in the homogeneous solution, it is necessary first to multiply $(y_x)_p$ by x^n where n is the smallest integer that will make $(y_x)_p$ different from $(y_x)_h$.

Example 8

For

$$y_{x+2} - 6y_{x+1} + 9y_x = 3^x,$$

$$\beta_1 = \beta_2 = 3 \qquad \text{and} \qquad (y_x)_h = (c_1 + c_2 x)3^x,$$

the particular solution would be $(y_x)_p = c(3^x)$. But, since 3^x and $x(3^x)$ are present in $(y_x)_h$ it is necessary to use $cx^2 3^x$ as $(y_x)_p$, i.e., $(y_x)_p = cx^2 3^x$.

Upon substitution, it is found that $c = 1/18$; thus

$$(y_x)_p = \frac{(x^2)3^x}{18}.$$

Example 9

For $y_{x+2} - 4y_{x+1} + 3y_x = x^2$ it is found that $\beta_1 = 1$, $\beta_2 = 3$; hence $(y_x)_h = c_1 + c_2 3^x$.

The trial form of $(y_x)_p$ is $(y_x)_p = A_0 + A_1 x + A_2 x^2$. Since A_0 and c_1 are similar, it is necessary to multiply $(y_x)_p$ by x. Hence $(y_x)_p = A_0 x + A_1 x^2 + A_2 x^3$. It is left as an exercise for the student to determine values of A_0, A_1, A_2.

Another point to be noticed is that the method of undetermined coefficients can be used to find the particular solution of $y_{x+1} = Ay_x + B$ where A, B are constants.

The nonhomogeneous term f_x may also have the following forms:

(a) $f_x = A^x + x^n$,
(b) $f_x = A^x x^n$.

In case (a), for A^x, $(y_x)_p = cA^x$, and for x^n, $(y_x)_p = A_0 + A_1 x + \cdots + A_n x^n$. Hence the general trial particular solution is

$$(y_x)_p = cA^x + A_0 + A_1 x + \cdots + A_n x^n.$$

In case (b),

$$(y_x)_p = A^x(A_0 + A_1 x + \cdots + A_n x^n).$$

The method of solution in these cases is similar to the previously explained methods.

PROBLEMS

Solve the following equations:

7-9. $3y_{x+1} = 6y_x + 9, \quad y_0 = 2.$

7-10. $y_{x+2} - 5y_{x+1} + 6y_x = 4^x.$

7-11. $y_{x+2} - 5y_{x+1} + 6y_x = 2^x.$

7-12. $y_{x+2} - 4y_{x+1} + 4y_x = x^2.$

7-13. $y_{x+2} + 2y_{x+1} + 4y_x = 0.$

7-14. $y_{x+1} = y_x + 5.$

7-15. Example 8.

7-16. Example 9.

7.11 Numerical Stability

Equations 7.99 and 7.101 together comprise the Milne method and are restated here for convenience.

Predictor (7.99):

$$y_{i+4} = y_i + \frac{4h}{3}(2y'_{i+1} - y'_{i+2} + 2y'_{i+3}) + \frac{14}{45}h^5y^5(\xi_1), \qquad (x_i < \xi_1 < x_{i+4}).$$

Corrector (7.101):

$$y_{i+2} = y_i + \frac{h}{3}(y'_i + 4y'_{i+1} + y'_{i+2}) - \frac{h^5y^{(5)}(\xi_2)}{90}, \qquad (x_i < \xi_2 < x_{i+2}).$$

For convenience, the subscripts are increased in these equations by 3 and 1 respectively. Let

$$\frac{dy}{dx} = f(x,y) = Ay, \tag{7.111}$$

where A is a constant, represent the differential equation. In general, the roots of β_i of the auxiliary equation (7.101) would be impossible to find. Furthermore, the difference equation for (7.111) will be sufficient to determine whether or not Eq. 7.101 is numerically stable.

The true solution of (7.111) is $y = Ce^{Ax}$ where C is a constant. Any numerical solution should converge toward the true solution. Using the method of solution for a difference equation in Sec. 7.10, the difference equation for Eq. 7.101, and the fact that $y' = Ay$, the difference equation becomes

$$(3 - Ah)y_{i+2} - 4Ahy_{i+1} - (3 + Ah)y_i = 0. \tag{7.112}$$

It should be noted that Eq. 7.112 is a linear homogeneous difference equation.

Let $y_i = \beta^i$, then the auxiliary equation is

$$(3 - Ah)\beta^2 - 4Ah\beta - (3 + Ah) = 0. \tag{7.113}$$

Solving this equation by the quadratic formula,

$$\beta = \frac{4Ah \pm \sqrt{36 + 12A^2h^2}}{2(3 - Ah)}.$$

The binomial theorem is used to expand $\sqrt{36 + 12A^2h^2}$ through the linear term, and then, after dividing by $2(3 - Ah)$, the roots β for small values of h have the values

$$\begin{aligned} \beta_1 &= 1 + Ah + 0(h^2), \\ \beta_2 &= -1 + Ah/3 + 0(h^2). \end{aligned} \tag{7.114}$$

Thus, the solution to the difference equation 7.112 is

$$\begin{aligned} y_i &= c_1[1 + Ah + 0(h^2)]^i + c_2\left[-\left(1 - \frac{Ah}{3}\right) + 0(h^2)\right]^i \\ &= c_1[1 + Ah + 0(h^2)]^i + c_2(-1)^i\left[1 - \frac{Ah}{3} - 0(h^2)\right]^i. \end{aligned}$$

For $n = i$, these equations become

$$y_n = c_1[1 + Ah + 0(h^2)]^n + c_2(-1)^n\left[\left(1 - \frac{Ah}{3}\right) + 0(h^2)\right]^n.$$

In calculus it is shown that

$$\lim_{\delta \to 0} (1 + \delta)^{1/\delta} = e.$$

Thus, for x_n fixed and $n = x_n/h$,

$$\lim_{h \to 0} [1 + Ah + 0(h^2)]^n = \lim_{h \to 0} [(1 + Ah)^{1/Ah}]^{(Ax_n)} = e^{Ax_n}.$$

Also from calculus,

$$\lim_{\delta \to 0} (1 - \delta)^{1/\delta} = e^{-1};$$

hence

$$\begin{aligned} \lim_{h \to 0} \left[1 - \frac{Ah}{3} + 0(h^2)\right]^n &= \lim_{h \to 0} (-1)^n\left[\left(1 - \frac{Ah}{3}\right)^{(1/Ah)/3}\right]^{Ax_n/3} \\ &= \lim_{n \to \infty} (-1)^n(e^{-Ax_n/3}). \end{aligned}$$

However, $\lim_{h\to 0}(-1)^n$ does not exist. But with some liberty, it is safe to say that as h approaches 0 the solution of (7.112) becomes

$$y_n = c_1 e^{Ax_n} + c_2(-1)^n e^{-Ax_n/3}. \tag{7.115}$$

Since the true solution of (7.111) is $y = ce^{Ax}$, it is seen that if $A > 0$, e^{Ax_n} is approaching the desired solution and $e^{-Ax_n/3}$ is exponentially decreasing. Hence, for $A > 0$, Milne's method is stable.

For $A < 0$, the term e^{Ax_n} will approach the desired solution, but here the term $e^{-Ax_n/3}$ is exponentially increasing and will quickly dominate the true solution, thereby leading to erroneous results. Therefore, for $A < 0$, Milne's method is unstable.[11] When the stability of a method depends upon the sign of A, the method is said to be *weakly unstable.*

If $\partial f/\partial y < 0$ for the differential equation $y' = f(x,y)$, weak instability can be expected. In retrospect, it should be pointed out that $f(x,y)$ was replaced by Ay, thereby leading to a linear homogeneous difference equation with constant coefficients. In the auxiliary equation 7.113, if $h \to 0$, the equation reduces to

$$\beta^2 - 1 = 0, \qquad (\beta_1 = 1, \beta_2 = -1).$$

For $A > 0$, β_1^n is the root leading to the desired solution of the differential equation. $\beta_2 = -1$ (the extraneous root) does not affect the solution. However, for $A < 0$, $\beta_2 = -1$ does affect the solution, since the errors caused by $e^{-Ax_n/3}$ are not damped as calculations proceed.

Thus to determine stability in a method, the following technique may be used. From the method itself and the use of Ay for $f(x,y)$, a homogeneous equation of order k is derived. If the roots of the auxiliary equation are β_i, $i = 1, \ldots, k$, then the general solution of the homogeneous difference equation is

$$y_n = C_1\beta_1^n + C_2\beta_2^n + \cdots + C_k\beta_k^n.$$

As $h \to 0$, one of these, say β_1, will be the root that leads to the true solution of the differential equation. All other roots are considered extraneous because they are caused by replacing a first-order differential equation by a higher-order difference equation.

If β_1 is the root leading to the true solution and if $|\beta_i| < 1$ for $i = 2, 3, \ldots, k$, then the method is said to be *strongly stable.* Errors under these conditions, once made, are damped as calculations proceed. If $|\beta_i| = 1$, $i = 2, 3, \ldots, k$, as in the example, there is a possi-

[11] For further study on stability of predictor–corrector methods, see R. W. Haming, "Stable Predictor–Corrector Methods for Ordinary Differential Equations," *Journal of the Association for Computing Machinery* 6(1):37–47, 1959.

bility of instability. If $|\beta_i| > 1$, $i = 2, 3, \ldots, k$, the method is unstable and the errors grow exponentially.

One-step methods such as Runge–Kutta methods are stable if h is chosen small enough. Methods requiring two or more initial values of y (called multistep methods) may be unstable for all values of h in some cases, or they may be unstable for a range of values of h.

7.12 Multistep Methods

The Milne predictor–corrector method (Eqs. 7.99 and 7.101) has already been described in some detail. For the starting values of this method, a Taylor series expansion can be used to find values for y_0, y_1, y_2, y_3, and y'_0, y'_1, y'_2, y'_3. Another technique for finding the initial values is to use a fourth-order Runge–Kutta method. When these initial values have been found, the Milne method can be used to continue the solution. More will be said later concerning the combination of a Runge–Kutta method and a predictor–corrector method.

Another multistep method combines the predictor formula known as the Adams–Bashforth method with the corrector formula known as the Adams–Moulton method. Referring to Table 7.2, y' may be approximated by

$$y' = y'_3 + (u - 3)\,\Delta y'_2 + \frac{(u-2)^{[2]}}{2!}\,\Delta^2 y_1 + \frac{(u-1)^{[3]}}{3!}\,\Delta^3 y'_0. \tag{7.116}$$

The value x_4 in the approximate solution of (7.1) can now be found by integrating Eq. 7.116 from x_3 to x_4, i.e.,

$$\int_{x_3}^{x_4} dy = h\int_3^4 \left[y'_3 + (u-3)\,\Delta y'_2 + \frac{(u-2)^{[2]}}{2!}\,\Delta^2 y'_1 + \frac{(u-1)^{[3]}}{3!}\,\Delta^3 y'_0\right] du. \tag{7.117}$$

The result is

$$y_4 = y_3 + h\left(y'_3 + \frac{1}{2}\,\Delta y'_2 + \frac{5}{12}\,\Delta^2 y'_1 + \frac{3}{8}\,\Delta^3 y'_0\right),$$

or, expressed in terms of y_i, y'_i,

$$y_4 = y_3 + \frac{h}{24}(55y'_3 - 59y'_2 + 37y'_1 - 9y'_0). \tag{7.118}$$

The error term of Eq. 7.118 may be found by extending the Newton backward formula (Table 7.2) to the term immediately following the last term in (7.116), and integrating this term with $h^4 y^5(\xi)$ replacing

$\Delta^4 y'_{0-1}$. Thus the error term is

$$E = h\int_3^4 \frac{u^{[4]}}{4!} h^4 y^5(\xi)\, du.$$

Since $u^{[4]}$ does not change sign on the interval [3,4], there exists a point ξ between x_3 amd x_4 such that

$$E = \frac{h^5 y^5(\xi)}{4!}\int_3^4 u^{[4]}\, du$$

or (7.119)

$$E = h^5 y^5(\xi)\frac{251}{720}.$$

Note that E is proportional to $y^5(\xi)$ since to begin with the function is y'.

The Adams–Bashforth method with error term is in general expressed as

$$y_{i+1} = y_i + \frac{h}{24}(55y'_i - 59y'_{i-1} + 37y'_{i-2} - 9y'_{i-3}) + E,$$

$$E = h^5 y^5(\xi)\frac{251}{720}. \qquad (7.120)$$

Equation 7.120 is an open-type formula, since it excludes the end values x_4, y'_4 and all differences based upon the end values. (The Euler method can also be derived in this manner.)

Because Eq. 7.120 predicts y_{i+1}, a corrector formula is now needed to correct y_{i+1}. Referring again to Table 7.2, y' may be approximated by the formula

$$y' = y'_4 + (u-4)\,\Delta y'_3 + \frac{(u-3)^{[2]}}{2}\,\Delta^2 y'_2 + \frac{(u-2)^{[3]}}{6}\,\Delta^3 y'_1. \qquad (7.121)$$

Using (7.121) as the approximation for y in the differential equation 7.1 and integrating from x_3 to x_4,

$$\int_{x_3}^{x_4} dy = h\int_3^4 \left(y'_4 + (u-4)\,\Delta y'_3 + \frac{(u-3)^{[2]}}{2}\,\Delta^2 y'_2 + \frac{(u-2)^{[3]}}{6}\,\Delta^3 y'_1\right) du.$$

When all differences are expressed in terms of y_i, the result is

$$y_4 = y_3 + \frac{h}{24}(9y'_4 + 19y'_3 - 5y'_2 + y'_1); \qquad (7.122)$$

the error for this formula is

$$E = \frac{-19}{720} h^5 y^5(\xi). \qquad (7.123)$$

Equation 7.122, which is obviously a closed type and a corrector, is known as the Adams–Moulton formula of order 4. In general, it is written in the form

$$y_{i+1} = y_i + \frac{h}{24}(9y'_{i+1} + 19y'_i - 5y'_{i-1} + y'_{i-2}). \qquad (7.124)$$

Equations 7.120 and 7.124 together are respectively the predictor and the corrector in the Adams–Bashforth–Moulton method. The error for the corrector is given by (7.123).

For the two predictor–corrector methods discussed here (there are others), namely the Milne method and the Adams–Bashforth–Moulton, more questions must be answered before a program is written.

First, for the Adams–Bashforth–Moulton method, we must find out if the method is stable. The conditions given in Sec. 7.11 state that if β_1 is the root of the auxiliary equation as $h \to 0$ leading to the true solution, and if $|\beta_i| < 1$, $i = 2, 3, \ldots,$ then the method is strongly stable. If, in the differential equation $y' = f(x,y)$, $f(x,y)$ is replaced by Ay, A a constant, then Eq. 7.124 becomes

$$y_{i+1} = y_i + \frac{h}{24}(9Ay_{i+1} + 19Ay_i - 5Ay_{i-1} + Ay_{i-2})$$

or (7.125)

$$\left(1 - \frac{9hA}{24}\right)y_{i+1} - \left(1 + \frac{19hA}{24}\right)y_i + \frac{5hA}{24}y_{i-1} - \frac{hA}{24}y_{i-2} = 0.$$

Let $y_i = \beta^i$; then the auxiliary equation is

$$\left(1 - \frac{9hA}{24}\right)\beta^3 - \left(1 + \frac{19hA}{24}\right)\beta^2 + \frac{5hA}{24}\beta - \frac{hA}{24} = 0. \qquad (7.126)$$

The roots of (7.126) can be found and are functions of h. If h approaches zero, Eq. 7.126 becomes $\beta^3 - \beta^2 = 0$ whose roots are $\beta_1 = 1$, $\beta_2 = \beta_3 = 0$.

Furthermore, for h small it can be shown that the root β_1^n of (7.126) corresponding to $\beta_1 = 1$ (when $h = 0$) leads to the true solution of the differential equation. Also, it should be seen that the roots β_2^n and β_3^n will be extraneous with magnitudes less than one. Hence the method is strongly stable.

Second, for any predictor–corrector method, the test for convergence of each y_{i+1} is usually based upon the relative error—i.e., for the

$(i + 1)$th y iterate, i.e., if

$$\left| \frac{y_{i+1}^{(j)} - y_{i+1}^{(j-1)}}{y_{i+1}^{(j)}} \right| < \epsilon,$$

ϵ prescribed and where the superscript j indicates iteration with the corrector, then the method converges. In the case of possible convergence, an estimate of the error should be made at this point. If the estimate shows that too much accuracy is being required, the step size h can be increased; if it shows there is not enough accuracy, the step size can be reduced.

An estimate of the error can be found by considering the error in the predictor in connection with the error in the corrector. For example, in the Milne method, the error in the predictor (7.99) is

$$E_p = \frac{14}{45} h^5 y^5(\xi), \tag{7.127}$$

and the error in the corrector (7.101) is

$$E_c = \frac{-h^5 y^5(\eta)}{90} \tag{7.128}$$

where ξ, η are within the interval of interest. These two errors can be expressed as

$$y(x_{i+1}) - y_{i+1}^{(0)} = \frac{14}{45} h^5 y^5(\xi) \tag{7.129}$$

and

$$y(x_{i+1}) - y_{i+1}^{(1)} = \frac{-h^5 y^5(\eta)}{90}. \tag{7.130}$$

In both equations it is assumed that $y(x_{i+1})$ represents the exact value of y at $x = x_{i+1}$ and that all values of $f(x,y)$ are exact at all points x_i, $i = 0, 1, 2, \ldots, n$. The values $y_{i+1}^{(0)}$ and $y_{i+1}^{(1)}$ represent respectively the values obtained from the predictor and one application of the corrector.

Although $\xi \neq \eta$ in general, but if it is assumed that $y^5(x)$ is almost constant over the interval, then $y^5(\xi) \cong y^5(\eta)$. By subtracting Eq. 7.130 from Eq. 7.129, the result is

$$y_{i+1}^{(1)} - y_{i+1}^{(0)} = \frac{29 h^5 y^5(\eta)}{90}$$

or (7.131)

$$h^5 y^5(\eta) = \frac{90}{29}(y_{i+1}^{(1)} - y_{i+1}^{(0)}).$$

Substituting this value for $h^5y^5(\eta)$ in the corrector error equation 7.130,

$$y(x_{i+1}) - y_{i+1}^{(1)} = \frac{-(y_{i+1}^{(1)} - y_{i+1}^{(0)})}{29}$$

or (7.132)

$$y(x_{i+1}) - y_{i+1}^{(1)} \cong \frac{-1}{30}(y_{i+1}^{(1)} - y_{i+1}^{(0)}) = E_{i+1}.$$

Thus, the error of the corrected value of $y(x_{i+1})$ is approximately $-1/30$ of $y_{i+1}^{(1)} - y_{i+1}^{(0)}$.

If the estimate of the error E_{i+1} is not sufficient to yield the required accuracy, the better procedure to follow is to reduce the step size and recompute the four starting values rather than using the corrector to correct again. If E_{i+1} shows that too much accuracy is being obtained, it is then a better procedure to increase the step size and start again with new starting values rather than use the corrector.

In view of the above procedure of reducing the step size in one case and increasing it in the other, an effortless way to accomplish these is to initially choose a step size h and then replace h by $h/2$ or by $2h$, depending on what is called for.

With the possibility of a variable step size, a good combination of formulas to obtain the best results is a fourth-order Runge–Kutta method and a fourth-order predictor–corrector method. Suppose it is desired that local error be bounded so that

$$e_1 \leq E_{i+1} \leq e_2. \tag{7.133}$$

The general steps are:

1. Use the Runge–Kutta method to find the first four starting values.
2. Use the predictor to compute $y_{i+1}^{(0)}$.
3. Use the corrector to compute $y_{i+1}^{(1)}$.
4. Compute E_{i+1}.
5. If $E_{i+1} \leq e_2$, transfer to step 6; otherwise transfer to step 7.
6. If $E_{i+1} \geq e_1$, continue with the normal procedure of integration (increment x and transfer to step 2); otherwise transfer to step 8.
7. Replace h by $h/2$ and transfer to step 1.
8. Replace h by $2h$ and transfer to step 1.

One might assume that a lower bound of the truncation error E_{i+1} (also called discretization error) in (7.133) is not necessary—that is, that the smaller the step size h is chosen, the better the convergence will be. But it should also be kept in mind that as h becomes smaller, the computer must perform more step computations, and therefore the accumulated round-off error that is also propagated becomes much larger. As truncation error is reduced, accumulated round-off error increases.

7.12.1 Program

For the Adams–Bashforth method, given:

$$\frac{dy}{dx} = .1(x^3 + y^2), \qquad (y = 1 \text{ at } x = 0),$$

the following program uses the formula

$$y_{i+1} = y_i + h(y_i' + \Delta y_{i-1}' + \frac{5}{12}\Delta^2 y_{i-2}' + \frac{3}{8}\Delta^3 y_{i-3}' + E),$$

$$\left(E = \frac{251}{720}\Delta^4 y_{i-4}'\right)$$

instead of Eq. 7.120. The first five starting values of y and y' were previously computed by means of Taylor's series expansion for $H = .1$

The output consists of the five starting values of y and y', and values of y and y' for $x = .5, .6, \ldots, 1$ as these are computed by the Adams–Bashforth method. A table of differences of y' is also printed.

```
      DOUBLE PRECISION Y(105),YPRIM(105,20),T(105),F,Z,X,A,H,DN
   10 FORMAT(3F10.3,I5,/(8F10.0))
   11 FORMAT(1H1,5X,4H X =,F12.3,3X,4H A =,F12.3,3X,4H H =,F12.3,3X,
    1 4H N =,I6,10X,1HY,15X,7HY PRIME/(75X,F20.8,3X,F20.8/))
  200 FORMAT(//10X,1HX,20X,1HY,13X,5HYPRIM)
  201 FORMAT(F20.9,F20.9,/(40X,5F15.8))
      F(X,Z)=(X**3+Z**2)*0.1
      READ(5,10)X,A,H,N,(Y(I),YPRIM(I,1),I=1,N)
      WRITE(6,11)X,A,H,N,(Y(I),YPRIM(I,1),I=1,N)
      J=1
   90 L=J+1
      I=J
   95 K=I+1
      YPRIM(K,L)=YPRIM(K,J)-YPRIM(I,J)
      IF(K-N)100,101,101
  100 I=I+1
      GO TO 95
  101 IF(L-N)102,103,103
  102 J=J+1
      GO TO 90
  103 Y(N+1)=Y(N)+H*(YPRIM(N,1)+YPRIM(N,2)/2.+YPRIM(N,3)*5./12.+
    1 YPRIM(N,4)*3./8.+YPRIM(N,5)*251./720.)
      K=N+1
      J=1
```

```
      DN=N
      X=A+DN*H
      T(K)=X
      Z=Y(K)
      YPRIM(K,J)=F(X,Z)
      J=J+1
104   YPRIM(K,J)=YPRIM(K,J-1)-YPRIM(K-1,J-1)
      IF(J-N)105,106,106
105   J=J+1
      GO TO 104
106   IF(X-1.)107,107,108
107   N=N+1
      GO TO 103
108   WRITE(6,200)
      DO 300 I=1,N
300   WRITE(6,201)T(I),Y(I),(YPRIM(I,J),J=1,5)
      STOP
      END
```

THE RESULTS ARE:

X=0.0 A=0.0 H=0.100 N=5

Y	Y PRIME
1.00000000	0.09999996
1.01000000	0.10210991
1.02021000	0.10488296
1.03070000	0.10893404
1.04159000	0.11489147

X	Y	YPRIM	ΔYPRIM
0.0	1.000000000		
		0.09999996	0.0
0.0	1.010000000		
		0.10210991	0.00210995
0.0	1.020210000		
		0.10488296	0.00277305
0.0	1.030700000		
		0.10893404	0.00405108
0.0	1.041590000		
		0.11489147	0.00595743
0.500000000	1.053480479		
		0.12348207	0.00859060
0.600000000	1.066398620		
		0.13532055	0.01183849
0.700000000	1.080677072		
		0.15108624	0.01576569
0.800000000	1.096765340		
		0.17148936	0.02040312
0.900000000	1.115155370		
		0.19725708	0.02576772
1.000000000	1.136420848		
		0.22914515	0.03188807

Δ^2YPRIM	Δ^3YPRIM	Δ^4YPRIM
0.0	0.0	0.0
0.0	0.0	0.0
0.00066310	0.0	0.0
0.00127803	0.00061493	0.0
0.00190635	0.00062832	0.00001339
0.00263317	0.00072682	0.00009850
0.00324789	0.00061472	−0.00011210
0.00392720	0.00067931	0.00006459
0.00463743	0.00071023	0.00003092
0.00536460	0.00072717	0.00001693
0.00612035	0.00075575	0.00002859

7.12.2 Flow Chart

The following is a general purpose flow chart for a predictor–corrector method. For the differential equation

$$\frac{dy}{dx} = \frac{1}{x^2} - \frac{1}{x}y, \qquad (y(1) = 1),$$

Flow Chart 7.12.2 is based upon the eight guidelines stated in Sec. 7.12.

The Runge–Kutta method of order 4 is used to find the starting values. The formulas for these values are (7.85) and (7.86), which are expressed as

$$y_{l+1} = y_l + \frac{h}{6}\sum_{j=1}^{4} a_j k_j, \qquad (l = 1, 2, \ldots)$$

where $a_1 = 1$, $a_2 = 2$, $a_3 = 2$, $a_4 = 1$ and

$$k_j = f[x_i + b_j(h), y_i + b_j(k_{j-1})]$$

where $b_1 = 0$, $b_2 = 1/2$, $b_3 = 1/2$, $b_4 = 1$, $(j = 1, 2, 3, 4)$.

A subroutine RUNGE (Flow Chart 7.6.2) is used to compute y_2, y_3, y_4. With the starting values y_1, y_2, y_3, y_4, the Milne method is now used to continue the solution. The formulas used are

Predictor:

$$y_{i+1}^{(1)} = y_{i-3} + \frac{4h}{3}(2y'_{i-2} - y'_{i-1} + 2y'_i) + \frac{14}{45}h^5 y^{(5)}(\xi_1),$$

$$(x_{i-3} < \xi_1 < x_{i+1});$$

Corrector:

$$y_{i+1}^{(j)} = y_{i-1} + \frac{h}{3}(y'_{i-1} + 4y'_i + y'_{i+1}) - \frac{h^5 y^{(5)}(\xi_2)}{90}, \qquad (x_{i-1} < \xi_2 < x_{i+1}).$$

These two formulas may be stated in a more general form as

$$y_{i+1}^{(1)} = y_{i-r_1} + h \sum_{k=0}^{r} a_{k+1} y'_{i-k}$$

where $r_1 = 3$, $r = 2$ and $a_1 = 8/3$, $a_2 = -4/3$, $a_3 = 8/3$, and

$$y_{i+1}^{(j+1)} = y_{i-p_1} + h \sum_{k=0}^{p} b_{k+1} y'_{i-k} + hC[y_{i+1}^{(j)}]^1$$

where $p_1 = 1$, $p = 1$, $b_1 = 4/3$, $b_2 = 1/3$, and $C = 1/3$. By using these equations, only one program is necessary regardless of the method; only the data of the coefficients have to be changed.

When $y_{i+1}^{(0)}$ and $y_{i+1}^{(1)}$ have been computed by the predictor and corrector, respectively, the error

$$E_{i+1} = \frac{1}{30}|y_{i+1}^{(1)} - y_{i+1}^{(0)}|$$

is computed. For the test

$$e_1 \leq E_{i+1} \leq e_2$$

where e_1 and e_2 have already been chosen, then if $E_{i+1} > e_2$, h is replaced by $h/2$ and the Runge–Kutta subroutine is called to compute y_l for $l = i-3, i-2, i-1, i$ and for $h/2$ step size. Thus, by an application of the Runge–Kutta method, new values of y_{i-2}, y_{i-1}, and y_i are computed. Then the predictor–corrector process can be applied again.

If $E_{i+1} < e_1$, h is replaced by $2h$ and the Runge–Kutta subroutine is used in a fashion similar to the above case for $E_{i+1} > e_2$. If the test for E_{i+1} is satisfied, x_i is incremented by h and the predictor–corrector process is continued.

The step size h is initially set equal to .01. Values of y are to be computed at the points x_i in the interval [1,2]. In Flow Chart 7.12.2:

$X, X0$, are initial values of X.
$XEND=2$.
$E1=10^{-8}$.
$E2=10^{-6}$.

FLOW CHART 7.12.2 General Predictor–Corrector Method

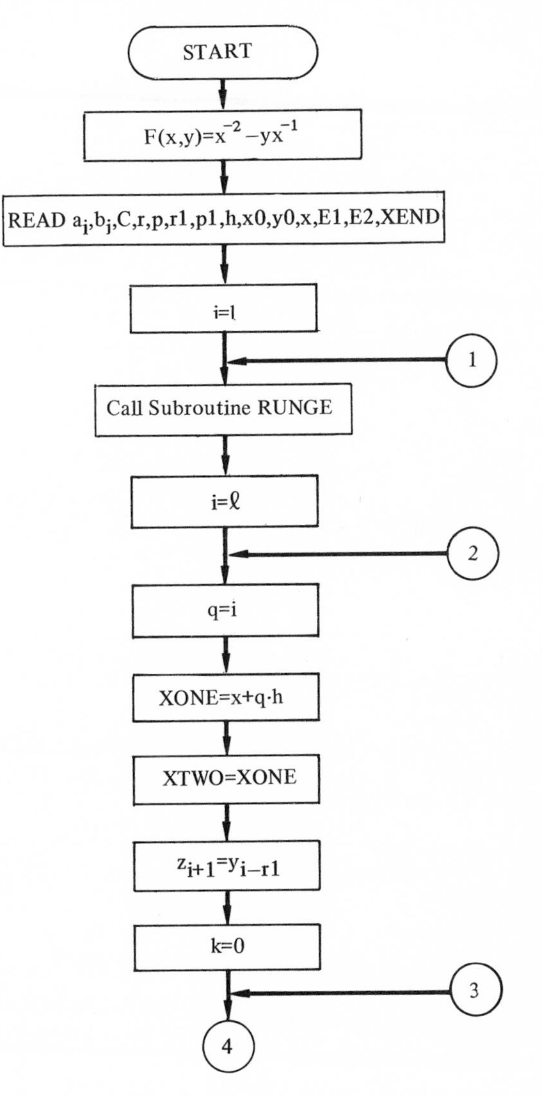

Flow Chart 7.12.2 (*Continued*)

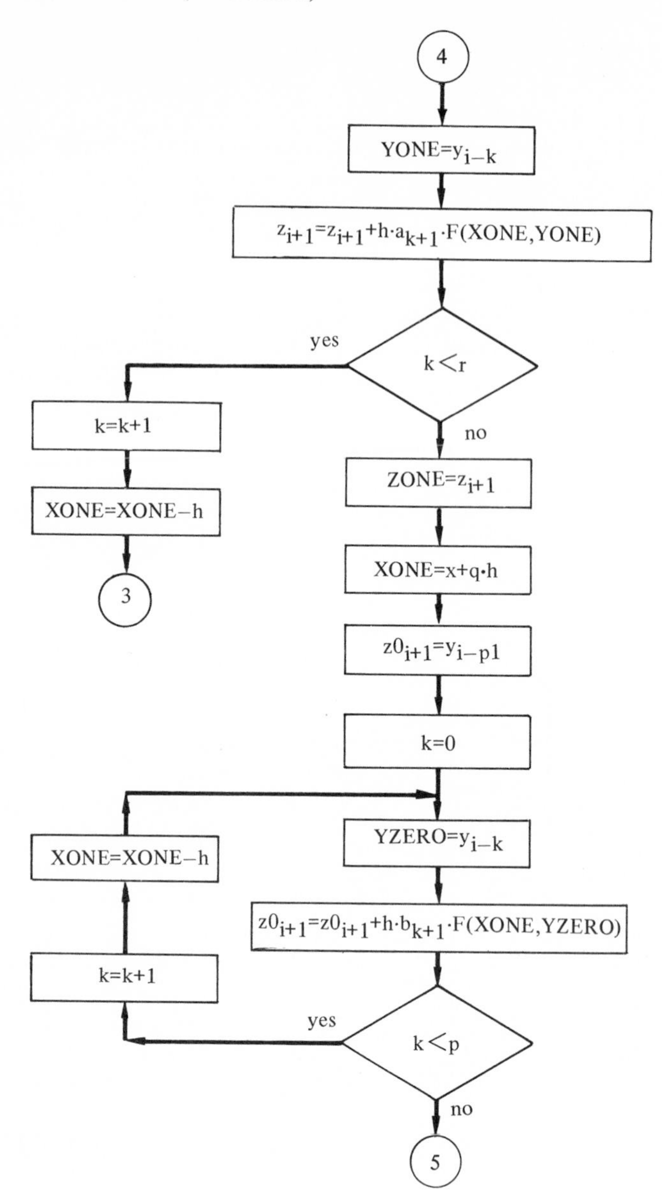

Flow Chart 7.12.2 (*Continued*)

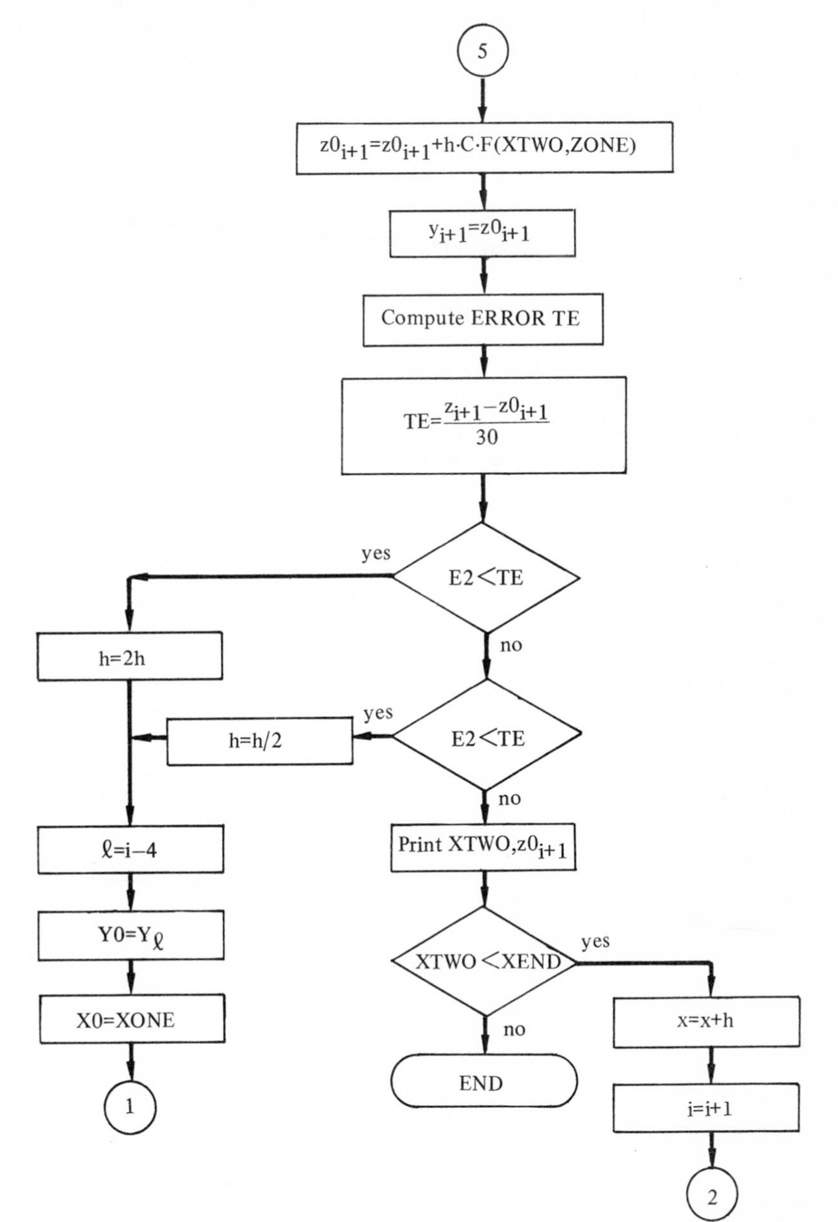

7.12.3 Comments on the Flow Chart

When the error TE is either too small or too large, i.e., when (in Flow Chart 7.12.2) $E1 > TE$ or $E2 < TE$, the subroutine RUNGE must be called to recompute $y_{i-3}, y_{i-2}, y_{i-1}, y_i$.[12] Thus, when $Z0_{i+1}$ is computed by the corrector formula, y_{i+1} is set equal to this value $Z0_{i+1}$ so that when RUNGE is called the most recent values of y shall be used. Then if $TE > E1$ or $E2 < TE$, the statement $l = i - 4$ and $Y0 = YL$, $X0 = XONE$ ($XONE$ having been decreased) are required to have the correct values for the subroutine.

In the subroutine itself, certain changes must be made so that it will agree in notation with the main program. The READ statement must be eliminated. The statement $i = 1$ will be changed to $l = i$ and the subscript i should be changed to l throughout. Note that in the main program after the CALL statement for RUNGE, i is reset equal to l, the current subscript of y.

The statement PRINT $X0$, Y_i should be used for only the first four iterates. For any subsequent use of the subroutine, the PRINT statement should be bypassed. If $l > 4$, one way of accomplishing this bypass is suggested by Flow Chart 7.12.3. The arguments for sub-

FLOW CHART 7.12.3 To Avoid the PRINT Statement $l > 4$ in the Subroutine RUNGE

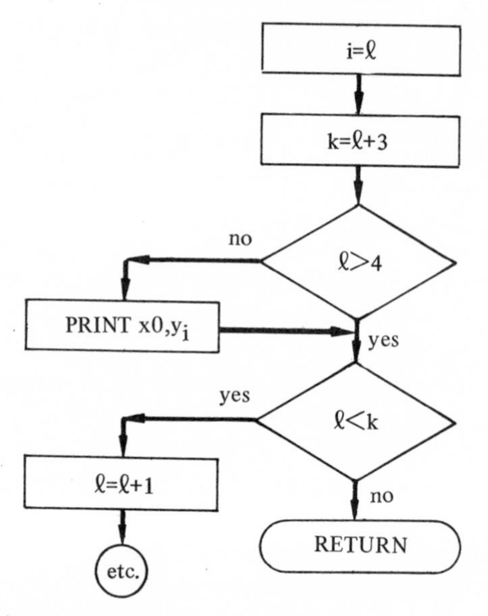

[12] At the $(i + 1)$th iteration, y_{i-3} is not recomputed by the subroutine RUNGE, but the value y_{i-3} is needed in the subroutine to compute y_{i-2}, y_{i-1}, and y_i.

routine RUNGE should include all variables appearing on the left sides of statements, i.e., y_i, AB, BA, RK_j, $X0$.

PROBLEMS

7-17. Test Euler's and Euler's modified methods for stability in solving $dy/dx = Ay$ where A is a real constant. Are these methods strongly stable, weakly unstable, or completely unstable?

7-18. For the Adams–Bashforth–Moulton predictor–corrector method (Eqs. 7.120, 7.123, 7.124), find an estimate of the local error E_{i+1}.

7-19. Write a complete program based on Flow Chart 7.12.2 to solve

$$\frac{dy}{dx} = \frac{1}{x^2} - \frac{1}{x}y, \qquad (y(1) = 1)$$

using

(a) Runge–Kutta, Milne combination, $1 \le x \le 2$, $h = .01$.

(b) Runge–Kutta, Adams–Moulton combination, $1 \le x \le 2$, $h = .01$.

7-20. Let $dy/dx = -y$. (Why this choice for A?)

(a) Find the difference equation for the Adams–Moulton formula (Eq. 7.124).

(b) Let $y_i = \beta^i$; let h have the values 0, .1, .2, ... Solve the resulting cubic equation for the smallest root for each value of h. When $|\beta_3| > 1$ the method will be unstable. Thus, find an upper bound of h beyond which the method is unstable.

NUMERICAL INTEGRATION OF ORDINARY BOUNDARY VALUE PROBLEMS

When conditions for an ordinary differential equation are specified at more than one point, the differential equation along with its conditions is called an *ordinary boundary value problem*. When these conditions are given at a single point, the differential equation with its conditions is known as an *initial value problem*. By definition, then, a problem involving a first-order differential equation is an initial value type. On the other hand, boundary value problems give rise to second and higher-order equations. Odd-order equations are sometimes more complicated numerically, since the number of conditions at one point is not usually the same as at other points. For this reason, odd-order differential equations are sometimes transformed into even-order equations by differentiation or integration.

An example of a second-order boundary value problem is $y'' - y = 0$, $y(0) = 0$, $y(1) = 1$. An example of a fourth-order boundary value problem is $y'''' + ky = q(x)$, k a constant with the conditions $y(0) = y'(0) = 0$, $y(1) = y''(1) = 0$.

Methods of solution to be considered here are of two types:

1. Methods based upon *finite differences*. Methods of this type transform integration of the differential equation into a system of algebraic equations. The roots of these equations are the approximations to the solutions of the differential equation at points within the specified region of interest.
2. Techniques based on methods considered previously in this chapter. These methods are sometimes called *shooting* methods.

7.13 Finite-difference Methods

Consider the linear second-order differential equation

$$y'' + f(x)y' + g(x)y = q(x) \tag{7.134}$$

with boundary conditions $y(a) = A$, $y(b) = B$. Let the interval $[a,b]$ be divided into n equal parts, and define h as $h = (b - a)/n$. Then the points on the interval including end points can be defined as

$$x_i = a + ih, \qquad (i = 0, 1, \ldots, n), \tag{7.135}$$

and the values of y at these points can be denoted as

$$y_i = y(a + ih), \qquad (i = 0, 1, \ldots, n). \tag{7.136}$$

Also the values of $f(x)$, $g(x)$ and $q(x)$ at the points x_i can be denoted as

$$f_i = f(a + ih), \qquad g_i = g(a + ih), \qquad q_i = q_i(a + ih). \tag{7.137}$$

In order to apply a method based upon finite differences, values of each derivative must be approximated by differences. To find approximations for y_i' and y_i'', the *average* of the Gauss forward and Gauss backward interpolation formulas is differentiated.[13] Either of these could be differentiated separately, but the error would be of order h rather than of order h^2.

$$\begin{aligned} y = y_0 &+ \frac{u}{2}\{\Delta y_{-1} + \Delta y_0\} + \frac{1}{2}\left\{\frac{(u+1)^{[2]}}{2} + \frac{u^{[2]}}{2}\right\}\Delta^2 y_{-1} \\ &+ \frac{1}{2}\left\{\frac{(u+1)^{[3]}}{3!}\right\}\{\Delta^3 y_{-2} + \Delta^3 y_{-1}\} + \frac{1}{2}\left\{\frac{(u+1)^{[4]}}{4!} + \frac{(u+2)^{[4]}}{4!}\right\}\Delta^4 y_{-2} \\ &+ \frac{1}{2}\left\{\frac{(u+2)^{[5]}}{5!}\right\}\{\Delta^5 y_{-3} + \Delta^5 y_{-2}\} + \cdots, \quad \left(u = \frac{x - x_0}{h}\right). \end{aligned} \tag{7.138}$$

[13] This polynomial is known as Stirling's formula and can be expressed in terms of central differences.

By differentiating, it is seen that

$$y' = \frac{1}{h}\left[\frac{1}{2}(\Delta y_{-1} + \Delta y_0) + \frac{u}{2}\Delta^2 y_{-1} + \left(\frac{3u^2 - 1}{12}\right)(\Delta^3 y_{-2} + \Delta^3 y_{-1})\right.$$

$$\left. + \left\{\frac{4u^3 - 2u}{24}\right\}\Delta^4 y_{-2} + \left\{\frac{5u^4 - 15u^2 + 4}{240}\right\}\{\Delta^5 y_{-3} + \Delta^5 y_{-4}\} + \cdots\right. \quad (7.139)$$

Thus, at $u = 0$,

$$y_0' = \frac{1}{2h}[\Delta y_{-1} + \Delta y_0] - \frac{1}{12h}[\Delta^3 y_{-2} + \Delta^3 y_{-1}]$$

$$+ \frac{1}{60h}[\Delta^5 y_{-3} + \Delta^5 y_{-4}] + \cdots. \quad (7.140)$$

Or the derivative through the linear terms is

$$y_0' = \frac{1}{2h}(y_1 - y_{-1}) \quad (7.141)$$

and the error is of order h^2.

In general

$$y_i' = \frac{y_{i+1} - y_{i-1}}{2h} + 0(h^2), \qquad (i = 0, 1, \ldots); \quad (7.142)$$

in like manner,

$$y_i'' = \frac{y_{i-1} - 2y_i + y_{i+1}}{h^2} + 0(h^2) \quad (7.143)$$

and

$$y_i'''' = \frac{y_{i-2} - 4y_{i-1} + 6y_i - 4y_{i+1} + y_{i+2}}{h^4} + 0(h^2),$$

$$(i = 0, 1, \ldots). \quad (7.144)$$

The differential equation 7.134 can now be approximated by a finite difference equation in which each derivative is approximated by a formula of order h^2. The finite difference approximation of Eq. 7.134 at the point x_i is

$$\frac{y_{i-1} - 2y_i + y_{i+1}}{h^2} + \frac{f_i(y_{i+1} - y_{i-1})}{2h} + g_i y_i = q_i. \quad (7.145)$$

After the necessary algebra has been performed, (7.145) simplifies to

$$(2 - hf_i)y_{i-1} + (-4 + 2h^2 g_i)y_i + (2 + hf_i)y_{i+1} = 2h^2 q_i,$$

$$(i = 0, 1, 2, \ldots, n - 1). \quad (7.146)$$

Since $y_0 = A$ and $y_n = B$ are known, Eq. 7.146 represents $(n-1)$ equations in $(n-1)$ unknowns, $y_1, y_2, \ldots, y_{n-1}$. These equations become

$$
\begin{aligned}
&(-4 + 2h^2g_1)y_1 + (2 + hf_1)y_2 &&= 2h^2q_1 + (2 - hf_1)A \\
&(2 - hf_2)y_1 + (-4 + 2h^2g_2)y_2 + (2 + hf_2)y_3 &&= 2h^2q_2 \\
&(2 - hf_3)y_2 + (-4 + 2h^2g_3)y_3 + (2 + hf_3)y_4 &&= 2h^2q_3 \\
&\cdots\cdots\cdots\cdots\cdots\cdots\cdots\cdots \\
&(2 - hf_{n-2})y_{n-3} + (-4 + 2h^2g_{n-2})y_{n-2} + (2 + hf_{n-2})y_{n-1} &&= 2h^2q_{n-2} \\
&(2 - hf_{n-1})y_{n-2} + (-4 + 2h^2g_{n-1})y_{n-1} &&= 2h^2q_{n-1} - (2 + hf_{n-1})B.
\end{aligned}
\tag{7.147}
$$

In each equation of (7.147) let the coefficient of each $y_j, j = 1, 2, \ldots, n-1$, be represented by a_{ij} and let the terms on the right side of the equation be denoted by b_i. Then Eqs. 7.147 may be expressed in the form

$$
\begin{aligned}
&a_{11}y_1 + a_{12}y_2 &&= b_1 \\
&a_{21}y_1 + a_{22}y_2 + a_{23}y_3 &&= b_2 \\
&a_{32}y_2 + a_{33}y_3 + a_{34}y_4 &&= b_3 \\
&\cdots\cdots\cdots\cdots\cdots\cdots \\
&a_{n-2,n-3}y_{n-3} + a_{n-2,n-2}y_{n-2} + a_{n-2,n-1}y_{n-1} &&= b_{n-2} \\
&a_{n-1,n-2}y_{n-2} + a_{n-1,n-1}y_{n-1} &&= b_{n-1},
\end{aligned}
\tag{7.148}
$$

or in matrix form,

$$
\begin{bmatrix}
a_{11} & a_{12} & & & & \\
a_{21} & a_{22} & a_{23} & & & \\
 & a_{32} & a_{33} & a_{34} & & \\
\cdot & \cdot & \cdot & \cdot & \cdot & \cdot \\
 & & & a_{n-2,n-3} & a_{n-2,n-2} & a_{n-2,n-1} \\
 & & & & a_{n-1,n-2} & a_{n-1,n-1}
\end{bmatrix}
\begin{bmatrix} y_1 \\ y_2 \\ \cdot \\ \cdot \\ \cdot \\ y_{n-1} \end{bmatrix}
=
\begin{bmatrix} b_1 \\ b_2 \\ \cdot \\ \cdot \\ \cdot \\ b_{n-1} \end{bmatrix}.
\tag{7.149}
$$

Thus, the system of equations to be solved is, in matrix notation,

$$AY = B \tag{7.150}$$

where A is a tridiagonal band type matrix, $Y = \{y_1, y_2, \ldots, y_{n-1}\}$ is a column vector, and $B = \{b_1, b_2, \ldots, b_{n-1}\}$ is also a column vector.

Any of the numerical methods of Ch. 4 applicable to such a system may be used to solve (7.150). However, for the problem at hand, Cholesky's method for a band type problem is well suited.

Before any method for solution is considered, it is best to examine the degree of accuracy obtainable by a finite difference method. Clearly, the accuracy depends upon the size of h and on the order of the finite difference approximation. As h is made smaller (halved), the number of equations to be solved increases, and the amount of computer time needed may become excessive. As a result, accuracy may diminish. On the other hand, if the order of approximation is decreased, say to $0(h^4)$, and h remains the same, greater accuracy can be achieved but at the expense of complicated numerical operations. This would be especially true near the end points where formulas of higher-order approximation would require values at points (not prescribed) outside the interval $[a,b]$.

Despite this dilemma, one practical way to obtain the desired accuracy is by trying several values of h in solving the linear system. Then a comparison of values at common points within the interval will indicate how accurate the solutions are. Also, the technique of extrapolation can be used.

In Sec. 6.3 the technique of extrapolation to a limit was used to improve the accuracy of approximating the derivative of a function of x, on the basis that error was caused more by truncation than by round-off. In general, this process of extrapolation can be applied to a boundary value problem to yield a more accurate approximation.

Let $y_i(h)$, $i = 1, 2, \ldots, n-1$, denote the values of the approximations of the solution. Then by halving the interval, let $y_i(h/2)$, $i = 1, 2, \ldots, 2n-1$, be the solutions based upon $2n$ divisions. At points common to both n and $2n$ divisions, extrapolation may be used. Thus, at

$$x_1 = a + h,\ x_2 = a + 2h, \ldots, x_{n-1} = a + (n-1)h,$$

the extrapolation

$$y_i^{(1)} = \frac{4y_i(h/2) - y_i(h)}{3}, \qquad (i = 1, 2, \ldots, n-1) \qquad (7.151)$$

will usually yield a better approximation to the solution.

In summary, the guidelines for solution of a boundary value problem by the method described above consist of five main steps:

1. Evaluate a_{ij} and b_i, $i, j = 1, 2, \ldots, n-1$, for step size h.
2. Solve the system of Eqs. 7.150 by Cholesky's method for a band type problem for y_i, $i = 1, 2, \ldots, n-1$.
3. For step size $h/2$, repeat steps 1 and 2 for $i = 1, 2, \ldots, 2n-1$.
4. For $x = a + h, a + 2h, \ldots, a + (n-1)h$ evaluate

$$y_i^{(1)} = \frac{4y_i(h/2) - y_i(h)}{3}, \qquad (i = 1, 2, \ldots, n-1).$$

5. Print y_i, $i = 1, 2, \ldots, n-1$;
   y_i, $i = 1, 2, \ldots, 2n-1$;
   $y_i^{(1)}$, $i = 1, 2, \ldots, n-1$.

Example

Consider the differential equation

$$y'' - 2(9x + 2)y = -2(9x + 2)e^x, \qquad (y(0) = 0, y(1) = 1). \qquad (7.152)$$

By means of Eq. 7.146, Eq. 7.152 is transformed into a corresponding difference problem:

$$y_{i-1} - \{2 + h^2(18x_i + 4)\}y_i + y_{i+1} = -2h^2(9x_i + 2)e^{x_i},$$
$$(i = 1, 2, \ldots, n - 1). \qquad (7.153)$$

For $n = 2$, $h = 1/2$, Eq. 7.153 becomes

$$-5.25y_1 + 1 = -3.25e^{0.5} = -5.359. \qquad (7.154)$$

Thus $y_1 = y(1/2) = 1.211$. For $n = 4$, $h = 1/4$, the approximation yields the following three equations:

$$\begin{aligned} &\text{at } x_1 = \tfrac{1}{4}, && -2.5312y_1 + y_2 = -0.6821, \\ &\text{at } x_2 = \tfrac{1}{2}, && y_1 - 2.8125y_2 + y_3 = -1.3396, \\ &\text{at } x_3 = \tfrac{3}{4}, && y_2 - 3.0938y_3 = -3.3156. \end{aligned} \qquad (7.155)$$

By Cholesky's method, the solution of the system (7.155) is

$$y_1 = y(1/4) = .7753, \; y_2 = y(1/2) = 1.2802,$$
$$y_3 = y(3/4) = 1.4855.$$

Also by means of extrapolation (Eq. 7.151), the value of y at $x = 1/2$ can be further approximated as

$$y_1^{(1)} = \frac{4(1.2802) - 1.2110}{3} \quad \text{or} \quad y_1^{(1)} = 1.3033.$$

For $n = 6$, $h = 1/6$, the approximation by means of (7.153) yields the value of y at $x = 1/2$ as $y_3 = y(1/2) = 1.3090$. The extrapolated value $y_1^{(1)}$ is off less than .006 from this value of y_3.

In general, approximately the same degree of accuracy can be obtained by extrapolation with $h = .1$ and $.05$ as with $h = .01$ without extrapolation at points common to both methods.

7.13.1 Flow Chart

For the differential equation 7.152, the difference equation is

$$y_{i-1} - (2 + h^2(18x_i + 4))y_i + y_{i+1} = -2h^2(9x_i + 2)e^{x_i},$$
$$(y_0 = 0, y_n = 1). \qquad (7.156)$$

The system of Eqs. 7.147 becomes

$$
\begin{aligned}
-[2 + h^2(18x_1 + 4)]y_1 + y_2 &= -2h^2(9x_1 + 2)e^{x_1}\\
y_1 - [2 + h^2(18x_2 + 4)]y_2 + y_3 &= -2h^2(9x_2 + 2)e^{x_2}\\
y_2 - [2 + h^2(18x_3 + 4)]y_3 + y_4 &= -2h^2(9x_3 + 2)e^{x_3}\\
\cdots\cdots\cdots\cdots &\\
y_7 - [2 + h^2(18x_8 + 4)]y_8 + y_9 &= -2h^2(9x_8 + 2)e^{x_8}\\
y_8 - [2 + h^2(18x_9 + 4)]y_9 &= -1 - 2h^2(9x_9 + 2)e^{x_9},\\
(h = .1,\ n = 10,\ x_i &= 0 + ih).
\end{aligned}
\tag{7.157}
$$

The only coefficients a_{ij} of (7.157) that have to be computed are the diagonal coefficients a_{ii}. Thus

$$
\begin{aligned}
a_{ii} &= -2 - h^2(18x_i + 4), \qquad (i = 1, 2, \ldots, 9),\\
b_j &= -2h^2(9x_j + 2)e^{x_j}, \qquad (j = 1, 2, \ldots, 8),
\end{aligned}
\tag{7.158}
$$

and

$$b_9 = -1 - 2h^2(9x_9 + 2)e^{x_9}. \tag{7.159}$$

To find the extrapolated values, the value of h will be reset to $h/2 = .05$ and the value of n to 20. Equations 7.158 will then be computed for $i = 1, 2, \ldots, 19$, $j = 1, 2, \ldots, 18$, and

$$b_{19} = -1 - 2h^2(9x_{19} + 2)e^{x_{19}}. \tag{7.160}$$

For the band type system of Eqs. 7.157, the matrix A in (7.150) is

$$
A = \begin{bmatrix}
a_{11} & 1 & 0 & 0 & \cdots & 0 & 0\\
1 & a_{22} & 1 & 0 & \cdots & 0 & 0\\
0 & 1 & a_{33} & 1 & \cdots & 0 & 0\\
\cdot & \cdot & \cdot & \cdot & \cdot & \cdot & \cdot\\
0 & 0 & \cdots & 1 & \cdots & a_{n-2,n-2} & 1\\
0 & 0 & \cdots & \cdot & \cdots & 1 & a_{n-1,n-1}
\end{bmatrix}
$$

and

$$
B = \begin{bmatrix} b_1\\ b_2\\ \cdot\\ \cdot\\ \cdot\\ b_{n-1} \end{bmatrix}
\tag{7.161}
$$

where a_{ii} and b_j are defined by Eqs. 7.158–160. Then the system (7.157) is $AY = B$, which by Cholesky's method (Sec. 4.15.2) becomes

$$\begin{aligned} LUY &= B \\ UY &= Z \\ LZ &= B \end{aligned} \tag{7.162}$$

where

$$l_{kk} = a_{kk} - l_{k,k-1}u_{k-1,k}, \qquad (k = 1, 2, \ldots, n-1, \; l_{1,0} = 0, \; u_{0,1} = 0)$$
$$l_{k+1,k} = a_{k+1,k}, \qquad (k = 1, 2, \ldots, n-2)$$

and (7.163)

$$u_{k,k+1} = \frac{1}{l_{kk}} a_{k,k+1}, \qquad (k = 1, 2, \ldots, n-2).$$

When these values of u_{ij} and l_{ij} have been computed,

$$z_k = \frac{1}{l_{kk}}[b_k - (l_{k,k-1})z_{k-1}], \qquad (l_{1,0} = 0, \; z_0 = 0, \; k = 1, 2, \ldots, n-1) \tag{7.164}$$

and

$$y_k = z_k - u_{k,k+1}y_{k+1}, \qquad (k = n-1, n-2, \ldots, 1); \tag{7.165}$$

($u_{n-1,n}$ and y_n are assumed to be zero).

Boundary values are: $y = 0$ at $xa = 0$,
$y = 1$ at $xb = 1$.

FLOW CHART 7.13.1 Solution of a Second-order Boundary Value Problem

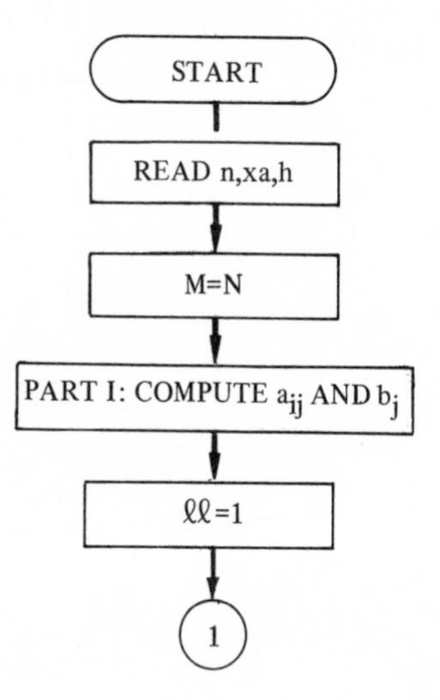

Flow Chart 7.13.1 *(Continued)*

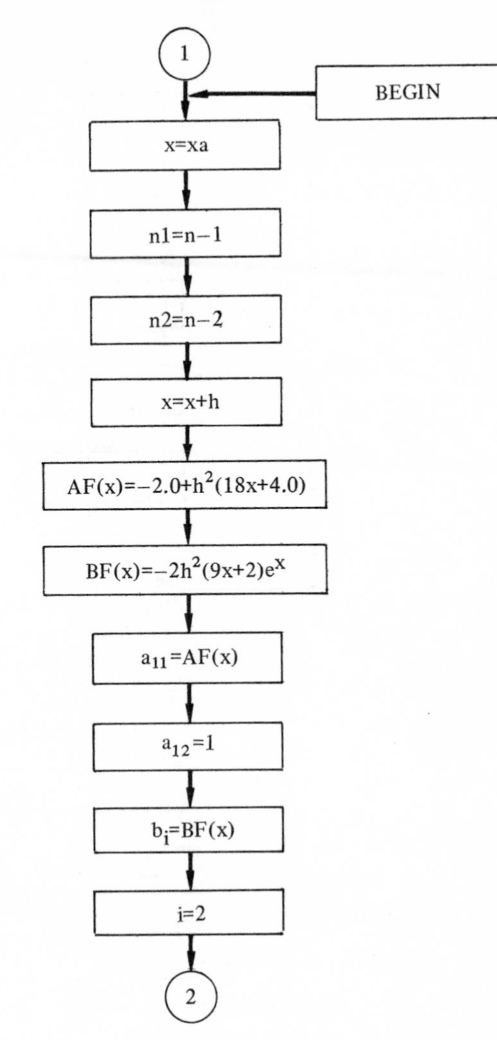

Flow Chart 7.13.1 *(Continued)*

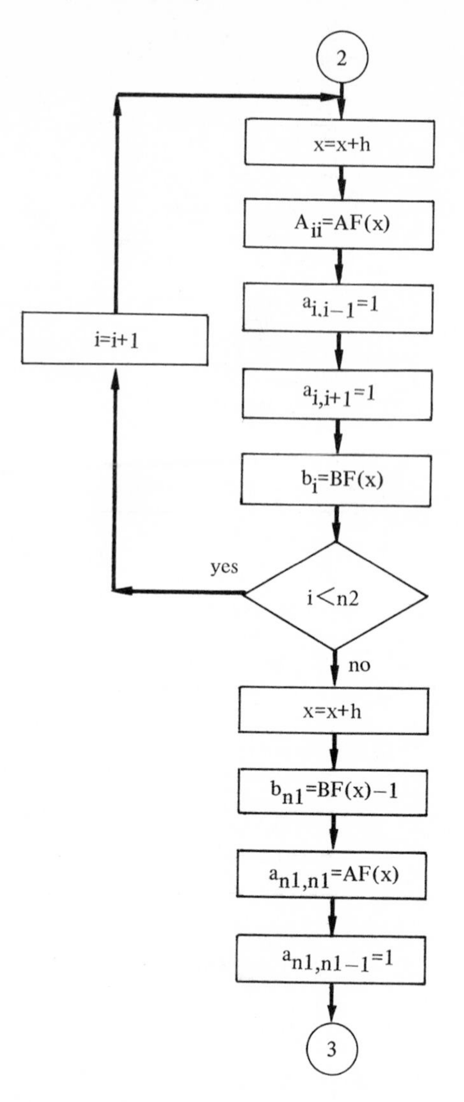

Flow Chart 7.13.1 *(Continued)*

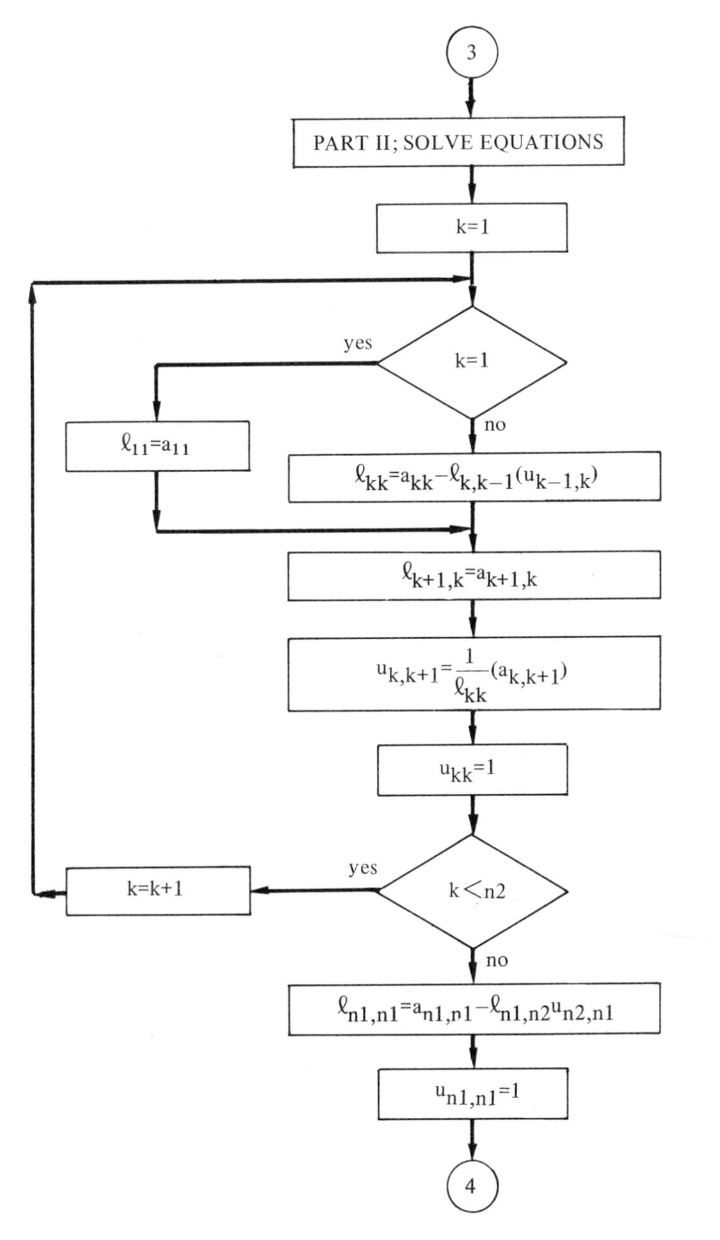

Flow Chart 7.13.1 *(Continued)*

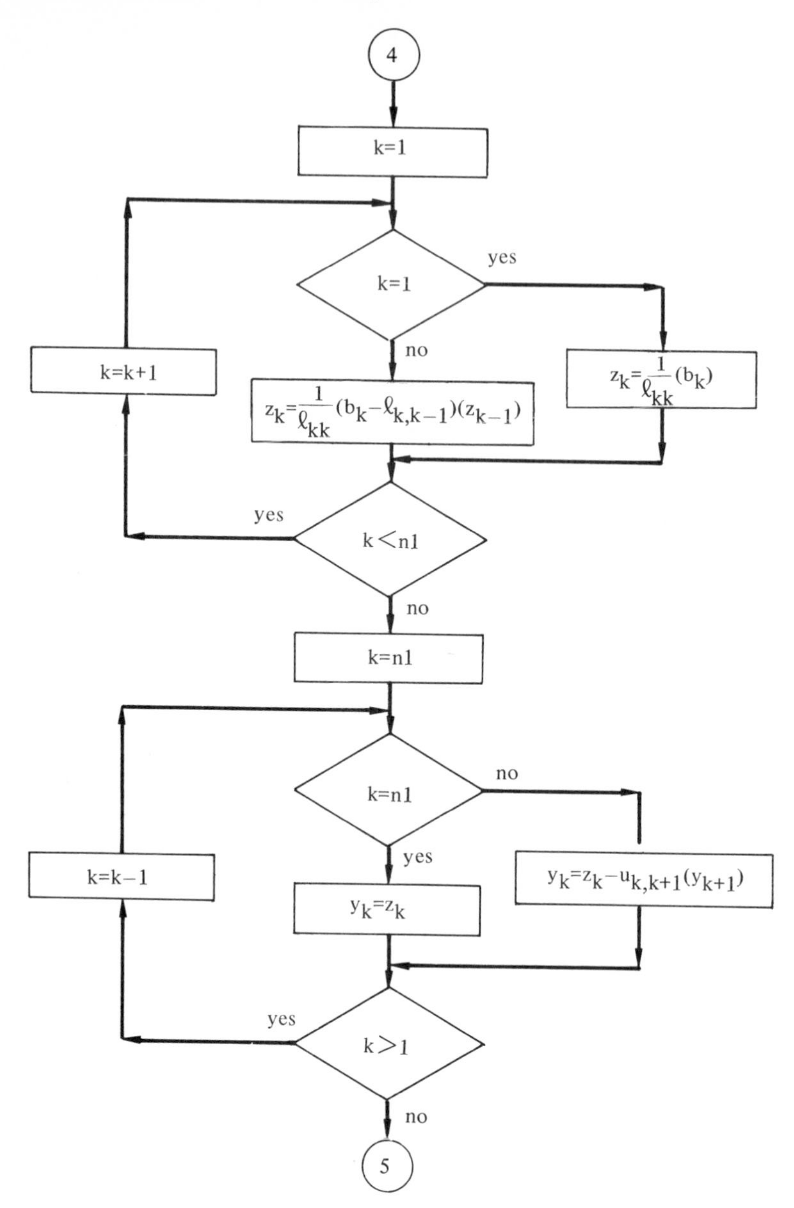

Flow Chart 7.13.1 *(Continued)*

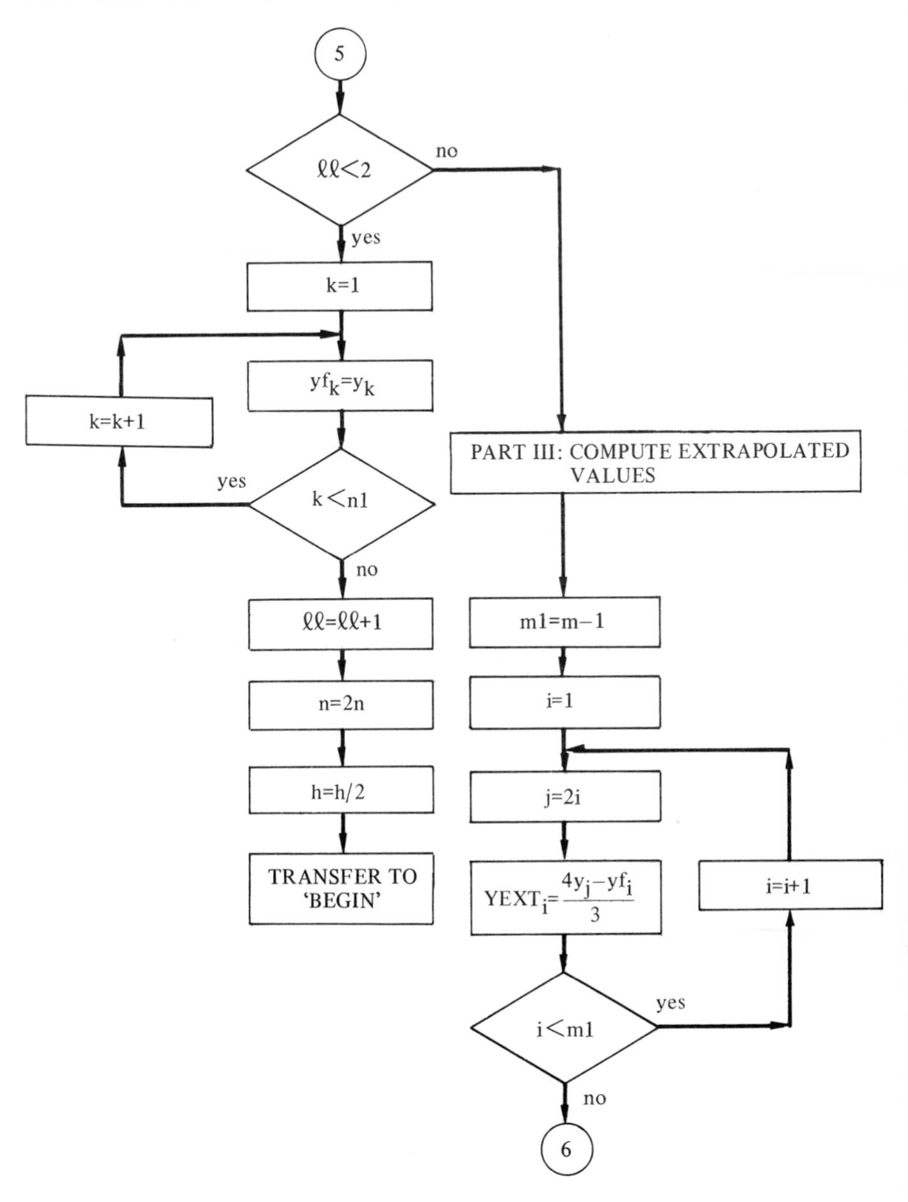

Flow Chart 7.13.1 *(Continued)*

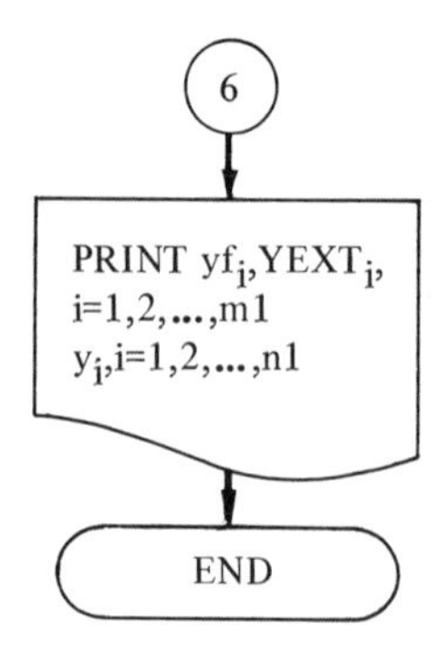

7.13.2 Program

Given the second-order boundary value problem:

$$y'' - 2(9x + 2)y = -2(9x + 2)e^x, \qquad (y(0) = 0, y(1) = 1).$$

Starting values: $x = 0.0$, $N = 10$, $H = .1$.
For $N = 10$, $H = .1$, the values of $Y(I) = YF(I)$ are computed. Then for $N = 20$, $H = .05$, the values of $Y(I)$ are computed. Finally the extrapolated values $YEXT(I)$ are computed.

```
      DIMENSION A(50,50),B(20),CL(50,50),U(50,50),Y(50),YF(50),Z(50)
      DIMENSION YEXT(50)
      AF(X)=-2.0-(H**2)*(18.0*X+4.0)
      BF(X)=-2.0*(H**2)*(9.0*X+2.0)*EXP(X)
      READ(5,10)N,XA,H
   10 FORMAT(I3,2F10.4)
      M=N
C
C       PART 1 COMPUTE A(I,J) AND B(J)
C
      L=1
  160 X=0.0
      N1=N-1
      N2=N-2
      X=X+H
      A(1,1)=AF(X)
      A(1,2)=1
      B(1)=BF(X)
      DO 20 I=2,N2
      X=X+H
      A(I,I)=AF(X)
      A(I,I-1)=1
```

```
      A(I,I+1)=1
   20 B(I)=BF(X)
      X=X+H
      B(N1)=BF(X)-1.0
      A(N1,N1)=AF(X)
      A(N1,N1-1)=1.0
C
C       PART 2 SOLVE EQUATIONS
C
      DO 30 K=1,N2
      IF(K-1)40,50,40
   50 CL(K,K)=A(K,K)
      GO TO 60
   40 CL(K,K)=A(K,K)-CL(K,K-1)*U(K-1,K)
   60 CL(K+1,K)=A(K+1,K)
      U(K,K+1)=A(K,K+1)/CL(K,K)
   30 U(K,K)=1
      CL(N1,N1)=A(N1,N1)-CL(N1,N2)*U(N2,N1)
      U(N1,N1)=1
      Z(1)=B(1)/CL(1,1)
      DO 70 K=2,N1
   70 Z(K)=(B(K)-CL(K,K-1)*Z(K-1))/CL(K,K)
      Y(N1)=Z(N1)
      K=N2
  120 Y(K)=Z(K)-U(K,K+1)*Y(K+1)
      IF(K-1)100,100,110
  110 K=K-1
      GO TO 120
  100 IF(L-2)130,140,140
  130 DO 150 K=1,N1
  150 YF(K)=Y(K)
      L=L+1
      N=N*2
      H=H/2.0
      GO TO 160
C
C       PART 3 COMPUTE EXTRAPOLATED VALUES
C
  140 M1=M-1
      DO 170 I=1,M1
      J=2*I
  170 YEXT(I)=(4.0*Y(J)-YF(I))/3.0
      WRITE(6,180)
  180 FORMAT('THE VALUES OF YF(I) AND YEXT(I) ARE ')
      WRITE(6,190)
  190 FORMAT('YF(I)',5X,'YEXT(I)')
      WRITE(6,200)(YF(I),YEXT(I),I=1,M1)
  200 FORMAT(2F10.4)
      WRITE(6,210)
  210 FORMAT('THE VALUES OF Y(I) ARE ')
```

```
      WRITE(6,220)(Y(I),I=1,N1)
  220 FORMAT(F10.4)
      STOP
      END
      THE VALUES OF YF(I) AND YEXT(I) ARE
      X     YF(I)      YEXT(I)
      .1    0.3468     0.3473
      .2    0.6497     0.6510
      .3    0.9091     0.9116
      .4    1.1270     1.1307
      .5    1.3041     1.3091
      .6    1.4364     1.4427
      .7    1.5117     1.5189
      .8    1.5035     1.5111
      .9    1.3626     1.3685
      THE VALUES OF Y(I) ARE
      X      Y(I)
      .05    0.1789
      .10    0.3472
      .15    0.5045
      .20    0.6507
      .25    0.7861
      .30    0.9109
      .35    1.0254
      .40    1.1298
      .45    1.2241
      .50    1.3079
      .55    1.3806
      .60    1.4411
      .65    1.4875
      .70    1.5171
      .75    1.5261
      .80    1.5092
      .85    1.4593
      .90    1.3670
      .95    1.2196
```

PROBLEMS

7-21. Consider the boundary value problem

$$y'' - 4y' + 4y = e^{3x}, \qquad (y(0) = 0,\ y(1) = -2).$$

The exact solution is

$$y = [-1 + (1 - e - 2e^{-2})x]e^{2x} + e^{3x}.$$

Write a program to solve the problem in the following manner:

(a) Compute the YT_i values of y at $x = .05, .1, .15, \ldots, .95$ by using the exact solution.

(b) Use Cholesky's method to compute YH_i values of y at $x = .1, .2, \ldots, .9$.
(c) Use Cholesky's method to compute the $YH2_i$ values of y at $x = .05, .10, .15, \ldots, .95$.
(d) Use the extrapolation technique to compute the $YEXT_i$ extrapolated values of y at $x = .1, .2, \ldots, .9$.
(e) The output can be listed in columns as suggested below:

X	YT	YH2	YH1	YEXT
.05	YT_1	$YH2_1$		
.1	YT_2	$YH2_2$	$YH1_2$	$YEXT_2$
.15	YT_3	$YH2_3$		
.2	YT_4	$YH2_4$	$YH1_4$	$YEXT_4$
. . .	. . .	. . .	. . .	. . .
.95	YT_{19}	$YH2_{19}$		

7-22. Consider the boundary value problem

$$y'''' + 6y = 100, \qquad (y(0) = y'(0) = y(1) = y''(1) = 0).$$

(a) Show that the difference equation for this problem by Eq. 7.144 becomes

$$y_{i-2} - 4y_{i-1} + 6(1 + h^4)y_i - 4y_{i+1} + y_{i+2} = 100h^4. \tag{a}$$

(b) Show also that the boundary conditions become

$$y_0 = 0, \qquad y_{-1} = y_1, \qquad y_n = 0, \qquad y_{n+1} = -y_{n-1} \tag{b}$$

where n is the number of subintervals.
(c) Let $n = 2$. Show that for $i = 1$, Eq. (a) simplifies to $y(1/2) = y_1 = .98$ (slide rule computation).
(d) For $n = 4$ and $h = 1/4$, show that Eq. (a) using Eq. (b) yields the following equations:

$$\text{at } x = x_1 = \frac{1}{4}, \qquad y_1 + 6\left(1 + \frac{1}{4^4}\right)y_1 - 4y_2 + y_3 = \frac{100}{(4)^4}$$

$$\text{at } x = x_2 = \frac{1}{2}, \qquad -4y_1 + 6\left(1 + \frac{1}{4^4}\right)y_2 - 4y_3 = \frac{100}{(4)^4}$$

$$\text{at } x = x_3 = \frac{3}{4}, \qquad y_1 - 4y_2 + 6\left(1 + \frac{1}{4^4}\right)y_3 - y_3 = \frac{100}{(4)^4}.$$

(e) Solve the equations in (d) for y_1, y_2, y_3.
Answers: $y_1 = y(1/4) = .34$
$y_2 = y(1/2) = .64$
$y_3 = y(3/4) = .51$

(f) By means of extrapolation for $n = 2$ and 4 show that $y(1/2) = .53$.

7-23. Consider the boundary value problem $y'''' + Ky = q(x)$, K a constant,
$y(0) = y'(0) = 0,$
$y'(0) = y'(1) = 0.$

Using difference approximation (7.144) and boundary conditions, show that for $i = 1, 2, \ldots, n-1$ and $h = 1/n$ the following set of equations is obtained:

$$(7 + kh^4)y_1 - 4y_2 + y_3 = h^4q(x_1),$$
$$-4y_1 + (6 + kh^4)y_2 - 4y_3 + y_4 = h^4q(x_2).$$

For $i = 3, 4, \ldots, n-3$,

$$y_{i-2} - 4y_{i-1} + (6 + kh^4)y_i - 4y_{i+1} + y_{i+2} = h^4q(x_i);$$

for $i = n - 2$,

$$y_{i-4} - 4y_{i-3} + (6 + kh^4)y_{i-2} - 4y_{i-1} = h^4q(x_i);$$

for $i = n - 1$,

$$y_{i-3} - 4y_{i-2} + (6 + kh^4)y_i = h^4q(x_i).$$

7-24. Write a flow chart and program to solve the boundary value problem in Prob. 7-22 by Cholesky's method, including extrapolation for $n = 4$ and 8.

7-25. (a) Show that Eqs. 7.163 for the differential equation 7.152 can be expressed as

$$l_{kk} = a_{kk} - u_{k-1,k}$$
$$l_{k+1,k} = 1$$
$$u_{k,k+1} = 1/l_{kk}.$$

(b) Write a program to solve (7.152) using the formulas in (a) above. Choose $n = 10$, $h = .1$.

7.14 Shooting Method

The techniques based upon finite differences for the solution of a linear boundary value problem are in general the best available methods. For a nonlinear equation, finite difference methods can be used, but there are certain disadvantages. For example, a program itself would require a method of finding a solution, and then by an iterative process improving this solution so that it would approximate the true solution within the desired degree of accuracy. Also, as in the method described below, there is no guarantee of convergence.

The *shooting* method is based upon the initial value problem methods that were discussed earlier. However, in the second-order initial value problem, both $y(0)$ and $y'(0)$ are known values, whereas in the boundary value problem $y'(0)$ is not prescribed. Thus, before using initial value problem techniques to solve a boundary value problem, some arbitrary value must be assigned to $y'(0)$.

For example, consider the nonlinear boundary value problem

$$yy'' + (y')^2 = 0, \qquad (y(0) = 1,\ y(1) = \sqrt{3}). \tag{7.166}$$

The exact solution is $y^2 = 2x + 1$, with $y'(0) = 1$. Now consider the initial value problem

$$yy'' + (y')^2 = 0, \qquad (y(0) = 1, y'(0) = 1), \tag{7.167}$$

whose exact solution is also $y^2 = 2x + 1$.

If one were intuitive enough to choose $y'(0)$ equal to 1 for the boundary value problem, then the initial value problem technique could be applied without further question in this regard. But almost always, a first guess of $y'(0)$ is not as exact. However, a reasonably good guess can be made on the basis of a knowledge of physical considerations of the problem, or possibly from a graph of the differential equation.

In practice, what one wishes to do is outlined in the following steps:

1. Given the nonlinear boundary value problem $y'' = f(x,y,y')$, $y(a) = A$, $y(b) = B$.
2. Let the true value of $y'(a) = C$, and let $c_1, c_2, \ldots$ be approximations to C (c_1 and c_2 can be chosen in an arbitrary manner based upon a knowledge of the problem).
3. Solve the initial value problems $y'' = f(x,y,y')$, $y(a) = A$, $y'(a) = c_k$, $k = 1, 2, \ldots$.
4. From (3), two values of $y(b)$ are obtained. Call these $y_{c_1,b}$ and $y_{c_2,b}$. Using linear interpolation (the secant method, see Fig. 7.1), the next approximation is found by the formula

$$c_{k+1} = c_{k-1} + (c_k - c_{k-1})\left\{\frac{B - y_{c_{k-1},b}}{y_{c_k,b} - y_{c_{k-1},b}}\right\}. \tag{7.168}$$

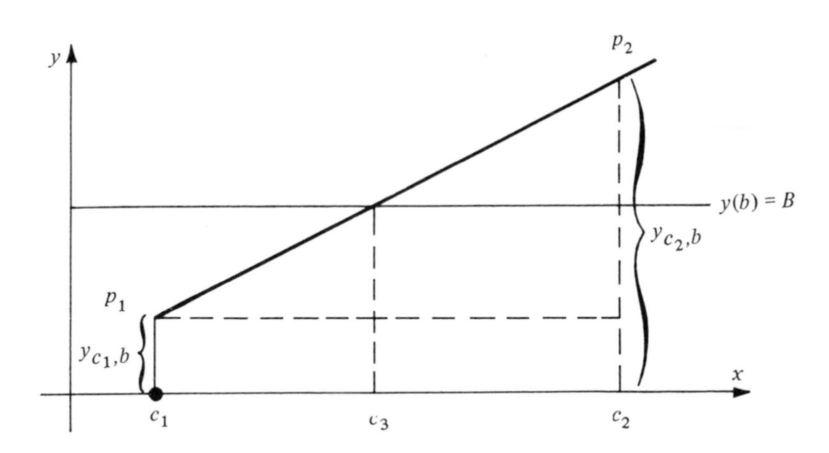

FIGURE 7.1 Secant Method for Approximation for c_3

5. Repeat steps 3 and 4 for each c_k, $k = 3, 4, \ldots$, until

$$|B - y_{c_k,b}| < \epsilon$$

where ϵ has been prescribed.

Before the nonlinear problem is considered in more detail, it is appropriate to comment on the numerical solution of a second-order linear boundary value problem.

Any second-order linear boundary value problem can be reduced to an initial value problem. For example, given the linear differential equation

$$y'' = f(x)y' + g(x)y + q(x), \qquad (y(a) = A,\ y(b) = B), \quad (7.169)$$

consider now the initial value problem

$$y'' = f(x)y' + g(x)y + q(x)$$

with two sets of initial conditions:

$$y(a) = A,\ y'(a) = c_1 \qquad \text{and} \qquad y(a) = A,\ y'(a) = c_2.$$

Denote the two solutions as $y_1(x)$ and $y_2(x)$, respectively, where c_1, c_2 are chosen arbitrarily with $c_1 \neq c_2$.

Let $y_1(b) = B_1$ and $y_2(b) = B_2$, then

$$y(x) = \frac{1}{B_2 - B_1}\{(B - B_1)y_2(x) + (B_2 - B)y_1(x)\} \qquad (7.170)$$

is a solution of (7.169). Hence, any initial value method (applied twice) with the use of (7.170) will lead to a solution of a linear second-order boundary value problem.

Example

Given the boundary value problem

$$y'' + y = 0, \qquad (y(0) = 0,\ y(\pi/2) = 1),$$

the exact solution is $y = \sin x$. Now consider

$$y'' + y = 0, \qquad (y(0) = 0,\ y'(0) = c_1).$$

The exact solution is $y_1(x) = c_1 \sin x$ and $y_1(\pi/2) = c_1$. Next consider

$$y'' + y = 0, \qquad (y(0) = 0,\ y'(0) = c_2,\ c_1 \neq c_2).$$

The exact solution is $y_2(x) = c_2 \sin x$ and $y_2(\pi/2) = c_2$. Then, by (7.169),

$$y(x) = \frac{1}{c_2 - c_1}\{(1 - c_1)c_2 \sin x + (c_2 - 1)c_1 \sin x\}$$

or

$$y(x) = \sin x, \qquad (y(0) = 0,\ y(\pi/2) = 1).$$

7.14.1 Flow Chart

Given: the nonlinear boundary value problem

$$yy'' + (y')^2 = 0, \qquad (y(0) = 1,\ y(1) = \sqrt{3}). \tag{7.171}$$

Equation 7.171 can be restated as two first-order differential equations. That is, let $y' = z$; then

$$z' = -\frac{z^2}{y}, \qquad (y(0) = 1,\ y(1) = \sqrt{3}). \tag{7.172}$$

Now consider the initial value problems

$$yy'' + (y')^2 = 0, \qquad (y(0) = 1,\ y'(0) = .6) \tag{7.173}$$

and

$$yy'' + (y')^2 = 0, \qquad (y(0) = 1,\ y'(0) = .9). \tag{7.174}$$

With an arbitrary choice of values of .6 and .7 for $y'(0)$, the initial value problems are

$$\begin{aligned} y' &= z \\ z' &= -z^2/y, \qquad (y(0) = 1,\ z(0) = .6 = c_1) \end{aligned} \tag{7.175}$$

and

$$\begin{aligned} y' &= z \\ z' &= -z^2/y, \qquad (y(0) = 1,\ z(0) = .9 = c_2). \end{aligned} \tag{7.176}$$

The general procedure is to solve each of these equations by the fourth-order Runge–Kutta method (which is modified here for the problem at hand).

Let the computed values of $y(1)$ be denoted by B_1 and B_2, respectively. If $|B - B_i| < \epsilon$ for a prescribed ϵ, and $i = 1$ or 2, where $B = y(1) = \sqrt{3}$, convergence is satisfactory. Otherwise, linear interpolation is used to find c_3 and the Runge–Kutta method is again applied.

The formulas (7.92) and (7.93) for two first-order differential equations are

$$y_{i+1} = y_i + \frac{h}{6} \sum_{j=1}^{4} a_j k_j$$

$$z_{i+1} = z_i + \frac{h}{6} \sum_{j=1}^{4} a_j l_j$$

where $a_1 = 1$, $a_2 = 2$, $a_3 = 2$, $a_4 = 1$, and

$$k_j = z_i + b_j(l_{j-1})$$

$$l_j = -\frac{[z_i + b_j(l_{j-1})]^2}{y_i + b_j k_{j-1}}$$

where $b_1 = 0$, $b_2 = 1/2$, $b_3 = 1/2$, $b_4 = 1$.

Let $h = .1$, $n = 10$, $c_1 = .6$, $c_2 = .9$, $BB = \sqrt{3} = y(1)$, $X0 = 0$, $yy = 1$, $EPS = 10^{-4}$, and $m = 4$, the number of allowable iterations through the Runge–Kutta method. $jn = 2$ is used as a control on c_i.

FLOW CHART 7.14.1 Shooting Method for a Second-order Boundary Value Problem

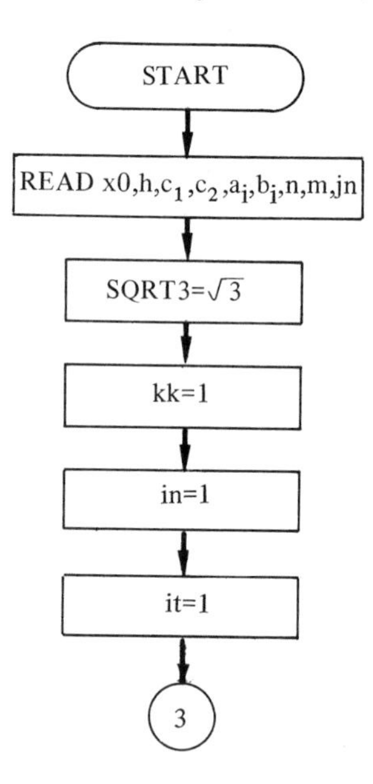

Flow Chart 7.14.1 *(Continued)*

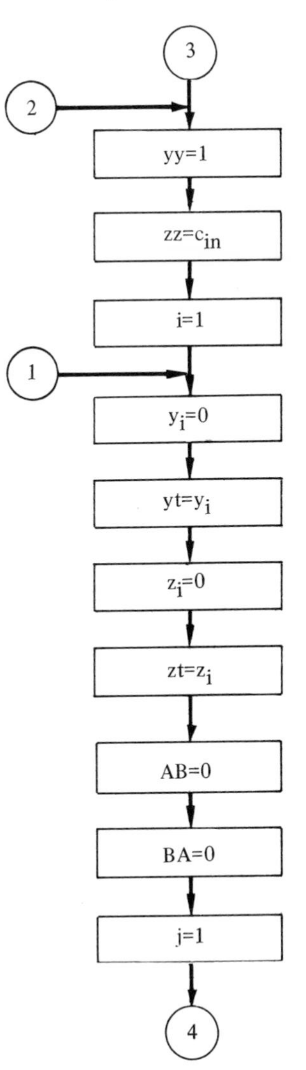

Flow Chart 7.14.1 *(Continued)*

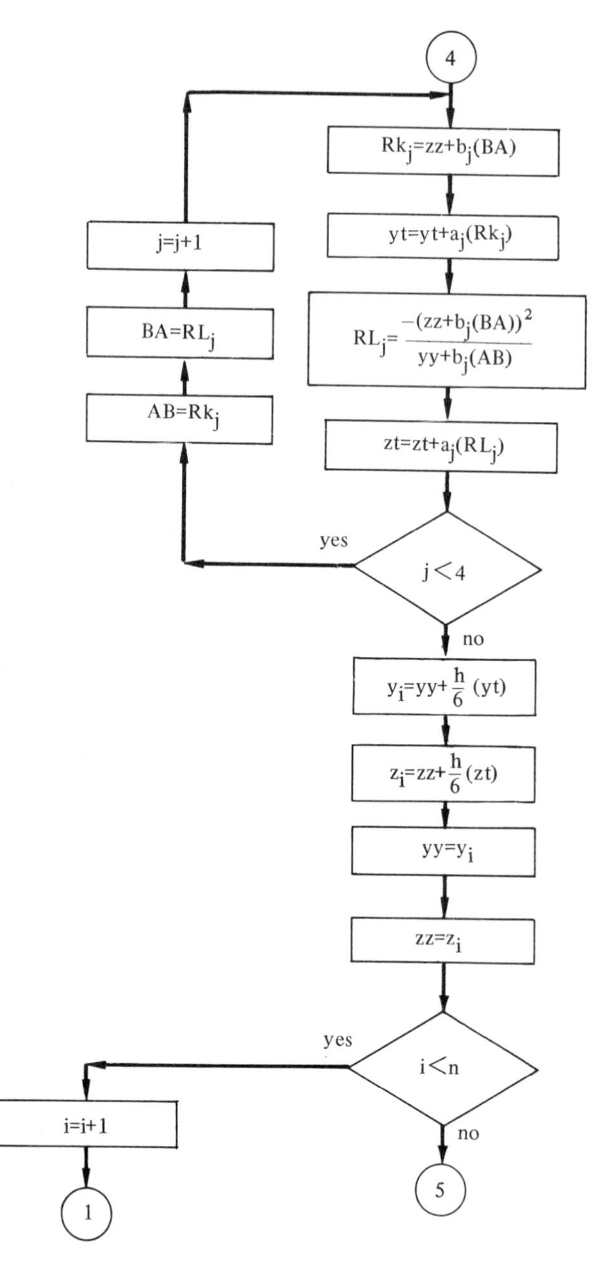

Flow Chart 7.14.1 *(Continued)*

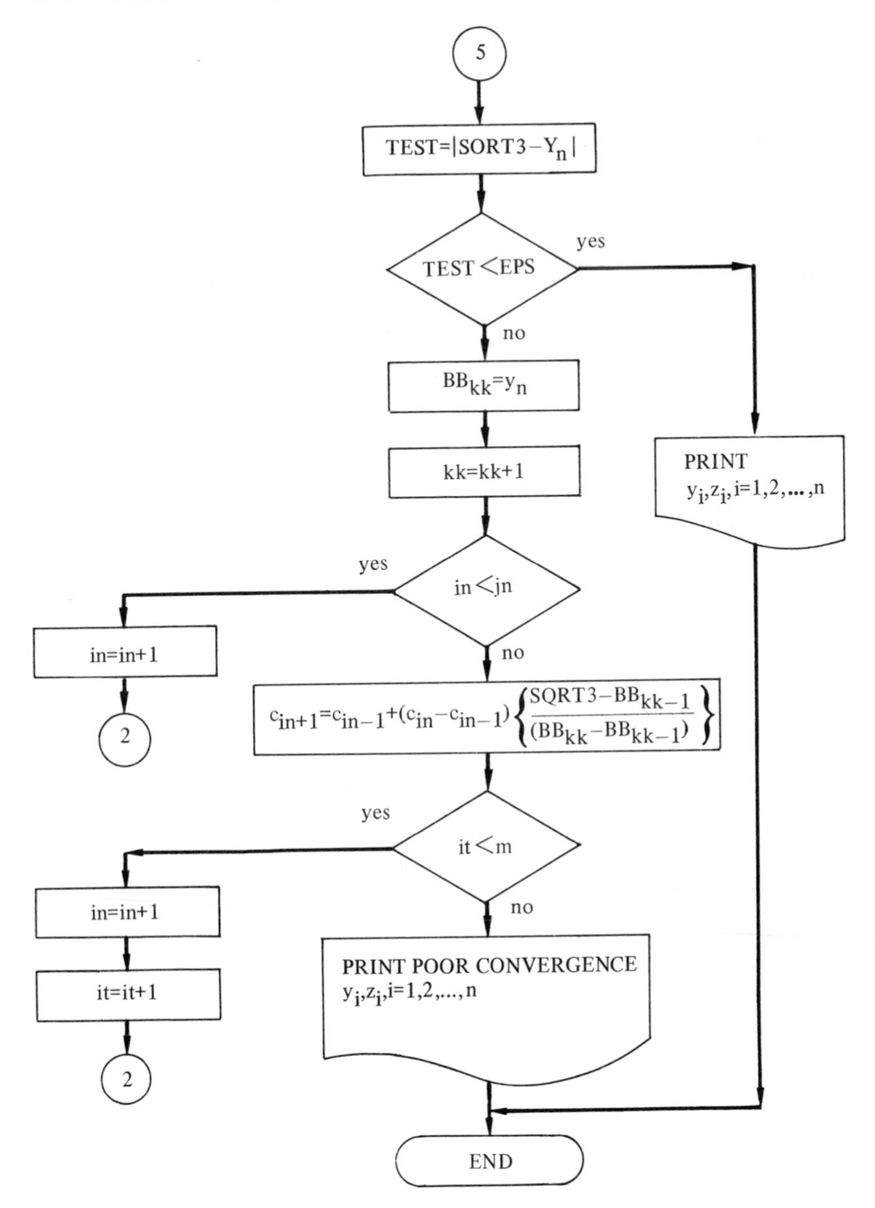

7.14.2 Program

The following program solves Eq. 7.171 by the Runge–Kutta method. The starting values are given in Sec. 7.14.1. As can be seen from the results, the convergence is poor. Had the program included a predictor–corrector technique, better convergence could be expected.

```
C SHOOTING METHOD FOR SECOND ORDER BOUNDARY VALUE PROBLEM
      DIMENSION A(4),B(4),C(4),BB(4),Y(10),Z(10),RK(4),RL(4)
      READ(5,100)X0,H,C(1),C(2),EPS,N,M,JN
      READ(5,101)(A(I),I=1,4)
      READ(5,101)(B(I),I=1,4)
      SQRT3=SQRT(3)
      KK=1
      IT=1
      IN=1
    2 YY=1
      ZZ=C(IN)
      DO 1 I=1,N
      Y(I)=0
      YT=Y(I)
      Z(I)=0
      ZT=Z(I)
      AB=0
      BA=0
      J=1
    4 RK(J)=ZZ+B(J)*BA
      YT=YT+RK(J)*A(J)
      RL(J)=-((ZZ+B(J)*BA)**2)/(YY+B(J)*AB)
      ZT=ZT+RL(J)*A(J)
      IF(J-4)5,6,6
    5 AB=RK(J)
      BA=RL(J)
      J=J+1
      GO TO 4
    6 Y(I)=YY+H*YT/6.
      Z(I)=ZZ+H*ZT/6.
      YY=Y(I)
      ZZ=Z(I)
    1 CONTINUE
      TEST=ABS(SQRT3-Y(N))
      IF(TEST-EPS)9,10,10
    9 WRITE(6,102)(Y(L),L=1,N),(Z(L),L=1,N)
    3 STOP
   10 BB(KK)=Y(N)
      K=KK+1
      IF(IN-JN)11,12,12
   11 IN=IN+1
      GO TO 2
```

```
 12 C(IN+1)=C(IN-1)+(C(IN)-C(IN-1))*((SQRT3-BB(KK-1))
   1/(BB(KK)-BB(KK-1)))
    IF(IT-M)13,14,14
 13 IT=IT+1
    IN=IN+1
    GO TO 2
 14 WRITE(6,103)
    GO TO 9
100 FORMAT(5F5.0,3I2)
101 FORMAT(4F5.0)
102 FORMAT(10F7.4)
103 FORMAT(//,'POOR CONVERGENCE',/)
    END
```

```
POOR CONVERGENCE

THE VALUES OF THE Y ITERATES ARE:

1.0648   1.1289   1.1920   1.2541   1.3152
1.3751   1.4339   1.4917   1.5484   1.6040

THE VALUES OF THE Z ITERATES ARE:

0.8619   0.8277   0.7969   0.7689   0.7432
0.7196   0.6978   0.6775   0.6588   0.6412
```

Problems

7-26. Solve the homogeneous linear boundary value problem[14]

$$y'' - 2y' + (1 + \pi^2)y = 0, \qquad y(0) = 0, y(1) = 0$$

by the shooting method. Let $c_1 = .4$, $c_2 = .6$, and $H = .1$. After two iterations by the Runge–Kutta method, use Eq. 7.170 to compute values of y_i at $x = .1, .2, \ldots, 1$. Also use the exact solution $y = e^x \sin \pi x$ to compute values of y_i.

7-27. Use the shooting method to solve the nonhomogeneous boundary value problem

$$y'' - 6y^2 = 0, \qquad y(0) = 1/4, y(1) = 1.$$

Let $c_1 = .1$ and $c_2 = .2$. The exact solution is $y = 1/(x - 2)^2$.

[14] It should be noted that a linear homogeneous problem is characterized by the fact that if $y(x)$ is a solution, then $cy(x)$ for any constant c is also a solution that satisfies the boundary conditions.

A nonhomogeneous problem has at least one term in the differential equation or in the boundary conditions that is independent of y and its derivatives. For example, $y'' + \pi^2 y = 0$, $y(0) = 0$, $y(1) = 1$, is linear but nonhomogeneous because of the condition $y(1) = 1$.

Bibliography

Boyce, W. E., and DiPrima, R. C., *Elementary Differential Equations and Boundary Value Problems,* John Wiley & Sons, Inc., New York, 2nd ed., 1969.

Coddington, E. A., and Levinson, N., *Theory of Ordinary Differential Equations,* McGraw-Hill Book Company, Inc., New York, 1955.

Davis, P. D., and Rabinowitz, P., *Numerical Integration,* Blaisdell Publishing Co., Waltham, Mass., 1967.

Esser, M., *Differential Equations.* W. B. Saunders Company, Philadelphia, 1968.

Fadeeva, V. N., *Computational Methods of Linear Algebra* (translated by C. D. Benster), Dover Publications, Inc., New York, 1959.

Fox, L., *Numerical Solution of Ordinary and Partial Differential Equations,* Addison-Wesley Publishing Company, Inc., Reading, Mass., 1962.

Goldberg, S., *Introduction to Difference Equations,* John Wiley & Sons, Inc., New York, 1961.

Haming, R. W., *Numerical Methods for Scientists and Engineers,* McGraw-Hill Book Company, New York, 1962.

Haming, R. W., "Stable Predictor-Corrector Methods for Differential Equations," *Journal of the Association for Computing Machinery* 6(1):37–47 (1959).

Henrici, P., *Elements of Numerical Analysis,* John Wiley & Sons, Inc., New York, 1964.

Hildebrand, F. B., *Introduction to Numerical Analysis,* McGraw-Hill Book Company, Inc., New York, 1956.

Hohn, F. E., *Elementary Matrix Algebra,* Macmillan Company, New York, 1958.

Householder, A. S., *Principles of Numerical Analysis,* McGraw-Hill Book Company, New York, 1953.

Ince, E. L., *Ordinary Differential Equations,* Dover Publications, Inc., New York, 1926.

Kunz, K. S., *Numerical Analysis,* McGraw-Hill Book Company, New York, 1957.

Milne, W. E., *Numerical Calculus,* Princeton University Press, Princeton, N.J., 1949.

Milne, W. E., *Numerical Solution of Differential Equations,* John Wiley & Sons, Inc., New York, 1953. (Paperback edition: Dover Publications, Inc., New York, 1970.)

Ralston, A., *A First Course in Numerical Analysis,* McGraw-Hill Book Company, New York, 1965.

Ralston, A., and Wilf, H. S., *Mathematical Methods for Digital Computers,* John Wiley & Sons, Inc., New York, 1960.

Scarborough, J. B., *Numerical Mathematical Analysis,* Johns Hopkins Press, Baltimore, 1962.

Southwell, R. V., *Relaxation Methods in Theoretical Physics,* Oxford University Press, Fair Lawn, N.J., 1946.

Steffensen, J. Z., *Interpolation,* Chelsea Publishing Company, New York, 1950.

Todd, J. (ed.), *Survey of Numerical Analysis,* McGraw-Hill Book Company, New York, 1962.

Wilks, S. S., *Mathematical Statistics,* John Wiley & Sons, Inc., New York, 1962.

APPENDIX

A Summary of Fortran Statements

ARITHMETIC

A=B

where:

A is a variable, subscripted or unscripted. B is an expression.

CALL

CALL SUB (A1,A2,...AN)

where:

SUB is the name of a subroutine subprogram being called.

A1, A2,...AN are arguments.

COMMON

COMMON A, B, C,...

where:

A,B,C,... are variable names and these may be dimensioned as COMMON A (n,m), B(l,j,k)

CONTINUE

CONTINUE

DATA

DATA

DIMENSION

DIMENSION ARR1(n,m), ARR2(I,J,K)...

where:

ARR1, ARR2 are variable names and n,m,I,J,K are unsigned integer constants or integer variables. Array names are separated by commas and the integer constants or integer variables are also separated by commas.

DO

DOK I=M,N,L

where:

I is an integer variable, K is a statement number. M,N,L are unsigned integer constants or unscripted integer variables. If L is omitted, it is assumed to be one.

END

END

EQUIVALENCE

EQUIVALENCE (A,B(I), C(K,L)),...(X,Y(I,K,L)),...

where:

A,B,C,X,Y are variable names and I,K,L are unsigned integer constants or variables.

FORMAT

K FORMAT (S1,S2,...Sn/SS1,SS2,...SSm/...)

where:

each SI is a format specification. K is a statement number.

FUNCTION

FUNCTION NAME (A1,A2,...AN)

where:

NAME is the symbolic name of a single valued function.

A1, A2,...AN are unsubscripted variable names. The type (real, integer, or double precision) is implied by the first letter in the name.

GO TO

GO TO N

where:

N is a statement number.

GO TO COMPUTED

Go to (N1, N2,...),I

where:

N1, N2,... are statement numbers and I is an unsubscripted integer variable.

IF (ARITHMETIC)

IF (A) M,N,L

where A is an arithmetic expression. M is the number of the statement to which control is directed if A (computed) is negative. Also control is directed to the statement N if A is zero and to the statement L if A is positive.

PAUSE

PAUSE

READ

READ (X,Y) List

where:

X is an unsigned integer constant or integer variable. Y is the number of a format statement. List is a list of variables and/or arrays. The list may be omitted.

RETURN

RETURN

Return is the logical end of a subprogram.

STOP

STOP

SUBROUTINE

SUBROUTINE NAME (A1,A2,...AN)

where:

NAME is the symbolic name of a subprogram. A1,A2,...AN are dummy names of SUBROUTINE arguments. A SUBROUTINE need not have arguments.

TYPE

Double PRECISION A(N1,N2,...NL), B(M1,M2,...ML)...

INTEGER A (...),...

REAL A (...),...

where:

A,B,C... are variable names appearing in the program. N1,N2,...NL and M1,M2,...ML are unsigned integer constants or variables.

WRITE

WRITE (X,Y) List

where:

X is an unsigned integer constant or variable and Y is the number of a format statement. LIST is a list of variables, arrays or expressions. LIST may be omitted.

Index

Numbers in parentheses refer to problem numbers